ESSENTIAL MECHANICS FOR A-LEVEL

DJ SIMMONS
DEPUTY HEADMASTER WATFORD GRAMMAR SCHOOL

PE NUN[illegible]
H[illegible] OF MATHEMATICS WATFO[illegible]AMMAR SCHOOL

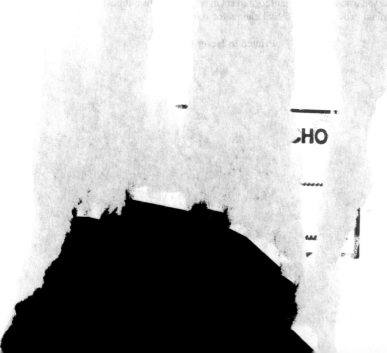

Thomas Nelson and Sons Ltd
Nelson House   Mayfield Road
Walton-on-Thames   Surrey
KT12 5PL   UK

51 York Place
Edinburgh
EH1 3JD   UK

Thomas Nelson (Hong Kong) Ltd
Toppan Building 10/F
22A Westlands Road
Quarry Bay   Hong Kong

Thomas Nelson Australia
102 Dodds Street
South Melbourne
Victoria 3205   Australia

Nelson Canada
1120 Birchmount Road
Scarborough   Ontario
M1K 5G4   Canada

First published by Thomas Nelson and Sons Ltd 1984

ISBN 0-17-431281-4
NPN 9 8 7 6 5

Printed in Hong Kong.

CONTENTS

1
Vectors

2
Kinematics

3
Dynamics

4
Motion in a straight line

5
Momentum and impulse

6
Work and energy

7
Statics

8
Elasticity and simple harmonic motion

9
Centre of gravity

PREFACE

This book has been written to provide the mechanics needed for the new single-subject Advanced-level syllabuses for most Schools' Examination Boards, and in particular optional topics in mechanics from the recommendations of the Standing Conference on University Entrance and the Council for National Academic Awards, the 'Core Syllabus' of which is covered in 'Essential Mathematics'. It is therefore a companion both to the latter book and to many other contemporary texts in pure mathematics.

It is our experience that many students find particular difficulty with mechanics at this level. With the recommendations of the Cockroft report in mind, our aim has been to produce a text which students will wish to read for themselves. Therefore explanations and background material have been included, which teachers may not necessarily cover in class.

There are few laws which govern dynamics and statics, but it is probably because of this that students have difficulty in relating them to a wide variety of real problems. Modelling a physical situation mathematically is a major problem for young mathematicians, and some appreciation of the drastic simplifications made, in order to make the mathematics manageable at this level, is felt desirable. To this end, particularly in the early stages of the book, the modelling of a situation is considered carefully. Time has been taken to discuss the physics of many everyday problems, since we are aware that an increasing number of mathematics students are not studying physics at A-level and, of those who do, many will not study classical mechanics in great detail. Many worked examples have been included to demonstrate different styles and methods of solution. Within the exercises there are problems which require greater insight, as well as many of a routine nature.

Extensive use has been made of photographs and diagrams, since a good illustration is often the start to the solution of a problem. Students must be able to visualise a problem before they can attempt to solve it.

Teachers may choose to teach the chapters from this book in sequence, but a number will prefer to teach statics at an earlier stage, in which case it can be taught at any time after chapter 3. This is a long chapter, and many teachers will wish to divide their teaching of it into several sessions. Chapters 4, 8 and 9 are dependent on calculus in places, and so these chapters may either be delayed until the appropriate techniques have been covered in pure mathematics, or the early parts may be taught and the chapters returned to at a later stage.

Clearly students will wish to make their own notes as they follow the course, and to assist we have included chapter summaries, when appropriate, and have highlighted important sections within the text. Revision exercises, which consist of questions taken from past examination papers, are given at the end of the book. In the main exercises there are no past examination questions.

In preparation are a number of computer programs to accompany this text and, although computer techniques have not been included in this book, it is hoped that computer simulations of real situations will emphasise a different approach to modelling.

DJ Simmons
PE Nunn

ACKNOWLEDGEMENTS

We should like to take this opportunity of thanking those people who have helped in the writing of this book: Dr Jerry Griffiths and Mr D Halfpenny who, in their different ways gave extremely valuable comments on the original manuscripts; Mary Nunn who so carefully and imaginatively drew the diagrams for the manuscript; and to all the staff at Thomas Nelson and Sons who patiently guided us through the process of producing the book.

Finally we are grateful to the following Examination Authorities for permission to use examination questions in the revision exercises:
Associated Examining Board
University of Cambridge Local Examinations Syndicate
University of London University Entrance and School Examination Council
Joint Matriculation Board
Oxford and Cambridge Joint Board.

The authors and publishers are grateful to the following for permission to use their photographs.

Ajax News and Feature Service page 194 (bottom); Allsport pages 92, 114 (left); The Angling Times page 11; BBC Hulton Picture Library pages 30, 34, 90; Camera Press pages 87, 174; Cementation Frank Pile Ltd page 163; Central Electricity Generating Board page 170; Jean Fraser pages 168, 199; The Ministry of Defence page 11 (bottom); Nelson pages 112, 139, 194, (top), 196, 222, 232; The Science Museum page 51; The Science Photo Library pages 113, 114 (right), 152; Sporting Pictures page 50; Tony Stone Associates pages 16, 109.

GLOSSARY OF MATHEMATICAL SYMBOLS

Logic

$\Rightarrow$	implies
$=$	equals
$\neq$	does not equal
$\approx$	is approximately equal to
$>$	is greater than
$\gg$	is much greater than
$\geqslant$	is greater than or equal to
$<$	is less than
$\ll$	is much less than
$\leqslant$	is less than or equal to

Algebra and vectors

$$\sum_{1}^{n} m_i u_i = m_1 u_1 + m_2 u_2 + \cdots m_n u_n$$

OP	the vector from O to P
$\boldsymbol{r}$	the vector $\boldsymbol{r}$
r or $\lvert\boldsymbol{r}\rvert$	the length or magnitude of $\boldsymbol{r}$
$\boldsymbol{i}, \boldsymbol{j}, \boldsymbol{k}$	unit vectors in the x-, y- and z-directions
$\begin{pmatrix} a \\ b \\ c \end{pmatrix} = a\boldsymbol{i} + b\boldsymbol{j} + c\boldsymbol{k}$	the vector with components a, b, c
$\boldsymbol{a} \cdot \boldsymbol{b} = ab\cos\theta$	the scalar product of vectors $\boldsymbol{a}$ and $\boldsymbol{b}$ where θ is the angle between them
$\boldsymbol{r}_{\mathrm{A}}(\mathrm{B})$	the displacement of B relative to A
$\hat{\boldsymbol{r}}$	the unit vector in the direction of $\boldsymbol{r}$

Mechanics

$[F]$	the dimensions of F, see appendix
g	acceleration due to gravity

Analysis

$f(t)$	the function of t
$\dot{f}(t)$	the first derivative of f with respect to t
$\ddot{f}(t)$	the second derivative of f with respect to t
$\dot{x}$ or $\dfrac{\mathrm{d}x}{\mathrm{d}t}$	the first derivative of x with respect to t
$\ddot{x}$ or $\dfrac{\mathrm{d}^2x}{\mathrm{d}t^2}$	the second derivative of x with respect to t
$\dot{\boldsymbol{r}}$ or $\dfrac{\mathrm{d}\boldsymbol{r}}{\mathrm{d}t}$	the first derivative of $\boldsymbol{r}$ with respect to t
$\ddot{\boldsymbol{r}}$ or $\dfrac{\mathrm{d}^2\boldsymbol{r}}{\mathrm{d}t^2}$	the second derivative of $\boldsymbol{r}$ with respect to t
δh	a small increment of h
$\rightarrow$	tends to
$\int f(x)\,\mathrm{d}x$	the indefinite integral of $f(x)$
$\int_a^b f(x)\,\mathrm{d}x$	the definite integral of $f(x)$ between $x = a$ and $x = b$
$\ln x$	the natural logarithm of x

$$[F(x)]_a^b = F(b) - F(a)$$

VECTORS 1

Most students will have met vectors before, either as part of their O-level work or in the pure mathematics part of their A-level course. This chapter gives a brief reminder of the main properties that will be used in later chapters of this book.

Vectors and vector addition 1.1

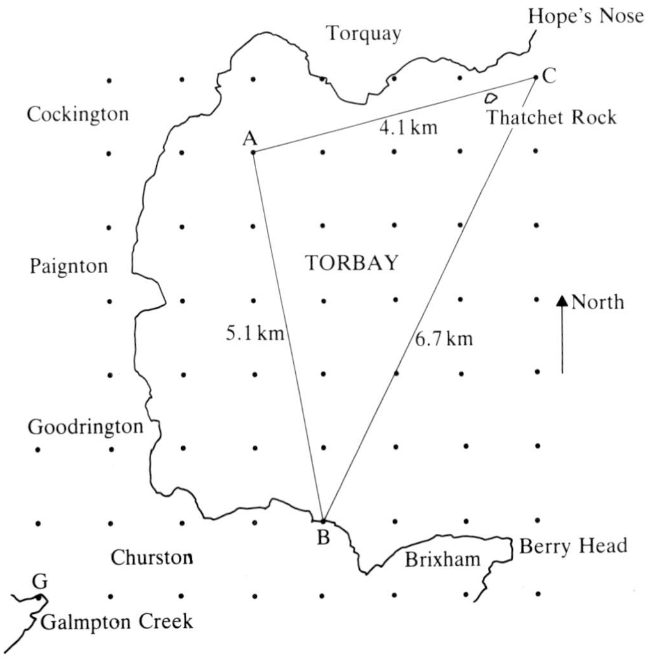

Figure 1.1

Figure 1.1 shows a section of coastline around Torbay, on which is marked a course for a yacht race, in which the boats have to sail around three buoys, A, B and C. Although yachts do not sail in straight lines, we can represent the displacement of a yacht from A to B by the vector **AB**, and from B to C by **BC**. The direct distances will be written as AB and BC. We can combine these displacements by the **triangle law of addition.**

$$\mathbf{AB} + \mathbf{BC} = \mathbf{AC},$$

and we say that **AC** is the **resultant** of **AB** followed by **BC**.

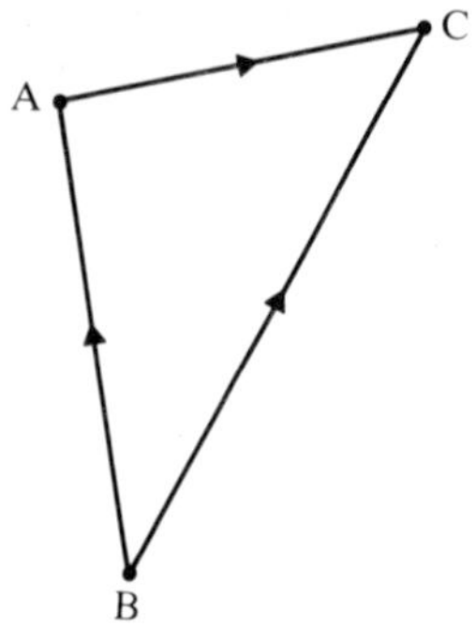

Figure 1.2

In figure 1.2 we have introduced arrows on the sides of the triangle to show the displacements. We can see that the displacement from A to B, **AB**, followed by the displacement from B to C, **BC**, is equivalent to the displacement from A to C, **AC**. Although the routes taken are different, the resulting displacement is the same.

Polygons

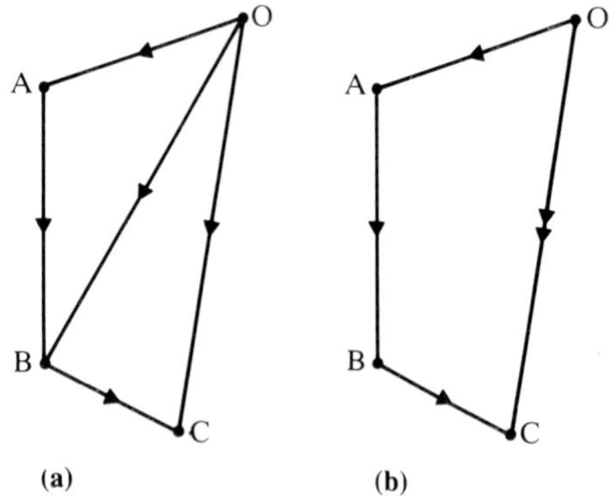

Figure 1.3

Clearly we will need to extend the idea of addition to more than two vectors. In figure 1.3a we see that

$$\mathbf{OA} + \mathbf{AB} = \mathbf{OB} \quad \text{and} \quad \mathbf{OB} + \mathbf{BC} = \mathbf{OC}.$$

So that $$\mathbf{OA} + \mathbf{AB} + \mathbf{BC} = \mathbf{OC}.$$

We usually write this result immediately and omit the first step. The resultant vector completes the polygon. It is sometimes convenient to stress the resultant vector by giving it a double arrow, as in figure 1.3b.

Zero and negative vectors

In figure 1.4 we note that

$$\mathbf{AB} + \mathbf{BC} + \mathbf{CA} = \mathbf{AA} = \mathbf{0},$$

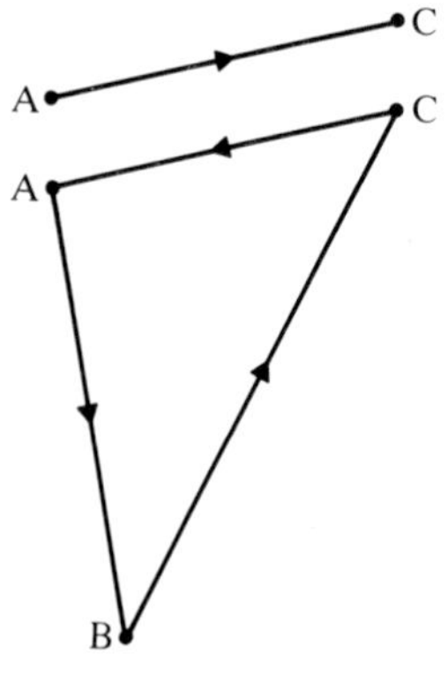

Figure 1.4

where **0** is the **zero vector** and represents zero displacement.

We also see that $$\mathbf{AC} + \mathbf{CA} = \mathbf{0},$$

and we write $$\mathbf{CA} = -\mathbf{AC},$$

where the negative of a vector is of the same length but is in the opposite direction.

We must take care to distinguish between vectors and lengths. Whilst $\mathbf{AB} + \mathbf{BC} + \mathbf{CA} = \mathbf{0}$ is true, it is not true that the lengths AB, BC and CA sum to zero. The displacement of a yacht after one complete circuit is zero, but it has covered a greater distance than one which has not left buoy A.

Description of displacements **1.2**

In sailing, each leg of the course is defined by its distance and bearing from its starting point, with reference to grid north. For example, B is 5.1 km from A on a bearing of 169°, so **AB** is defined by the number pair (5.1, 169°). Similarly, **BC** is defined by (6.7, 027°) and **AC** by (4.1, 076°).

It is not easy to combine vectors in this form. **AB** + **BC** = **AC**, but the three number pairs for these vectors are not related in a simple way and we would find it easier to find **AC** from a scale diagram rather than from its connection with **AB** and **BC**. In general, therefore, we will describe displacements in mathematics using base vectors. There are two ways of doing this.

a) Let $\begin{pmatrix}1\\0\end{pmatrix}$ be a unit vector due east and let $\begin{pmatrix}0\\1\end{pmatrix}$ be a unit vector due north. Then, in figure 1.1,

$$\mathbf{AB} = \begin{pmatrix}1\\-5\end{pmatrix} \quad \text{and} \quad \mathbf{BC} = \begin{pmatrix}3\\6\end{pmatrix},$$

and we can check that

$$\mathbf{AB} + \mathbf{BC} = \begin{pmatrix}1\\-5\end{pmatrix} + \begin{pmatrix}3\\6\end{pmatrix} = \begin{pmatrix}4\\1\end{pmatrix} = \mathbf{AC},$$

$$\mathbf{CA} = \begin{pmatrix}-4\\-1\end{pmatrix} = -\begin{pmatrix}4\\1\end{pmatrix} = -\mathbf{AC}.$$

The numbers in each column vector are called its **components**.

b) Let $\boldsymbol{i}$ be a unit vector due east and $\boldsymbol{j}$ a unit vector due north. Then

$$\mathbf{AB} = (1)\boldsymbol{i} + (-5)\boldsymbol{j} = \boldsymbol{i} - 5\boldsymbol{j},$$

and

$$\begin{aligned}\mathbf{AB} + \mathbf{BC} &= (\boldsymbol{i} - 5\boldsymbol{j}) + (3\boldsymbol{i} + 6\boldsymbol{j})\\ &= 4\boldsymbol{i} + \boldsymbol{j}\\ &= \mathbf{AC}.\end{aligned}$$

In solving problems it does not matter which of the above two notations we use, as long as we are consistent within a particular example. Clearly the two notations are equivalent:

$$\boldsymbol{i} = \begin{pmatrix}1\\0\end{pmatrix}, \quad \boldsymbol{j} = \begin{pmatrix}0\\1\end{pmatrix}.$$

In mathematics the unit vectors we use are based on the cartesian coordinate system in two or three dimensions, as shown in figure 1.5.

In three dimensions, unit vectors $\boldsymbol{i}$, $\boldsymbol{j}$ and $\boldsymbol{k}$ are taken along the x-, y- and z-axes, respectively. In terms of components these are

$$\boldsymbol{i} = \begin{pmatrix}1\\0\\0\end{pmatrix}, \quad \boldsymbol{j} = \begin{pmatrix}0\\1\\0\end{pmatrix}, \quad \boldsymbol{k} = \begin{pmatrix}0\\0\\1\end{pmatrix}.$$

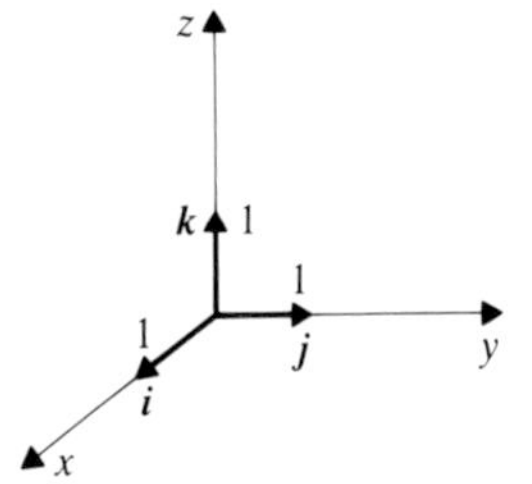

Figure 1.5

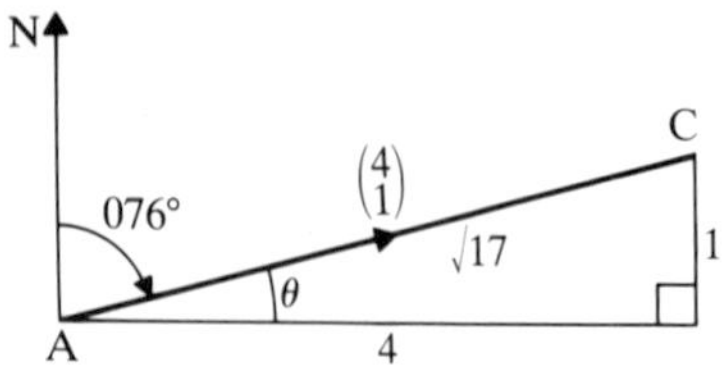

Figure 1.6

In later examples which involve motion in a vertical plane, $\boldsymbol{i}$ is chosen to be horizontal and $\boldsymbol{j}$ vertical.

We can now see a simple relationship between the mathematical description of vectors and the navigational description. Consider the displacement **AC**, as shown in figure 1.6.

$$\mathbf{AC} = \begin{pmatrix} 4 \\ 1 \end{pmatrix},$$

so that $AC^2 = 4^2 + 1^2 = 17$, giving $AC = \sqrt{17} = 4.1$, which is equal to the distance from A to C. We say that $\sqrt{17}$ is the **modulus** or length of the vector **AC**. Also $\tan\theta = \frac{1}{4}$, so $\theta = 14°$. The bearing from C to A is $90° - \theta = 076°$.

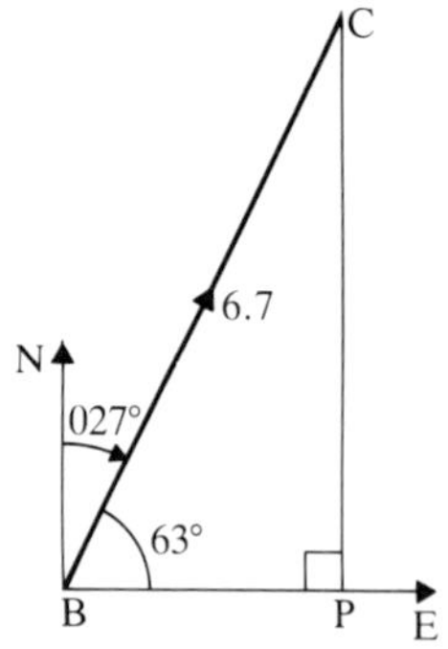

Figure 1.7

Since combining vectors is easier when they are in component form, it is important to be able to reverse this process, i.e. to convert a vector given by its magnitude and direction into one in component form.

For example, $\mathbf{BC} = (6.7, 027°)$ is shown in figure 1.7, in which

$$BP = 6.7 \cos 63° \approx 3 \qquad \text{and} \qquad CP = 6.7 \sin 63° \approx 6.$$

Thus, using base vectors $\boldsymbol{i}$ east and $\boldsymbol{j}$ north, $\mathbf{BC} = 3\boldsymbol{i} + 6\boldsymbol{j}$. Note that the slight inaccuracy has come from the original drawing. The process of converting a vector of known length and direction into component form is called **resolution into components**.

1.3 Different types of vector quantity

So far we have used vectors to describe displacements. Later in this book we will use them to describe other physical quantities such as velocity, acceleration, force, impulse and momentum. Indeed, any quantity which can be shown to have both magnitude (size) and direction can be represented by a vector. Quantities which have magnitude only, like temperature, are called scalars.

Localised vectors

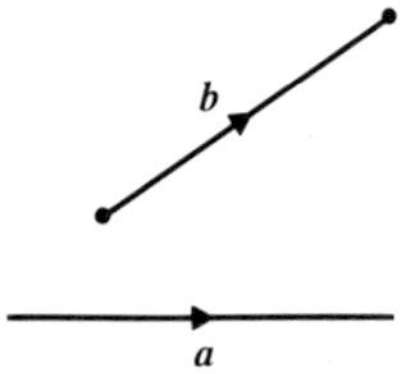

Figure 1.8

In section 1.1, **BC** was defined as a vector describing the displacement from B to C. It has definite start and end points and is called a **localised vector**.

Free vectors

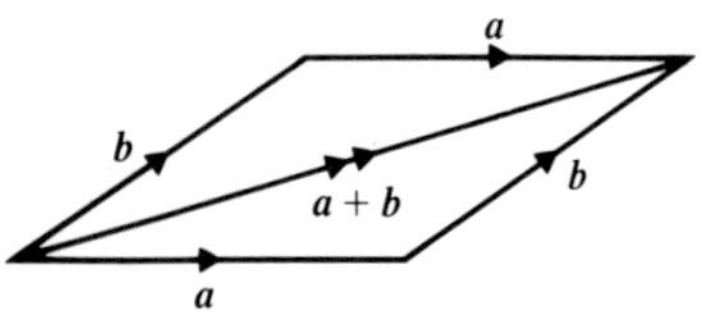

Figure 1.9(a)

In figure 1.1 **AC** = **GB**, the displacement from Galmpton Creek to Fishcombe Point. These vectors are equivalent, although they begin and end at different points. They are parallel and of the same length. We often wish to emphasise that there is an infinite set of vectors equivalent to a given vector. To show the fact that the starting point does not matter we use a single small letter e.g. $\boldsymbol{a}$, to represent what we call a **free vector**. We denote the modulus (length) of $\boldsymbol{a}$ by a.

To add two free vectors, such as those shown in figure 1.8, we use the triangle law, by placing them 'tip-to-tail', as shown in figure 1.9a.

To add two vectors localised at the same point, as often happens in problems in mechanics, we use the fact that vector addition is commutative and the two vectors form a parallelogram, of which their sum is the diagonal drawn through the same start point. This is referred to as the **parallelogram law of addition.** Figure 1.9a shows the method.

In practice we do not need to draw the complete parallelogram; we can draw one of the two triangles of figure 1.9a, using the triangle law. It is also worth noting that the second diagonal of the parallelogram is either $\boldsymbol{b} - \boldsymbol{a}$ or $\boldsymbol{a} - \boldsymbol{b}$, depending on its direction,as in figure 1.9b.

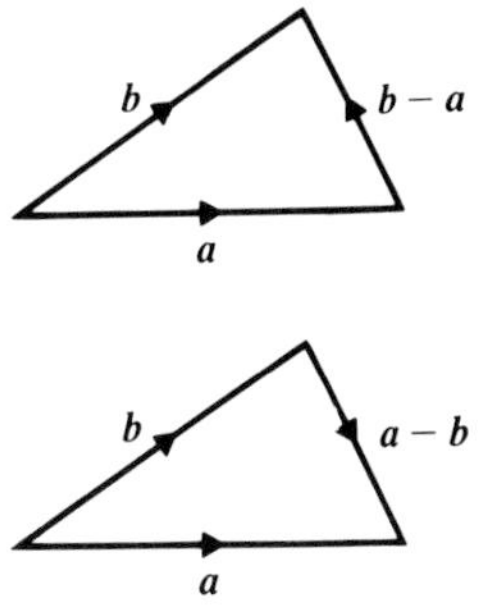

Figure 1.9(b)

Vectors with parameters **1.4**

In mechanics we will be interested in vectors which change, and we can illustrate some simple cases.

a) Suppose a man is standing 40 m from the edge of a road and suppose a car initially 100 m up the road is travelling down the road towards him at 20 m s^{-1}. The position of the car from the man at various times is shown in the table.

Time, t	0	1	2	3 ...	6
Displacement, **MC**	$\begin{pmatrix}40\\100\end{pmatrix}$	$\begin{pmatrix}40\\80\end{pmatrix}$	$\begin{pmatrix}40\\60\end{pmatrix}$	$\begin{pmatrix}40\\40\end{pmatrix}$ ...	$\begin{pmatrix}40\\-20\end{pmatrix}$

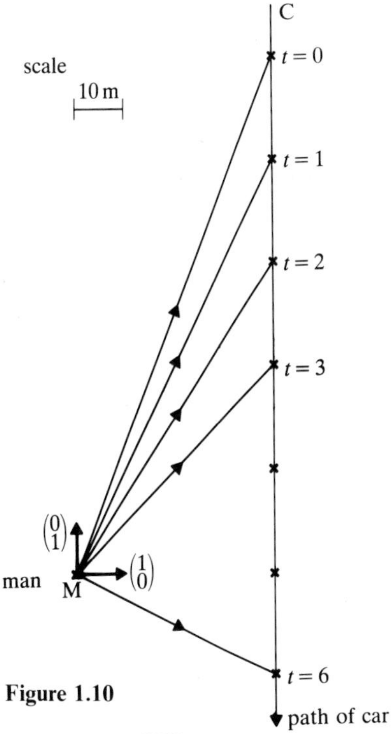

Figure 1.10

MC is the displacement of the car from the man and unit vectors are taken as in figure 1.10. We see that t seconds after the car has started,

$$\mathbf{MC} = \begin{pmatrix}40\\100\end{pmatrix} + t\begin{pmatrix}0\\-20\end{pmatrix} = \begin{pmatrix}40\\100-20t\end{pmatrix},$$

where t, representing time, is called a parameter.
Note that both the length and direction of **MC** vary, although the end point C is moving in a straight line.

b) Suppose the man is now standing in the middle of a roundabout of radius 10m, as in figure 1.11. As the car goes round, the position vector **MC** will be

$$\mathbf{MC} = \begin{pmatrix}10\cos\theta\\10\sin\theta\end{pmatrix}.$$

The parameter in this case is θ, the angle turned through by **MC**. The modulus of the vector **MC** is always 10, the radius of the circle.

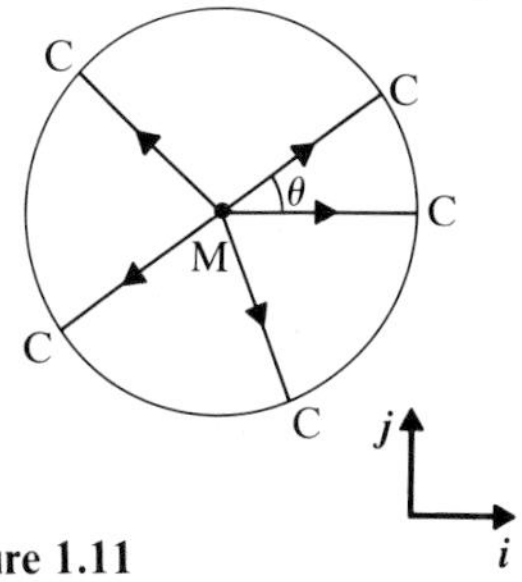

Figure 1.11

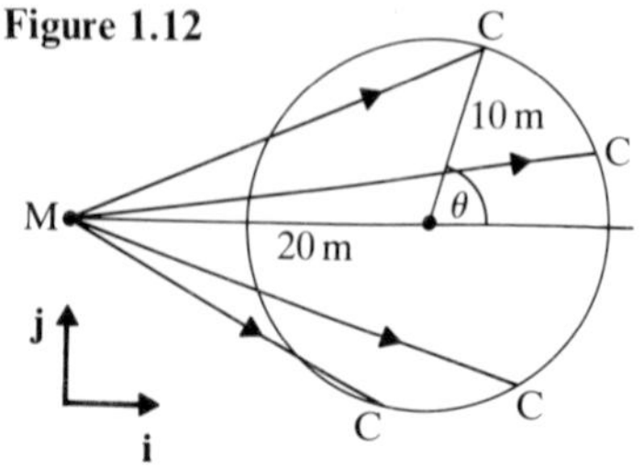

Figure 1.12

c) Suppose finally that the man is 20 m from the middle of the roundabout, watching the car go round, as in figure 1.12. Although C still describes a circle, the vector **MC** varies both in modulus and direction:

$$\mathbf{MC} = \begin{pmatrix} 20 \\ 0 \end{pmatrix} + \begin{pmatrix} 10\cos\theta \\ 10\sin\theta \end{pmatrix}.$$

EXERCISE 1A

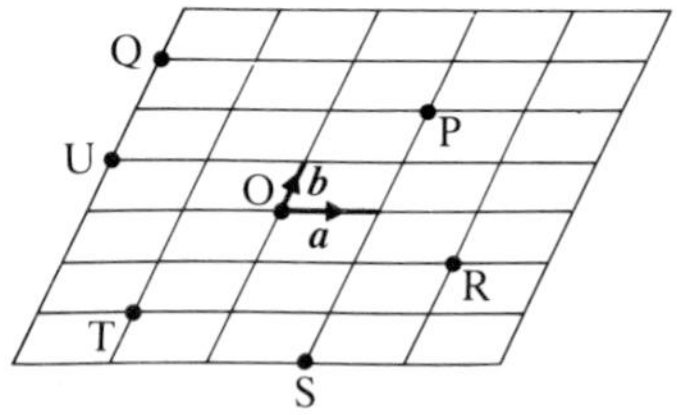

Figure 1.13

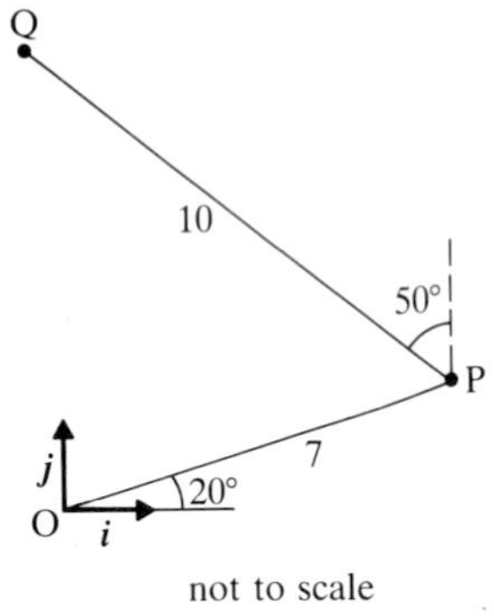

Figure 1.14

1. Express the position vectors of the points P, Q, R, S, T and U relative to O, in terms of the vectors $\boldsymbol{a}$ and $\boldsymbol{b}$ in figure 1.13.

2. A and B are the points (2, 4) and (0, 2), respectively, and O is the origin. Find the coordinates of C, D and E, if
   a) $\mathbf{OC} = \frac{1}{2}\mathbf{OA} + \frac{1}{2}\mathbf{OB}$
   b) $\mathbf{OD} = \frac{1}{4}\mathbf{OA} + \frac{3}{4}\mathbf{OB}$
   c) $\mathbf{OE} + \frac{1}{2}\mathbf{OB} - \frac{3}{2}\mathbf{OA} = \mathbf{0}$

3. A point P moves so that

$$\mathbf{OP} = \begin{pmatrix} 3 \\ 1 \end{pmatrix} + t\begin{pmatrix} -2 \\ 1 \end{pmatrix}.$$

   a) Plot P for $t = 0$, 1, 2, 3, and 4.
   b) What is the equation of the path of P?

4. A point P moves so that

$$\mathbf{OP} = t\,\boldsymbol{i} + t^2\boldsymbol{j}.$$

   a) Plot P for $t = 0, 1, \dots .6$.
   b) What is the equation of the path of P?

5. If $\mathbf{OP} = t\,\boldsymbol{i} + 3\sin t\,\boldsymbol{j}$, draw the path of P for $0 \leqslant t \leqslant 4\pi$.

6. Express the vectors **OP**, **PQ** and **OQ** in figure 1.14 in terms of the vectors $\boldsymbol{i}$ and $\boldsymbol{j}$, by resolving into components.

7. A yacht leaves Torbay on a bearing of 165° and sails for 80 nautical miles. How far east and south of Torbay is the yacht at the end of the trip? How far west should the yacht then sail in order to return home by sailing due north?

8. A light aircraft flies from Biggin Hill on a bearing of 285° for 50 km and then on a bearing of 080° for a further 80 km. How far east and north of Biggin Hill is the plane at the end of this leg?

9. A rocket is launched so that initially it rises vertically a distance of 50 km, then rises at 15° to the vertical for 80 km and then at 35° to the vertical for 130 km. Taking unit vectors horizontally and vertically, find how far in each direction it has moved from the launch pad and hence how far it then is from the pad.

10. A vector **OP** is of magnitude 10 units due south. Find its components in the directions of unit vectors $\hat{\boldsymbol{u}}$ and $\hat{\boldsymbol{v}}$ in the directions 050° and 320°, respectively.

The scalar product 1.5

So far we have shown how to add and subtract vectors. We now consider multiplication. Suppose that

$$\mathbf{AB} = \begin{pmatrix} 2 \\ 3 \end{pmatrix} \text{ and } \mathbf{BC} = \begin{pmatrix} -1 \\ 2 \end{pmatrix},$$

then we could define the product $\mathbf{AB} \times \mathbf{BC}$ as

$$\begin{pmatrix} 2 \\ 3 \end{pmatrix} \times \begin{pmatrix} -1 \\ 2 \end{pmatrix} = \begin{pmatrix} 2 \times -1 \\ 3 \times 2 \end{pmatrix} = \begin{pmatrix} -2 \\ 6 \end{pmatrix}.$$

This is a perfectly reasonable definition, but unfortunately does not have any practical use.

There are in fact a large number of different ways in which two vectors can be multiplied. We will consider just one, known as the scalar product, which does have a wide number of applications.

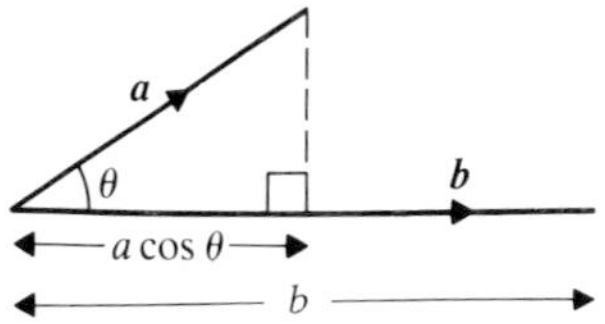

Figure 1.15

Definition

The **scalar product** of two vectors $\boldsymbol{a}$ and $\boldsymbol{b}$ is defined by

$$\boldsymbol{a} \cdot \boldsymbol{b} = ab \cos \theta,$$

where a and b are the lengths of the vectors and θ is the angle between them. It is sometimes called the 'dot' product. The result is a scalar and not a vector.

In figure 1.15, we see that

$$\begin{aligned} \boldsymbol{a} \cdot \boldsymbol{b} &= (a \cos \theta) b \\ &= (\text{the projection of } \boldsymbol{a} \text{ on } \boldsymbol{b}) \times \text{the length of } \boldsymbol{b} \end{aligned}$$

We define the scalar product of two vectors which do not meet, as in figure 1.16, as follows:

$$\begin{aligned} \boldsymbol{c} \cdot \boldsymbol{b} &= (\mathrm{XY})(b) \\ &= (c \cos \phi)(b) \\ &= cb \cos \phi. \end{aligned}$$

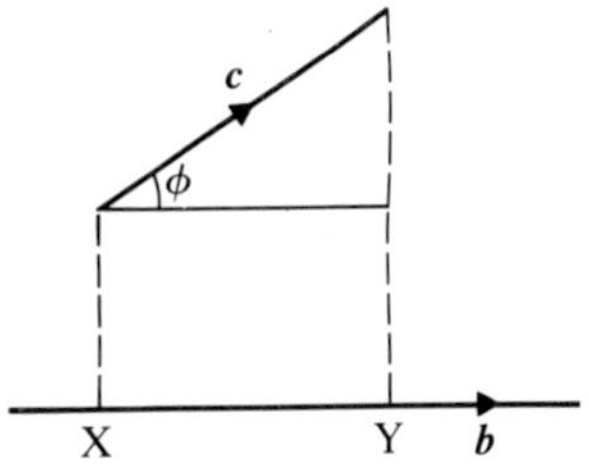

(a)

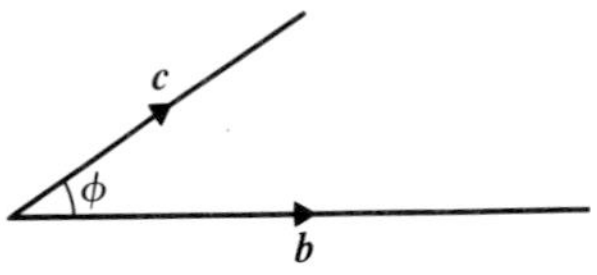

(b)

Figure 1.16

We note that this is the same result as the case when $\boldsymbol{b}$ and $\boldsymbol{c}$ are placed 'tip-to-tail'.

The angle between two vectors is the angle between their positive directions. To see this we usually locate the two vectors at the same origin, as in figure 1.17.

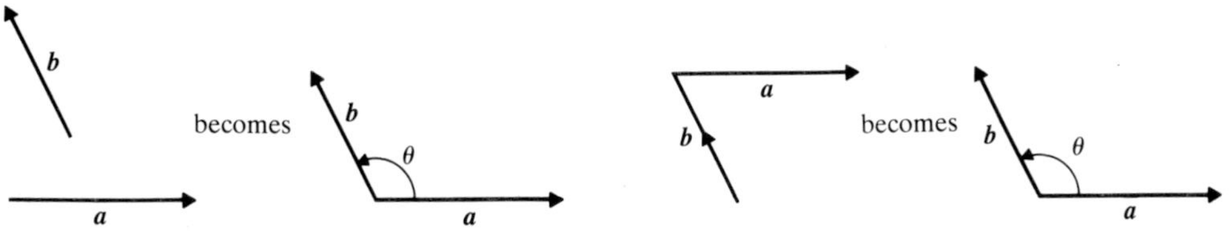

Figure 1.17

Properties of the scalar product

1. The commutative law applies:

$$\begin{aligned} \boldsymbol{a}\cdot\boldsymbol{b} &= ab\cos\theta \\ &= ba\cos\theta \\ &= \boldsymbol{b}\cdot\boldsymbol{a} \end{aligned}$$

2. The associative law does not apply since the product of any two vectors is a scalar.

3. The distributive law. Consider figure 1.18, where

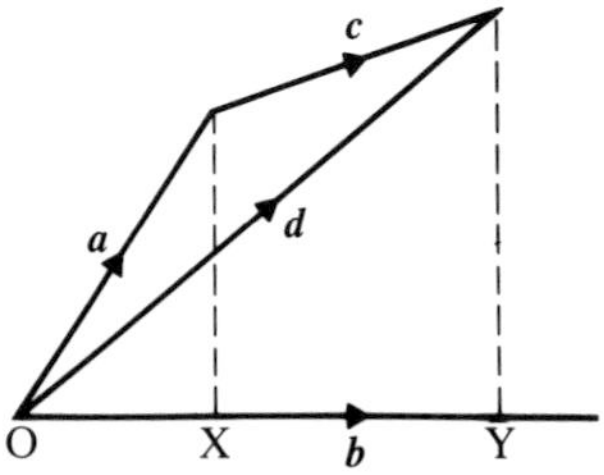

Figure 1.18

$$\begin{aligned} (\boldsymbol{a}+\boldsymbol{c})\cdot\boldsymbol{b} &= \boldsymbol{d}\cdot\boldsymbol{b} \\ &= (\mathrm{OY})(b) \\ &= (\mathrm{OX}+\mathrm{XY})(b) \\ &= (\mathrm{OX})(b)+(\mathrm{XY})(b) \\ &= \boldsymbol{a}\cdot\boldsymbol{b}+\boldsymbol{c}\cdot\boldsymbol{b} \end{aligned}$$

So the distributive law of the scalar product over the addition of vectors is true.

4. Multiplication by scalars. It is clear that

$$(k\boldsymbol{a})\cdot(l\boldsymbol{b}) = (kl)\boldsymbol{a}\cdot\boldsymbol{b},$$

where k and l are scalars.

5. The scalar product of a vector with itself gives the square of its modulus:

$$\boldsymbol{a}\cdot\boldsymbol{a} = aa\cos 0^\circ = a^2.$$

6. If $\boldsymbol{a}$ is perpendicular to $\boldsymbol{b}$, then

$$\boldsymbol{a}\cdot\boldsymbol{b} = ab\cos 90^\circ = 0.$$

Conversely, if $\boldsymbol{a}\cdot\boldsymbol{b}=0$, then either $\boldsymbol{a}$ or $\boldsymbol{b}$ is zero (or both) or $\boldsymbol{a}$ and $\boldsymbol{b}$ are perpendicular vectors.

A particular use of result 6 arises when vectors are expressed in terms of components.
Let $\boldsymbol{i}$ and $\boldsymbol{j}$ be unit vectors along perpendicular axes, then

$$\boldsymbol{i}\cdot\boldsymbol{i}=\boldsymbol{j}\cdot\boldsymbol{j}=1 \qquad \text{and} \qquad \boldsymbol{i}\cdot\boldsymbol{j}=\boldsymbol{j}\cdot\boldsymbol{i}=0.$$

If $\boldsymbol{a}=a_1\boldsymbol{i}+a_2\boldsymbol{j}$ and $\boldsymbol{b}=b_1\boldsymbol{i}+b_2\boldsymbol{j}$, we can write

$$\begin{aligned} \boldsymbol{a}\cdot\boldsymbol{b} &= (a_1\boldsymbol{i}+a_2\boldsymbol{j})\cdot(b_1\boldsymbol{i}+b_2\boldsymbol{j}) \\ &= a_1b_1+a_2b_2, \end{aligned}$$

using the distributive law. In three dimensions $\boldsymbol{a}=a_1\boldsymbol{i}+a_2\boldsymbol{j}+a_3\boldsymbol{k}$ and $\boldsymbol{b}=b_1\boldsymbol{i}+b_2\boldsymbol{j}+b_3\boldsymbol{k}$, and the result above extends to give

$$\boldsymbol{a}\cdot\boldsymbol{b} = a_1b_1+a_2b_2+a_3b_3,$$

since $\boldsymbol{k}\cdot\boldsymbol{k}=1$ and $\boldsymbol{k}\cdot\boldsymbol{i}=\boldsymbol{k}\cdot\boldsymbol{j}=0$.

The angle between two vectors

In two dimensions it is easy to find the angle between two vectors, as the example shows.

EXAMPLE 1

Find the angle between the vectors $\binom{1}{2}$ and $\binom{3}{4}$. In figure 1.19:

$\psi = \tan^{-1} 2 = 63.4^\circ$ and $\phi = \tan^{-1} \frac{4}{3} = 53.1^\circ$.

The angle between the vectors is $\psi - \phi = 10.3^\circ$

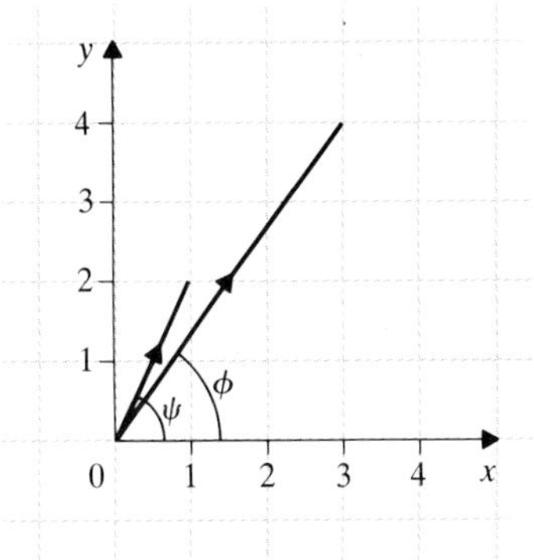

Figure 1.19

The scalar product provides us with an alternative method. By definition,

$$\boldsymbol{a} \cdot \boldsymbol{b} = ab \cos \theta.$$

Rearranging this $\cos \theta = \dfrac{\boldsymbol{a} \cdot \boldsymbol{b}}{ab} = \dfrac{\text{scalar product}}{\text{length product}}.$

Now $\boldsymbol{a} \cdot \boldsymbol{b} = 1 \times 3 + 2 \times 4 = 11$, and $a = \sqrt{5}$, $b = 5$. So that

$$\cos \theta = \frac{11}{5\sqrt{5}} = 0.984,$$

giving $\theta = 10.3^\circ$. This method is particularly useful in three dimensions.

EXAMPLE 2

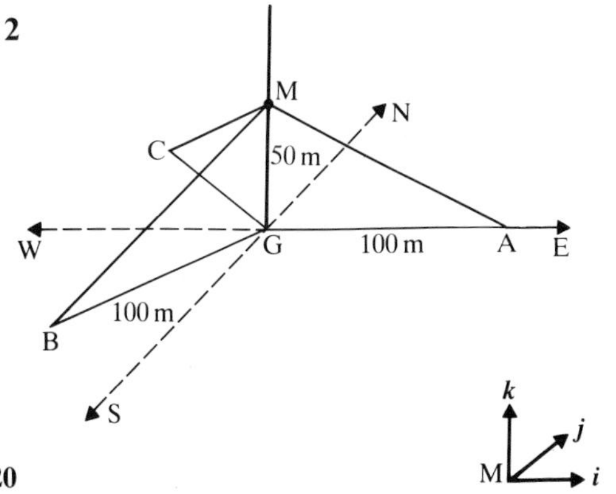

Figure 1.20

In figure 1.20, three guy ropes are supporting a television mast at a point 50 m above its base. The other end of each rope is fixed to the ground 100 m from the base of the mast, at three points due east, southwest and northwest of the mast. Find the angles between pairs of ropes.

Let M be the origin and take unit vectors in the directions east, north and vertically upwards.

$$\mathbf{MA} = \begin{pmatrix} 100 \\ 0 \\ -50 \end{pmatrix}, \quad \mathbf{MB} = \begin{pmatrix} -100 \cos 45^\circ \\ -100 \sin 45^\circ \\ -50 \end{pmatrix}, \quad \mathbf{MC} = \begin{pmatrix} -100 \cos 45^\circ \\ 100 \sin 45^\circ \\ -50 \end{pmatrix}$$

By Pythagoras' theorem:

$$MA = MB = MC = \sqrt{12\,500}\ \text{m}.$$

Hence $\cos A\hat{M}B = \dfrac{\mathbf{MA}\cdot\mathbf{MB}}{MA \times MB}$

$$= \frac{100 \times -70.7 + 50 \times 50}{12\,500} = -0.364,$$

$$A\hat{M}B = 111^\circ.$$

So by symmetry, $A\hat{M}C = 111^\circ$. Also

$$\cos B\hat{M}C = \frac{\mathbf{MB}\cdot\mathbf{MC}}{MB \times MC}$$

$$= \frac{(-70.7 \times -70.7) + (-70.7 \times 70.7) + (-50 \times -50)}{12\,500}$$

$$= 0.2,$$

$$B\hat{M}C = 78.5^\circ.$$

The angles between pairs of ropes are 111°, 111° and 78.5°.

1.6 Unit vectors

In our work so far we have taken unit vectors either in the directions east and north or along cartesian axes. Sometimes we need to form unit vectors in other directions.

EXAMPLE 1

Find a unit vector in the direction of the vector $4\boldsymbol{i} + \boldsymbol{j}$.

The modulus of $4\boldsymbol{i} + \boldsymbol{j}$ is $\sqrt{(4^2 + 1^2)} = \sqrt{17}$. So a unit vector in the direction of $\binom{4}{1}$ is $\binom{4/\sqrt{17}}{1/\sqrt{17}}$, written $\hat{\boldsymbol{u}}$. The ˆ reminds us that we have a unit vector, although it is often omitted from the **base unit vectors *i*, *j*,** and ***k***. Note also that

$$\hat{\boldsymbol{u}} = \frac{4}{\sqrt{17}}\boldsymbol{i} + \frac{1}{\sqrt{17}}\boldsymbol{j}.$$

In general, $$\hat{\boldsymbol{u}} = \frac{\boldsymbol{u}}{u},$$

1.7 Forces

A fundamental concept that will be used in later chapters is that of a force. We all have an intuitive idea of what forces are, since we experience them in everyday life through different agencies. Some examples will illustrate this.

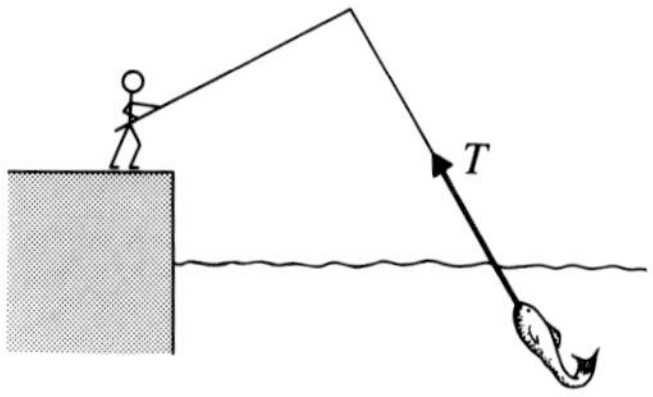

Figure 1.21

a) In figure 1.21 a fisherman is trying to land a fish. The force pulling on the fish comes from the tension in the line. The arrow labelled $\boldsymbol{T}$ shows the force on the fish from the line.

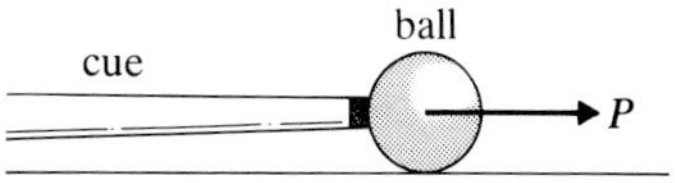

Figure 1.22

b) Figure 1.22 shows a snooker ball being struck by a cue. The force on the ball comes from a thrust in the cue, and is labelled $\boldsymbol{P}$.

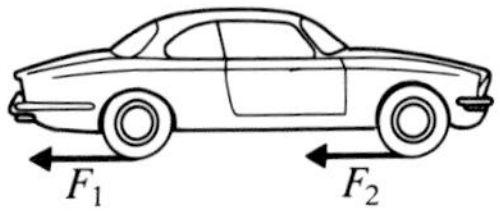

Figure 1.23

c) If a car is in a skid with its wheels locked it will slow down and eventually stop. This is mainly due to the frictional forces acting between the wheels and the ground. In figure 1.23 the arrows labelled $\boldsymbol{F}_1$ and $\boldsymbol{F}_2$ indicate the frictional forces acting on the wheels of the car.

d) Jet fighters often land at high speeds on runways which are restricted in length. Conventional braking and the reverse thrust of the engines is assisted by the use of a parachute and this increases air resistance to help slow down the plane.

Figure 1.24

A jaguar landing at Farnborough air show

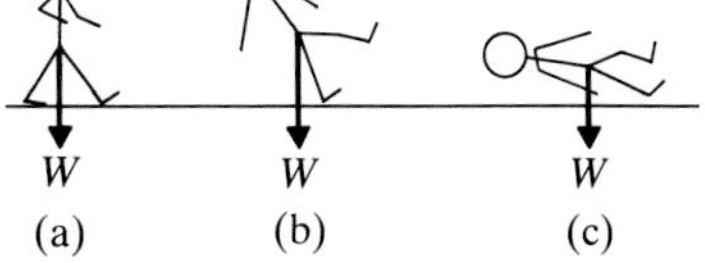

Figure 1.25

e) In figure 1.25 a man who has slipped on ice will fall to the ground because there is a weight force pulling him down. The weight force is always acting on the man, but in figure 1.25a this is balanced by contact forces between his feet and the ice. In parts b and c, he has 'lost contact' with the ice.

It is important to realise that the above examples only illustrate our intuitive ideas about forces. Whilst forces are concerned with motion, they are not necessarily required to maintain it. Furthermore, motion is possible in the absence of forces. A space rocket far out in space does not need any force acting on it to keep it going at a constant speed in a straight line. This will be discussed in more detail in chapter 3, where the units of force will be given, which for the present we will refer to simply as units.

1.8 Force vectors

A force, however produced, will be specified by its magnitude (to distinguish between large and small forces) and its direction (to distinguish, for example, between a push and a pull). Forces, therefore, can be described mathematically by vectors.

Figure 1.26 shows a man opening a door. If he exerts the same force in (a) and (b), it is clear that the door will open more easily in (b). Although the forces labelled ***P*** are equal in magnitude and direction, they have different effects because of their different points of application. Thus, force vectors are not necessarily free vectors and for the rest of this book we will usually regard them as localised vectors.

When more than one force acts at a point we can find their resultant by the methods of sections 1.1 and 1.2.

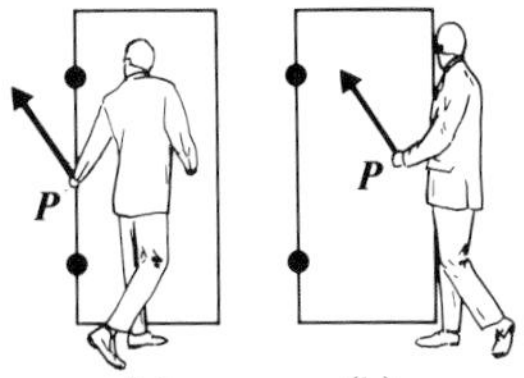

(a) (b)

Figure 1.26

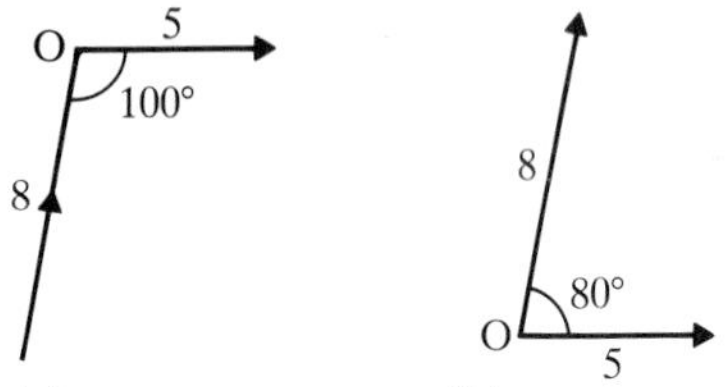

(a) (b)

Figure 1.27

EXAMPLE 1

Two forces act at a point, as shown in figure 1.27a. Find the magnitude and direction of their resultant.

We redraw the diagram with all the forces coming away from the point O, as in figure 1.27b. This gives a figure equivalent to the original one.

There are three methods we can use to solve this problem.

Method 1

We draw a vector polygon to scale and find the resultant by measurement, as in figure 1.28. From this figure ***R*** has magnitude 10.14 units and makes an angle of 51° with the force of 5 units.

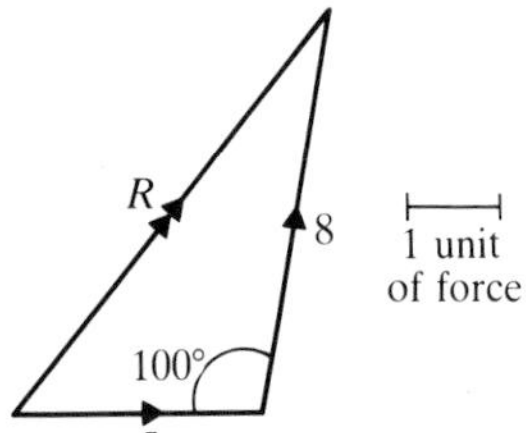

Figure 1.28

Method 2

We draw a sketch vector polygon, as in figure 1.29 (not to scale). ***R*** is then given by the cosine rule:

$$R^2 = 5^2 + 8^2 - 2 \times 5 \times 8 \cos 100^\circ,$$

$$R = 10.14.$$

θ is given by the sine rule:

$$\frac{8}{\sin\theta} = \frac{R}{\sin 100^\circ},$$

$$\theta = 51^\circ.$$

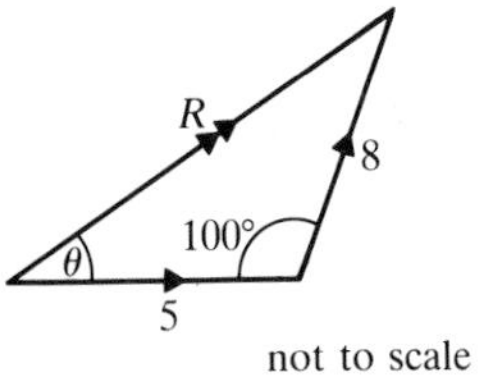

Figure 1.29

Method 3

We resolve the forces into components, taking $\boldsymbol{i}$ and $\boldsymbol{j}$ in the directions shown in figure 1.30. The force of magnitude 8 units is resolved as

$$8\cos 80^\circ\,\boldsymbol{i} + 8\sin 80^\circ\,\boldsymbol{j},$$

to give $\boldsymbol{R}$ as $\qquad \boldsymbol{R} = (5 + 8\cos 80^\circ)\boldsymbol{i} + 8\sin 80^\circ\,\boldsymbol{j}.$

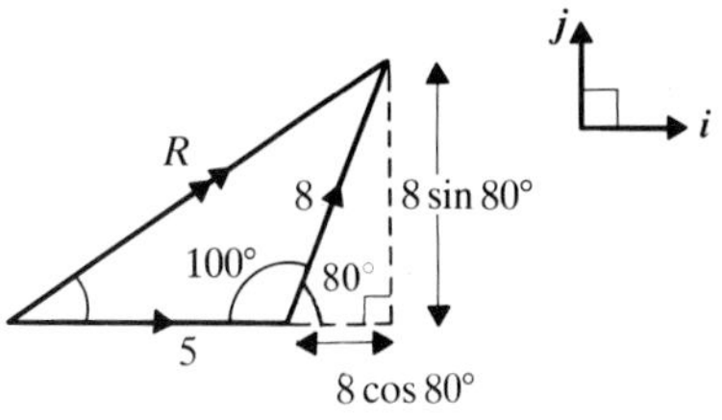

Figure 1.30

The best method to use depends on the number of forces acting in any given problem and the degree of accuracy required. Method 2 is very useful when the polygon reduces to a triangle, and method 3 is usually applied when more than three forces are present.

EXAMPLE 2

Three forces act at a point, as shown in figure 1.31. If their resultant acts due north or south, find the magnitudes of the unknown force, $\boldsymbol{P}$, and the resultant, $\boldsymbol{R}$.

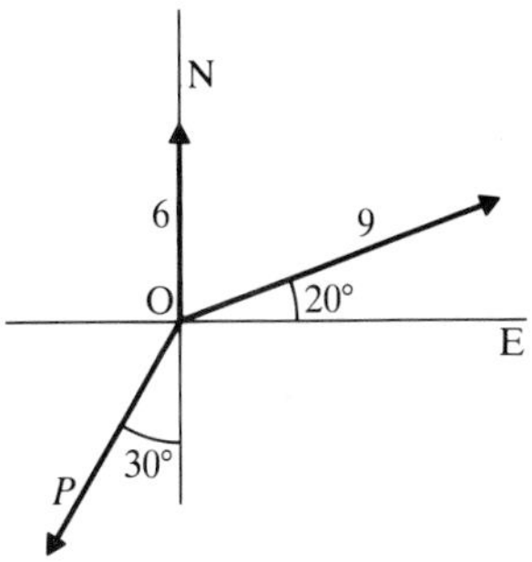

Figure 1.31

It seems as if method 3 is the best to use, but a sketch of the vector polygon, as in figure 1.32, gives us a triangle. From this figure we can calculate P and R using the sine rule.

$$\frac{P}{\sin 110^\circ} = \frac{9}{\sin 30^\circ} = \frac{6+R}{\sin 40^\circ},$$

which gives $P = 16.9$ and $R = 5.57$ due south. This simplification is possible because we have a triangle of forces, since the angle between $\boldsymbol{R}$ and the force of 6 units is 180°.

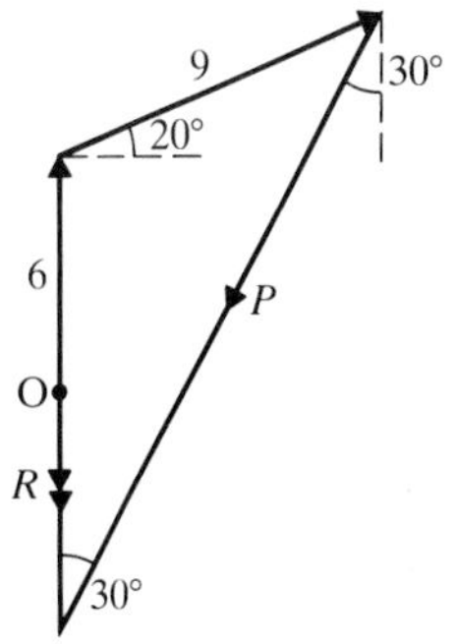

Figure 1.32

EXAMPLE 3

Given the same conditions as example 2, except that the 6 unit force is now acting at 10° west of the north line, as shown in figure 1.33, find the resultant, $\boldsymbol{R}$.

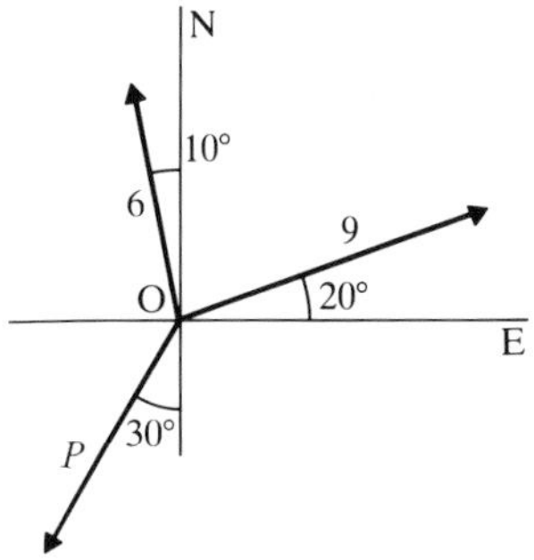

Figure 1.33

Figure 1.34 shows the polygon of forces. The geometry is not as simple in this case, and we have to use method 3. We take unit base vectors east and north. Thus

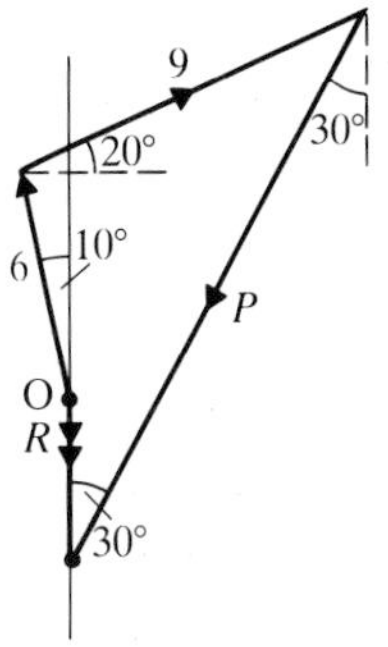

Figure 1.34

$$\boldsymbol{R} = \begin{pmatrix} 9\cos 20^\circ \\ 9\sin 20^\circ \end{pmatrix} + \begin{pmatrix} -6\sin 10^\circ \\ 6\cos 10^\circ \end{pmatrix} + \begin{pmatrix} -P\sin 30^\circ \\ -P\cos 30^\circ \end{pmatrix}$$

$$= \begin{pmatrix} 9\cos 20^\circ - 6\sin 10^\circ - P\sin 30^\circ \\ 9\sin 20^\circ + 6\cos 10^\circ - P\cos 30^\circ \end{pmatrix}.$$

Since $\boldsymbol{R}$ has no component in the east direction,

$$9\cos 20^\circ - 6\sin 10^\circ - P\sin 30^\circ = 0,$$

giving $P = 14.8$, and hence

$$\begin{aligned} R &= 9\sin 20^\circ + 6\cos 10^\circ - P\cos 30^\circ \\ &= -3.86. \end{aligned}$$

The resultant force is 3.86 units due south.

In practice, once we have decided to use method 3, we do not draw a vector polygon, but proceed directly as follows. In figure 1.33
a) resolving along OE,

$$9\cos 20^\circ - 6\sin 10^\circ - P\sin 30^\circ = 0, \qquad \textbf{(1)}$$

b) resolving along OS,

$$P\cos 30^\circ - 6\cos 10^\circ - 9\sin 20^\circ = R. \qquad \textbf{(2)}$$

Equations (**1**) and (**2**) are then solved as above.

Equilibrium

When the resultant of a number of forces acting at a point is zero, the forces are said to be in equilibrium.

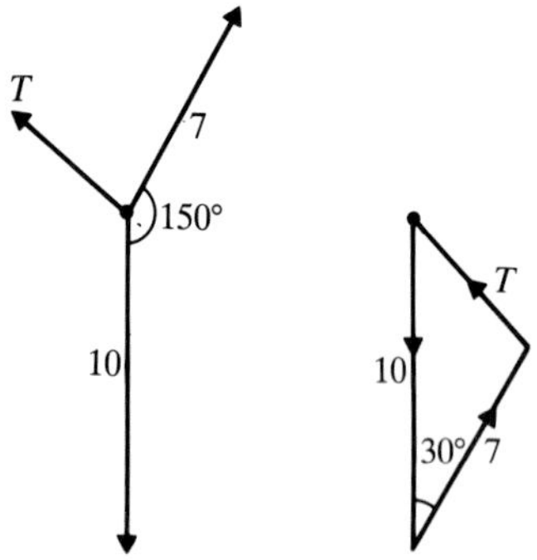

(a) **(b)**

Figure 1.35

EXAMPLE 4

If the three forces in figure 1.35a are in equilibrium, find the magnitude of the force $\boldsymbol{T}$.

The resultant is zero and so we have a triangle of forces (figure 1.35b) and use the cosine rule as in method 2.

$$T^2 = 10^2 + 7^2 - 2 \times 10 \times 7\cos 30^\circ = 27.76.$$

Hence $T = 5.26$.

Consider now three general forces in equilibrium acting at a point, as in figure 1.36.

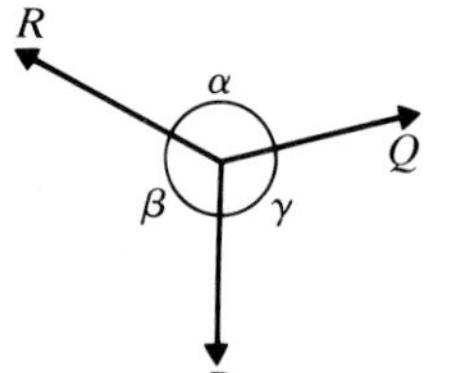

Figure 1.36

The vector polygon is shown in figure 1.37 (not to scale). From the sine rule:

$$\frac{P}{\sin(180^\circ - \alpha)} = \frac{Q}{\sin(180^\circ - \beta)} = \frac{R}{\sin(180^\circ - \gamma)}$$

$$\frac{P}{\sin\alpha} = \frac{Q}{\sin\beta} = \frac{R}{\sin\gamma}$$

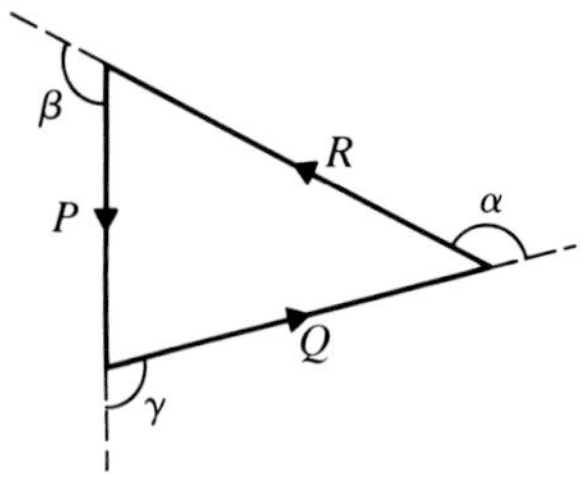

Figure 1.37

This result is known as **Lami's theorem**.

EXERCISE 1B

1. Find the angle between the following pairs of vectors:

   a) $\begin{pmatrix} 1 \\ 1 \end{pmatrix}$ and $\begin{pmatrix} 2 \\ -4 \end{pmatrix}$. b) $\boldsymbol{i} + \boldsymbol{j}$ and $\boldsymbol{i} + \boldsymbol{k}$. c) $\begin{pmatrix} 1 \\ 2 \\ 3 \end{pmatrix}$ and $\begin{pmatrix} 5 \\ -2 \\ 1 \end{pmatrix}$.

   d) $\boldsymbol{i} - 3\boldsymbol{j} + \boldsymbol{k}$ and $2\boldsymbol{i} + 2\boldsymbol{j} - \boldsymbol{k}$.

2. a) Find the modulus of the vector $\begin{pmatrix} 1 \\ 2 \\ 3 \end{pmatrix}$.

   b) Find the unit vector in the direction of the vector $\begin{pmatrix} 1 \\ 2 \\ 3 \end{pmatrix}$.

3. A particle moves so that its position at time t is given by

$$\boldsymbol{r} = 6t^2\boldsymbol{i} + 4t\boldsymbol{j}$$

   a) When is $\boldsymbol{r}$ parallel to $3\boldsymbol{i} + 2\boldsymbol{j}$?

   b) When is $\boldsymbol{r}$ perpendicular to $3\boldsymbol{i} - 2\boldsymbol{j}$?

4. Calculate the component of the vector $\begin{pmatrix} 10 \\ 7 \end{pmatrix}$ in the direction of the vector $\begin{pmatrix} 2 \\ 1 \end{pmatrix}$. Illustrate your answer on a diagram.

5. Two forces $\boldsymbol{X}$ and $\boldsymbol{Y}$ act away from a point and the angle between them is α. Find the magnitude of the resultant and its inclination to the force $\boldsymbol{X}$ in the following cases:

   a) $X = 10$, $Y = 15$, $\alpha = 50°$.

   b) $X = 4$, $Y = 7$, $\alpha = 90°$.

   c) $X = 9$, $Y = 11$, $\alpha = 140°$.

6. A particle is acted on by forces 2 units in the direction northwest and 3 units in the direction northeast.

   a) What is the magnitude and direction of the resultant force acting on the particle?

   b) What is the magnitude and direction of the force needed so that the resultant force on the particle is zero?

7. Find the magnitude and direction of the resultant of forces 80 units on a bearing of 010°, 100 units at 070° and 50 units at 150°, (a) by scale drawing and (b) by calculation.

8. Two forces $\boldsymbol{X}$ and $\boldsymbol{Y}$ act at an angle of 80° to each other. A third force of magnitude 10 units acts at an angle of 120° with the force $\boldsymbol{X}$ and 160° with the force $\boldsymbol{Y}$. If the system is in equilibrium, find the magnitudes of $\boldsymbol{X}$ and $\boldsymbol{Y}$.

2 KINEMATICS

Kinematics is the study of motion, that is, of velocity and acceleration, without consideration of what causes or constrains it. Use is made in this chapter of the idea of differentiation of displacement to give both velocity and acceleration, which is extended to motion in two or three dimensions by the use of vectors.

2.1 Velocity

On a slalom run, a skier frequently changes his speed and direction.

The photograph shows part of a slalom ski run. Suppose we want to find the average speed of the skier between two successive gates. We would need to calculate the fraction distance/time, but the path taken is clearly not a straight line, having deviations both sideways and due to the uneven ground, so we do not know the exact distance travelled. Figure 2.1 represents a similar problem which has been reduced to two dimensions. Notice that a scale has been included, together with the timings at each gate. In addition we have replaced the actual path taken by a series of straight-line segments.

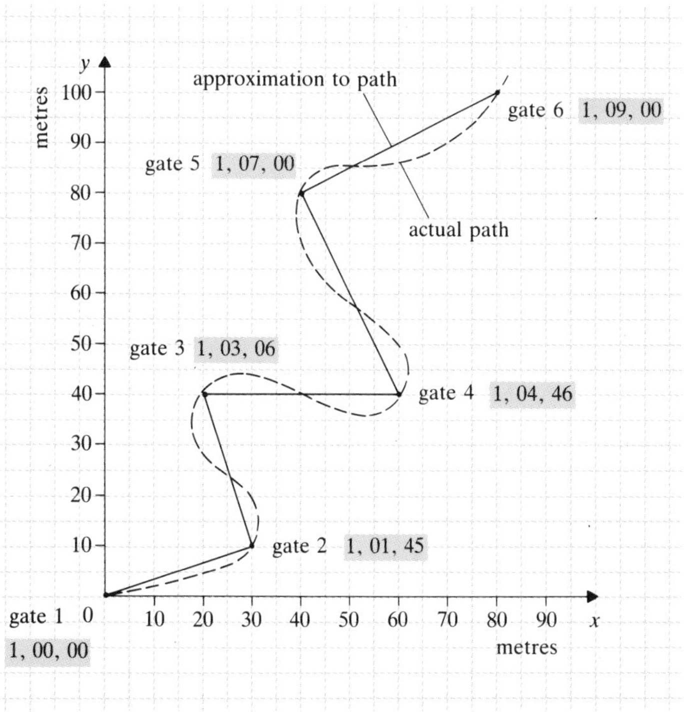

Figure 2.1

The following table, based on figure 2.1 shows the calculation of the approximate average speed at various points on the course.

Gate	1–2	2–3	3–4	4–5	5–6
Distance (m)	32	32	40	45	45
Time (s)	1.45	1.61	1.40	2.14	2.00
Approximate average speed ($m\ s^{-1}$)	22	20	29	21	23

We have calculated the approximate average speed of the skier for different legs of his run, but we have not given any indication about his direction, which changes every time he passes through a gate. To account for this we consider his displacement at each stage using vectors, as shown in the table below. His average velocity is defined to be (displacement vector / time).

Gate	1–2	2–3	3–4	4–5	5–6
Displacement vector (m)	$\begin{pmatrix}30\\10\end{pmatrix}$	$\begin{pmatrix}-10\\30\end{pmatrix}$	$\begin{pmatrix}40\\0\end{pmatrix}$	$\begin{pmatrix}-20\\40\end{pmatrix}$	$\begin{pmatrix}40\\20\end{pmatrix}$
Average velocity (ms^{-1})	$\begin{pmatrix}20.7\\6.9\end{pmatrix}$	$\begin{pmatrix}-6.2\\18.7\end{pmatrix}$	$\begin{pmatrix}29\\0\end{pmatrix}$	$\begin{pmatrix}-9.4\\18.7\end{pmatrix}$	$\begin{pmatrix}20\\10\end{pmatrix}$

In general, the **average velocity** in going from a point P_1 with position vector $\boldsymbol{r}_1$ at a time t_1 to a point P_2 with position vector $\boldsymbol{r}_2$ at a time t_2 is given by the expression: $(\boldsymbol{r}_2 - \boldsymbol{r}_1)/(t_2 - t_1)$.

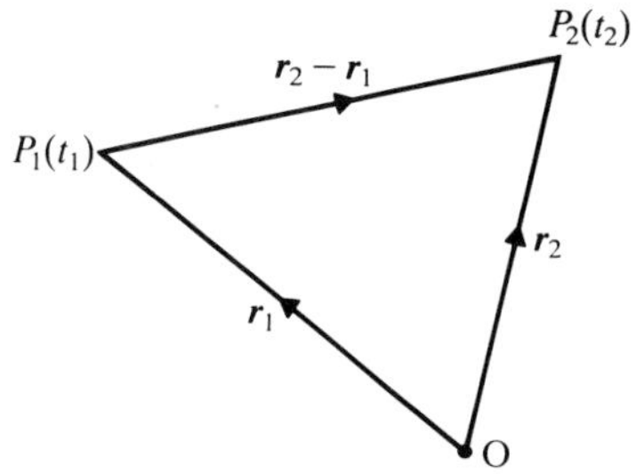

Figure 2.2

Let us look again at the progress of the skier between gates 1 and 2, as in figure 2.1. His average velocity is $\binom{20.7}{6.9}$ m s^{-1} and the magnitude of this is $(20.7^2 + 6.9^2)^{1/2} \simeq 22$ m s^{-1}. In practice his average speed is greater than this since he has actually travelled more than 32 m between gates 1 and 2. The following example will reinforce this idea.

EXAMPLE 1

A driver approaches a roundabout of circumference 600 m, as shown in figure 2.3. Realising that she is in the wrong part of town, she leaves by the same road as she entered. Her time on the roundabout is one minute.

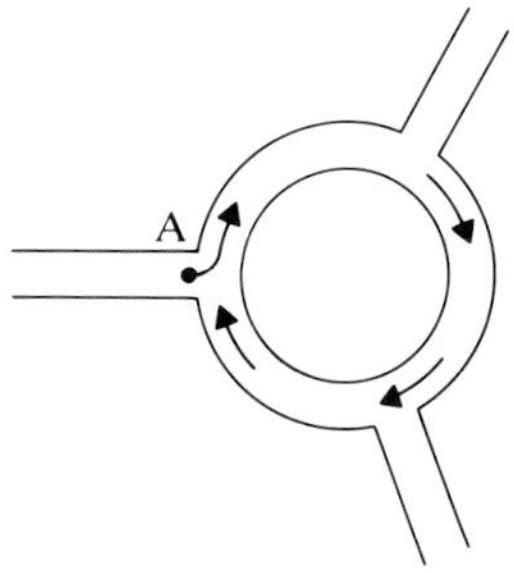

Figure 2.3

Her average speed is 600 m/min = 10 m s^{-1}. However, her displacement in that minute is **AA** = **0** and so her average velocity is **0**, with magnitude 0 m s^{-1}. The magnitude of the average velocity vector is only equal to the average speed when the motion is in a straight line.

For the situation in figure 2.4, as the particle moves from P to Q along the curve we obtain:
average velocity = PQ/t,
magnitude of average velocity = PQ/t,
average speed = $s/t >$ PQ/t:

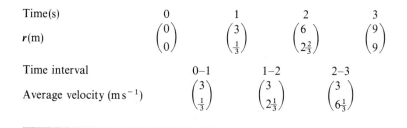

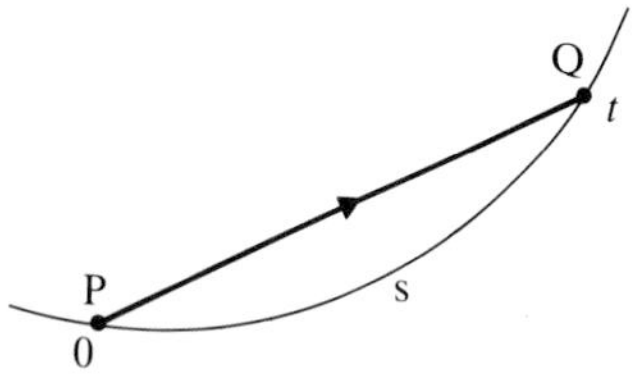

Figure 2.4

Velocity at an instant

EXAMPLE 2

Suppose a point moves so that its position vector after t seconds is given by $\boldsymbol{r} = 3t\boldsymbol{i} + \frac{1}{3}t^3\boldsymbol{j}$. Find its average velocity over the first three one-second periods.

We will generally find it more useful to use column vector notation:

$$3t\boldsymbol{i} + \tfrac{1}{3}t^3\boldsymbol{j} \equiv \begin{pmatrix} 3t \\ \frac{1}{3}t^3 \end{pmatrix}.$$

We can set out the calculation in a table as follows:

Time(s)	0		1		2		3
$\boldsymbol{r}$(m)	$\begin{pmatrix} 0 \\ 0 \end{pmatrix}$		$\begin{pmatrix} 3 \\ \frac{1}{3} \end{pmatrix}$		$\begin{pmatrix} 6 \\ 2\frac{2}{3} \end{pmatrix}$		$\begin{pmatrix} 9 \\ 9 \end{pmatrix}$
Time interval		0–1		1–2		2–3	
Average velocity (m s^{-1})		$\begin{pmatrix} 3 \\ \frac{1}{3} \end{pmatrix}$		$\begin{pmatrix} 3 \\ 2\frac{1}{3} \end{pmatrix}$		$\begin{pmatrix} 3 \\ 6\frac{1}{3} \end{pmatrix}$	

Suppose we want to find the velocity when $t = 2$. Clearly the velocity is not constant, but we could improve our average velocity near $t = 2$

by taking successively smaller intervals of time near $t = 2$, as with motion in a straight line. Figure 2.5 shows the path taken by the particle, with line segments drawn from $t = 2$ to $t = 3$ and from $t = 2$ to $t = 2.5$ to give the average velocities over those intervals. The calculation for smaller intervals can be shown in a table.

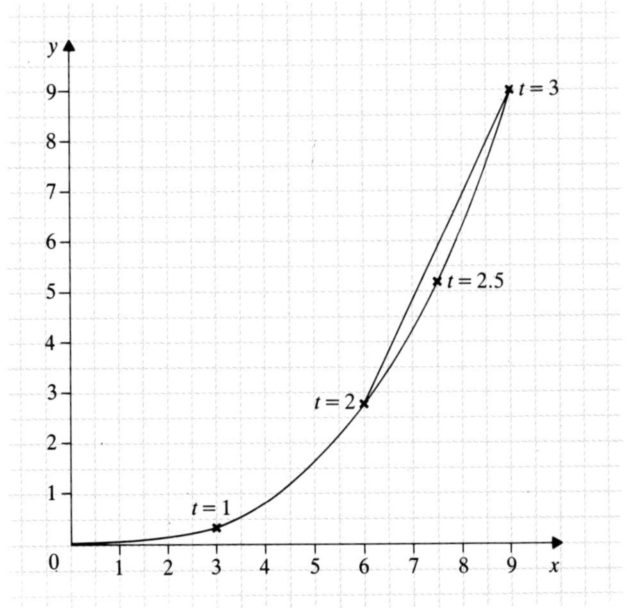

Figure 2.5

Time(s)	2		2.5		2.1		2.01
$\boldsymbol{r}$(m)	$\begin{pmatrix} 6 \\ 2\frac{2}{3} \end{pmatrix}$		$\begin{pmatrix} 7.5 \\ 5.208 \end{pmatrix}$		$\begin{pmatrix} 6.3 \\ 3.087 \end{pmatrix}$		$\begin{pmatrix} 6.03 \\ 2.7068 \end{pmatrix}$
Interval		2–2.5		2–2.1		2–2.01	
Average velocity (m s^{-1})		$\begin{pmatrix} 3 \\ 5.08 \end{pmatrix}$		$\begin{pmatrix} 3 \\ 4.203 \end{pmatrix}$		$\begin{pmatrix} 3 \\ 4.016 \end{pmatrix}$	

As the time interval gets smaller we can see that the average velocity appears to tend to $\binom{3}{4}$. To confirm this we consider the time interval 2 to $2 + h$.

Time(s)	2	$2 + h$
$\boldsymbol{r}$(m)	$\begin{pmatrix} 6 \\ 2\frac{2}{3} \end{pmatrix}$	$\begin{pmatrix} 3(2+h) \\ \frac{1}{3}(2+h)^3 \end{pmatrix}$

Now $(2 + h)^3 = 8 + 12h + 6h^2 + h^3$, so the average velocity is:

$$\frac{1}{h}\begin{pmatrix} 3h \\ \frac{1}{3}(12h + 6h^2 + h^3) \end{pmatrix} = \begin{pmatrix} 3 \\ 4 + 2h + \frac{1}{3}h^2 \end{pmatrix}.$$

As $h \to 0$, the average velocity $\to \binom{3}{4}$ m s^{-1}.

We recognise the process of differentiation in the last stage of the above calculation. We have merely differentiated the components of the vector separately. Thus

$$\boldsymbol{r} = \begin{pmatrix} 3t \\ \frac{1}{3}t^3 \end{pmatrix},$$

gives
$$\boldsymbol{v} = \frac{\mathrm{d}\boldsymbol{r}}{\mathrm{d}t} = \begin{pmatrix} 3 \\ t^2 \end{pmatrix}.$$

$\boldsymbol{v}$ is called the velocity vector. When $t = 2$,

$$\boldsymbol{v} = \begin{pmatrix} 3 \\ 2^2 \end{pmatrix} = \begin{pmatrix} 3 \\ 4 \end{pmatrix}.$$

In general, suppose P has position vector $\boldsymbol{r}(t)$, where the components of $\boldsymbol{r}$ are both functions of t so that we can write

$$\boldsymbol{r}(t) = \begin{pmatrix} f(t) \\ g(t) \end{pmatrix}.$$

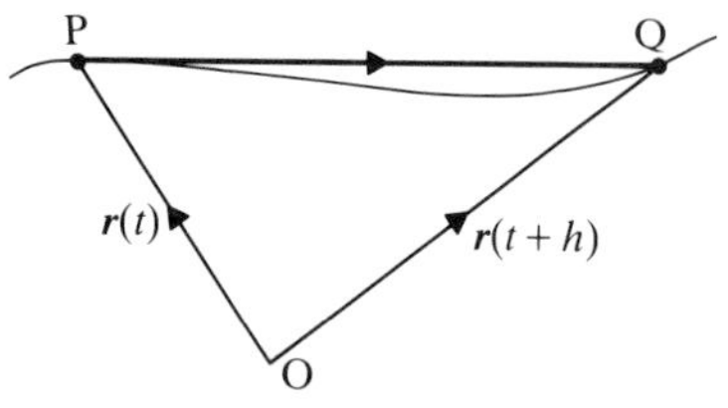

Figure 2.6

Let Q have position vector $\boldsymbol{r}(t+h)$ as shown in figure 2.6.

The **average velocity** from P to Q is

$$\frac{\boldsymbol{r}(t+h) - \boldsymbol{r}(t)}{h}.$$

As $h \to 0$
$$\frac{\boldsymbol{r}(t+h) - \boldsymbol{r}(t)}{h} = \lim_{h \to 0} \frac{1}{h}\begin{pmatrix} f(t+h) - f(t) \\ g(t+h) - g(t) \end{pmatrix} = \begin{pmatrix} \dot{f}(t) \\ \dot{g}(t) \end{pmatrix}.$$

Hence
$$\boldsymbol{v} = \dot{\boldsymbol{r}} = \frac{\mathrm{d}\boldsymbol{r}}{\mathrm{d}t}.$$

We define **speed** at an instant to be the magnitude of the velocity at that instant. Thus

$$\text{speed} = v = |\boldsymbol{v}| = \sqrt{(\boldsymbol{v} \cdot \boldsymbol{v})}.$$

In the above example, when $\boldsymbol{v} = \binom{3}{4}$, the speed $v = (3^2 + 4^2)^{1/2} = 5\ \mathrm{m\,s^{-1}}$.

□□□□□

We often use an alternative notation as follows:

If $\boldsymbol{r} = x\boldsymbol{i} + y\boldsymbol{j}$, where x and y are functions of t,

$$\boldsymbol{v} = \frac{\mathrm{d}\boldsymbol{r}}{\mathrm{d}t} = \frac{\mathrm{d}x}{\mathrm{d}t}\boldsymbol{i} + \frac{\mathrm{d}y}{\mathrm{d}t}\boldsymbol{j} = \begin{pmatrix} \mathrm{d}x/\mathrm{d}t \\ \mathrm{d}y/\mathrm{d}t \end{pmatrix},$$

$$\boldsymbol{v} = \dot{\boldsymbol{r}} = \dot{x}\boldsymbol{i} + \dot{y}\boldsymbol{j} = \begin{pmatrix} \dot{x} \\ \dot{y} \end{pmatrix}.$$

$$v = (\dot{x}^2 + \dot{y}^2)^{1/2}.$$

All the above work applies to problems in three dimensions, as example 3 shows.

EXAMPLE 3

The position of a boy on a helter skelter relative to a point on the bottom of the run, after t seconds, is given by

$$\boldsymbol{r} = 1.5\cos 3t\,\boldsymbol{i} + 1.5\sin 3t\,\boldsymbol{j} + (16 - 0.25t^2)\boldsymbol{k},$$

where $\boldsymbol{i}, \boldsymbol{j}$ and $\boldsymbol{k}$ are unit vectors, as shown in figure 2.7. Find the time taken for him to reach the bottom, and his speed when he gets there.

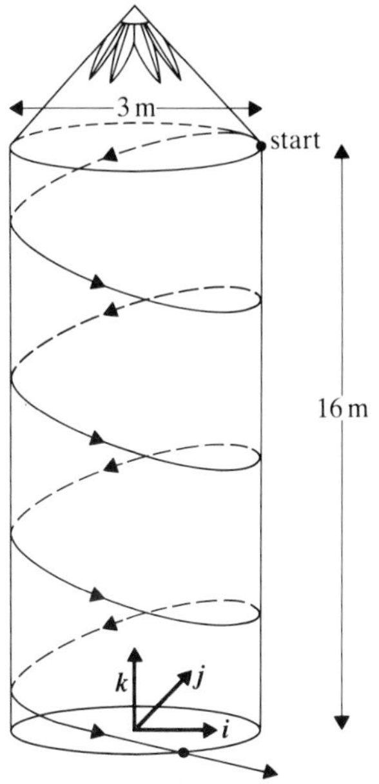

Figure 2.7

The boy reaches the bottom when $16 - 0.25t^2 = 0$ i.e. when $t = 8$. The general expression for his velocity vector is

$$\boldsymbol{v} = \frac{\mathrm{d}\boldsymbol{r}}{\mathrm{d}t} = -4.5\sin 3t\,\boldsymbol{i} + 4.5\cos 3t\,\boldsymbol{j} - \tfrac{1}{2}t\boldsymbol{k}$$

At the bottom, when $t = 8$, we have

$$\boldsymbol{v} = -4.5\sin 24\,\boldsymbol{i} + 4.5\cos 24\,\boldsymbol{j} - 4\boldsymbol{k}.$$

His speed at this point is given by

$$v^2 = 20.25\sin^2 24 + 20.25\cos^2 24 + 16 = 36.25.$$

His speed at the bottom is $6.02\,\mathrm{m\,s^{-1}}$, and since $24 \approx 8\pi$, he will have done approximately 4 'turns' on descent.

EXERCISE 2A

1. A particle goes through the points P, Q, R and S at two-second intervals. The position vectors of the points are:

$$\boldsymbol{p} = \boldsymbol{i} + 3\boldsymbol{j}, \quad \boldsymbol{q} = -2\boldsymbol{i} + 4\boldsymbol{j}, \quad \boldsymbol{r} = 7\boldsymbol{i} - 2\boldsymbol{j}, \quad \boldsymbol{s} = -2\boldsymbol{i} - 5\boldsymbol{j}$$

   Find the average velocity for the following stages:

   a) P → Q, b) Q → R, c) R → S, d) P → S.

2. Let $\boldsymbol{i}$ and $\boldsymbol{j}$ be unit vectors east and north, respectively. A boat is travelling with a speed of 12 knots on a bearing of 215°. Express this as a velocity vector.

In questions 3–8, $\boldsymbol{r}$ is the position vector of a particle at time t.

3. $\boldsymbol{r} = (4t + 5)\boldsymbol{i} + 6\boldsymbol{j}$. Calculate the average velocity between $t = 2$ and $t = 5$.

4. $\boldsymbol{r} = 2t\boldsymbol{i} + (t^2 - 1)\boldsymbol{j}$.

   a) Plot $\boldsymbol{r}$ for $0 \leqslant t \leqslant 4$ and find the average velocity over the first four one-second intervals.

   b) Find $\boldsymbol{v}$ when $t = 0, 1, 2, 3, 4$.

5. $\boldsymbol{r} = t\boldsymbol{i} + 3\sin t\boldsymbol{j}$. Plot $\boldsymbol{r}$ for $0 \leq t \leq 4$ and find $\boldsymbol{v}$ when $t = 2$.

6. $\boldsymbol{r} = \binom{3}{0} + t^2\binom{5}{1}$. What is $\boldsymbol{v}$ when $t = 3$?

7. $\boldsymbol{r} = 10t(\boldsymbol{i} + \boldsymbol{j}) + 5t^2\boldsymbol{k}$. What is the speed when $t = 2$?

8. $\boldsymbol{r} = 4\cos \pi t\,\boldsymbol{i} + 4\sin \pi t\,\boldsymbol{j}$. What is the path of the particle? Plot the path and mark the points corresponding to $t = 0, \frac{1}{2}, 1, 1\frac{1}{2}, 2$. Calculate the average velocity over the half-second intervals 0–$\frac{1}{2}$ and $\frac{1}{2}$–1, and over the one-second intervals 0–1 and 1–2.

9. A golf ball is hit so that its position t seconds later is $\boldsymbol{r} = 30t\boldsymbol{i} + (10t - 5t^2)\boldsymbol{j}$, where $\boldsymbol{i}$ and $\boldsymbol{j}$ are unit vectors horizontally and vertically and the distances are in metres. Find the position of the ball when $t = \frac{1}{2}, 1, 1\frac{1}{2}, 2, 2\frac{1}{2}$. Hence estimate the velocity of the ball when $t = 1$ and $t = 2$. Check your answers by differentiation.

10. A particle moves along a straight line $y = 2x + 1$ with a constant speed of $\frac{4}{5}$. What is the velocity vector? If the particle starts at (0, 1) write down the displacement vector at time t.

2.2 Acceleration

In example 2, of section 2.1, where $\boldsymbol{r} = 3t\boldsymbol{i} + \frac{1}{3}t^3\boldsymbol{j}$, we found $\boldsymbol{v} = 3\boldsymbol{i} + t^2\boldsymbol{j}$. The table shows some values for $\boldsymbol{v}$ over the first three seconds.

t(s)	0	1	2	3
v(m s^{-1})	$\begin{pmatrix}3\\0\end{pmatrix}$	$\begin{pmatrix}3\\1\end{pmatrix}$	$\begin{pmatrix}3\\4\end{pmatrix}$	$\begin{pmatrix}3\\9\end{pmatrix}$

Since $\boldsymbol{v}$ depends on t, it is clear that the velocity is not constant, and the table shows this. We can define average acceleration to be the change in velocity divided by the change in time, along similar lines to the definition of average velocity.
Thus for the above periods of time we get:

Time interval	0–1	1–2	2–3
Average acceleration	$\begin{pmatrix}0\\1\end{pmatrix}$	$\begin{pmatrix}0\\3\end{pmatrix}$	$\begin{pmatrix}0\\5\end{pmatrix}$

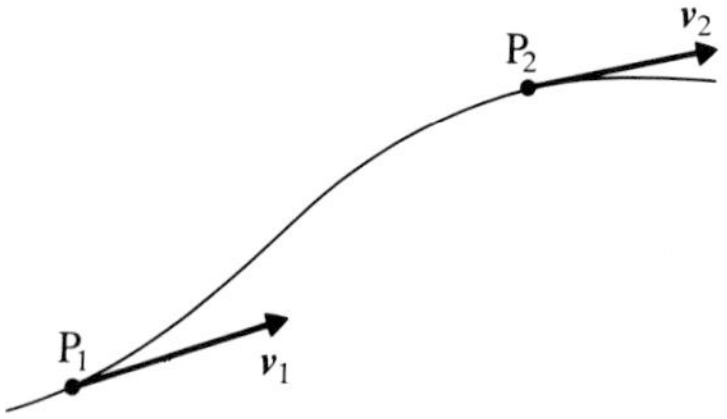

Figure 2.8

In general, as in figure 2.8, the average acceleration as a point moves from P_1 with velocity $\boldsymbol{v}_1$ at time t_1 to P_2 with velocity $\boldsymbol{v}_2$ at time t_2 is given by

$$\frac{\boldsymbol{v}_2 - \boldsymbol{v}_1}{t_2 - t_1}.$$

This expression is very similar to the one we obtained for the average velocity, from which we deduced that the velocity at an instant is the derivative of displacement with respect to time. The acceleration at an instant is defined to be the derivative with respect to time of velocity:

$$\boldsymbol{a} = \frac{\mathrm{d}\boldsymbol{v}}{\mathrm{d}t}.$$

Acceleration is a vector quantity. We can also write:

$$\boldsymbol{v} = \dot{\boldsymbol{r}} = \dot{x}\boldsymbol{i} + \dot{y}\boldsymbol{j} = \begin{pmatrix}\dot{x}\\ \dot{y}\end{pmatrix},$$

$$\boldsymbol{a} = \ddot{\boldsymbol{r}} = \ddot{x}\boldsymbol{i} + \ddot{y}\boldsymbol{j} = \begin{pmatrix}\ddot{x}\\ \ddot{y}\end{pmatrix}.$$

In example 2 of section 2.1,

$$\boldsymbol{v} = 3\boldsymbol{i} + t^2\boldsymbol{j} = \begin{pmatrix} 3 \\ t^2 \end{pmatrix},$$

$$\boldsymbol{a} = \frac{\mathrm{d}\boldsymbol{v}}{\mathrm{d}t} = 0\boldsymbol{i} + 2t\boldsymbol{j} = \begin{pmatrix} 0 \\ 2t \end{pmatrix}.$$

We can now fully describe the motion of the object.

a) Path

To find this we substitute values for t in the expression for $\boldsymbol{r}$,

$$\boldsymbol{r} = 3t\boldsymbol{i} + \tfrac{1}{3}t^3\boldsymbol{j}.$$

Time (t)	0	1	2	3
Displacement ($\boldsymbol{r}$)	$0\boldsymbol{i} + 0\boldsymbol{j}$	$3\boldsymbol{i} + \frac{1}{3}\boldsymbol{j}$	$6\boldsymbol{i} + \frac{8}{3}\boldsymbol{j}$	$9\boldsymbol{i} + 9\boldsymbol{j}$

This is shown in figure 2.9. We note that, since $x = 3t$ and $y = \frac{1}{3}t^3$ the cartesian equation of the path is $y = \frac{1}{81}x^3$.

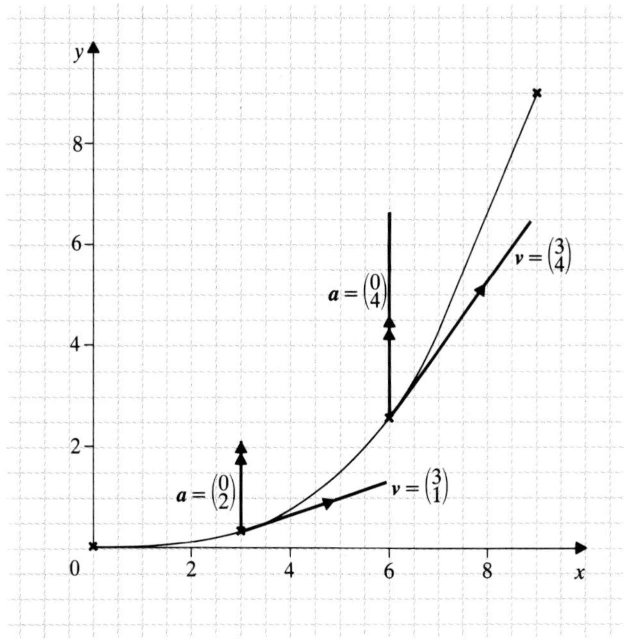

Figure 2.9

b) Velocity

The velocity is given by

$$\boldsymbol{v} = \frac{\mathrm{d}\boldsymbol{r}}{\mathrm{d}t} = 3\boldsymbol{i} + t^2\boldsymbol{j}.$$

We can produce a table of values for t, $\boldsymbol{v}$ and the speed, v.

Time (t)	0	1	2	3
Velocity ($\boldsymbol{v}$)	$3\boldsymbol{i}+0\boldsymbol{j}$	$3\boldsymbol{i}+\boldsymbol{j}$	$3\boldsymbol{i}+4\boldsymbol{j}$	$3\boldsymbol{i}+9\boldsymbol{j}$
Speed (v)	3	$\sqrt{10}$	5	$\sqrt{90}$

Two of these velocity vectors have been drawn in figure 2.9 and we note that $\boldsymbol{v}$ is tangential to the curve at each instant.

We can also see this another way. The equation of the curve is $y = \frac{1}{81}x^3$, so that at any point its gradient is $dy/dx = \frac{1}{27}x^3$. But $x = 3t$, so as a function of t, $dy/dx = \frac{1}{3}t^2$. Now, $\boldsymbol{v} = 3\boldsymbol{i} + t^2\boldsymbol{j}$, so that the direction of $\boldsymbol{v}$ at time t is also inclined at an angle whose tangent is $\frac{1}{3}t^2$ to the $\boldsymbol{i}$-direction.

c) Acceleration

This is given by $\boldsymbol{a} = d\boldsymbol{v}/dt = 2t\boldsymbol{j}$ and is shown in figure 2.9 by double-headed arrows, and indicates the way in which $\boldsymbol{v}$ is changing.

EXERCISE 2B

In questions 1–5, $\boldsymbol{r}$ is the position vector of a particle at time t

1. $\boldsymbol{r} = 2t\boldsymbol{i} + (t^2 - 1)\boldsymbol{j}$.
   a) Write down $\boldsymbol{v}$ when $t = 0, 1, 2, 3, 4$, and calculate the average acceleration over the first four one-second intervals.
   b) Write down $\boldsymbol{a}$ when $t = 0, 1, 2, 3, 4$.
   c) Plot $\boldsymbol{r}$ for $0 \leqslant t \leqslant 4$ and mark $\boldsymbol{v}$ and $\boldsymbol{a}$ at points corresponding to $t = 0, 1, 2, 3, 4$.
   d) Write down the equation of the path.
2. $\boldsymbol{r} = 10t(\boldsymbol{i} + \boldsymbol{j}) + 5t^2\boldsymbol{k}$. Write down $\boldsymbol{r}$, $\boldsymbol{v}$, $\boldsymbol{a}$ when $t = 3$.
3. $\boldsymbol{r} = t\boldsymbol{i} + 3\sin t\boldsymbol{j}$. Write down $\boldsymbol{v}$, $\boldsymbol{a}$ and $\boldsymbol{v}\cdot\boldsymbol{a}$ at time t.
4. $\boldsymbol{r} = (2t^2 + 8t)\boldsymbol{i} + (20t - t^3)\boldsymbol{j}$.
   Write down a) $\boldsymbol{v}$, b) $\boldsymbol{a}$, c) $\boldsymbol{v}\cdot\boldsymbol{a}$.
   When is the particle moving parallel to $2\boldsymbol{i} + \boldsymbol{j}$?
5. $\boldsymbol{r} = \binom{3}{0} + t^2\binom{-1}{-2}$. Write down $\boldsymbol{v}$ and $\boldsymbol{a}$ when $t = 2$. Plot the path of the particle and find when $\boldsymbol{r}\cdot\boldsymbol{a} = 0$.
6. An aircraft is flying horizontally over Dover at a height of 2 km in a northwesterly direction at a speed of 600 km h^{-1}. Taking unit vectors $\hat{\boldsymbol{u}}$ upwards, $\hat{\boldsymbol{n}}$ north, $\hat{\boldsymbol{e}}$ east, write down the position vector of the aircraft t h after passing over Dover.
7. A golf ball is hit so that its position t s later is $\boldsymbol{r} = 30t\boldsymbol{i} + (10t - 5t^2)\boldsymbol{j}$, where $\boldsymbol{i}$ and $\boldsymbol{j}$ are unit vectors horizontally and vertically and distances are in metres (see exercise 2A question 9). Plot the path of the ball for $0 \leqslant t \leqslant 3$ and calculate $\boldsymbol{v}$ and $\boldsymbol{a}$ when $t = 0, 1, 2$. Put these vectors on your diagram.

8. $\boldsymbol{r} = 2\cos t\,\boldsymbol{i} + 2\sin t\,\boldsymbol{j}$. Find the velocity and acceleration vectors when $t = 0, \frac{1}{2}\pi, \pi$. Sketch the path of the particle and mark on $\boldsymbol{v}$ and $\boldsymbol{a}$ at $t = 0, \frac{1}{2}\pi, \pi$.

9. $\boldsymbol{r} = \cos t^2\,\boldsymbol{i} + \sin t^2\,\boldsymbol{j}$. Find $\boldsymbol{v}$ and $\boldsymbol{a}$ at time t. Plot the path of the particle for $0 \leqslant t \leqslant 4$ and mark on $\boldsymbol{v}$ and $\boldsymbol{a}$ when $t = 0, 1$.

10. $\boldsymbol{r} = 2(1+t)^{-1}\boldsymbol{i} + 2(1+t)\boldsymbol{j}$. Find expressions for $\boldsymbol{v}$ and $\boldsymbol{a}$ at time t. Plot the path of the particle for $0 \leqq t \leqq 4$.

Uniform acceleration **2.3**

So far we have found the velocity and acceleration in situations where the path is given. Very often we need the reverse process, i.e. when we are given the acceleration and need to find the path. It is frequently the case that the acceleration is constant, as when bodies fall freely under gravity. In these cases the evaluation of $\boldsymbol{v}$ and $\boldsymbol{r}$ is straightforward.

Suppose that an object moves so that its acceleration is given by

$$\boldsymbol{a} = \begin{pmatrix} 2 \\ 3 \end{pmatrix}.$$

This is constant, so integrating with respect to t, we get

$$\boldsymbol{v} = \begin{pmatrix} 2t \\ 3t \end{pmatrix} + \boldsymbol{u} = t\begin{pmatrix} 2 \\ 3 \end{pmatrix} + \boldsymbol{u},$$

where $\boldsymbol{u}$ is the constant vector of integration, so that when $t = 0$, the initial velocity is $\boldsymbol{u}$.

In general, with constant acceleration $\boldsymbol{a}$, we get

$$\boldsymbol{v} = \boldsymbol{u} + t\boldsymbol{a}. \qquad \textbf{(1)}$$

Integrating equation (1) with respect to t, we get

$$\boldsymbol{r} = t\boldsymbol{u} + \tfrac{1}{2}t^2\boldsymbol{a} + \boldsymbol{c}.$$

where $\boldsymbol{c}$ is a constant of integration which can be interpreted as the position vector when $t = 0$. We can generally choose the origin so that $\boldsymbol{c} = \boldsymbol{0}$. Thus

$$\boldsymbol{r} = t\boldsymbol{u} + \tfrac{1}{2}t^2\boldsymbol{a}. \qquad \textbf{(2)}$$

We can rearrange this as

$$\boldsymbol{r} = t\boldsymbol{u} + \tfrac{1}{2}t(t\boldsymbol{a}),$$

and using (1),

$$\boldsymbol{r} = t\boldsymbol{u} + \tfrac{1}{2}t(\boldsymbol{v} - \boldsymbol{u}),$$

so that

$$\boldsymbol{r} = \tfrac{1}{2}t(\boldsymbol{u} + \boldsymbol{v}). \qquad \textbf{(3)}$$

Equation (3) gives the displacement as the mean of initial and final velocities multiplied by the time.

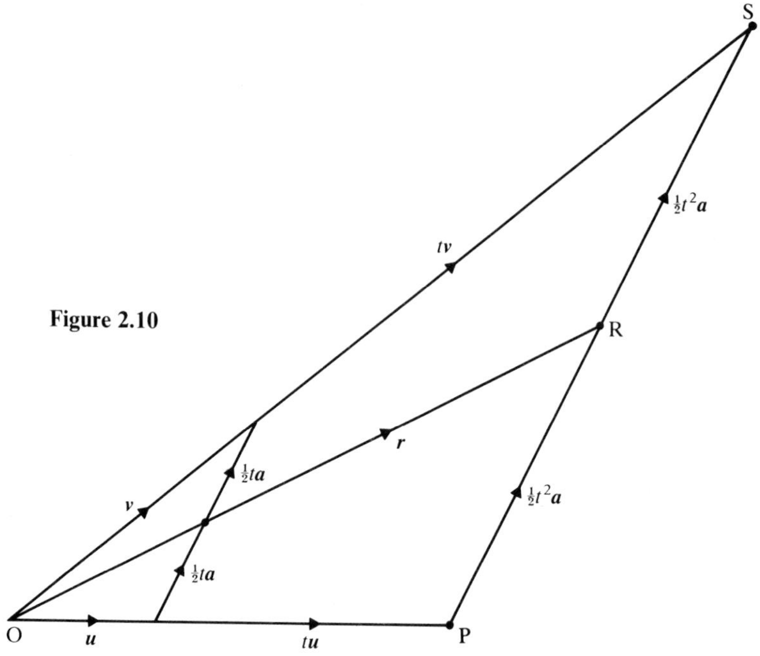

Figure 2.10

We can demonstrate the equivalence of equations (2) and (3) on a diagram, as in figure 2.10, where

$$\boldsymbol{r} = \mathbf{OR} = \mathbf{OP} + \mathbf{PR} = t\boldsymbol{u} + \tfrac{1}{2}t^2\boldsymbol{a},$$

or

$$\boldsymbol{r} = \mathbf{OR} = \tfrac{1}{2}(\mathbf{OP} + \mathbf{OS}),$$

by the midpoint theorem, which gives,

$$\boldsymbol{r} = \tfrac{1}{2}t(\boldsymbol{u} + \boldsymbol{v}).$$

From equations (1) and (2) we can obtain a further equation.

From (1) $$t\boldsymbol{a} = \boldsymbol{v} - \boldsymbol{u}.$$

From (2) $$\frac{2}{t}\boldsymbol{r} = \boldsymbol{v} + \boldsymbol{u}.$$

Forming the scalar product of these two equations,

$$2(\boldsymbol{a}\cdot\boldsymbol{r}) = (\boldsymbol{v} - \boldsymbol{u})\cdot(\boldsymbol{v} + \boldsymbol{u}) = v^2 - u^2, \qquad \textbf{(4)}$$

where $v^2 = \boldsymbol{v}\cdot\boldsymbol{v}$ and $u^2 = \boldsymbol{u}\cdot\boldsymbol{u}$.
Summarising the above equations we have

$$\boldsymbol{v} = \boldsymbol{u} + t\boldsymbol{a},$$
$$\boldsymbol{r} = t\boldsymbol{u} + \tfrac{1}{2}t^2\boldsymbol{a},$$
$$\boldsymbol{r} = \tfrac{1}{2}t(\boldsymbol{u} + \boldsymbol{v}),$$
$$v^2 = u^2 + 2\boldsymbol{a}\cdot\boldsymbol{r}.$$

When the motion is in one dimension the equations reduce to:

$$v = u + ta,$$
$$s = tu + \tfrac{1}{2}t^2a,$$

$$s = \tfrac{1}{2}t(u + v),$$
$$v^2 = u^2 + 2as.$$

where s (or x) is used to denote the distance travelled from the initial point.

Note that motion in one dimension is still concerned with vector quantities, since we can still have two directions, e.g. forward or back, up or down. However, we can condense the notation provided we distinguish the positive and negative directions with + or − signs.

A common constant acceleration is that experienced by bodies falling freely near the surface of the Earth. This is called the acceleration due to gravity and has a magnitude of approximately 9.8 m s^{-2}. (See also sections 2.4 and 3.4.)

EXAMPLE 1

A ball is thrown vertically upwards with a speed of 20 m s^{-1}. How high does it rise?

The information we have is: $u = 20$, and $v = 0$ at the highest point. $a = -9.8$, the acceleration due to gravity, where the coordinate direction is increasing upwards and so a is negative. Using $v^2 = u^2 + 2as$, we get

$$0 = 400 - 2 \times 9.8s$$
$$s = 20.4.$$

The ball rises 20.4 m.

EXAMPLE 2

A tile falls off a roof 20 m high. How long does it take to hit the ground if air resistance is neglected?

We have $u = 0$, $s = 20$ and $a = 9.8$, since the positive coordinate distance is now taken as downwards. Using $s = tu + \frac{1}{2}t^2a$, we get

$$20 = \tfrac{1}{2}t^2 \times 9.8,$$
$$t^2 = 40/9.8,$$
$$t = 2.02.$$

The tile takes about 2 s to reach the ground.

EXAMPLE 3

A particle starts at the point (6, −11) with initial velocity $\boldsymbol{i} + 3\boldsymbol{j}$ and constant acceleration $-2\boldsymbol{i} + \boldsymbol{j}$. Find the time when the particle passes through the point (−6, 9).

We have

$$\boldsymbol{c} = \begin{pmatrix} 6 \\ -11 \end{pmatrix}, \quad \boldsymbol{u} = \begin{pmatrix} 1 \\ 3 \end{pmatrix}, \quad \boldsymbol{a} = \begin{pmatrix} -2 \\ 1 \end{pmatrix}.$$

Using $\boldsymbol{r} = \boldsymbol{c} + t\boldsymbol{u} + \frac{1}{2}t^2\,\boldsymbol{a}$ we obtain

$$\boldsymbol{r} = \begin{pmatrix} 6 \\ -11 \end{pmatrix} + t\begin{pmatrix} 1 \\ 3 \end{pmatrix} + \tfrac{1}{2}t^2\begin{pmatrix} -2 \\ 1 \end{pmatrix}.$$

The particle passes through $(-6, 9)$ when $\boldsymbol{r} = \binom{-6}{9}$, giving

$$6 + t - t^2 = -6$$
$$-11 + 3t + \tfrac{1}{2}t^2 = 9,$$

giving $t = 4$. The reader should plot the path of the particle for $0 \leqslant t \leqslant 4$, showing $\boldsymbol{v}$ and $\boldsymbol{a}$ at $t = 0, 1, 2$.

EXAMPLE 4

A stone is dropped out of a tall building at the same instant as a ball is thrown vertically upwards from the ground. If the stone and the ball have the same speed when they collide, prove that the ball has travelled three times as far as the stone.

Let g be the acceleration due to gravity, v the common speed of the ball and stone on collision, and t the time taken.
If s_1 is the distance travelled by the stone,

$$s_1 = \tfrac{1}{2}g\,t^2,$$
$$v = g\,t.$$

If s_2 is the distance travelled by the ball, and u is its initial speed,

$$s_2 = ut - \tfrac{1}{2}gt^2,$$
$$v = u - gt.$$

Hence $\qquad u = v + gt = 2gt$

and $\qquad s_2 = 2gt^2 - \tfrac{1}{2}gt^2 = \tfrac{3}{2}gt^2.$

Hence $s_2 = 3s_1$, as required.
More complicated examples of motion in a straight line are discussed in chapter 4.

EXERCISE 2C

1. A car accelerates uniformly in a straight line from rest to 30 m s^{-1} in 10 s. Calculate the acceleration and the distance travelled in that time.

2. What acceleration is needed to increase the speed of a car from 0 to 30 m s^{-1} in 100 m?

3. A particle has an initial velocity of $\boldsymbol{i} + 2\boldsymbol{j}$ and is at the point (3, 4). It accelerates uniformly with acceleration $-2\boldsymbol{i} + \boldsymbol{j}$. Find its velocity and position after 2 s.

4. A particle starts at the origin with velocity $\boldsymbol{i} + 2\boldsymbol{j}$, and is subject to a constant acceleration of $3\boldsymbol{i} - 4\boldsymbol{j}$. Find expressions for $\boldsymbol{v}$ and $\boldsymbol{r}$ after t seconds. When will the particle be moving perpendicularly to its original direction?

5. A dart is thrown at a board with a horizontal velocity of 20 m s^{-1}. It is subject to a constant acceleration of 10 m s^{-2} vertically

downwards. Taking unit vectors $\boldsymbol{i}$ and $\boldsymbol{j}$ horizontally and vertically upwards, write down an expression for $\boldsymbol{v}$ at time t. What is the speed after one second, and in what direction is it travelling?

6. A man is running in a straight line and covers 6 m, 9 m and 21 m in successive intervals of 3 s, 2 s and 3 s. Show that this is consistent with constant acceleration. Find the acceleration and the speed of the man at the end of the 8 s period.

7. A ball is dropped from a high-rise block. The distance between floors in the block is constant. The ball takes 1 s to fall from the 10th to the 9th floor and 0.5 s to fall from the 9th floor to the 8th. What is the distance between floors? Take g as 10 m s^{-2}.

8. A ball is thrown vertically upwards with a speed u. After time t another ball is thrown vertically upwards from the same point with the same speed. Show that the balls will collide at a height of $(4u^2 - g^2t^2)/8g$.

9. In a rally, cars are set off at intervals of two minutes. If two cars accelerate uniformly from rest to a maximum 60 mph in one minute, find how far the first car will have gone when the second car starts. How far apart will they be at top speed?

10. At the end of a race, athlete A is 190 m from the tape and is running at a constant 10 m s^{-1}. Athlete B is 200 m from the tape with a speed of 8 m s^{-1}. B accelerates uniformly at $\frac{1}{2}$ m s^{-2}, until she reaches a speed of 12 m s^{-1}. Prove that B wins the race and find how far from the tape she overtakes A.

Projectiles 2.4

The last two examples show the use of the equations for uniform acceleration in one-dimensional form. A very common use of the equations in vector form is in connection with projectiles.

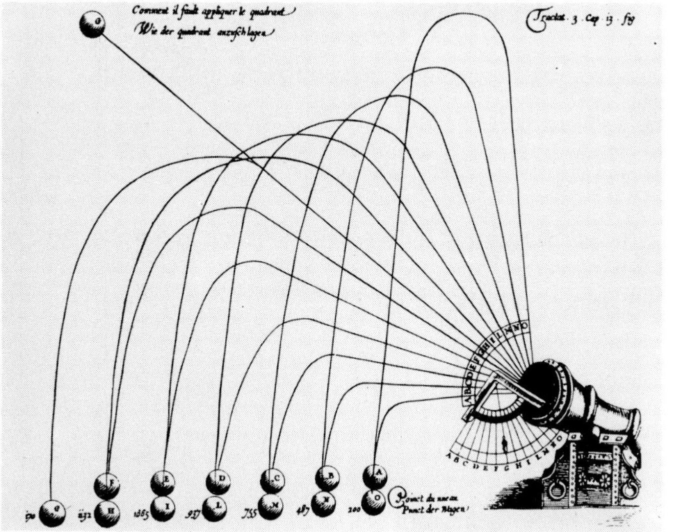

This illustration from a gunner's handbook of 1621 shows the true parabolic path of a missile.

The photograph shows a stunt rider trying to jump a river. Suppose he takes off at 40 m s^{-1} up a ramp at 30° to the horizontal and the river is 60 m wide. Will he clear it?

Motor cyclist Eddie Kidd leaps the broken span of a railway bridge in the film Flying High.

Major factors affecting his motion will be air resistance, lift and side winds. At this stage these are too difficult for us to analyse. As with many problems in applied mathematics we try to answer a much simpler problem. We replace the cyclist by a single particle, upon which we assume all the above effects are negligible. The only remaining force is that of gravitation which causes a constant acceleration vertically downwards.

In this example, the information we have is:

a) The total displacement

$$\boldsymbol{r} = \begin{pmatrix} s \\ 0 \end{pmatrix},$$

since over the motion as a whole the vertical displacement is zero.

b) The initial velocity

$$\boldsymbol{u} = \begin{pmatrix} 40 \cos 30° \\ 40 \sin 30° \end{pmatrix} = \begin{pmatrix} 34.6 \\ 20 \end{pmatrix},$$

where we resolve the given velocity into two components.

c) The acceleration

$$\boldsymbol{a} = \begin{pmatrix} 0 \\ -9.8 \end{pmatrix},$$

where the acceleration due to gravity is taken as 9.8 m s^{-2} vertically downwards.

Using equation (2) we get

$$\begin{pmatrix} s \\ 0 \end{pmatrix} = t\begin{pmatrix} 34.6 \\ 20 \end{pmatrix} + \tfrac{1}{2}t^2\begin{pmatrix} 0 \\ -9.8 \end{pmatrix}.$$

The y-component of this vector equation gives

$$0 = 20t - 4.9t^2,$$

$$t = 4.08 \text{ or } 0.$$

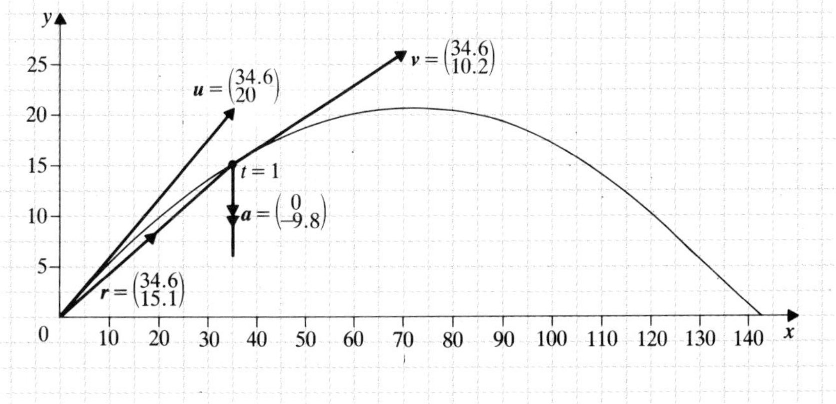

Figure 2.11

The point at which $t = 0$ is the initial point and the particle is again on the same horizontal plane when $t = 4.08$. The x-component of the equation gives:

$$s = 34.6t = 141.$$

Thus, the particle travels 141 m and is well clear of the river, leaving a considerable margin of error. The path of the particle is shown in figure 2.11. In particular, when $t = 1$,

$$\boldsymbol{v} = \boldsymbol{u} + t\boldsymbol{g} = \begin{pmatrix} 40 \cos 30^\circ \\ 40 \sin 30^\circ \end{pmatrix} + \begin{pmatrix} 0 \\ -9.8 \end{pmatrix} = \begin{pmatrix} 34.6 \\ 10.2 \end{pmatrix},$$

$$\boldsymbol{r} = t\boldsymbol{u} + \tfrac{1}{2}t^2\boldsymbol{g} = \begin{pmatrix} 40 \cos 30^\circ \\ 40 \sin 30^\circ - 4.9 \end{pmatrix} = \begin{pmatrix} 34.6 \\ 15.1 \end{pmatrix}.$$

Notice that $\boldsymbol{v}$ is tangential to the path, as required. We recognise the path as a parabola and it is often useful to find its equation. We will derive this for the most general case, since it is applicable to all projectile problems in which a particle is given an initial velocity and is acted on only by a constant force of gravitation.

Suppose a particle is initially thrown with a velocity $\boldsymbol{u}$ at an angle θ to the horizontal, and is subject to a constant acceleration due to gravity of $\boldsymbol{g}$ vertically downwards.

Taking unit vectors horizontally and vertically, we have

$$\boldsymbol{u} = \begin{pmatrix} u \cos \theta \\ u \sin \theta \end{pmatrix}, \qquad \boldsymbol{a} = \begin{pmatrix} 0 \\ -g \end{pmatrix}, \qquad \text{and let } \boldsymbol{r} = \begin{pmatrix} x \\ y \end{pmatrix}$$

at any point on the path. Using $\boldsymbol{r} = t\boldsymbol{u} + \frac{1}{2}t^2\boldsymbol{a}$, we get

$$\begin{pmatrix} x \\ y \end{pmatrix} = \begin{pmatrix} tu \cos \theta \\ tu \sin \theta \end{pmatrix} + \tfrac{1}{2}t^2 \begin{pmatrix} 0 \\ -g \end{pmatrix}.$$

The x-component gives

$$t = \frac{x}{u \cos \theta}.$$

The y-component gives

$$y = tu \sin \theta - \tfrac{1}{2}t^2 g.$$

Substituting for t

$$y = x \tan \theta - \tfrac{1}{2}g \frac{x^2}{u^2 \cos^2 \theta},$$

or

$$y = x \tan \theta - \frac{gx^2}{2u^2} \sec^2 \theta,$$

which is the equation of a parabola.

The time of flight is found by putting $u = 0$ in the y-component to give

$$0 = tu \sin \theta - \tfrac{1}{2}t^2 g,$$

$$\Rightarrow \quad t = \frac{2u \sin \theta}{g}, \quad \text{since } t \neq 0$$

The horizontal range is found by putting this value of t in the x-component to give

$$\begin{aligned} x &= tu \cos \theta \\ &= \frac{2u^2 \sin \theta \cos \theta}{g} \\ &= \frac{u^2 \sin 2\theta}{g}. \end{aligned}$$

The maximum range will occur when $\sin 2\theta = 1$, i.e. when $\theta = 45^\circ$, in which case the range is u^2/g.

The maximum height is found to be

$$\frac{u^2 \sin^2 \theta}{2g}.$$

EXERCISE 2D

Take g as 10 m s^{-2}, where necessary.

1. Humpty Dumpty fell off a wall 3 m high. With what speed did he hit the ground?

2. A ball is dropped from a board 10 m above a pool. At the same time a dolphin rises vertically from the water at 8 m s^{-1}. Where and when does the dolphin head the ball?

3. A golf ball is hit at 30 m s^{-1} at an angle of 30° to the horizontal. Find its time of flight and distance covered before the first bounce.

4. A stone is thrown up at an angle of 30° to the horizontal with a speed of 30 m s^{-1} from the edge of a cliff 50 m above sea level. If the stone lands in the sea, calculate:

   a) how long it is in the air,

   b) how far from the base of the cliff it lands,

   c) the speed and direction of the stone as it hits the water.

5. A cricket ball is hit with a speed of 25 m s^{-1} at an angle of 40° to the horizontal. Will it score a six if the boundary is 70 m away?

6. A goal is scored from a place kick in rugby. The ball is initially 15 m from the posts and just passes over the bar 3 m above the ground, at the highest point in its flight. With what speed was the ball kicked and what was the angle of projection with the horizontal?

7. a) A golfer is 80 m from the hole and hits the ball, which leaves the club head at 30 m s^{-1} at an elevation of 60°. How far from the hole will the ball land?

   b) If, in addition, there were a tree 15 m high, 10 m from the player and directly between the ball and the hole, would the ball clear the tree?

8. Figure 2.12 shows a girl taking a shot at goal in a netball match. What are the speed and angle of projection if the ball drops into the net at 30° to the vertical?

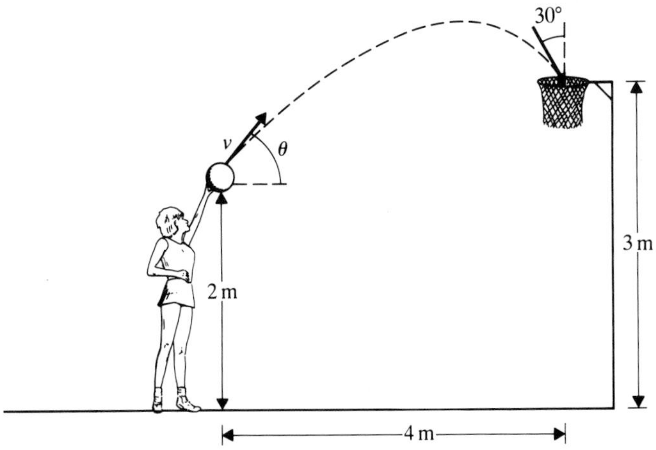

Figure 2.12

9. A boy is standing 4 m away from a wall which is 5 m high. He throws a ball at 10 m s^{-1} at an elevation of 40° above the horizontal from his hand which is 1 m above the ground. Will the ball pass over the wall?

10. A shell is fired at a gun tower on a cliff from a boat at sea, as shown in figure 2.13. The shell just passes over the tower and lands behind it. Prove:

    a) $\tan\alpha + \tan\theta = 2h/x$,

    b) $1/R = (\tan\alpha)/h - 1/x$.

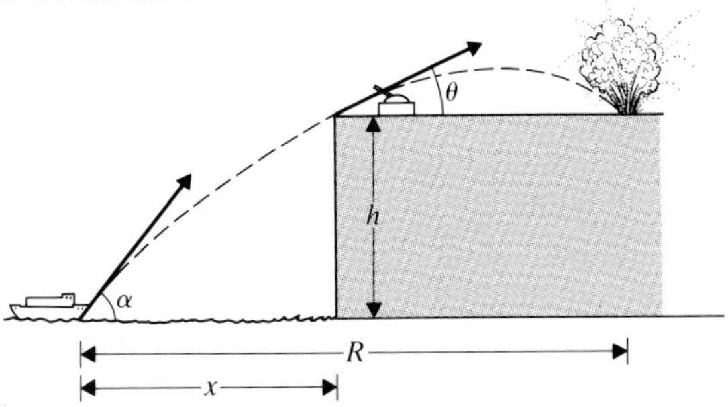

Figure 2.13

11.* A golfer is trying to hit a ball over two lines of trees, as shown in figure 2.14. Prove that if θ is the angle of projection of the ball, $\tan\theta = h(x+y)/xy$

Prove also that the maximum height of the ball is $h(x+y)^2/4xy$.

Figure 2.14

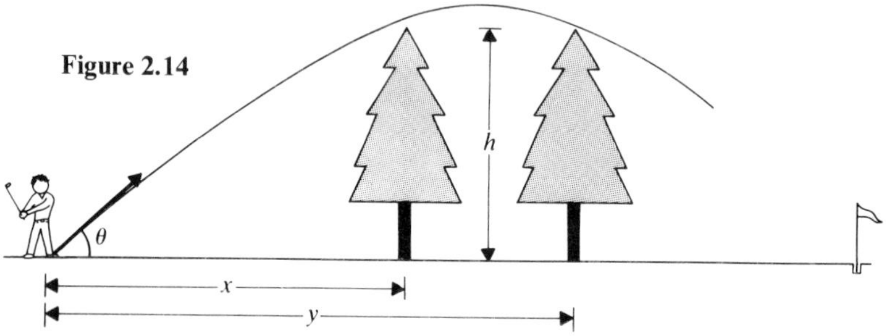

12.* A particle is projected with speed v at an angle α to the horizontal up the line of greatest slope of a plane inclined at an angle β ($\beta < \alpha$) to the horizontal. The particle strikes the plane at right angles, a distance s up the plane. Prove:

a) $\cot(\alpha - \beta) = 2\tan\beta$,

b) $s = v^2[\sin(2\alpha - \beta) - \sin\beta]/g\cos^2\beta$

2.5 Motion in a circle

a) Uniform motion

As the line of skaters rotates, those on the outside move with a greater speed than those near the centre.

In the photograph we see a long line of skaters each skating in a circle on the ice. Since the line remains straight it is clear that all the skaters turn through the same angle in the same time. We say they have the same **angular velocity** about the centre of the circle. This is usually denoted by the letter ω and we will assume in this section that it is constant.

Suppose the skaters do one complete circle in 10 s. They will have turned through 2π rad. Their angular velocity is $2\pi/10 = \frac{1}{5}\pi$ rad s^{-1}.

The skaters are not all moving at the same linear speed. A skater trying to join the line has to skate very fast whereas the skaters near the middle are moving very slowly, with the skater at the centre spinning on the spot. This is because each skater's path has a different radius and hence a different circumference to be covered in the same interval of time. We can find a connection between the angular velocity ω and the linear speed v.

Consider a point moving on a circle of radius r with angular velocity ω. After time t, the point will have moved from X to P, as shown in figure 2.15. The arc length XP is $s = r(\omega t)$. The speed is

$$\frac{ds}{dt} = r\omega,$$

i.e. $$v = r\omega.$$

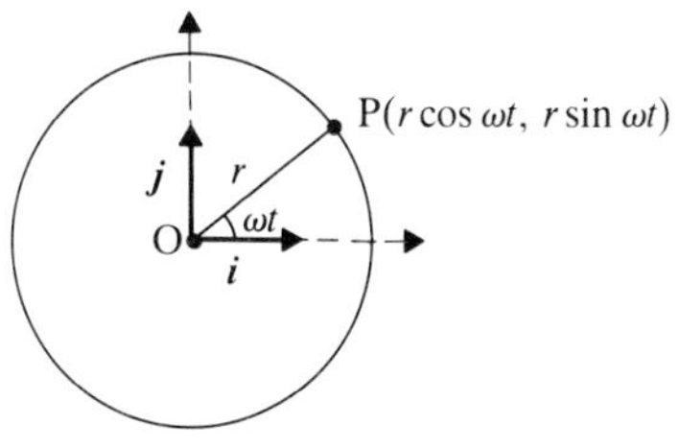

Figure 2.15

The speed v is directly proportional to the radius and so the larger the circle the greater the speed. The direction of the speed will be along the tangent since velocity is always tangential to the path. We can confirm this by using vectors.

In figure 2.15 let

$$\boldsymbol{r} = r(\cos\omega t\,\boldsymbol{i} + \sin\omega t\,\boldsymbol{j}). \tag{5}$$

Differentiating with respect to t gives

$$\boldsymbol{v} = r\omega(-\sin\omega t\,\boldsymbol{i} + \cos\omega t\,\boldsymbol{j}) \tag{6}$$
$$= r\omega\hat{\boldsymbol{n}},$$

where $\hat{\boldsymbol{n}}$ is a unit vector at right angles to the unit vector $\hat{\boldsymbol{r}}$, as shown in figure 2.16. Hence $v = r\omega$.

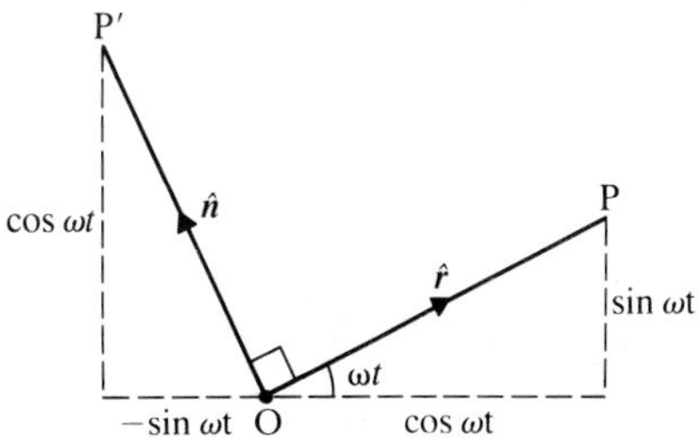

Figure 2.16

It can be seen that, although the speed is constant, the velocity and acceleration are not.

Differentiating equation (6), we get

$$\boldsymbol{a} = r\omega(-\omega\cos\omega t\,\boldsymbol{i} - \omega\sin\omega t\,\boldsymbol{j})$$
$$= -r\omega^2(\cos\omega t\,\boldsymbol{i} + \sin\omega t\,\boldsymbol{j})$$
$$= -\omega^2 r(\cos\omega t\,\boldsymbol{i} + \sin\omega t\,\boldsymbol{j})$$
$$= -\omega^2\boldsymbol{r}. \tag{7}$$

So the acceleration has a constant magnitude $r\omega^2 = v^2/r$ and, from (7), is directed towards the centre O.

EXAMPLE 1

What is the speed of the tip of the minute hand of a clock, where the hand is of length 7 cm?

The hand rotates 1 revolution in each hour, which is equivalent to 2π rad in 3600 s, so that

$$\omega = 2\pi/3600.$$

The speed $v = r\omega = 7 \times 2\pi/3600 = 0.012$. The tip of the hand has a constant speed of $0.012\ \text{cm s}^{-1}$.

EXAMPLE 2

A particle has position vector at time t, in seconds, given by

$$\boldsymbol{r} = \begin{pmatrix} 2 + 3\cos 2t \\ 4 + 3\sin 2t \end{pmatrix}.$$

Show that the motion is circular and find its velocity and acceleration.

a) Path

$$\boldsymbol{r} = \begin{pmatrix} 2 + 3\cos 2t \\ 4 + 3\sin 2t \end{pmatrix} = \begin{pmatrix} x \\ y \end{pmatrix},$$

so that $\quad x = 2 + 3\cos 2t, \qquad y = 4 + 3\sin 2t,$

$$\Rightarrow \quad x - 2 = 3\cos 2t, \qquad y - 4 = 3\sin 2t,$$

$$\Rightarrow \quad (x-2)^2 = 9\cos^2 2t, \qquad (y-4)^2 = 9\sin^2 2t,$$

and hence $\quad (x-2)^2 + (y-4)^2 = 9.$

The path is a circle of radius 3 and centre (2, 4) and is shown in figure 2.17.

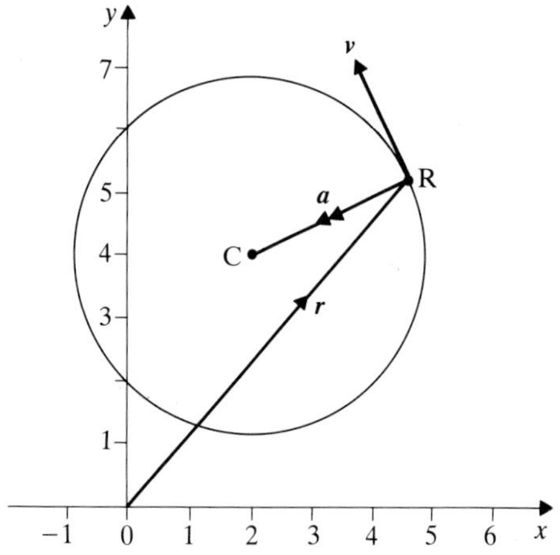

Figure 2.17

b) Velocity

$$\boldsymbol{v} = \begin{pmatrix} -6\sin 2t \\ 6\cos 2t \end{pmatrix} = 6\begin{pmatrix} -\sin 2t \\ \cos 2t \end{pmatrix}.$$

The speed, v, is $6\ \text{m s}^{-1}$ and is constant.

c) Acceleration

$$\boldsymbol{a} = -12\begin{pmatrix}\cos 2t \\ \sin 2t\end{pmatrix}$$

The magnitude of the acceleration is 12 m s^{-2}. In the diagram

$$\mathbf{CR} = \begin{pmatrix}3\cos 2t \\ 3\sin 2t\end{pmatrix},$$

and hence $\boldsymbol{a} = -4\mathbf{CR}$,

i.e. the acceleration is directed towards C and has magnitude 4CR = 12. Note also that $\boldsymbol{v}\cdot\mathrm{CR} = 0$, as expected.

*b) Non-uniform motion

Suppose a point P is moving on a circle of radius r and centre O, with angular velocity $\omega = \dot{\theta}$, where $\dot{\theta}$ is not constant so that $\ddot{\theta} \neq 0$.

Proceeding along lines similar to those in section 2.5a,

$$\boldsymbol{r} = \mathbf{OP} = r(\cos\theta\,\boldsymbol{i} + \sin\theta\,\boldsymbol{j}) = r\hat{\boldsymbol{r}}, \qquad \mathbf{(8)}$$

$$\boldsymbol{v} = \dot{\boldsymbol{r}} = r\dot{\theta}(-\sin\theta\,\boldsymbol{i} + \cos\theta\,\boldsymbol{j}) = r\dot{\theta}\hat{\boldsymbol{n}}, \qquad \mathbf{(9)}$$

where $\hat{\boldsymbol{r}}$ and $\hat{\boldsymbol{n}}$ are unit vectors along and at right angles to the radius. Differentiating equation (**9**) with respect to t,

$$\begin{aligned}\boldsymbol{a} &= r\ddot{\theta}(-\sin\theta\,\boldsymbol{i} + \cos\theta\,\boldsymbol{j}) + r\dot{\theta}(-\cos\theta\,\boldsymbol{i} - \sin\theta\,\boldsymbol{j})\dot{\theta} \\ &= r\ddot{\theta}\hat{\boldsymbol{n}} - r\dot{\theta}^2\hat{\boldsymbol{r}}.\end{aligned}$$

Thus the acceleration $\boldsymbol{a}$ has two components:

$r\ddot{\theta}$ along the tangent,

$r\dot{\theta}^2$ towards the centre.

Clearly, if $\theta = \omega = \text{constant}$, we produce the original acceleration $r\omega^2$ towards the centre, as in section 2.5a.

EXAMPLE 3

A particle is moving in a circle of radius r so that its position at time t is given by

$$\boldsymbol{r} = r\cos t^2\,\boldsymbol{i} + r\sin t^2\,\boldsymbol{j}.$$

Write down expressions for its velocity and acceleration at time t. Sketch its path and draw vectors to represent the velocity and acceleration vectors at time $t = 0$, 1 and 2 s.

Differentiating $\boldsymbol{r}$ with respect to t,

$$\begin{aligned}\boldsymbol{v} = \dot{\boldsymbol{r}} &= r(-2t\sin t^2\,\boldsymbol{i} + 2t\cos t^2\,\boldsymbol{j}) \\ &= 2rt(-\sin t^2\,\boldsymbol{i} + \cos t^2\,\boldsymbol{j}) = 2rt\hat{\boldsymbol{n}},\end{aligned}$$

$$\begin{aligned}\boldsymbol{a} = \dot{\boldsymbol{v}} &= 2r(-\operatorname{in} t^2\,\boldsymbol{i} + \cos t^2\boldsymbol{j}) + 4rt^2(-\cos t^2\boldsymbol{i} - \sin t^2\boldsymbol{j}) \\ &= 2r\hat{\boldsymbol{n}} + -4rt^2\hat{\boldsymbol{r}}.\end{aligned}$$

Thus, at time t, the speed is $v = 2rt$ and is along the tangent. The acceleration has a component of $2r$ along the tangent and one of $4rt^2$ directed towards the centre.

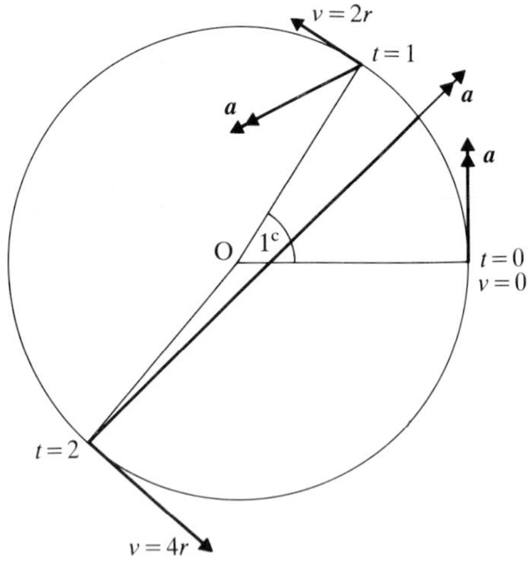

Figure 2.18

We compile a table of values for these when $t = 0, 1$ and 2, and figure 2.18 shows the circular path.

t	v (along tangent)	a (along tangent)	a (towards centre)
0	0	$2r$	0
1	$2r$	$2r$	$4r$
2	$4r$	$2r$	$16r$

At the time given the particle has turned through 0, 1 and 4 rad, respectively. The velocity and acceleration vectors are shown at these positions.

EXERCISE 2E

1. A fly is sitting on the edge of an old '78' record, rotating at 78 rpm, whose radius is 12.5 cm. Find the speed and acceleration of the fly.
2. An electric drill has a speed of 2400 rpm. Convert this into angular velocity in rad s^{-1}.
3. The Earth orbits around the Sun once every 365 days. Assuming that the orbit is circular with radius 149×10^6 km, find the orbital speed and the magnitude of the acceleration of the Earth.
4. A space shuttle orbits the Earth 72 times in two days. What is its average angular velocity?
5. A car wheel has a radius of 27 cm. If it rolls without slipping find its angular velocity when the car is travelling at 60 km h^{-1}.
6. At a certain stage in its flight a discus of radius 12 cm is moving horizontally and spinning about its axis, which is vertical, at 5 rps. If the centre of the discus is moving at 20 m s^{-1}, what are the maximum and minimum speeds of points on the rim?

7. Figure 2.19 shows the fan belt of a car. If the belt is moving without slipping on the pulleys at a speed of $2\ \mathrm{m\,s^{-1}}$, calculate the angular velocities of the pulleys.

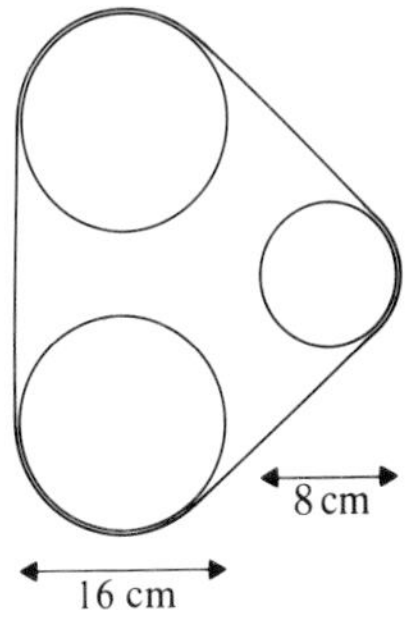

Figure 2.19

8. Figure 2.20 shows two gear wheels. If the driver gear is rotating at $10\ \mathrm{rad\,s^{-1}}$, calculate the angular velocity of the driven gear, assuming that there is no slipping.

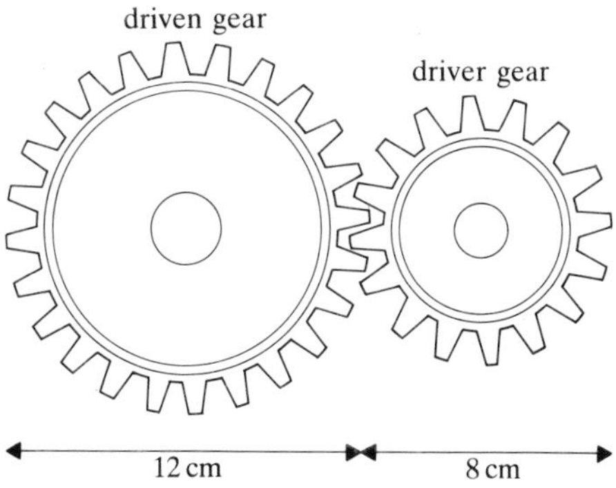

Figure 2.20

9. A diver performs two and a half somersaults from a 10 m board. What is her average angular velocity?

10. Figure 2.21 shows a pulley system. If there is no slipping and the free end of the rope is pulled down with a speed of $1\ \mathrm{m\,s^{-1}}$ calculate:

    a) how fast pulley 2 rises.

    b) the angular velocities of the pulleys.

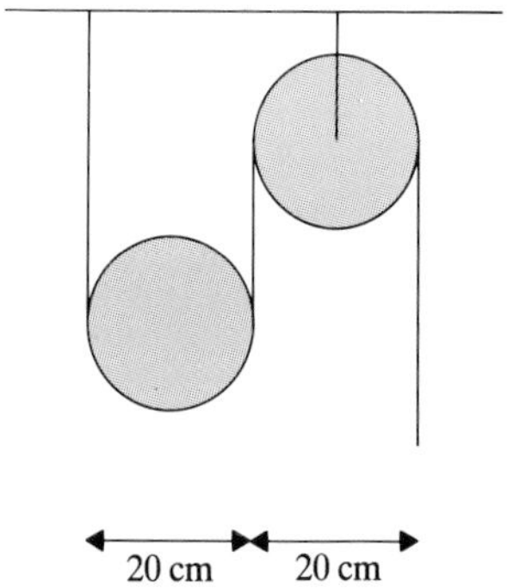

Figure 2.21

11.* A car wheel rotates at a constant $\omega\ \mathrm{rad\,s^{-1}}$. Mud is picked up by the wheel and thrown off at a tangent to the wheel as shown in figure 2.22. Find in terms of r, ω, g and θ, how far from the bottom of the wheel the mud will land.

Figure 2.22

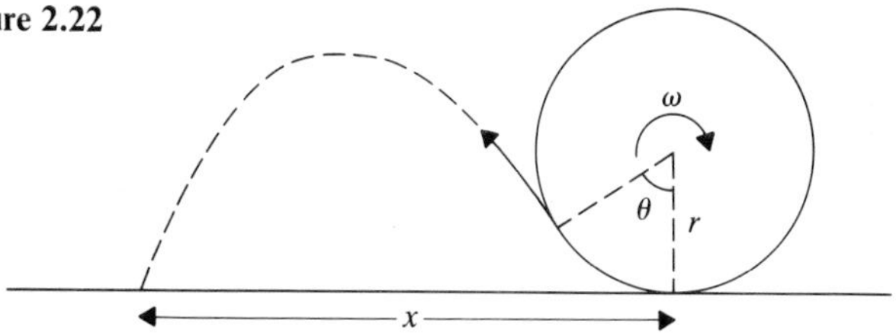

12.* A particle moves on a circle of radius 2 m. Its angular velocity after t seconds is $3t^2\ \mathrm{rad\,s^{-1}}$. (a) Calculate the velocity and acceleration at time t. (b) Calculate the magnitude and direction of the acceleration after 2 s.

13.* A car enters a corner which is in the shape of a quadrant of a circle of radius 50 m. It is travelling at $30\ \mathrm{m\,s^{-1}}$, but is decelerating at a constant $5\ \mathrm{m\,s^{-2}}$. Calculate the magnitude and direction of the acceleration of the car on entering and leaving the bend.

14.* Figure 2.23 shows a simplified version of a piston connected to a crank shaft. If the details are as shown, find the speed and the acceleration of the piston at the top of the stroke. Form an expression for the speed at the general position.

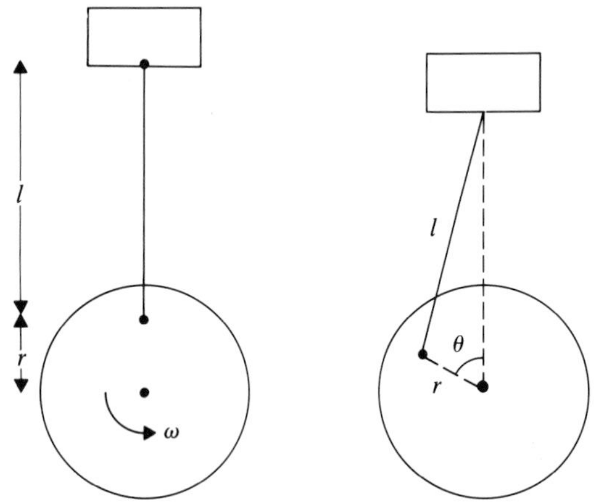

Figure 2.23

2.6 Relative motion

A still from the James Bond film Octopussy. As the man leaps from the train he is moving very fast relative to the ground.

Suppose a car which is moving at 70 km h^{-1} is being overtaken by a car moving at 80 km h^{-1} on a motorway. To a passenger in the front of the faster car who looks back, the slower car may seem to be moving backwards. To a passenger in the slower car, the faster car is only pulling away from him slowly. The speed of the faster car relative to the slower car is

$$(80\text{–}70)\,\text{km}\,\text{h}^{-1} = 10\,\text{km}\,\text{h}^{-1}$$

The speed of the slower car relative to the faster car is

$$(70-80)\,\mathrm{km\,h^{-1}} = -10\,\mathrm{km\,h^{-1}}.$$

The negative sign shows that the slower car is moving backwards relative to the faster car.

Suppose the cars are approaching each other at the above speeds on the same road. Their speed of approach is $(70+80)\,\mathrm{km\,h^{-1}} = 150\,\mathrm{km\,h^{-1}}$. If the slower car is moving in the positive direction, the speed of the slower relative to the faster is

$$70-(-80) = 150$$

which is their speed of approach.

This example illustrates the idea of relative motion which we shall consider in more detail in this section. There is a sense in which all motion is relative. When we stand still and watch objects move, we imagine we are at rest, but in fact the Earth, relative to which we are at rest, is both spinning on its axis and rotating in orbit around the Sun.

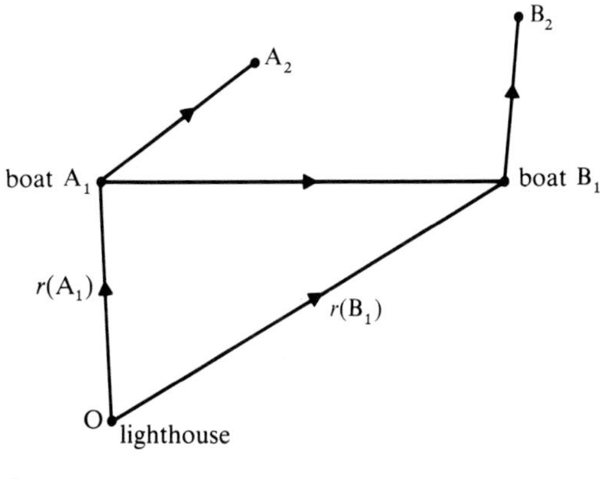

Figure 2.24

Figure 2.24 shows the positions of two sailing cruisers A and B at some time t. The positions of A and B relative to the lighthouse at O are written as $\boldsymbol{r}(\mathrm{A})$ and $\boldsymbol{r}(\mathrm{B})$. This notation is slightly different from that used in chapter 1, but is convenient for relative motion. The position of boat B relative to boat A is given by the vector **AB**, which we write as $\boldsymbol{r}_{\mathrm{A}}(\mathrm{B})$. From the triangle law,

$$\boldsymbol{r}_{\mathrm{A}}(\mathrm{B}) = \boldsymbol{r}(\mathrm{B}) - \boldsymbol{r}(\mathrm{A}).$$

Suppose at time t_1, A is at A_1 and B at B_1; and at time t_2, A is at A_2 and B at B_2, both having moved with constant velocity. The position of B_1 relative to A_1 is

$$\boldsymbol{r}_{\mathrm{A}_1}(B_1) = \boldsymbol{r}(B_1) - \boldsymbol{r}(A_1).$$

The position of B_2 relative to A_2 is

$$\boldsymbol{r}_{\mathrm{A}_2}(\mathrm{B}_2) = \boldsymbol{r}(\mathrm{B}_2) - \boldsymbol{r}(\mathrm{A}_2),$$

The displacement of B relative to A in the time interval $t_2 - t_1$ is given by $\boldsymbol{r}_{A_2}(B_2) - \boldsymbol{r}_{A_1}(B_1)$, i.e. the change in its relative position. Now

$$\begin{aligned}\boldsymbol{r}_{A_2}(B_2) - \boldsymbol{r}_{A_1}(B_1) &= \boldsymbol{r}(B_2) - \boldsymbol{r}(A_2) - (\boldsymbol{r}(B_1) - \boldsymbol{r}(A_1)) \\ &= \boldsymbol{r}(B_2) - \boldsymbol{r}(B_1) - (\boldsymbol{r}(A_2) - \boldsymbol{r}(A_1)) \\ &= \mathbf{B_1 B_2} - \mathbf{A_1 A_2}.\end{aligned}$$

Thus the displacement of B relative to A is the displacement of B minus the displacement of A.

Relative velocity

Since, in the above, both A and B are moving with constant velocity, the velocity of B relative to A is given by

$$\begin{aligned}\frac{\boldsymbol{r}_{A_2}(B_2) - \boldsymbol{r}_{A_1}(B_1)}{t_2 - t_1} &= \frac{\mathbf{B_1B_2} - \mathbf{A_1A_2}}{t_2 - t_1} \\ &= \frac{\mathbf{B_1B_2}}{t_2 - t_1} - \frac{\mathbf{A_1A_2}}{t_2 - t_1},\end{aligned}$$

i.e. $\boldsymbol{v}_A(B) = \boldsymbol{v}(B) - \boldsymbol{v}(A)$.

The velocity of B relative to A is the velocity of B minus the velocity of A.

In all cases in this chapter we deal with objects which move with constant velocity. However, the analysis for the more general case is straightforward.

Suppose A and B are at positions $\boldsymbol{r}(A)$ and $\boldsymbol{r}(B)$ at time t and are moving with velocities $\boldsymbol{v}(A)$ and $\boldsymbol{v}(B)$, respectively as in figure 2.25a, then

$$\boldsymbol{r}_A(B) = \boldsymbol{r}(B) - \boldsymbol{r}(A).$$

Differentiating with respect to t,

$$\begin{aligned}\frac{d}{dt}(\boldsymbol{r}_A(B)) &= \frac{d}{dt}(\boldsymbol{r}(B) - \boldsymbol{r}(A)) \\ \Rightarrow \quad \boldsymbol{v}_A(B) &= \boldsymbol{v}(B) - \boldsymbol{v}(A). \qquad \textbf{(10)}\end{aligned}$$

The velocity of B relative to A is $\boldsymbol{v}(B) - \boldsymbol{v}(A)$.

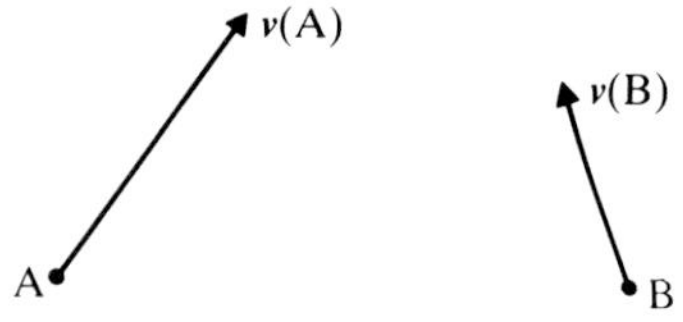

(a)

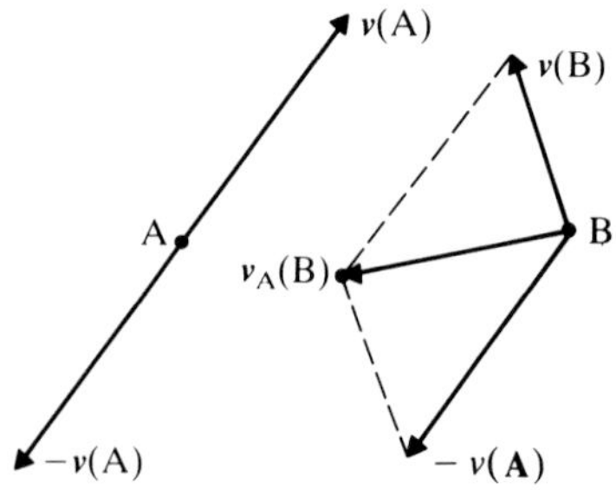

(b)

Figure 2.25

We can show this in a vector diagram as in figure 2.25b. The vector $-\boldsymbol{v}(A)$ has been added to the velocity of both B and A. This makes figures (a) and (b) equivalent. We note that A is now at rest and B moves with its velocity relative to A. This idea is useful in solving problems in which we have no 'fixed origin'.

EXAMPLE 1

Two cars are approaching a crossroads, as shown in figure 2.26. A is moving at $30\ \mathrm{m\,s^{-1}}$ due east and is 200 m from the crossroads, whilst B is 50 m away and is moving due north at $10\ \mathrm{m\,s^{-1}}$. Find the displacement of B relative to A in the next 2 s, and its relative velocity in that time.

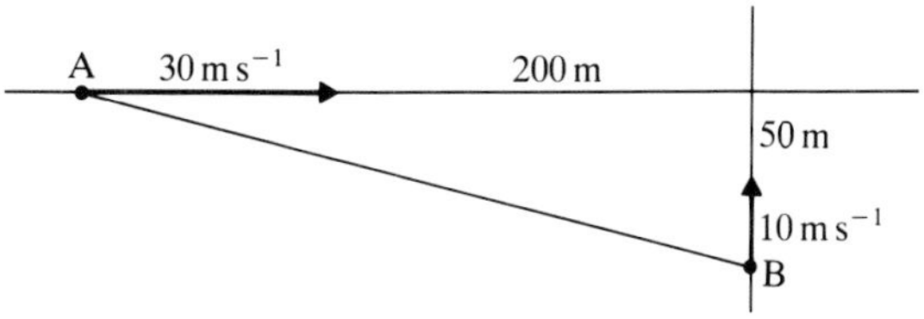

Figure 2.26

Initially

$$\boldsymbol{r}(\mathrm{A}) = \begin{pmatrix} -200 \\ 0 \end{pmatrix}, \qquad \boldsymbol{r}(\mathrm{B}) = \begin{pmatrix} 0 \\ -50 \end{pmatrix},$$

taking the origin at the crossroads and unit base vectors east and north. The position of B relative to A is

$$\begin{aligned} \boldsymbol{r}_{\mathrm{A}}(\mathrm{B}) &= \boldsymbol{r}(\mathrm{B}) - \boldsymbol{r}(\mathrm{A}) \\ &= \begin{pmatrix} 0 \\ -50 \end{pmatrix} - \begin{pmatrix} -200 \\ 0 \end{pmatrix} = \begin{pmatrix} 200 \\ -50 \end{pmatrix}. \end{aligned}$$

After 2 s, A has moved to A′ and B to B′, where

$$\boldsymbol{r}(\mathrm{A}') = \begin{pmatrix} -140 \\ 0 \end{pmatrix}, \qquad \boldsymbol{r}(\mathrm{B}') = \begin{pmatrix} 0 \\ -30 \end{pmatrix}.$$

The position of B′ relative to A′ is

$$\begin{aligned} \boldsymbol{r}_{\mathrm{A}'}(\mathrm{B}') &= \boldsymbol{r}(\mathrm{B}') - \boldsymbol{r}(\mathrm{A}') \\ &= \begin{pmatrix} 0 \\ -30 \end{pmatrix} - \begin{pmatrix} -140 \\ 0 \end{pmatrix} = \begin{pmatrix} 140 \\ -30 \end{pmatrix}. \end{aligned}$$

The displacement of B relative to A is

$$\boldsymbol{r}_{\mathrm{A}'}(\mathrm{B}') - \boldsymbol{r}_{\mathrm{A}}(\mathrm{B}) = \begin{pmatrix} 140 \\ -30 \end{pmatrix} - \begin{pmatrix} 200 \\ -50 \end{pmatrix} = \begin{pmatrix} -60 \\ 20 \end{pmatrix}.$$

The velocity of B relative to A is

$$\begin{aligned} \boldsymbol{v}_{\mathrm{A}}(\mathrm{B}) &= \tfrac{1}{2}(\boldsymbol{r}_{\mathrm{A}'}(\mathrm{B}') - \boldsymbol{r}_{\mathrm{A}}(\mathrm{B})) \\ &= \tfrac{1}{2}\begin{pmatrix} -60 \\ 20 \end{pmatrix} = \begin{pmatrix} -30 \\ 10 \end{pmatrix}. \end{aligned}$$

Note that $\boldsymbol{v}(\mathrm{B}) = \begin{pmatrix} 0 \\ 10 \end{pmatrix}$ and $\boldsymbol{v}(\mathrm{A}) = \begin{pmatrix} 30 \\ 0 \end{pmatrix}$, giving

$\boldsymbol{v}_{\mathrm{A}}(\mathrm{B}) = \boldsymbol{v}(\mathrm{B}) - \boldsymbol{v}(\mathrm{A}) = \begin{pmatrix} -30 \\ 10 \end{pmatrix}$, as above.

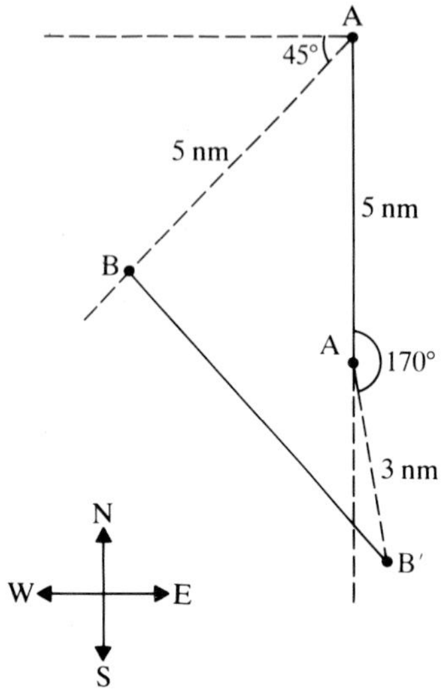

Figure 2.27

EXAMPLE 2

At noon a ship A, which is moving with a constant speed of 10 knots due south, sees a ship B 5 nautical miles southwest. At 12.30 p.m. B is 3 nautical miles from A on a bearing of 170°. What is the velocity of B? (1 knot = 1 nautical mile per hour.)

Figure 2.27 shows the displacements of A and B. The displacement of B relative to A is

$$\boldsymbol{r}_{A'}(B') - \boldsymbol{r}_A(B) = \begin{pmatrix} 3\cos 70^\circ \\ -3\sin 70^\circ \end{pmatrix} - \begin{pmatrix} -5\cos 45^\circ \\ -5\sin 45^\circ \end{pmatrix} = \begin{pmatrix} 4.5616 \\ 0.7165 \end{pmatrix}.$$

The velocity of B relative to A is

$$\boldsymbol{v}_A(B) = \frac{1}{0.5}\begin{pmatrix} 4.5616 \\ 0.7165 \end{pmatrix} = \begin{pmatrix} 9.123 \\ 1.43 \end{pmatrix}.$$

Now $\boldsymbol{v}_A(B) = \boldsymbol{v}(B) - \boldsymbol{v}(A)$, so the velocity of B is

$$\boldsymbol{v}(B) = \boldsymbol{v}_A(B) + \boldsymbol{v}(A)$$

$$= \begin{pmatrix} 9.123 \\ 1.43 \end{pmatrix} + \begin{pmatrix} 0 \\ -10 \end{pmatrix},$$

since A moves due south at 10 knots. So

$$\boldsymbol{v}(B) = \begin{pmatrix} 9.123 \\ -8.57 \end{pmatrix}.$$

The speed of B is $\sqrt{[(9.123)^2 + (-8.57)^2]} = 12.5$. Thus, B moves at 12.5 knots on a bearing of 136.8°.

EXAMPLE 3

An aeroplane A is moving at 100 m s^{-1} on a bearing of 040°. A second tanker aeroplane B which is to refill A is 100 km due east of A and is moving at 80 m s^{-1} on a bearing of 310°. They are both flying on the same level. Will the two planes meet and, if not, what is their closest distance of approach?

The velocities of A and B are

$$\boldsymbol{v}(A) = \begin{pmatrix} 100\sin 40^\circ \\ 100\cos 40^\circ \end{pmatrix} = \begin{pmatrix} 64.2 \\ 76.6 \end{pmatrix},$$

$$\boldsymbol{v}(B) = \begin{pmatrix} -80\sin 50^\circ \\ 80\cos 50^\circ \end{pmatrix} = \begin{pmatrix} -61.3 \\ 51.4 \end{pmatrix}.$$

The velocity of B relative to A is

$$\boldsymbol{v}_A(B) = \boldsymbol{v}(B) - \boldsymbol{v}(A)$$

$$= \begin{pmatrix} -61.3 \\ 51.4 \end{pmatrix} - \begin{pmatrix} 64.2 \\ 76.6 \end{pmatrix} = \begin{pmatrix} -125.5 \\ -25.2 \end{pmatrix}.$$

The magnitude of this vector is $\sqrt{[(-125.5)^2 + (-25.5)^2]} = 128$, giving the relative speed of B as 128 m s^{-1}. Its bearing is 258.6°, i.e. at an angle of 11.4° with the line AB in figure 2.28a. Thus, since $\boldsymbol{v}_A(B)$ is not due west, B will not meet A.

Figure 2.28

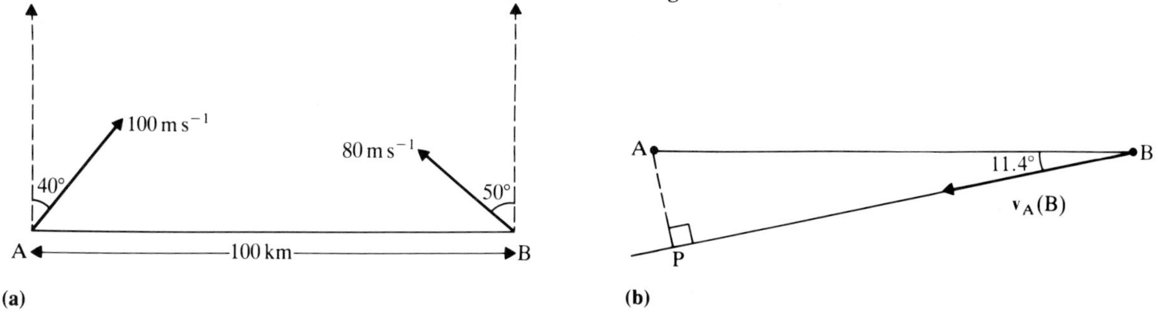

In figure 2.28b

$$AP = 100 \sin 11.4° = 19.8,$$

giving the closest distance of approach as 19.8 km. The time taken to this point is

$$t = \frac{PB}{128} = \frac{10^5 \cos 11.4°}{128} = 766,$$

giving approximately 12.8 min.

Figure 2.29

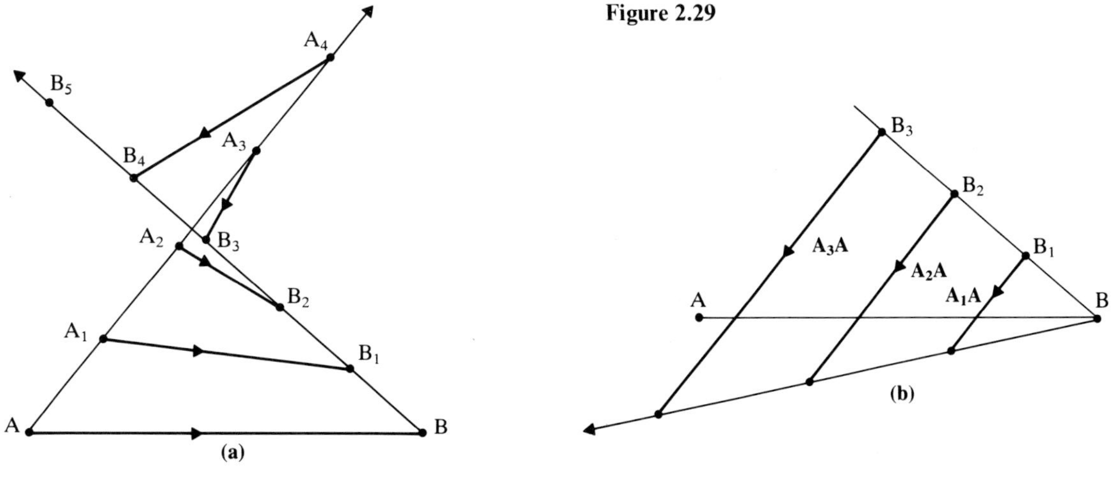

It is of interest to note the positions of A and B at several times during the motion, as shown in figure 2.29. Figure 2.29a shows the position of both planes at 5 min intervals, with the displacements of B relative to A shown by A_1B_1, A_2B_2 $\cdots$. Figure 2.29b shows the displacement of B relative to A, with A assumed stationary (see figure 2.25). Clearly, if B is to meet A it must be due west. If B maintains the speed of 80 m s^{-1}, the direction it must take to intercept A is as shown in figure 2.30. The angle α is given by the sine rule:

$$\frac{\sin \alpha}{\sin 50°} = \frac{100}{80},$$

$$\alpha = 73.2°$$

The direction of the velocity of B must be on a bearing of 286.8°.

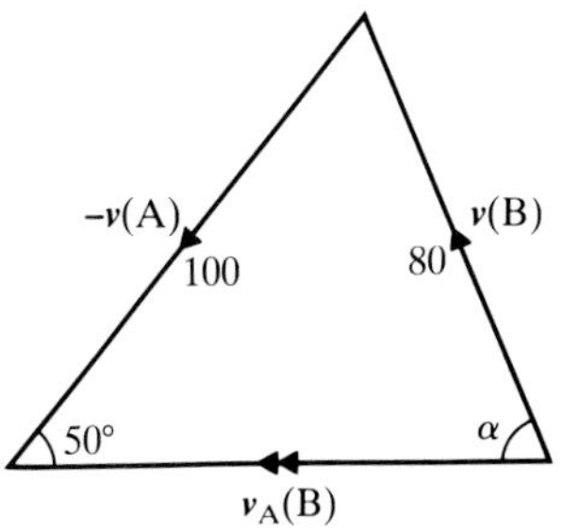

Figure 2.30

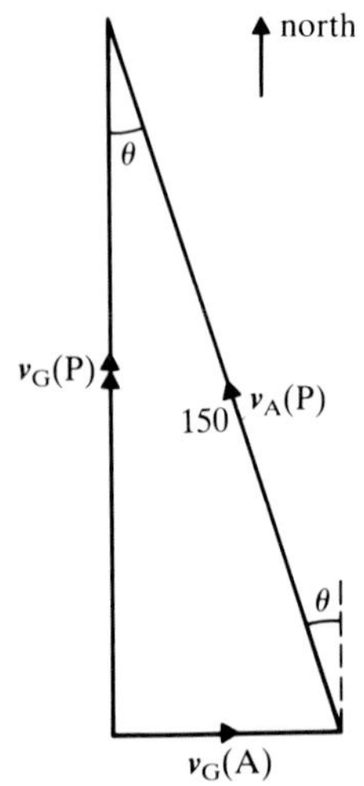

Figure 2.31

EXAMPLE 4

A light aeroplane has an airspeed of 150 km h^{-1}. The wind speed is 50 km h^{-1} and is from the west. Find the course to be set if the track to be made good is due north. What would the groundspeed then be?

Let $\boldsymbol{v}_G(P)$ be the velocity of the plane relative to a fixed point on the ground. This has a track due north.

Let $\boldsymbol{v}_G(A)$ be the velocity of the air relative to the ground. This is 50km h^{-1} from the west.

Let $\boldsymbol{v}_A(P)$ be the velocity of the plane relative to the air, the magnitude of which is the airspeed, 150km h^{-1}.

From equation (10)

$$\boldsymbol{v}_A(P) = \boldsymbol{v}_G(P) - \boldsymbol{v}_G(A),$$

where the origin is a fixed point on the ground, G. This can be re-arranged to give

$$\boldsymbol{v}_G(P) = \boldsymbol{v}_A(P) + \boldsymbol{v}_G(A),$$

and we draw a triangle of velocities as in figure 2.31.
Since $v_G(A) = 50$ and $v_A(P) = 150$, clearly $\sin\theta = \frac{50}{150} = \frac{1}{3}$, and hence $\theta = 19.5°$. The plane should set a course of $(360 - 19.5) = 340.5°$. The groundspeed is given by $v_G(P) = 150\cos\theta = 141.4$ km h^{-1}.
This problem could also be solved using a scale diagram.

*Suppose that, following a sudden gust, the wind speed increases to 100 km h^{-1}, and after engine failure the airspeed drops to 80 km h^{-1}. The pilot will no longer be able to make a track north. How near can he come to his required direction?

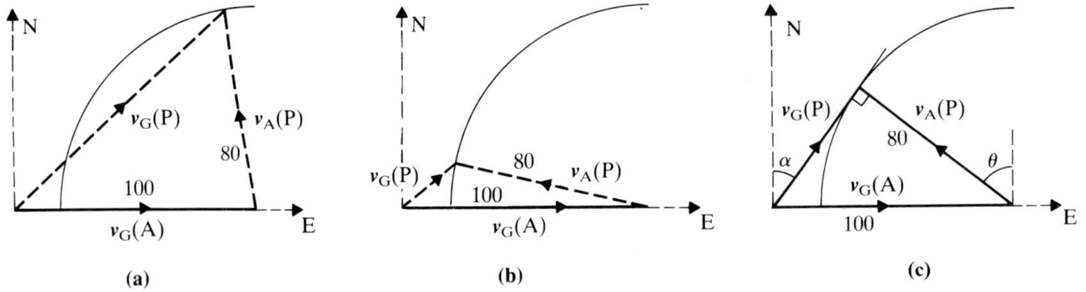

Figure 2.32

Again we use $\boldsymbol{v}_G(P) = \boldsymbol{v}_A(P) + \boldsymbol{v}_G(A)$, where $v_A(P) = 80$ and $v_G(A) = 100$. The first part of the diagram is as before and figure 2.32 shows several possible directions for $\boldsymbol{v}_A(P)$, but no matter what direction is taken, $\boldsymbol{v}_G(P)$ is not due north.

The closest the pilot can get to tracking north is given by the position in figure 2.32c, where $\boldsymbol{v}_G(P)$ is tangential to the circle of all possible directions for $\boldsymbol{v}_A(P)$. In this case the angle α will be a minimum, which is the angle 'off course' that the plane will actually be flying.

$$\alpha = \cos^{-1} \tfrac{80}{100} = 36.9^\circ$$

The course to be steered is $\theta = 90 - \alpha = 53.1^\circ$ west of north, i.e. a bearing of 306.9°.

EXERCISE 2F

1. A man can row a boat at 5 m s^{-1} in still water. He wishes to row straight across a river which is 50 m wide and flows at a constant speed of 3 m s^{-1} parallel to the banks.

   a) At what angle to the bank should he row?

   b) How long does he take to cross?

2. If the river in question 1 were flowing at 6 m s^{-1} instead of 3 m s^{-1}, what would be the minimum drift downstream?

3. A man is running due west at 8 m s^{-1}. The wind is blowing from the west and rain is falling at 10 m s^{-1} at 20° to the vertical. At what angle should the man hold his umbrella for maximum effect?

4. To an observer in a train travelling due east at 40 km h^{-1}, an aeroplane appears to be travelling north at 70 km h^{-1}. Find the true speed and course of the plane.

5. A speedboat has to round three buoys A, B, C starting from A. ABC is an equilateral triangle of side 200 m with BC due north and A west of B and C. The current is a steady 5 m s^{-1} from the west, and the boat can make 20 m s^{-1} in still water. Calculate the time taken for each leg.

6. A ship A is 100 km due west of a ship B. A is travelling at 10 km h^{-1} on a bearing of 030°. B is travelling at 20 km h^{-1} on a bearing of 270°. Find their closest distance of approach.

7. Two cyclists are on roads approaching the same junction at right angles. Cyclist A is 100 m from the junction cycling at a steady 10 m s^{-1}. Cyclist B is also 100 m from the junction cycling at a steady 15 m s^{-1}. Find their shortest distance of approach, and their distances from the junction when this occurs.

8. A woman is jogging west at a speed of 6 mph and observes that the wind appears to be coming from the north. When she increases her speed to 12 mph in the same direction the wind appears to be coming from the north west. Find the true speed and direction of the wind.

9. An aircraft which can fly at $180\ \text{km h}^{-1}$ in still air is to travel from Metz to Roubaix. Aachen is 200 km due north of Metz and Roubaix is 200 km due west of Aachen. A steady wind of $60\ \text{km h}^{-1}$ is blowing from the north east. Find the time taken to go from Metz to Roubaix a) direct, and b) via Aachen.

10. At 12 noon a destroyer travelling at 20 knots sights a ship travelling at 10 knots due north. When first seen the ship is 15 nautical miles north east of the destroyer. Find the direction in which the destroyer must be steered in order to intercept the ship. Find the time at which the ships will meet.

11.* The displacement at time t of a gnat from the centre of a pond is by $\boldsymbol{r} = 2t\hat{\boldsymbol{e}} + 4t\hat{\boldsymbol{n}} - 2t\hat{\boldsymbol{u}}$, where $\hat{\boldsymbol{e}}$, $\hat{\boldsymbol{n}}$ and $\hat{\boldsymbol{u}}$ are unit vectors in the east, north and up directions. If a hornet has displacement $\boldsymbol{r} = (t+1)\hat{\boldsymbol{e}} - 2t\hat{\boldsymbol{n}} + t\hat{\boldsymbol{u}}$ at a time t measured from the same origin, find:
   a) The displacement of the hornet relative to the gnat at time t.
   b) The velocity of the hornet relative to the gnat at time t.
   c) The time when they are closest together.

12.* Two cyclists are racing on a circular track. A is cycling at $20\ \text{m s}^{-1}$ and B is cycling at $25\ \text{m s}^{-1}$. The initial positions are shown in figure 2.33. Taking unit vectors $\boldsymbol{i}$ and $\boldsymbol{j}$ as shown, find an expression for their relative velocity at time t. How long is it before they are 50 m apart?

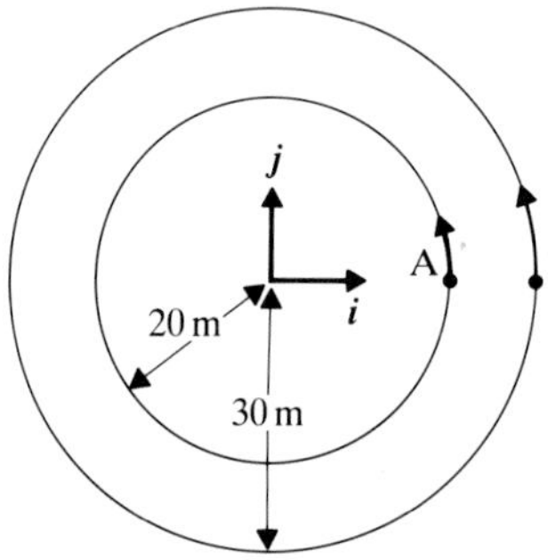

Figure 2.33

Summary

Velocity and acceleration

If $\boldsymbol{r} = \begin{pmatrix} x \\ y \end{pmatrix}$, then

$$\boldsymbol{v} = \dot{\boldsymbol{r}} = \begin{pmatrix} \dot{x} \\ \dot{y} \end{pmatrix}, \qquad \boldsymbol{a} = \ddot{\boldsymbol{r}} = \begin{pmatrix} \ddot{x} \\ \ddot{y} \end{pmatrix}.$$

Formulae for constant acceleration

$$\boldsymbol{v} = \boldsymbol{u} + t\boldsymbol{a},$$
$$\boldsymbol{r} = t\boldsymbol{u} + \tfrac{1}{2}t^2\boldsymbol{a} = \tfrac{1}{2}t(\boldsymbol{u} + \boldsymbol{v}),$$
$$v^2 = u^2 + 2\boldsymbol{a}\cdot\boldsymbol{r}.$$

In one dimension, these reduce to:

$$v = u + at,$$
$$s = ut + \tfrac{1}{2}at^2 = \tfrac{1}{2}(u + v)t,$$
$$v^2 = u^2 + 2as.$$

Motion under gravity

For an initial speed u at an angle of projection θ,

equation of the path $y = x \tan\theta - \dfrac{gx^2}{2u^2}\sec^2\theta,$

time of flight $T = \dfrac{2u\sin\theta}{g},$

horizontal range $R = \dfrac{u^2 \sin 2\theta}{g},$

maximum height $h = \dfrac{u^2\sin^2\theta}{2g}.$

Motion in a circle

The acceleration $\boldsymbol{a}$ has two components:
$r\ddot{\theta}$ along the tangent,
$r\dot{\theta}^2$ towards the centre.

If $\dot{\theta} = \omega = \text{constant}$, the acceleration $a = r\omega^2 = v^2/r$ towards the centre.

Relative motion

The displacement of B relative to A,

$$\boldsymbol{r}_{\text{A}}(\text{B}) = \boldsymbol{r}(\text{B}) - \boldsymbol{r}(\text{A})$$

The velocity of B relative to A,

$$\boldsymbol{v}_{\text{A}}(\text{B}) = \boldsymbol{v}(\text{B}) - \boldsymbol{v}(\text{A}).$$

3 DYNAMICS

3.1 Introduction

Figure 3.1

The photograph (figure 3.1) shows a man engaged in the sport of paraflying. He is attached to a fast boat by a long rope and is wearing a small parachute. Whilst in flight he is subjected to a number of forces which cause him to rise, fall, or stay in steady level flight.

At the end of chapter 1 we discussed some of the different types of forces and their representation as vectors. Dynamics is the study of the effects of forces on the motion of objects and, in the following exercise, we shall investigate a number of problems in which forces are acting.

EXERCISE 3A

1. In the example of the paraflier, describe what forces are acting on the man and the parachute. Discuss what might happen if:
   a) the boat suddenly accelerated,
   b) the boat stopped,
   c) there was a sudden gust of wind, blowing against the flier.

2. a) What forces make racing cars accelerate?
   b) Why do racing cars have large back tyres?
   c) Would the situation be very different if racing cars had front-wheel drive?

3. A stunt rider in an aeroplane performs a 'loop the loop' in a vertical circle without wearing a harness. What is the direction of the acceleration of the pilot at the top and at the bottom of the circle? What forces are acting on the pilot in those positions?

4. Which of the following are more likely to win a race over 10 m from rest: a) a top class sprinter, b) a racing car, c) a top class cyclist? Explain your answer.
   d) How would the answer differ if the race were over (i) 50 m, (ii) 200 m?

5. a) Why are passengers 'thrown forward' when a bus brakes suddenly?
   b) On the other hand, why do standing passengers in a tube train tend to fall backwards as the tube pulls out of the station?

6. Describe the forces acting:
   a) on the roller skates of a girl as she freewheels,
   b) on a man on an escalator.

Newton's laws of motion 3.2

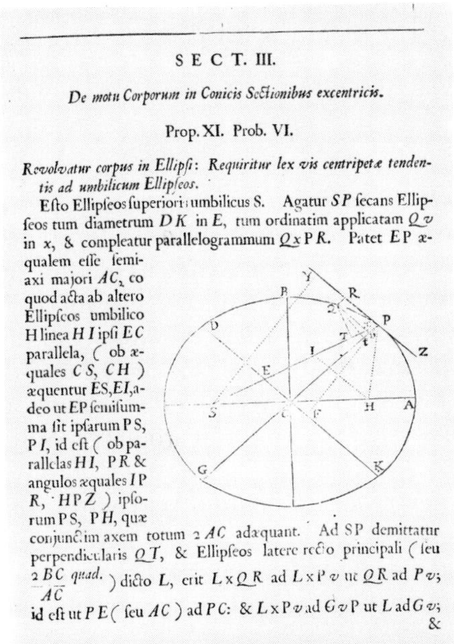

S E C T. III.

De motu Corporum in Conicis Sectionibus excentricis.

Prop. XI. Prob. VI.

Revolvatur corpus in Ellipſi: Requiritur lex vis centripetæ tendentis ad umbilicum Ellipſeos.

Eſto Ellipſeos ſuperioris umbilicus S. Agatur *SP* ſecans Ellipſeos tum diametrum *DK* in *E*, tum ordinatim applicatam *Qv* in *x*, & compleatur parallelogrammum *Qx*P*R*. Patet *E*P æqualem eſſe ſemiaxi majori *AC*, eo quod acta ab altero Ellipſeos umbilico H linea *HI* ipſi *EC* parallela, (ob æquales *CS*, *CH*) æquentur ES, *EI*, adeo ut EP ſemiſumma ſit ipſarum PS, P*I*, id eſt (ob parallelas *HI*, P*R* & angulos æquales *I*P*R*, *H*P*Z*) ipſorum PS, P*H*, quæ conjunctim axem totum 2 *AC* adæquant. Ad SP demittatur perpendicularis *QT*, & Ellipſeos latere recto principali (ſeu $\frac{2\,BC\ quad.}{AC}$) dicto *L*, erit *L*x*QR* ad *L*xP*v* ut *QR* ad P*v*; id eſt ut *PE* (ſeu *AC*) ad *PC*: & *L*xP*v* ad *G*vP ut *L* ad *Gv*;

&

Left, *A page from* Principia *by Isaac Newton and* right, *a portrait of Isaac Newton.*

The foundations of classical mechanics were laid by an English mathematician called Isaac Newton (1642–1727), who summarised his work in his *Principia* published in 1686.

Before Newton it was generally assumed that

a) All motion required a cause, and

b) The laws governing bodies on or near the Earth were essentially different from those governing the planets and stars.

Whilst Galileo had questioned the validity of the first assumption, it was Newton who finally gave a convincing argument against both propositions. Firstly, he asserted that it was not motion itself, but only a change in motion, i.e. acceleration, which requires a cause. Secondly, he proposed that the laws governing all bodies are the same, whether they are on the Earth or in space.

These essential ideas are contained in three basic propositions and his theory of gravitation. Since they accurately explained all relevant observable phenomena at the time, Newton's laws became generally accepted. It is well known that just after the turn of this century phenomena were observed which were not properly explained by Newton's laws, and it was Albert Einstein who provided the necessary alternative in his theories of relativity. However, these theories are far more complicated than Newton's, and, for the problems we will be investigating, Newton's model is very reasonable. We will refer to Newton's laws using the abbreviations N1, N2 and N3. Simple though Newton's theory is, the laws are commonly misunderstood, and we will look at them in some detail.

Figure 3.2 *A pike dive*

Newton's first law (N1)

Any body will move with constant speed in a straight line, unless there is a resultant external force acting on it.

There are words and phrases used here which need some explanation.

a) A body

Strictly N1 applies only to particles, a particle being an object of negligible dimensions, concentrated at a single point, which experiences no deformation or rotation during its motion. In an attempt to model physical situations mathematically, we will often treat large bodies as if they were particles. A few examples will illustrate this.

i) If we ignore its size and rotation we can deduce that the path of a golf ball after it has been hit is an approximate parabola.

ii) For the purposes of calculating its orbit around the Sun, we treat the Earth as a particle.

We cannot explain how a high board diver controls the number of somersaults he performs before he enters the water if we treat him as a particle. In fact, the number is partly controlled by the amount the diver bends during the motion, two standard positions being the 'tuck' and the 'pike'.

N1, and also N2 and N3, can be applied to the motion of an object whose size is small compared with the distance it travels. The laws apply only to the translational motion of such bodies and give no immediate information about their orientation or rotational motion.

b) Constant speed in a straight line

In vectorial language this means constant velocity and includes the possibility of a body being at rest. However, it is not easy to decide whether a body has constant velocity or is at rest. When velocity is measured it is done relative to an observer who may or may not be at rest. Observers often imagine themselves at an origin, and then set up the normal $\boldsymbol{i}$, $\boldsymbol{j}$, and $\boldsymbol{k}$ axes, often referred to as a **frame of reference**. For example, when a snooker player looks at a cue ball on a table, he imagines it to be at rest before he strikes it, but, due to the spin of the Earth, the ball is moving on a circle with a speed of perhaps 200 m s^{-1} and, due to the Earth's orbit about the Sun, it is moving on a circle with a speed of 32 km s^{-1} (see figure 3.3).

At this point it is sufficient simply to assume that a frame of reference can be found in which N1 is true. Such a frame is called an **inertial** or **newtonian frame** and a proper discussion of this topic is beyond the scope of this book. However, we may think of an inertial frame as one which is 'fixed' relative to the directions to the farthest stars out at the 'edge' of the universe. Fortunately, a frame of reference fixed on the Earth's surface is an approximate newtonian frame. This may seem to be questionable in view of the high speeds quoted for the Earth's spin and its speed about the Sun. However, although the speeds are large, the corresponding angular velocities are small:

for the Earth spinning about its axis, ω_1 is 7.3×10^{-5} rad s^{-1}.
for the Earth's rotation about the Sun, ω_2 is 2×10^{-7} rad s^{-1}.

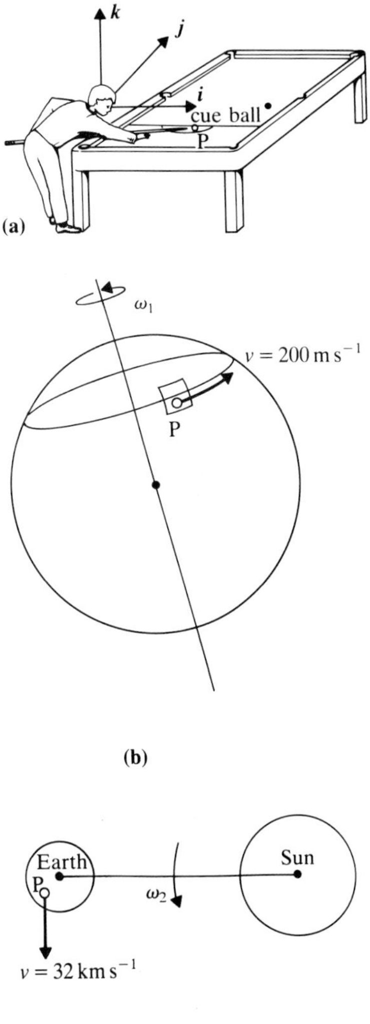

Figure 3.3

c) Resultant external force

It is important to realise that in general there are many forces acting on a body, even when it is moving with constant velocity.

EXAMPLE 1

Suppose the paraflier in section 3.1 has a constant velocity. In this case N1 states that the external forces acting on the man and the parachute must be in equilibrium, i.e. have zero resultant. The external forces are shown in figure 3.4a. We simplify this by regarding the man and the parachute as a particle, so that the forces act at a point, as in figure 3.4b. The condition for constant velocity can now be interpreted by a closed vector polygon of forces, as in figure 3.4c. Conversely, when there is a resultant force acting on a body, it will not move with constant velocity.

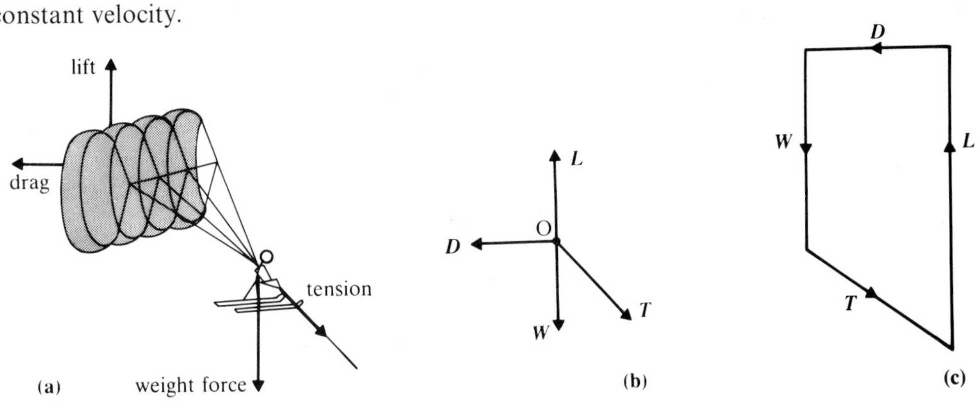

Figure 3.4

EXAMPLE 2

If a car is travelling along horizontal ground at a constant velocity and the engine is switched off, it will not continue with uniform velocity, but will slow down and eventually stop. This is because there is a resultant horizontal force acting on the car. This will be due to reaction between the wheels and the ground, friction on the bearings and air resistance etc.

Newton's second law (N2)

> The acceleration of a body is proportional to the resultant external force and takes place in the direction of the force.

At the end of the discussion of N1 we anticipated that, if there is a resultant external force on a body, then the velocity is not constant. In this case both the magnitude and the direction of the acceleration are specified by N2.

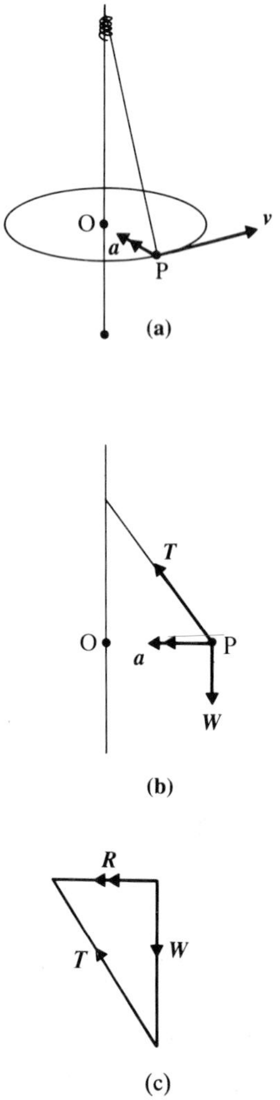

Figure 3.5

a) The direction of the acceleration is in the direction of the force

Most people have had some experience of bump-starting a car when the battery is flat. The car must be accelerated from rest to a certain speed before the gears are engaged. In this case the acceleration and the velocity are in the same direction. This is not always so, as we now show.

Suppose the swingball in figure 3.5a is moving in a circle with constant speed. Although the speed is constant, its direction and hence its velocity is changing, and the acceleration is towards the centre of rotation, O (see section 2.5). The forces on the ball are the tension in the string and the weight force, whose resultant **R** must be along **PO**, the direction of the acceleration as in figure 3.5b and c.

b) The acceleration is proportional to the force

Common experience tells us that some objects accelerate faster than others, given the same force. It takes longer to produce the required speed when pushing a large car than when pushing a small car. The quantity associated with a body which determines its reluctance to move when a force is applied is called its **mass**.

We see that $\mathbf{F} \propto \mathbf{a}$,

and also $F \propto m$.

Combining these we get $\mathbf{F} \propto m\mathbf{a}$.

In SI units we define a force of magnitude 1 newton (1N) to be that force which gives a mass of 1 kilogram (1 kg) an acceleration of 1 m s^{-2}. Provided that the mass is in kilograms, the acceleration in m s^{-2}, and the force in newtons, we can write N2 as a vector equation:

$$\mathbf{F} = m\mathbf{a}$$

EXAMPLE 1

In figure 3.6a the trolley has mass 20 kg and it contains a boy of mass 40 kg. The boy who is pushing applies a force of 100 N horizontally. Neglecting all resistances, calculate the acceleration of the trolley.

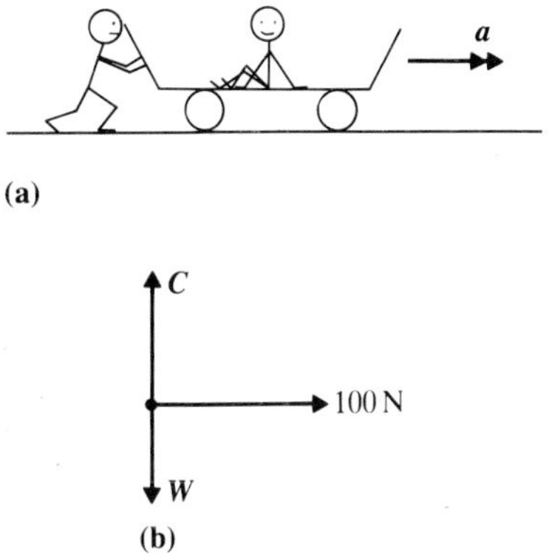

Figure 3.6

We assume that the boy and the trolley can be treated as a single particle of mass $m = 60$, so that all the forces acting on it can be at one point, as in figure 3.6b. We are justified in doing this provided

a) the boy in the trolley does not move relative to the trolley

b) there is no rotation of the trolley, i.e. it does not swing round or tip.

N2 is a vector equation, but the conditions of the question indicate that there will be no motion vertically. Thus, there is no component of the acceleration vertically, and no component of the resultant force vertically. Hence, the forces labelled $\boldsymbol{C}$ and $\boldsymbol{W}$ in figure 3.6b are not relevant to the problem. Whatever the value of C, it merely 'balances' W. The acceleration (and velocity) is in one dimension.

$$\boldsymbol{F} = m\boldsymbol{a} \qquad (1)$$

becomes

$$100 = 60a,$$

which is a scalar equation, giving a as 1.67 m s^{-2}.

What we have actually done here is to take components of vectors on both sides of equation (1) in the horizontal direction. Writing out the full justification of what we have done above is tedious and we will not do it in future. The reader should be clear in his or her own mind, however, what implicit assumptions are being made at each stage.

In future we will write:

Applying N2 horizontally to the trolley and the boy,

$$100 = 60a,$$

giving a as 1.67 m s^{-2}.

EXAMPLE 2

Suppose two boys now push the trolley in example 1. What is the acceleration?

Applying N2 horizontally to the trolley and the boy, as in figure 3.7a

$$F = ma,$$

$$200 = 60a,$$

giving a as approximately 3.33 m s^{-2}.

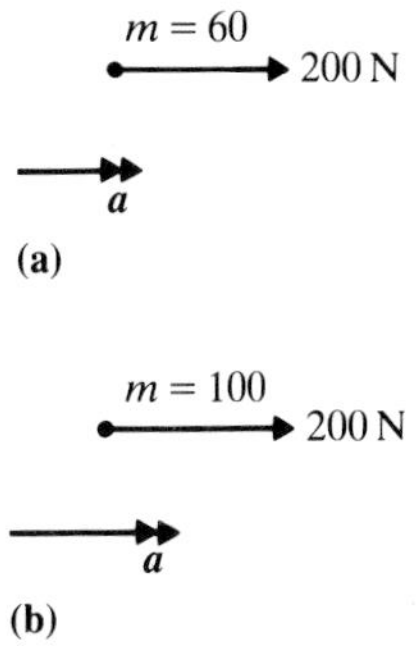

Figure 3.7

EXAMPLE 3

Suppose there are now two boys each of mass 40 kg in the trolley. What is its acceleration?

Applying N2 horizontally to the trolley and both boys, as in figure 3.7b.

$$F = ma,$$

$$200 = 100a,$$

a is 2 m s^{-2}.

EXAMPLE 4

A golf ball of mass 40 g is hit so that at time t its position vector is given by

$$\boldsymbol{r} = 25t\boldsymbol{i} + (15t - 5t^2)\boldsymbol{j},$$

where $\boldsymbol{i}$ and $\boldsymbol{j}$ are base vectors horizontally and vertically. Find the position, velocity and acceleration after 2 s. What is the force on the ball at that time?

The position vector at time t is

$$\boldsymbol{r} = 25t\boldsymbol{i} + (15t - 5t^2)\boldsymbol{j}.$$

Differentiating with respect to t gives the velocity vector as

$$\boldsymbol{v} = 25\boldsymbol{i} + (15 - 10t)\boldsymbol{j}.$$

Differentiating again gives the acceleration as

$$\boldsymbol{a} = -10\boldsymbol{j}.$$

When $t = 2$,

$$\boldsymbol{r} = 50\boldsymbol{i} + 10\boldsymbol{j},$$
$$\boldsymbol{v} = 25\boldsymbol{i} - 5\boldsymbol{j},$$
$$\boldsymbol{a} = -10\boldsymbol{j}.$$

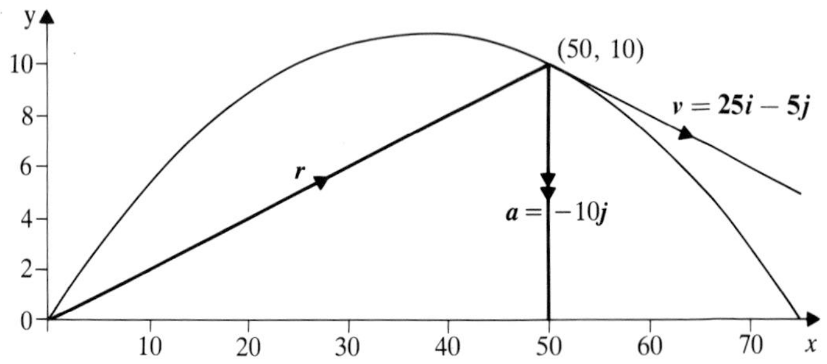

Figure 3.8

Figure 3.8 shows the displacement, velocity and time vectors drawn on a sketch of the path of the ball. The force is given by N2 as

$$\boldsymbol{F} = m\boldsymbol{a} = 0.04 \times -10\boldsymbol{j}$$
$$= -0.4\boldsymbol{j},$$

i.e. $\boldsymbol{F}$ has magnitude 0.4 N and acts vertically downwards.

Dimensions

N2 gives $\boldsymbol{F} = m\boldsymbol{a}$, and both sides of this equation must have the same dimensions (see appendix), so that

$$[\boldsymbol{F}] = [m\boldsymbol{a}],$$

and since $[m\boldsymbol{a}] = \mathrm{M\,L\,T^{-2}}$,

so $[\boldsymbol{F}] = \mathrm{M\,L\,T^{-2}}.$

EXERCISE 3B

1. What is the magnitude of the force required to give a particle of mass 3 kg an acceleration of magnitude: (a) $3\,\mathrm{m\,s^{-2}}$, (b) $25\,\mathrm{m\,s^{-2}}$, (c) $0.2\,\mathrm{m\,s^{-2}}$, (d) $0.2\,\mathrm{cm\,s^{-2}}$, (e) $15\,\mathrm{mm\,s^{-2}}$?

2. A jet of mass 10^5 kg is flying horizontally. The net forward force after resistances have been taken in account is 1.2×10^6 N. How long will it take to break the sound barrier, starting from a speed of $100\,\mathrm{m\,s^{-1}}$? (The speed of sound is $300\,\mathrm{m\,s^{-1}}$.)

3. A particle of mass 3 kg is acted on by a force of $\begin{pmatrix} 9 \\ -6 \end{pmatrix}$ N. The particle is initially at rest at a point with position vector $\begin{pmatrix} -1 \\ 2 \end{pmatrix}$ m. How long must the force be applied for the particle to reach a velocity of $\begin{pmatrix} 12 \\ -8 \end{pmatrix}\,\mathrm{m\,s^{-1}}$? What will be its position vector at that time?

4. A trolley of mass 50 kg is pushed with a force of 200 N. What is its acceleration?

5. A girl of mass 30 kg is seated on the trolley in question 4 when it is pushed with a force of 250 N. What is the acceleration?

6. A ball of mass 100 g has an acceleration of $200\,\mathrm{m\,s^{-2}}$. With what force is it hit?

7. A skater of mass 60 kg is moving at $5\,\mathrm{m\,s^{-1}}$ across the ice. She slows down in a distance of 30 m. What is the constant force causing her to slow down to rest?

8. A particle of mass 2 kg is moving in a horizontal circle of radius 3 m at a steady speed of $3\,\mathrm{m\,s^{-1}}$. Find its acceleration and hence the force acting on it.

9. A car of mass 1 t is brought to rest in 10 s from a speed of $50\,\mathrm{km\,h^{-1}}$. What is the constant force needed to produce the retardation?

10. A particle of mass 3 kg moves so that at time t its position is $\begin{pmatrix} 2\cos t \\ 2\sin t \end{pmatrix}$. Find its velocity and acceleration at time t, and hence the magnitude and direction of the force acting on it.

11. A particle of mass 6×10^{-31} kg is moving at a speed of $2 \times 10^8\,\mathrm{m\,s^{-1}}$ when it is acted on by a force of 1.5×10^{-15} N (a) in the same direction and (b) at right angles to its path. Find the magnitude of its velocity in each case after 3×10^{-8} s.

12. Two engines each having a thrust of 5500 N give an aeroplane of mass 36000 kg a horizontal acceleration of $0.25\,\mathrm{m\,s^{-2}}$. What is the magnitude of the air resistance?

13. A particle of mass 2 kg is moving at $15\,\mathrm{m\,s^{-1}}$ when a force of 10 N is applied at (a) 90° (b) 120° and (c) 150°, to its line of motion. In each case find its speed and direction after 5 s.

14. A coin of mass 10^{-2} kg is lying without slipping on the edge of a long-playing record of diameter 30 cm, which is rotating at $33\frac{1}{3}$ rpm. What is the horizontal force acting on the coin?

15. A fairground aeroplane consists of a rotating arm which can be raised or lowered, with a model aeroplane fixed at the 'free' end. The mass of the plane is 100 kg and its position vector at time t is

$$\mathbf{OP} = 4\cos 2t\,\boldsymbol{i} + 4\sin 2t\,\boldsymbol{j} + \sin 3t\,\boldsymbol{k}.$$

a) What is the resultant force acting on the aeroplane at time t?

b) How is this force provided?

c) If a child of mass 40 kg were to sit in the plane, what would be the force on him? How is this force provided? (Assume the child does not move relative to the plane.)

16. What are the dimensions of: a) angle, (b) angular velocity, (c) pressure (force per unit area)?

17.* A car of mass 1 t can be pushed on a horizontal road with an acceleration of $0.2\,\mathrm{m\,s^{-2}}$ by one man. When another man, exerting the same force, comes to his aid the acceleration is $0.5\,\mathrm{m\,s^{-2}}$. Assume there is a constant resistance of R N horizontally on the car. Calculate: (a) the value of R, (b) the force exerted by each man.

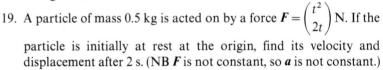

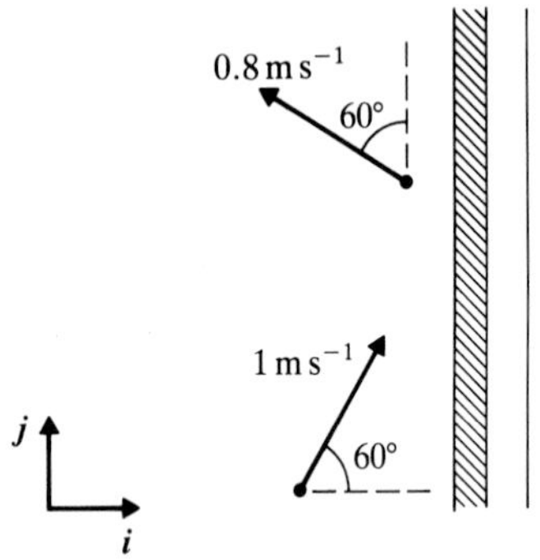

Figure 3.9

18.* Figure 3.9 shows a billiard table with a ball of mass 0.25 kg rebounding from the cushion. If the time of contact between the ball and the cushion is 0.1 s, calculate: (a) the average acceleration of the ball, (b) the average force on the ball.
Treat the billard ball as a particle. What assumptions are you making? Are they reasonable? Discuss the nature of the force acting on the ball.

19. A particle of mass 0.5 kg is acted on by a force $\boldsymbol{F} = \begin{pmatrix} t^2 \\ 2t \end{pmatrix}$ N. If the particle is initially at rest at the origin, find its velocity and displacement after 2 s. (NB $\boldsymbol{F}$ is not constant, so $\boldsymbol{a}$ is not constant.)

20. After t s, the position vector of a particle of mass 8 kg is given by $\boldsymbol{r} = t^{1/2}\boldsymbol{i} + \sin t\,\boldsymbol{j}$. Calculate: (a) the velocity when $t = 4$ s, (b) the force acting on the particle when $t = 4$ s.

3.3 Newton's third law (N3)

When two bodies A and B interact they exert forces on one another which are equal in magnitude and opposite in direction.

Thus, if body A exerts a force $\boldsymbol{F}$ on body B, then body B exerts a force $-\boldsymbol{F}$ on body A.

Contact forces

EXAMPLE 1

Figure 3.10a shows a man leaning against a wall. There will be contact forces between

a) the man and the wall b) the man and the floor.

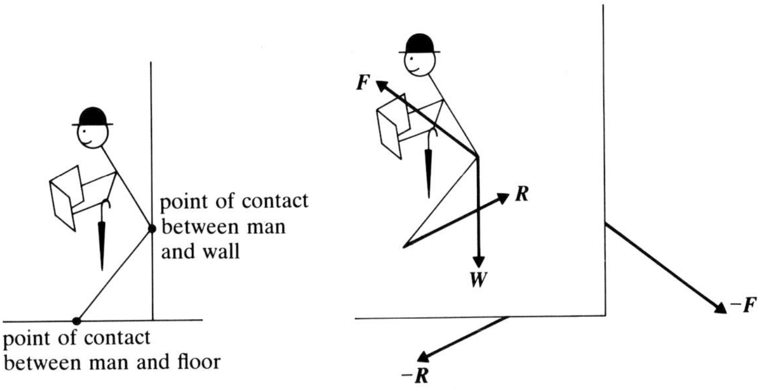

(a) **(b)**

Figure 3.10

We may show all the forces acting in a 'free body' diagram, as in figure 3.10b. $\boldsymbol{R}$ and $\boldsymbol{F}$ are the contact forces between the man and the floor and wall respectively, and $\boldsymbol{W}$ is the weight force on the man (see section 3.4).

EXAMPLE 2

Figure 3.11 shows a simplified version of the paraflier in figure 3.1. There are contact forces acting at P and Q arising from the tension in the rope. These are shown more clearly in figure 3.11b. Notice that the forces on the ends of the rope are outward since the rope is taut (tense).

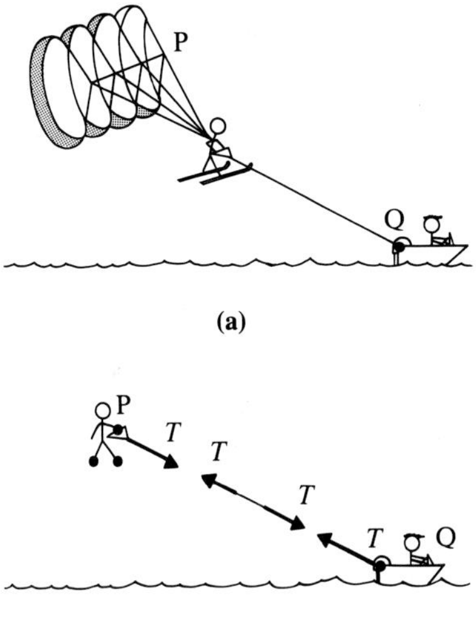

Figure 3.11

□□□□□

As a first approximation, we will often consider the wires or strings which join objects together to be 'light' (i.e. to have negligible mass) and to be inextensible (i.e. to be of fixed length).

Consider a light string which is in tension. Suppose that the tensions either side of a particular length are $\boldsymbol{T}_1$ and $\boldsymbol{T}_2$, as shown in figure 3.12. If $T_2 > T_1$, the forces on the element at P are not in equilibrium, and the element, having no mass, will have an infinite acceleration from left to right. Similarly, if $T_2 < T_1$, it will have an infinite acceleration to the left. Thus, $T_2 = T_1$. Hence, the tension in a light string is constant. This is also true for light extensible strings, since we cannot allow infinite accelerations (see section 8.1).

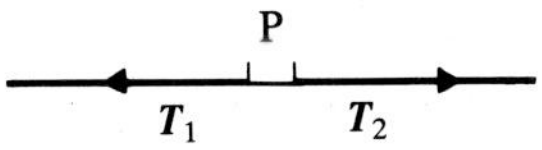

Figure 3.12

EXAMPLE 3

At the instant a golfer hits a golf ball with a club there will be a contact force between them, and we note:

a) This force is only in operation while the club head is in contact with the ball, and will not be constant throughout that time.

b) The effect of the forces is different for the two objects in contact. The ball is light and free to fly off initially in the direction in which it is hit. The club, on the other hand, is a large object which is constrained by other forces, e.g. those induced by the golfer's hands.

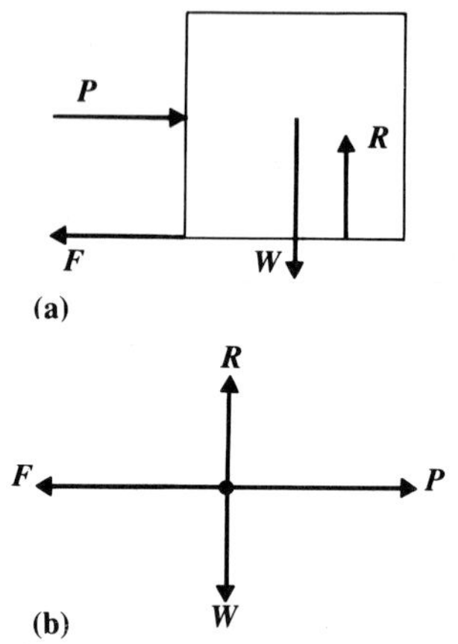

Figure 3.13

EXAMPLE 4

A large heavy packing case is pushed along the floor, as in figure 3.13. The forces acting on the case are:

P – the pushing force,
W – the weight force,
R, ***F*** – both components of the contact force.

R is called the normal contact force, and ***F*** is called the frictional force. ***F*** is usually present when there is slipping between surfaces in contact, or when there is a tendency to slip. If $\mathbf{F} = \mathbf{0}$, while slipping occurs, the surfaces are said to be smooth. We will discuss friction in more detail in section 7.2.

We would hesitate to use N2 if we thought that the packing case was likely to tip. Provided this is not the case, we can approximate to figure 3.13a by figure 3.13b.

EXERCISE 3C

1. Draw sketches illustrating the contact forces (omit others) in the following situations:
   a) a suitcase on a conveyor belt, with no slipping between the case and the belt, when the belt is (i) moving at steady speed, (ii) accelerating forward.
   b) a child sliding down a playground slide.
   c) a child walking up a playground slide.
2. Show the contact forces on the child on the roundabout at the points A and B in figure 3.14 when the roundabout is turning with constant angular velocity, and the child is at rest relative to the roundabout.

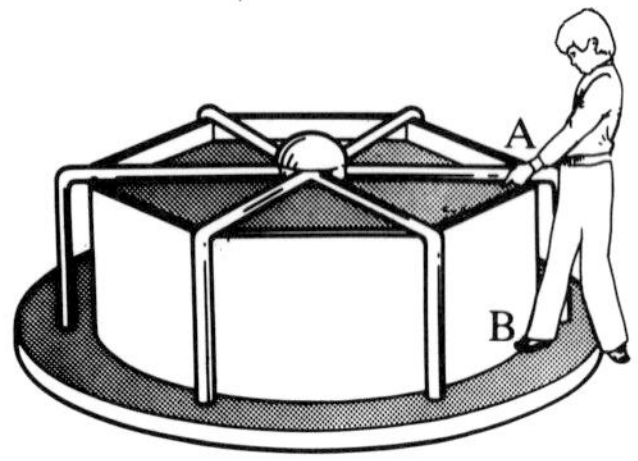

Figure 3.14

3. Show the forces at the point on the front wheel which is in contact with the ground, when a motorcycle is cornering. Draw two versions, one end on and the other a plan (the view from above).
4. Show the contact forces on a bicycle at the points where the front and rear wheels are in contact with the road under the following conditions:
   a) the cyclist is accelerating,
   b) the cyclist is freewheeling.
5. Under normal conditions, the fan belt in figure 3.15 is driven by pulley A, and drives pulleys B and C. Show the contact forces on the belt and the pulleys at P, Q and R. Assume the belt is under constant tension.

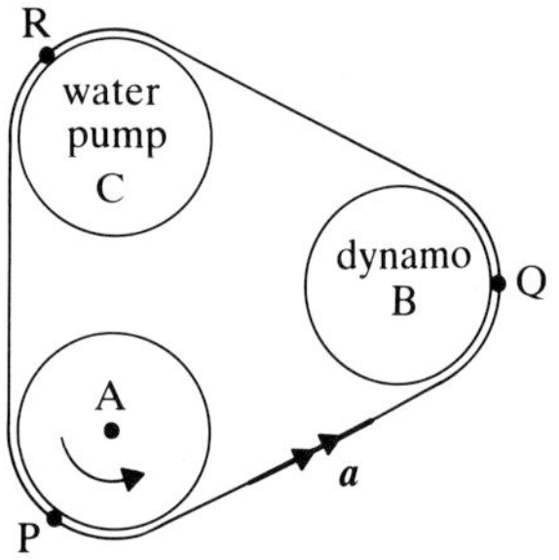

Figure 3.15

3.4 Newton's law of gravitation

In common with most scientists and mathematicians of his day, Newton was interested in astronomy, and we will briefly trace some of the fundamental ideas that led to his theory of gravitation.

a) From about 150 AD, the prevailing theory concerning planetary motion was due to Ptolemy as contained in his work *Almagest*. The scheme is geocentric with other planets, including the Sun, moving on crystal spheres (orbs). The looping of planets' motion was explained by the use of epicycles, as in figure 3.16.

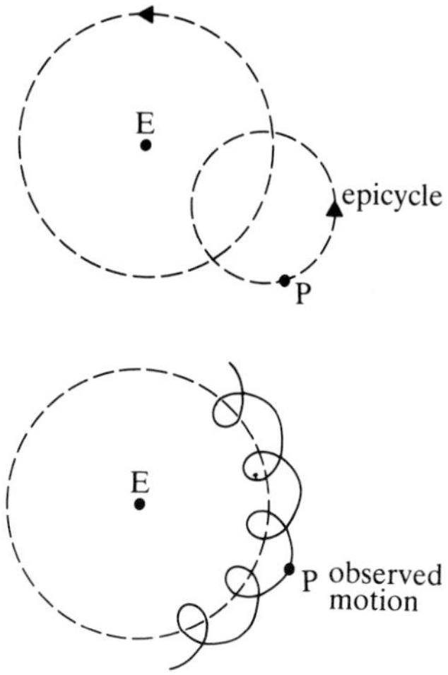

Figure 3.16

b) In 1543 Copernicus published *de Revolutionibus* in which he proposed that simplifications could be made if the Sun, rather than the Earth, were regarded as the centre of the system.

c) All observations had, of course, been made with the naked eye, since the astronomical telescope was not to appear until 1609. However, in 1576 the Danish astronomer Tycho Brahe built an observatory at Uraniborg, using sophisticated geometrical equipment. He also saw the need to dispense with the notion of crystal orbs to allow for the motion of comets, and he replaced them with circular paths or 'orbits'. Towards the end of his life, Tycho was joined by a mathematician, Kepler, who studied Tycho's results to try to formulate a mathematical description of planetary motion. After a number of false starts, Kepler finally arrived at three laws of planetary motion. The first two were published in 1609, and the third in 1619. We will refer to these as K1, K2 and K3.

Kepler's laws

K1: The orbit of each planet is an ellipse with the Sun at one focus.

K2: The radius vector from the Sun to a planet sweeps out equal areas in equal times.

K3: If R is the mean distance from the Sun to a planet and T is the periodic time of the orbit, then R^3/T^2 has a constant value for all planets.

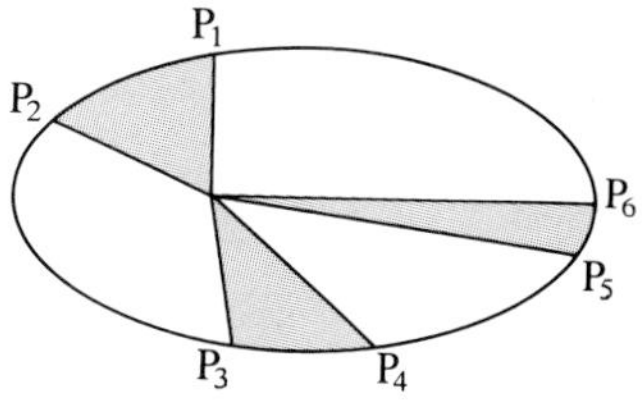

Figure 3.17

Illustration of K2. If, in figure 3.17, P_1P_2, P_3P_4, P_5P_6 are described in equal times, then the shaded areas are equal. The rate at which the areas are swept out is known as the areal velocity, and K2 states that this is constant. An immediate implication is that planets do not maintain a constant speed in their orbit. Note, however, that the eccentricities for planetary orbits are quite small. For the Earth's orbit, $e \approx \frac{1}{60}$. Thus, the orbits are nearly circular.

d) Galileo was one of the first astronomers to use a telescope, and was a keen defended of Copernican ideas, in spite of the Church's insistence on the validity of Ptolemy's geocentric system. He also clearly identified the concept of acceleration and investigated the kinematics of falling bodies. He was able to explain free fall and parabolic motion in terms of constant acceleration at the Earth's surface, but was unable to relate acceleration clearly to the idea of force. Galileo died in 1642, the same year that Newton was born.

e) In 1682 the astronomer Halley calculated the orbit of a bright comet (now called Halley's comet) and noted its close resemblance to those he had calculated for earlier comets in 1531 and 1607. He deduced that they were successive appearances of the same comet, having a period of about 76 years. The next return of this comet is in 1986. Figure 3.18 shows the orbit of Halley's comet, which is an 'eccentric' ellipse i.e. one which is *not* nearly circular.

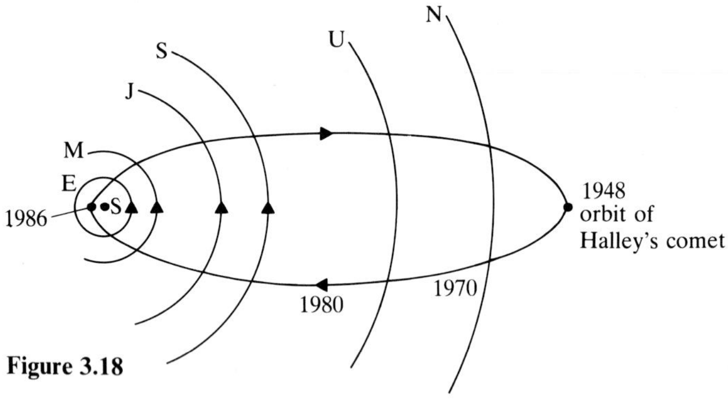

Figure 3.18

Although orbits could be calculated accurately, forces were not introduced since it was assumed that they could only act with contact. In 1684 Halley went to Newton at Cambridge to ask him if he could account for the orbits, along the lines suggested by Hooke. Newton claimed to have a proof already that elliptic orbits were consistent with an inverse square law of attraction. Halley persuaded Newton to publish, and this ultimately resulted in the *Principia* of 1686.

The theory of gravitation

An inverse square law of attraction can be deduced as follows.

Suppose that a planet P orbits the Sun S in an approximate circle of radius r, with speed v. If T is the period.

$$T = \frac{2\pi r}{v}. \qquad \textbf{(2)}$$

There is an acceleration of magnitude v^2/r towards S. Applying N2 towards S on the planet P,

$$\begin{aligned} F &= m\frac{v^2}{r} = \frac{m}{r}(v^2) \\ &= \frac{m}{r}\left(\frac{2\pi r}{T}\right)^2, \quad \text{(from equation } \textbf{(2)}\text{)} \\ &= (4\pi^2 m)\frac{r}{T^2}. \end{aligned}$$

Now K3 gives $T^2 = kr^3$, thus

$$F = (4\pi^2 m)\frac{r}{kr^3} = \frac{4\pi^2 m}{k}\frac{1}{r^2}$$

i.e. $F \propto (m/r^2)$. Thus, the net forces which act on planets are approximately proportional to their mass and inversely proportional to the square of their mean orbital radius. Since these forces are considered to be caused by the planet's interaction with the Sun, an application of N3 would also suggest that an equal (but opposite) force acts on the Sun. The Sun however has a mass which is considerably greater than that of any planet, so such a force would produce an acceleration which is so small that it would not normally be noticed.

The force on the planet had been found to be proportional to its mass, and it is logical now to assume also that the force on the Sun is similarly proportional to its mass. Since these forces are equal they must therefore be proportional to both masses.

By extending a more detailed version of this argument to include the moons of Saturn and Jupiter, Newton was led to suggest that all bodies attract each other with forces which are proportional to the product of their masses and inversely proportional to the square of the distance between them. This result is known as Newton's law of gravitation:

Any two bodies of mass m_1 and m_2 attract each other with a force whose magnitude is given by

$$F = \frac{Gm_1m_2}{d^2},$$

where d is their distance apart, and G is the constant of gravitation.

This law has been found to describe accurately the motion of bodies near the Earth's surface as well as that of planets and their satellites.

Acceleration due to gravity

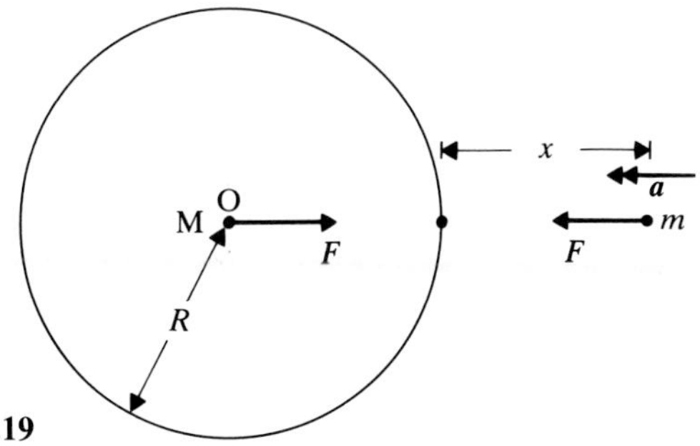

Figure 3.19

Consider a particle of mass m near the surface of the Earth, as in figure 3.19. To calculate the gravitational effect of the Earth on the particle we will make the following assumptions.

a) The Earth is a sphere of uniform density and radius R.

b) The Earth is not spinning on its axis.

Given (a), Newton proved that the gravitational field of the Earth is the same as that of a particle of equal mass concentrated at its centre. Using this result we have, from the law of gravitation,

$$F = \frac{GMm}{(R+x)^2}.$$

If $x \ll R$,
$$F = \frac{GMm}{R^2}.$$

Since $M \gg m$, the Earth accelerates very little under this force, so we may regard the Earth as fixed. The acceleration of m towards O is given by N2:

$$F = ma = \frac{GMm}{R^2},$$

so that
$$a = \frac{GM}{R^2},$$

which is a constant. This constant is usually denoted by g and is called the acceleration due to gravity. Thus:

$$g = \frac{GM}{R^2}.$$

In SI units, g is observed to be approximately $9.8\,\mathrm{m\,s^{-2}}$, but for ease of calculation and for most of this book this is often taken as $10\ \mathrm{m\ s^{-2}}$. The value of g will only be approximate since the initial assumptions are not strictly true, and the value of g will vary at different points on the surface of the Earth.

Dimensions and units of G

We have seen that Gm_1m_2/d^2 is the magnitude of a force.

$$\left[\frac{Gm_1m_2}{d^2}\right] = [F] = \mathrm{M\,L\,T^{-2}},$$

$$[G]\frac{\mathrm{M}^2}{\mathrm{L}^2} = \mathrm{M\,L\,T^{-2}}$$

$$[G] = \mathrm{M^{-1}\,L^3\,T^{-2}}.$$

The units of G are therefore $\mathrm{kg^{-1}\,m^3\,s^{-2}}$.

The first approximate value of G was found experimentally by Cavendish in 1798. It is approximately $6.67 \times 10^{-11}\,\mathrm{kg^{-1}m^3s^{-2}}$. We must remember that the law of gravitational attraction applies to all bodies, not just planets and stars. However the low value of G means that, under normal circumstances on the Earth's surface, the gravitational attractions between separate bodies are very small.

EXAMPLE 1

Two ten tonne trucks are parked 10 m apart. Find the attraction between them.

Now, $10\ t = 10^4$ kg, so treating the trucks as particles, N2 gives

$$F = 6.67 \times 10^{-11} \times \frac{10^4 \times 10^4}{10^2} = 6.67 \times 10^{-5}.$$

Hence the force is 0.000 067 N, which is very small indeed.

EXAMPLE 2

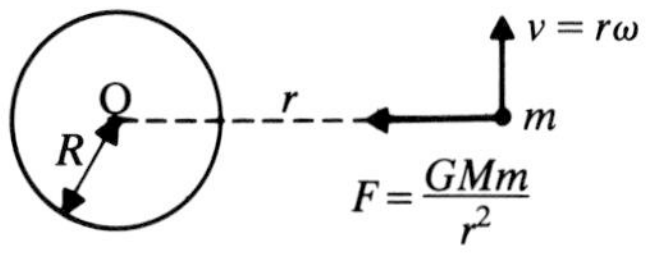

Figure 3.20

Suppose the Moon rotates about the Earth in a circular orbit of radius r, such that $r = 60R$, where R is the radius of the Earth, as in figure 3.20. If the period of the Moon's orbit is 27.5 days, calculate R.

Let M be the mass of the Earth and m be the mass of the Moon. By the law of gravitation,

$$F = \frac{GMm}{r^2}.$$

Let ω be the angular velocity of the Moon about the Earth. Applying N2 on the Moon toward O, the centre of the Earth,

$$mr\omega^2 = \frac{GMm}{r^2},$$

$$\omega^2 = \frac{GM}{r^3}$$

$$= \frac{GM}{R^2} \times \frac{R^2}{r^3}$$

$$= \frac{g}{r}\left(\frac{R}{r}\right)^2.$$

$$r = \frac{g}{\omega^2} \times \frac{1}{60^2},$$

$$R = \frac{g}{4\omega^2} \times \frac{1}{60^3}.$$

Now $\omega = 2\pi/T$, where $T = 27.5 \times 24 \times 60^2$, hence

$$R = \frac{g}{4\pi^2} \times \frac{(27.5 \times 24 \times 60^2)^2}{60^3} = 6.5 \times 10^6,$$

giving the radius of the Earth as 6500 km.

EXAMPLE 3

Given that the mass of the Moon is approximately $\frac{1}{81}$ times the mass of the Earth, and the radius of the Moon is $\frac{1}{4}$ times the radius of the Earth, calculate an approximate value for the acceleration due to gravity on the surface of the Moon.

Let M_E, R_E be the mass and radius of the Earth and g_E the acceleration due to gravity near the surface of the Earth. Let M_M, R_M and g_M be the corresponding values on the Moon.
On the Moon the acceleration due to gravity is given by

$$g_M = \frac{GM_M}{R_M^2}. \quad (3)$$

On the Earth,

$$g_E = \frac{GM_E}{R_E^2}. \quad (4)$$

Dividing equation (4) by equation (3),

$$\frac{g_M}{g_E} = \frac{M_M}{M_E}\left(\frac{R_E}{R_M}\right)^2 = \frac{4^2}{81} \simeq \tfrac{1}{5}.$$

$$g_M \approx 10 \times \tfrac{1}{5}.$$

The acceleration due to gravity on the Moon is approximately 2 m s^{-2}.

Mass and weight

When asked their weight young children might give their answer in kilograms. The kilogram, as we have seen, is a measure of mass, and people often confuse the terms mass and weight. Mass is a fundamental property of a body, measuring its reluctance to accelerate (see section 3.2) and is independent of where it is measured.

The term 'weight' is used in science to describe the force due to gravitational attraction on a body. Its value depends on

a) the body which is doing the attracting, and

b) the relative positions of the attracting and the attracted bodies.

Figure 3.21

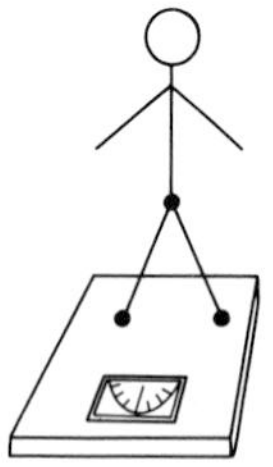

(a) at rest

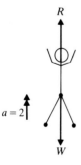

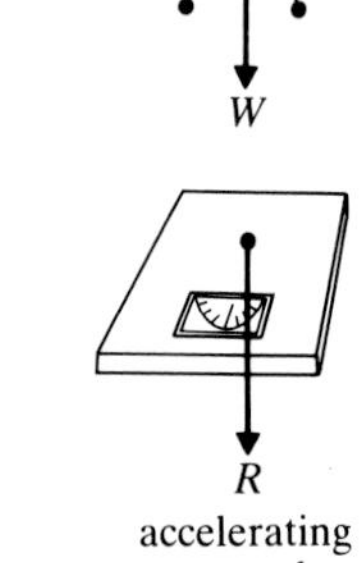

accelerating upwards

(b)

EXAMPLE 4

Suppose a man has a mass of 70 kg.

On the surface of the Earth, $F = mg_E = 70 \times 10 = 700$. The weight of the man is 700 N.

On the surface of the Moon, $F = mg_M = 70 \times 2 = 140$ (see example 3). The weight of the man on the Moon is 140 N.

□□□□□

An attempt is sometimes made to resolve the confusion between mass and weight by defining a kilogram-force (kgf) or kilogram-weight. These are equal to the weight of 1 kilogram near the surface of the Earth, and therefore have an approximate value of 9.8 (or 10) N. Thus, if a man stands on bathroom scales and registers 70 kg, this really means that his weight is 70 kilogram-weight or approximately 700 N.

When different bodies are measured under exactly the same circumstances, their weights are proportional to their masses, and so

$$W = mg,$$

where g is the acceleration due to gravity. When the man stands on the bathroom scales, as in figure 3.21a, the contact force on the scales depresses a spring which operates a pointer. The scales have responded to a force of 700 N. Applying N2 vertically upwards on the man,

$$R - W = 0,$$

$$R = 70g = 700.$$

This is a force of 70 kgf.

Suppose, however, as in figure 3.21b, that the man is in a lift which is accelerating upwards at 2 m s^{-2}. In this case, applying N2 vertically upwards to the man,

$$R - W = 70 \times 2,$$
$$R - 70g = 140,$$
$$R = 840.$$

The scales would register an 'apparent weight' of 84 kg.

Suppose the lift were to accelerate downwards at g m s^{-2} (free fall), as in figure 3.21c. Applying N2 vertically downwards on the man,

$$R + W = -70g,$$
$$R - 70g = -70g.$$
$$R = 0.$$

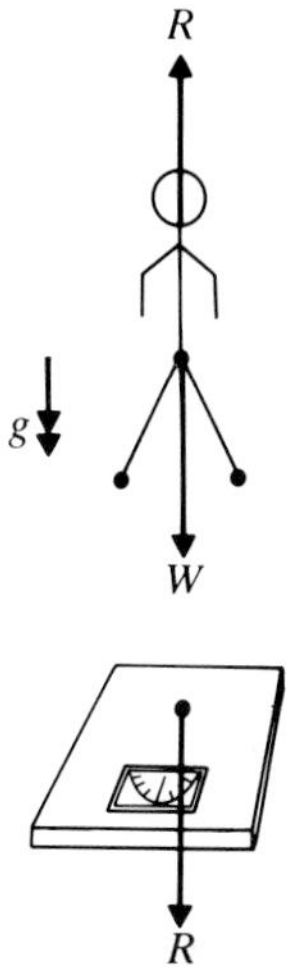

(c)

The man is apparently weightless (see example 3, section 3.7). Clearly, what the scales have measured is the contact force between the man's feet and the scales. In all three cases, the man's weight, which is 700 N, is the force on him due to gravitational attraction.

We will not refer to the kilogram-force or kilogram-weight at any later stage in this book since they are unnecessary.

We may summarise as follows:

The weight of an object is the force of gravitational attraction on it towards a specific body. When the body is not specified it can automatically be assumed to be the Earth. The units of weight are newtons.

A man of mass 70 kg near the surface of the Earth has a weight of 700 N whether at rest, in free fall or in a rocket blasting vertically.

EXERCISE 3D

Take G as 6.67×10^{-11} kg^{-1} m^3 s^{-2}.

1. Calculate the gravitational attraction between two particles of of masses 9 kg and 11 kg placed 10 cm apart.

2. Given the acceleration due to gravity, $g = 9.8$ m s^{-2}, and the radius of the Earth, $R_E = 6400$ km, calculate M_E, the mass of the Earth.

3. Given that the Moon orbits the Earth once a month on a circle of radius 3.8×10^5 km, and the Earth orbits the Sun once a year on a circle of radius 1.5×10^8 km, calculate the ratio of the mass of the Earth, M_E, to the mass of the Sun, M_S.

4. Titan (one of the moons of Saturn) describes an orbit around Saturn in 16 days. If the orbit is circular and has a radius 3.2 times the radius of the orbit of the Earth's moon, calculate the ratio of the masses of the Earth and Saturn.

5. Find the period of revolution of an artificial satellite orbiting just above the surface of the Earth.

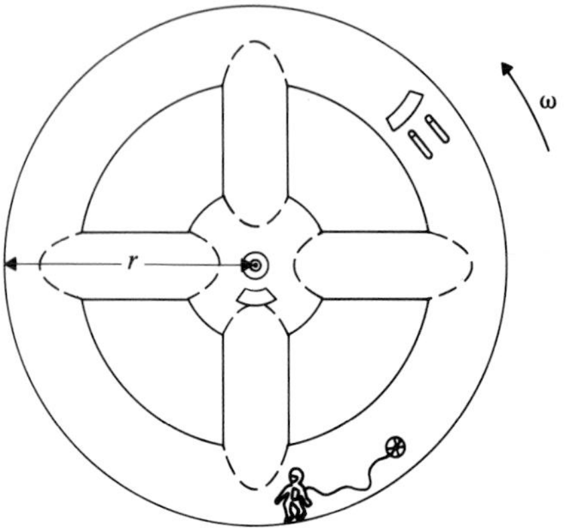

Figure 3.22

6. The mass of the Moon is approximately $\frac{1}{80}$ of the mass of the Earth and its radius is approximately $\frac{3}{11}$ of the radius of the Earth. What is the weight of a 70 kg man on the surface of the Moon?

7. Taking the Earth as a sphere of radius 6400 km, find the percentage change in the acceleration due to gravity in going from sea level to a height of 10 km.

8. If a satellite is to remain hovering over the same point on the Earth's equator, what will be the radius of its orbit? Ignore the Sun, Moon and other gravitational attractions.

9. Figure 3.22 shows a space station of radius r, rotating with angular speed ω.

   a) What is the relation between r and ω necessary for the man to have apparent Earth 'weight'?

   b) Discuss the forces on the man as he walks round at various speeds clockwise and anti-clockwise.

10.

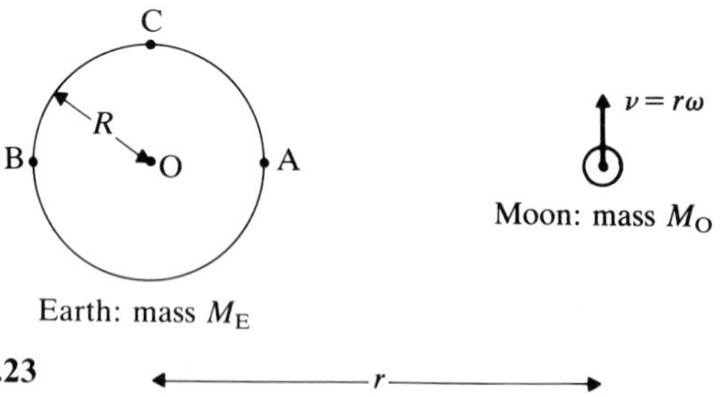

Figure 3.23

Figure 3.23 shows the Moon orbiting the Earth. Consider particles all of mass m at A, B, C and O. Let the magnitude of the force exerted by the Moon on the particle at O be F_O etc. Assuming that (R/r) is small, so that $(R/r)^2$ can be neglected, use the binomial theorem to estimate F_A/F_O and F_B/F_O. Calculate the component of F_C towards O, in terms of F_O. Assuming that the Earth is fixed and covered with a thin layer of liquid (i.e. the oceans), what do your results suggest about the height of the sea at A, B, and C. Illustrate your answer with a sketch.

11. Does a laboratory balance measure mass or weight? Should you refer to 'standard masses' or 'standard weights'?

3.5 Several forces

So far we have looked at examples where there has been just one force acting on each body considered. We now discuss cases where there are several forces acting. In each example we will look at particles, or bodies which may be treated as particles, so that all the forces may be thought of as acting at a single point. However, we must take care not to make this assumption too readily in all cases. For example, consider a ladder slipping down a wall, as shown in figure 3.24.

The forces acting may be simplified as shown and are:

R*, *C the contact forces with the wall

F*, *S the contact forces with the ground

W the weight force of the ladder, assumed to be acting through the centre of mass.

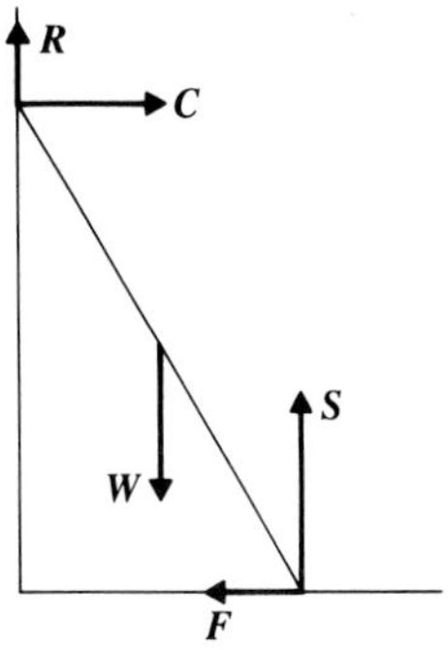

Figure 3.24

Clearly, all these forces act at different parts of the ladder and, if we wish to consider whether the ladder will slip on the ground or on the wall, we will have to consider these parts separately, and so cannot think of the ladder as a particle.

Some simplification is possible if the body is rigid, that is one in which all its parts remain at fixed distances from each other. Provided we can ignore rotation, we can treat large bodies as particles, but often the problem is to determine whether or not rotation takes place anyway. In the above example, the ladder is clearly rotating, but if it were to be dropped from a tall building with no rotational motion, we could treat it as a particle.

Assuming that we can reduce problems to those of particle motion, we solve examples where several forces are acting on a body by finding the resultant of those forces and then applying N2 to find its acceleration. In the special case in which the resultant is zero, the body is said to be in equilibrium, and it then either remains at rest or moves with constant velocity. Initially we consider particles which move or are constrained to move in a straight line.

EXAMPLE 1

A man of mass 70 kg is being hoisted vertically by a cable attached to him and to a helicopter, which is hovering above him. If the tension in the cable is 800 N, find the vertical acceleration of the man, neglecting air and other resistances. Take g as $10\,\mathrm{m\,s^{-2}}$.

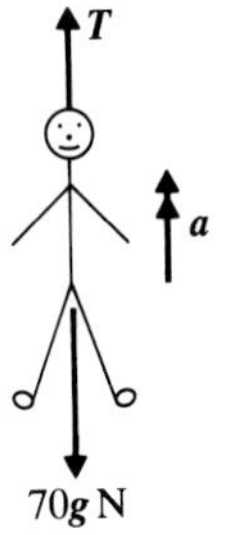

Figure 3.25

We concentrate only on the forces acting on the man, who is treated as a particle. There are two forces acting on him shown in figure 3.25,

a) the tension, ***T***, in the cable, and

b) his own weight force, 70***g*** N.

Taking the upward vertical direction as positive and applying N2 we get

$$T - 70g = 70a,$$

where a is the upward acceleration of the man.
Given that $T = 800$ and $g = 10$, we get

$$a = \frac{800 - 700}{70} = 1.43.$$

The acceleration is $1.43\ \mathrm{m\,s^{-2}}$.

We often write the weight force as a multiple of g in our initial equation and diagram and then evaluate it later in the problem. Similarly, with other forces, like ***T***, it is customary not to evaluate them in our initial equation.

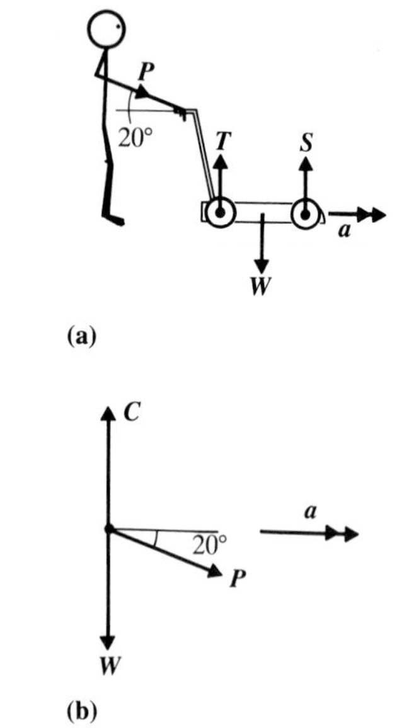

Figure 3.26

EXAMPLE 2

A toddler is pushing a Baby-walker of mass 3 kg along the ground with a force of 1.5 N downwards at 20° to the horizontal. What is the acceleration of the toy and the normal contact force between the toy and the ground if (a) the resistances to motion are ignored, and (b) the resistances total 0.5 N? Take g as 10 m s^{-2}.

There are several forces acting on the toy, as shown in figure 3.26a, namely

the push, $\boldsymbol{P}$, exerted by the child,

the weight force, $\boldsymbol{W}$, of the toy,

the contact forces, $\boldsymbol{S}$ and $\boldsymbol{T}$, between the wheels and the ground.

There is a tendency for the toy to tip up and so the reactions on the front and back wheels will not be equal. However, provided the toy does not actually rotate, we will assume that it can be treated as a particle and the normal contact force is represented by $\boldsymbol{C} = \boldsymbol{T} + \boldsymbol{S}$, as in figure 3.26b.

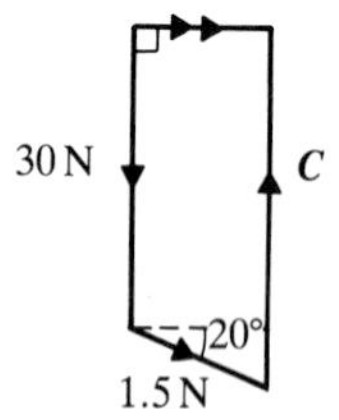

Figure 3.27

a) Since the motion and any acceleration is horizontal, the resultant force must be horizontal. Let the acceleration be **a** m s^{-2}. We compile a vector polygon of forces as in figure 3.27. The magnitude of the resultant is $P\cos 20°$, which is the component of $\boldsymbol{P}$ in the horizontal direction.
N2 horizontally on the toy gives

$$P\cos 20° = 3a,$$
$$a = \tfrac{1}{3}(1.5\cos 20°) = 0.47.$$

Ignoring the resistance, the acceleration is 0.47 m s^{-2}. The normal reaction $\boldsymbol{C}$ has magnitude given by applying N2 vertically downwards

$$3g + P\sin 20° - C = 0,$$

giving C as 30.5 N.

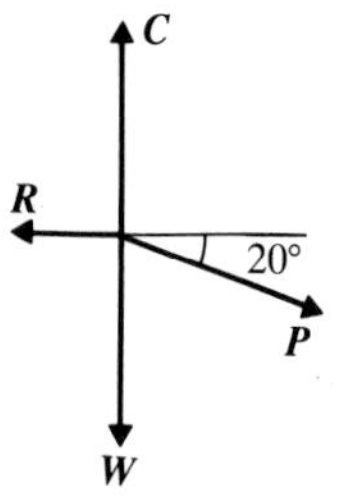

Figure 3.28

b) Suppose the resistance to motion is 0.5 N. We now include this force, as shown in figure 3.28. From N2, $\boldsymbol{F} = m\boldsymbol{a}$ is a vector equation, but we can think of it as a number of scalar equations obtained from each of its components, and so we can equate components of the equation. In our example, $\boldsymbol{R} + \boldsymbol{C} + \boldsymbol{W} + \boldsymbol{P} = 3\boldsymbol{a}$ is the vector equation of N2.
Taking components:

horizontally $$P\cos 20° - R = 3a. \qquad \textbf{(5)}$$

vertically $$-3g - P\sin 20° + C = 0. \qquad \textbf{(6)}$$

Equation (6) gives $C = 30.5$ N, as in part (a). From equation (5)

$$a = \tfrac{1}{3}(1.5\cos 20° - 0.5) = 0.3.$$

The acceleration is 0.3 m s^{-2}.

EXAMPLE 3

Suppose the toddler in example 2 pushes the Walker at a steady speed up a slope inclined at 10° to the horizontal. The child still pushes at an angle of 20° to the ground. Find the magnitude of the push exerted by the child and the normal contact force between the wheels and the ground, if the resistance to motion is 0.5 N.

Figure 3.29 shows the forces on the Walker, treated as a particle. In vector form N2 is $\boldsymbol{R} + \boldsymbol{C} + \boldsymbol{P} + \boldsymbol{W} = \boldsymbol{0}$, since the baby pushes at steady speed. Parallel to the slope N2 gives

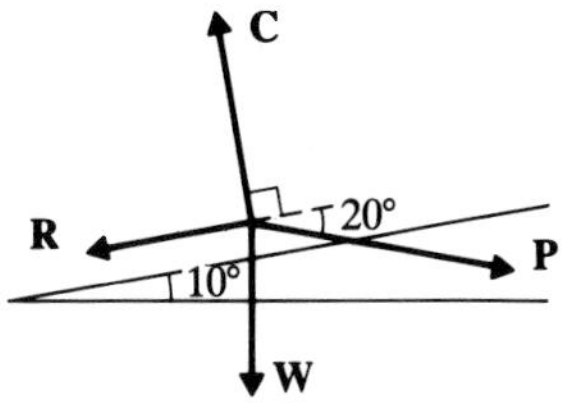

Figure 3.29

$$P \cos 20^\circ - 0.5 - 3g \sin 10^\circ = 0,$$

$$P = \frac{0.5 + 30 \sin 10^\circ}{\cos 20^\circ} = 6.08.$$

Perpendicular to the slope N2 gives

$$P \sin 20^\circ + 3g \cos 10^\circ - C = 0.$$

$$C = 16.5 \sin 20^\circ + 30 \cos 10^\circ = 35.2.$$

Thus the push has a magnitude 6.08 N, and the normal contact force is of magnitude 35.2 N.

□□□□□

Note that, in general, a weight force $\boldsymbol{W}$, which acts vertically, has components along and perpendicular to a slope inclined at an angle α of $W \sin \alpha$ and $W \cos \alpha$. Often the inclination of the slope is given as $\sin^{-1} k$, where k is some fraction, in which case the component along the slope is Wk.

EXERCISE 3E

Take g as 9.8 m s^{-2}, where necessary.

1. Draw labelled diagrams showing all the forces acting on the following bodies (not particles).
   a) A bicycle being pedalled forward on rough ground.
   b) Someone running on rough ground.
   c) A member of a tug of war team.
   d) A sailing dinghy which is 'tacking'.
   e) A parachutist.
   f) The parachute in (e).
2. A girl of mass 40 kg is in a lift. Find the thrust on her feet from the floor of the lift when:
   a) the lift is ascending at a steady speed of 2 m s^{-1}.
   b) the lift is decelerating upwards at 2 m s^{-2}.
   c) the lift is accelerating downwards at 1 m s^{-2}.

   Assume that the girl is at rest relative to the lift throughout. (Hint: Consider the forces acting on the girl alone.)

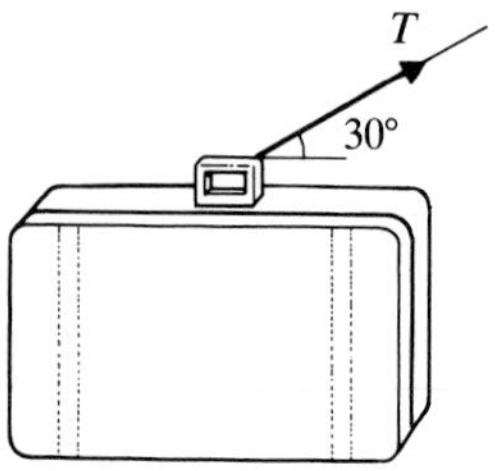

Figure 3.30

3. Figure 3.30 shows a suitcase of mass 40 kg in a corridor. Contact between the suitcase and the floor is smooth. The case is pulled by a woman using a string attached to the case at an angle of 30°. The tension in the string is 600 N.
   a) Show all the forces acting on the suitcase.
   b) Find the magnitude of the acceleration of the case when: (i) the corridor is level, (ii) the floor becomes a ramp inclined downwards at an angle of 10° to the horizontal.

4. A toboggan of mass 15 kg is on a smooth icy slope of angle 18°. What is the acceleration of the toboggan when it is released from rest?

5. A train of total mass 50 t is moving on a horizontal track with a tractive (pulling) force produced by the engine of 5000 N. If its acceleration is 0.08 m s^{-2}, find the total resistance to its motion.

6. One man who pushes a car of mass 800 kg can accelerate it at 0.08 m s^{-2}, whereas two men, each pushing with the same force as the one man, can produce an acceleration of 0.2 m s^{-2}. What is the resistance to motion, assumed to be the same in both cases?

7. A car of mass 950 kg is moving at a steady speed of 50 km h^{-1} up a hill inclined at an angle α to the horizontal, where $\sin\alpha = \frac{1}{10}$. There is a constant resistance to motion of 600 N. What is the tractive force of the engine?
   On reaching the top of the hill, as the road levels out, the driver keeps her foot on the 'accelerator' pedal, so that the tractive force is the same. What is the initial acceleration, assuming the resistance remains the same?

8. A punt of mass 200 kg contains 4 passengers each of mass 60 kg. It is moving at a steady speed of 2 m s^{-1}, when the 'driver' pushes on the pole to give the punt a horizontal force forward of 100 N, at which instant he falls out of the punt. What is the initial acceleration of the punt?

9. A parachutist of mass 70 kg is wearing a parachute of mass 15 kg and free falls to reach a constant speed of 35 m s^{-1}. The parachute opens and provides a further lift force of 500 N. What is the initial acceleration of the man? Calculate his speed after 2 s, and how far he will have moved vertically during this time. (Assume that the forces on the man are constant over this period.)

10. A lorry of mass 2 t is at rest on a hill of slope $\sin^{-1}\frac{1}{6}$ when its brakes fail. What is the speed of the lorry when it hits a wall 200 m away? Assume there is a constant resistance to motion of 1500 N.

11. A miners' lift cage has a mass of 100 kg and will take up to 5 passengers of average mass 70 kg each. What is the tension in the lift cable if, when slowing down and moving downwards, the lift is full and has a retardation of 3 m s^{-2}? What is the force between the floor of the lift and each passenger?

12. A boy of mass 30 kg and a girl of mass 20 kg are sitting on a toboggan of mass 50 kg. It is at the top of a hill of slope $\sin^{-1}\frac{1}{4}$, when it is pushed with an initial speed of $2\,\mathrm{m\,s^{-1}}$. There is a resistance of 50 N on the toboggan and 10 N on each of the children. What is the initial acceleration of the toboggan down the slope? What is its speed after 5 s?

    At this instant the boy and girl both fall off. What is the speed of the toboggan after a further 5 s?

13. A car of mass 1000 kg has an engine which exerts a constant tractive force of 900 N. The car moves up a hill inclined at an angle of $\sin^{-1}\frac{1}{10}$. There is a constant resistance of 400 N to its motion. The initial speed of the car is $30\,\mathrm{m\,s^{-1}}$. How long is it before the car comes to rest and how far has it then travelled?

14. If the car in question 13 starts downhill from rest at the top of the hill, when will it reach a speed of $20\,\mathrm{m\,s^{-1}}$ and how far will it have gone?

15. A train of mass 300 t travelling at $100\,\mathrm{km\,h^{-1}}$ reaches a rising incline of slope $\sin^{-1}\frac{1}{200}$ to the horizontal. The tractive force of the engine is 30 000 N and there is a resistance to motion of 20 000 N. What is its speed after it has travelled 0.5 km ?

More complicated problems 3.6

In the previous examples we have been able to solve problems by taking components of the forces in the direction of motion which has been specified, and this has greatly simplified the work. We now look at problems where this direction may be unknown.

EXAMPLE 1

A particle of mass 2 kg is acted upon by two forces of 10 N and 8 N with an angle of 60° between them, as in figure 3.31. Find the acceleration $\boldsymbol{a}$ of the particle.

Figure 3.3b shows the triangle of forces, not drawn to scale. From the cosine rule,

$$R^2 = 10^2 + 8^2 - 2 \times 10 \times 8 \cos 120 = 244.$$

Hence, $R \approx 15.6$N, and $a = 15.6/2 = 7.81\ \mathrm{m\,s^{-2}}$. From the sine rule,

$$\frac{R}{\sin 60^\circ} = \frac{8}{\sin\theta},$$

$$\sin\theta \approx \frac{8 \sin 60^\circ}{15.6},$$

$$\theta \approx 26.3^\circ.$$

The acceleration is $7.81\ \mathrm{m\,s^{-2}}$ at an angle of 26.3° to the 10 N force.

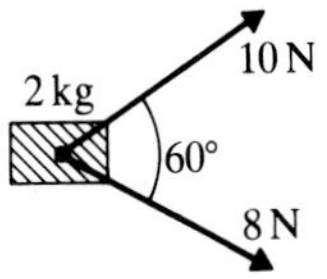

(a)

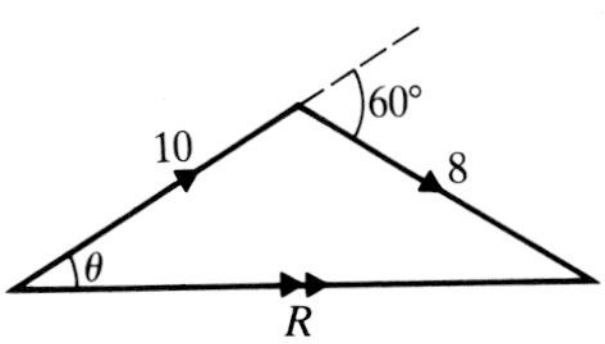

(b)

Figure 3.31

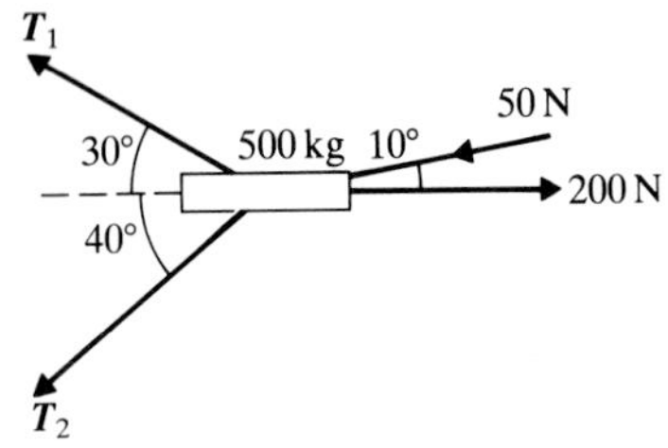

Figure 3.32

EXAMPLE 2

A speedboat of mass 500 kg is pulling two water skiers each of mass 70 kg with a total forward force of 200 N. Due to water resistance there is a force of 50 N at an angle of 10° to the direction of the fore and aft line of the boat on its port (left) side. At a particular instant, the ropes joining the skiers to the boat are inclined at 30° and 40° to the line of the boat, as shown in figure 3.32. Find the tension in each rope at this instant, if the boat is moving at a steady speed.

We will illustrate several methods which may be used to solve this problem. We concentrate solely on the forces on the boat, which is treated as a particle.

Method 1 Scale drawing

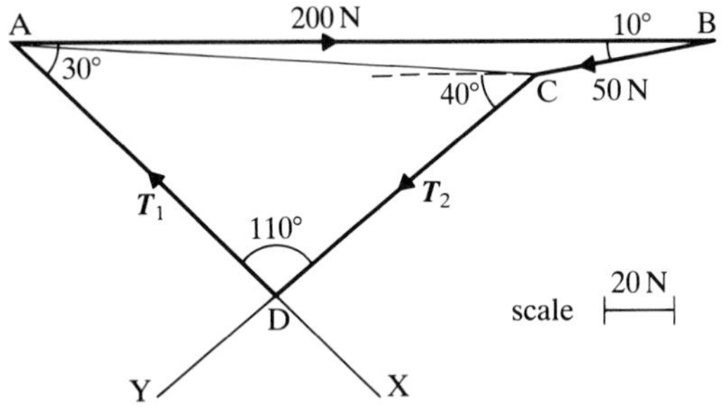

Figure 3.33

We compile figure 3.33 as follows:

a) The known vectors **AB** and **BC** are drawn representing the forward force of the boat and the water resistance.

b) The vectors **CY** and **AX**, each of unknown length, are drawn to represent the two tensions. They meet at D to form a closed polygon, since the boat is moving at steady speed.

c) By measurement, the magnitude of $\boldsymbol{T}_1$ is given by the length AD, so $T_1 = 110$ N. Similarly, $T_2 = 72$ N.

Method 2 Geometrical solution

The polygon of forces is drawn as in figure 3.33, but not to scale. The quadrilateral ABCD is split into two triangles $\triangle$ABC and $\triangle$ACD. The cosine rule for $\triangle$ABC gives

$$\begin{aligned} AC^2 &= AB^2 + BC^2 - 2 \times AB \times BC \cos 10^\circ, \\ &= 200^2 + 50^2 - 2 \times 200 \times 50 \cos 10^\circ, \end{aligned}$$

giving AC as 151 N.

From the sine rule,

$$\sin B\hat{A}C = \frac{50 \sin 10^\circ}{151},$$

$$B\hat{A}C = 3.3^\circ.$$

Hence, $A\hat{C}D = 43.3°$. Using the sine rule in $\triangle ACD$,

$$T_1 = \sin 43.3° \frac{151}{\sin 110°} = 110.$$

$$T_2 = \sin(30° - 3.3°) \frac{151}{\sin 110°} = 72.2.$$

Methods 3 Using components

a) Taking components of N2 (figure 3.34):
along the line of the boat

$$200 - 50\cos 10° - T_1 \cos 30° - T_2 \cos 40° = 0, \qquad (7)$$

perpendicular to the line of the boat

$$-50\sin 10° + T_1 \sin 30° - T_2 \sin 40° = 0. \qquad (8)$$

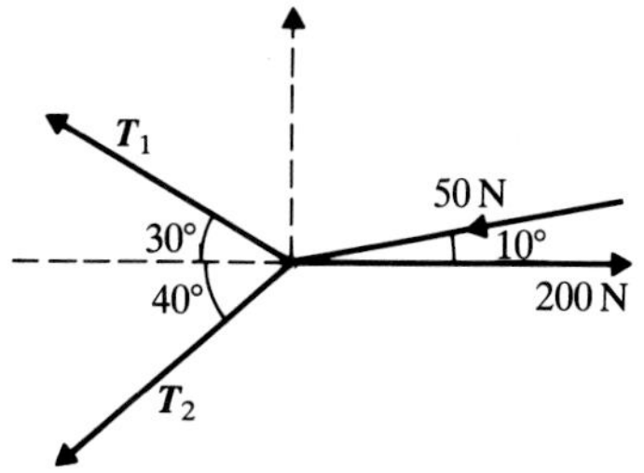

Figure 3.34

Equations (7) and (8) reduce to

$$0.866\, T_1 + 0.766\, T_2 = 150.8, \qquad 0.500\, T_1 - 0.643\, T_2 = 8.68.$$

These are two simultaneous equations in T_1 and T_2, the solution of which is not easy since the coefficients are not whole numbers. It is left to the reader to check that $T_1 = 110$ and $T_2 = 72.2$.

b) Since N2 is a vector equation we can take components in other directions, and it is convenient to take them at right angles to each of $\boldsymbol{T}_1$ and $\boldsymbol{T}_2$ in turn. To find T_1, we take components of N2 perpendicular to $\boldsymbol{T}_2$, as in figure 3.35:

$$200\cos 50° - T_1 \cos 20° - 50\cos 60° = 0,$$

$$T_1 = \frac{200\cos 50° - 50\cos 60°}{\cos 20°} = 110.$$

To find T_2, we take components of N2 perpendicular to $\boldsymbol{T}_1$:

$$200\cos 60° - 50\cos 80° - T_2 \cos 20° = 0,$$

$$T_2 = \frac{200\cos 60° - 50\cos 50°}{\cos 20°} = 72.2.$$

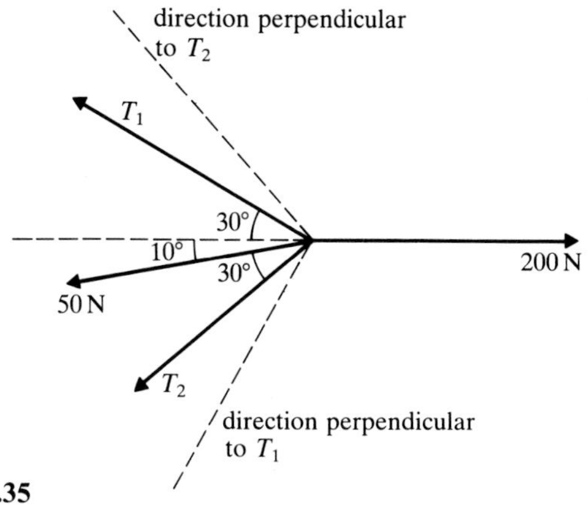

Figure 3.35

EXERCISE 3F

Take g as 10 m s^{-2}, where necessary.

1.

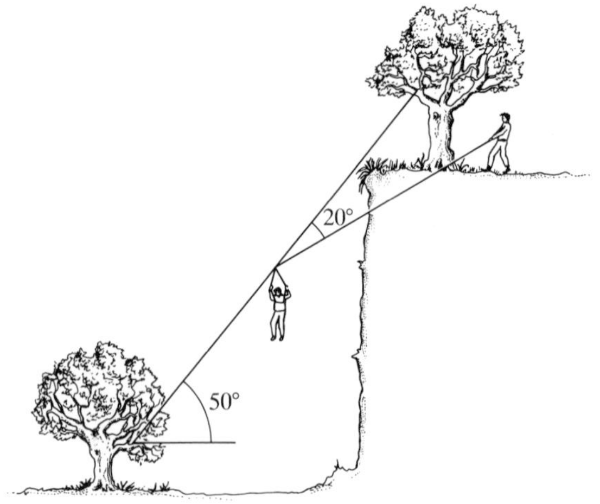

Figure 3.36

Figure 3.36 shows a Scout on an aerial runway. The mass of the Scout and pulley is 60 kg, and the friction between the pulley and runway is negligible. A friend is holding him in position (at rest) by pulling on a rope attached to the pulley as shown in the diagram. Find the tension in the rope:

a) by drawing a vector polygon of forces,

b) by taking components horizontally and vertically,

c) by taking components parallel and perpendicular to the runway.

2. A toboggan of mass 15 kg is on an icy slope of 18°. A horizontal force holds it at rest. Find the magnitude of the force and the acceleration of the toboggan if the force is removed.

3. Two horses on opposite banks of a canal are pulling a small barge of mass 20 t, so that it is moving parallel to the banks. On one side the rope is at 30° to the line of the barge, and on the other side it is at 35°. If the tension in the first rope is 4000 N and there is a resistance of 1000 N due to the water (which acts parallel to the canal banks), what is the tension in the second rope, and what is the acceleration of the barge?

4. Two tugs are pulling a tanker of mass 4000 t forwards with forces of 1.5×10^5 N and 2.5×10^5 N making angles of 30° and 25° on opposite sides of the line of the tanker at a particular instant. What is the magnitude of the acceleration of the tanker at that instant, if we ignore all resistances?

5. Three children think that the parcel has stopped at them in a game of pass the parcel. They pull on parts of the parcel with forces

of 20 N, 40 N and 35 N at angles of 120°, 150° and 90° with each other, as shown in figure 3.37. If the parcel does not break, in which direction will it move?

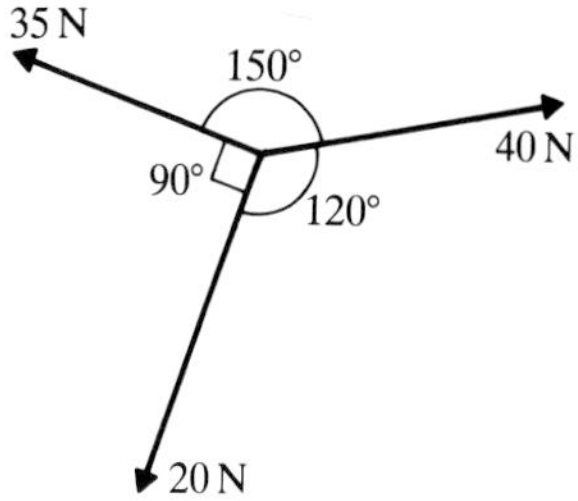

Figure 3.37

6. Two motor boats are pulling a number of sailing dinghies which are unable to move due to lack of wind. Assume that the dinghies may be treated as a single particle of total mass 1200 kg. The tensions in the ropes attached to the motor boats are 200 N and 300 N, and the angle between the ropes is 40°. If the total water resistance on the dinghies is 150 N and directly opposes the motion, calculate the magnitude of the acceleration of the dinghies.

7. Two boys A and B are pulling a heavy trunk of mass 50 kg with two ropes across a floor with forces of 30 N and 40 N, respectively, at an angle of 50° between them. There is a constant resistance to motion of 20 N. What is the acceleration of the trunk and in which direction does it move relative to the rope from A?

8. Two dogs are pulling a sledge of mass 25 kg. One dog pulls south-west with a force of 45 N and the other pulls due west with a force of 55 N. There is a resistance to motion of 30 N. What is the acceleration of the sledge and in what direction does it move?

9. Two men are pulling a light truck along a railway track by ropes on each side of the track. The mass of the truck is 900 kg and they pull with forces of 200 N and 300 N at angles of 20° and 25° to the track, respectively. The truck moves at a steady speed. What is the resistance to the motion of the truck?

10. An aircraft of mass 7×10^5 kg is climbing on a straight path at 25° to the horizontal with an acceleration of 2.5 m s^{-2}. The thrust of the engine is 4.8×10^6 N along the path. Find the drag (air resistance) and the lift (upward force perpendicular to the path).

11. An aircraft of mass 70 t is climbing at an angle of 10° to the horizontal. The thrust of the engines is 2.5×10^5 N and there is a drag of 6×10^4 N. Find the acceleration of the plane and its lift.

12. An aircraft of mass 80 t is climbing at an angle of 15°. The thrust of the engines is 3.5×10^5 N and the drag is 7.5×10^4 N. Find the lift and the acceleration.

Connected particles **3.7**

In previous sections we have restricted ourselves to problems involving the motion of a single particle under the influence of one or more external forces. We now examine the motion of several connected particles. We illustrate the methods used by means of examples.

EXAMPLE 1

A breakdown truck of mass 1.5 t is towing a car of mass 1 t along a horizontal road. The frictional resistance is a constant $500\ \mathrm{N\,t^{-1}}$ on both the car and the truck. The truck has a driving force of 3000 N.

Taking the value of g as $10\ \mathrm{m\,s^{-2}}$ and treating the car and the truck as particles, show the forces acting on the truck and on the car, and hence calculate (a) the tension in the towrope, and (b) the acceleration of the system.

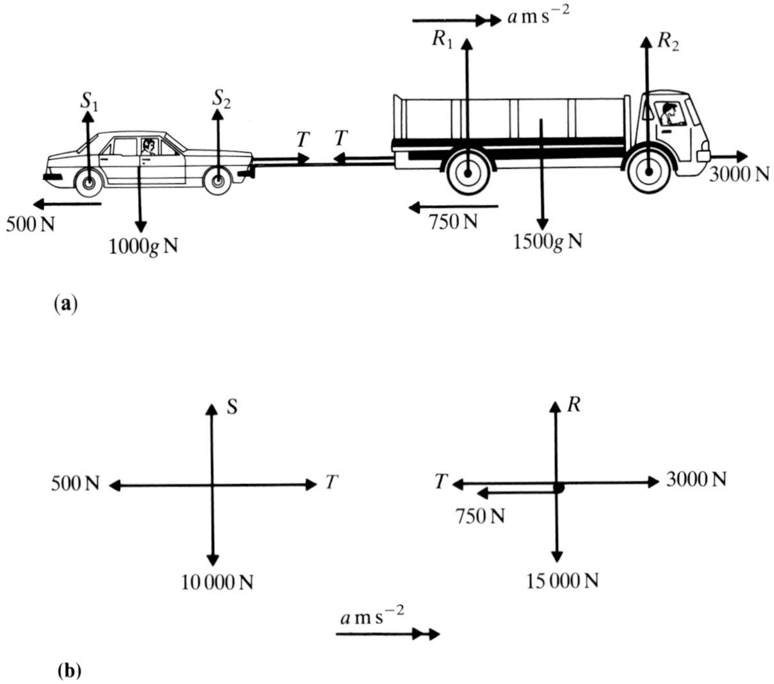

Figure 3.38

Figure 3.38b shows the main forces acting on the two parts of the system. The tension T in the towrope acts as a forward force on the car and a backward force on the truck. The tractive force of 3000 N acts between the wheels of the truck and the road and operates through friction. The weight forces and the normal contact forces act vertically in opposite directions. The resistances of 500 N and 750 N act backwards on the car and truck, respectively.

To solve the problem we look at the system as a whole, the car alone or the truck alone, as in figure 3.39. We omit the vertical forces since they do not affect the horizontal motion. Note that in the figure showing the system as a whole we have omitted the tensions at both ends of the towrope. These forces are internal to the system and, by N3, produce equal and opposite forces on the car and on the truck. We have shown the total mass of the car and the truck as a single particle, and have indicated the total resistance.

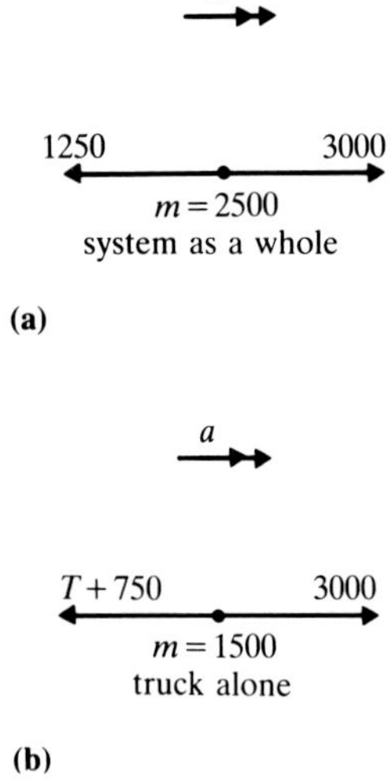

Figure 3.39

Applying N2 horizontally:

to the truck $3000 - T - 750 = 1500a$, **(9)**

to the car $T - 500 = 1000a$. **(10)**

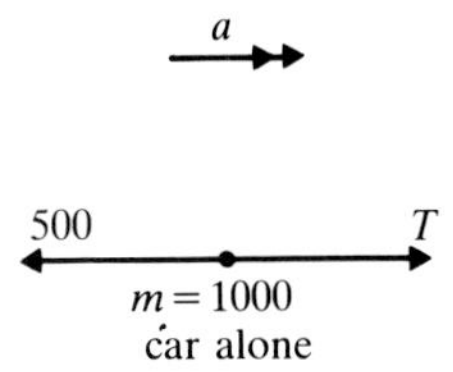

(c)

Adding the equations gives

$$3000 - 1250 = 2500a,$$

which is the same as the equation of motion for the system as a whole (figure 3.39a). Thus $a = 1750/2500 = 0.7$.

This value can be substituted back into either equation (9) or (10) to give T as 1200 N.

EXAMPLE 2

The truck in example 1 attempts to pull the car, with the same force, up a hill whose inclination to the horizontal is given by $\alpha = \sin^{-1} \frac{1}{10}$. Does it succeed? Take g as 10 m s^{-2}.

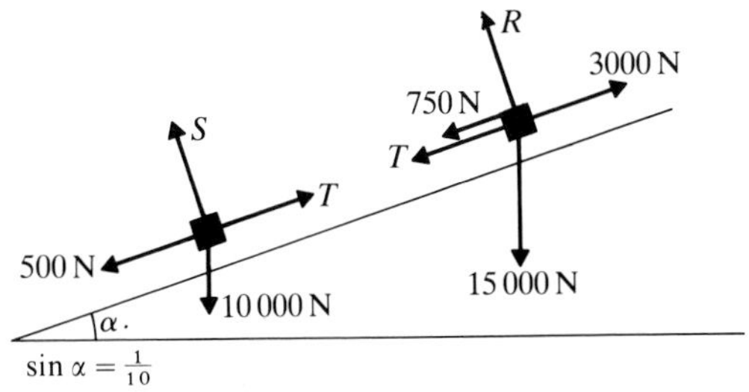

Figure 3.40

Figure 3.40 shows the forces on the truck and the car. Since we are not interested in the normal contact forces R and S, we apply N2 along the road. On the truck,

$$3000 - T - 750 - 15\,000 \sin \alpha = 1500a, \qquad \textbf{(11)}$$

where the weight force has a component $15\,000 \sin \alpha$ along the track. On the car,

$$T - 500 - 10\,000 \sin \alpha = 1000a \qquad \textbf{(12)}$$

Adding equations (11) and (12)

$$1750 - 25\,000 \sin \alpha = 2500a,$$

so a is -0.3 m s^{-2}. Since the acceleration up the slope is negative, the truck will slow down and thus how far it can climb depends on the speed at the bottom.

In this problem we are only interested in the acceleration and not the tension and so we could consider the system as a whole and produce an equation for N2 along the slope by treating the truck and the car as a single particle:

$$3000 - 750 - 500 - 25\,000 \sin \alpha = 2500a,$$

giving a as -0.3 m s^{-2}, as before.

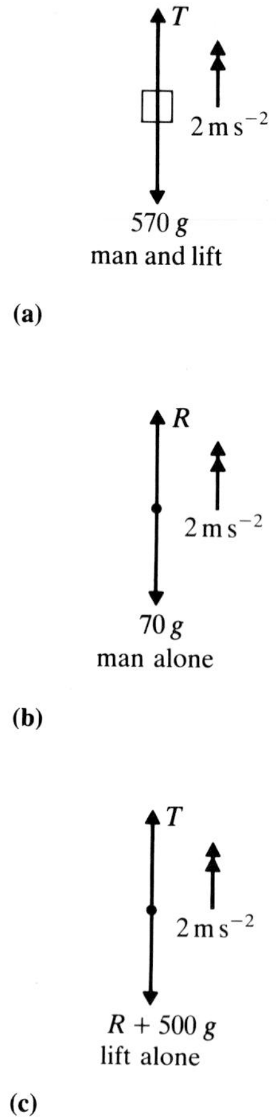

Figure 3.41

EXAMPLE 3

A man of mass 70 kg is standing in a lift of mass 500 kg. Find the force exerted by the floor on the man and the total tension in the cables which raise the lift (a) when the lift is accelerating upwards at $2\,\mathrm{m\,s^{-2}}$, and (b) when the lift is accelerating downwards at $2\,\mathrm{m\,s^{-2}}$. Take g as $10\,\mathrm{m\,s^{-2}}$.

Figure 3.41 shows the system as a whole, the forces on the man alone and the forces on the lift alone.

In (a) the tension in the cable is shown as T and the combined mass is 570 kg. The contact forces between the man and the lift are internal forces and have been omitted (see example 1). In figure 3.41b, the only force on the man, apart from his weight force, is the contact force R between his feet and the lift. The effect of the tension in the cable is felt through R.

a) The lift accelerating upwards at 2 m s⁻²

Applying N2 vertically upwards to the man,

$$R - 70g = 70 \times 2,$$
$$R = 840.$$

Applying N2 vertically upwards to the man and the lift

$$T - 570g = 570 \times 2,$$
$$T = 6870.$$

The reaction on the man is 840 N and the tension is 6870 N.

b) The lift accelerating downwards at 2 m s⁻²

Applying N2 vertically upwards to the man,

$$R - 70g = 70 \times -2,$$
$$R = 560.$$

Applying N2 vertically upwards to the man and the lift,

$$T - 570g = 570 \times -2,$$
$$T = 4560.$$

The reaction is 560 N and the tension is 4560 N.

Note that when the lift is accelerating upwards the contact force between the man and the lift is greater than his weight force, but when it is accelerating downwards the contact force is less. If the lift were falling freely with an acceleration of $g\,\mathrm{m\,s^{-2}}$, N2 on the man would give

$$R - 70g = 70 \times -g,$$
$$R = 0$$

Thus, there would be no contact force between the man and the lift and he would appear to be 'weightless' (see section 3.4).

EXERCISE 3G

Take g as $10\ \text{m s}^{-2}$ where necessary.

1. An engine of mass 300 t is pulling 20 trucks each of mass 5 t. The resistance to motion is 2×10^4 N on the train and 500 N on each of the trucks. If the engine moves at a steady speed, find the tractive force of the engine.
   Suddenly the last 10 trucks become disengaged. What is the acceleration of the train at that instant?

2. In question 1, what is the tension in the coupling between the 10th and 11th trucks before disengaging. What is the tension in the coupling between the engine and the first truck: (a) before the disengaging of the last ten, and (b) after the disengaging of the last ten?

3. A car of mass 1200 kg is pulling a glider of mass 200 kg by means of a cable which is inclined at an angle of 30° to the horizontal at a particular instant. The car is moving at a constant speed of $100\ \text{km h}^{-1}$ in a straight line, and the tension in the cable is 1000 N. Apart from the weight force and the tension, the forces on the glider are drag (horizontally) and lift (vertically). If the glider is flying horizontally, find the magnitude of the drag and the lift. If the cable is then released, what is the initial acceleration of the glider?

4. A lift of mass 1 t has a man of mass 100 kg inside. Find the tension in the lift cable and the thrust of the floor on the man when: a) the lift is ascending at steady speed, b) the lift is accelerating upwards at $2\ \text{m s}^{-2}$, c) the lift is moving upwards, but decelerating at $2\ \text{m s}^{-2}$.

5. A miniature train of mass 1 t pulls a carriage of mass 500 kg up an incline of $\sin^{-1}\frac{1}{100}$ at a steady speed. The resisting force of the track on the train is 100 N and on the carriage is 50 N. Calculate: (a) the tractive force of the train, and (b) the tension in the coupling.

6. Three trucks each of mass 8 kg are being pulled along a smooth horizontal table by a force of 12 N. (a) What is the acceleration of the trucks? (b) What is the tension in the rope between the second and last trucks?

7. A man of mass 75 kg is in the basket of a balloon whose total mass is 1500 kg. The balloon is drifting upwards at a steady speed of $3\ \text{m s}^{-1}$.
   a) What is the lift force on the balloon?
   b) If 100 kg of ballast is thrown out from the basket, (i) what is the acceleration of the balloon, and (ii) what is the speed of the balloon 20 s later?
   c) If gas is released from the balloon to reduce the lift force by 3000 N, (i) what is the new acceleration, and (ii) what is the speed of the balloon after a further 20 s? (Neglect the mass of the gas released.)

8. A car of mass 1000 kg is pulling a caravan of mass 500 kg along a straight road. The tractive force of the car is 2500 N and there is a total resistance of 500 N to the car and 300 N to the caravan. What is the acceleration of the car: (a) if the road is level, and (b) if the road is inclined at 6° to the horizontal?

9. An engine of mass 150 t is pulling 5 coaches each of mass 80 t up a slope inclined upwards at an angle of $\sin^{-1}\frac{1}{150}$ to the horizontal. The constant tractive force of the engine is 200×10^3 N and there is a resistance of $100\,\mathrm{N\,t^{-1}}$ on the engine and $60\,\mathrm{N\,t^{-1}}$ on each coach. What is the acceleration of the train and how long will it take to increase its speed from $15\,\mathrm{m\,s^{-1}}$ to $30\,\mathrm{m\,s^{-1}}$. Find the tension in the coupling between (a) the engine and the first coach, and (b) the fourth and fifth coaches.

10. A car of mass 1800 kg tows a caravan of mass 850 kg up a road inclined at an angle of $\sin^{-1}\frac{1}{10}$ to the horizontal. There is a resistance of $300\,\mathrm{N\,t^{-1}}$ opposing both the car and the caravan. The engine produces a constant tractive force of 400 N. Find (a) the acceleration of the car and the caravan, and (b) the tension in the tow bar.

11. A woman of mass 50 kg is standing in a lift of mass 750 kg. Find (a) the force exerted by the floor on the woman, and (b) the total tension in the lift cable when:

    i) the lift is moving upwards at a steady speed of $3\,\mathrm{m\,s^{-1}}$,

    ii) the lift is accelerating upwards at $3\,\mathrm{m\,s^{-2}}$,

    iii) the lift is accelerating downwards at $3\,\mathrm{m\,s^{-2}}$.

12. A man of mass 70 kg is in a lift of mass 750 kg when it is descending with an acceleration of $1.5\,\mathrm{m\,s^{-2}}$. Calculate the tension in the lift cable and the contact force between the man and the floor. What is the corresponding tension when it is moving upwards with the same acceleration?

13. An engine of mass 200 t is pulling 15 trucks each of mass 8 t. The resistance to motion is 1.5×10^4 N on the train and 600 N on each truck. What is the tractive force of the train if it moves at steady speed? What is the tension in the coupling between the last two coaches?

    If the last 5 trucks break away, what is the acceleration of the train? What is the tension in the coupling between the engine and the first truck?

3.8 Pulleys and smooth pegs

An example of the behaviour of several connected bodies occurs when they are joined by a light inextensible string which passes over smooth pulleys or pegs. It is assumed that the tension in a string remains constant throughout its length (see section 3.3).

EXAMPLE 1

Figure 3.42 shows a simplified version of a pulley attached to the top of a building on a building site. The man of mass 70 kg, with some assistance, hauls the bricks to the top of the building which is 10 m high. The mass of the barrel is 40 kg and the bricks have a mass of 100 kg. When the bricks are at the top of the building, the man forgets to secure the rope attached to them. Assuming that (i) the pulley is light, (ii) there is no friction at the pulley, and (iii) the rope is light and inextensible, discuss the subsequent motion. (Take g as 10 m s^{-2})

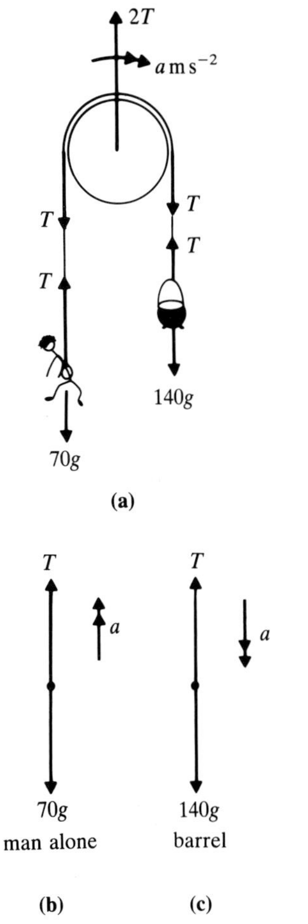

Figure 3.42

Applying N2 vertically upwards to the man in figure 3.42b,

$$T - 70g = 70a,$$

where a is his upward acceleration. Applying N2 vertically downwards to the barrel and bricks,

$$140g - T = 140a.$$

Adding these equations,

$$70g = 210a,$$

$$a = \tfrac{1}{3}g.$$

Thus, if the man holds on to the rope, he will take off from the ground with an acceleration of about 3.3 m s^{-2}. Provided he does not let go, he will continue to rise until the barrel hits the ground. The speed, v, at which it does so is given by $v^2 = u^2 + 2as$, where $u = 0$, $s = 10$ and $a = \frac{1}{3}g$, so that

$$v^2 = 2 \times \tfrac{1}{3}g \times 10,$$

giving the speed as 8 m s^{-1}. Note also that, since the pulley itself does not accelerate, it must be supported by a vertical force of magnitude $2T$.

EXAMPLE 2

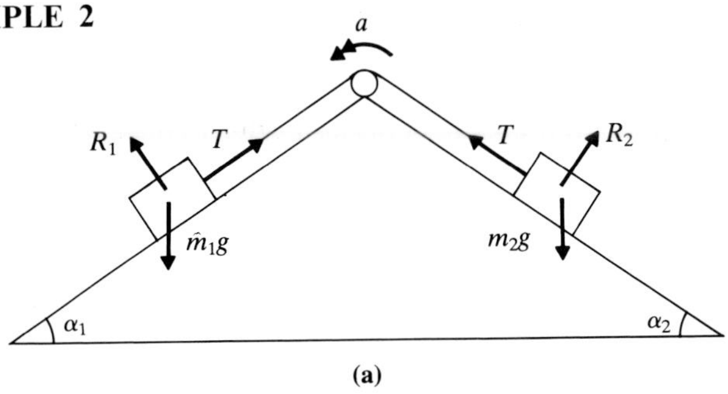

Figure 3.43

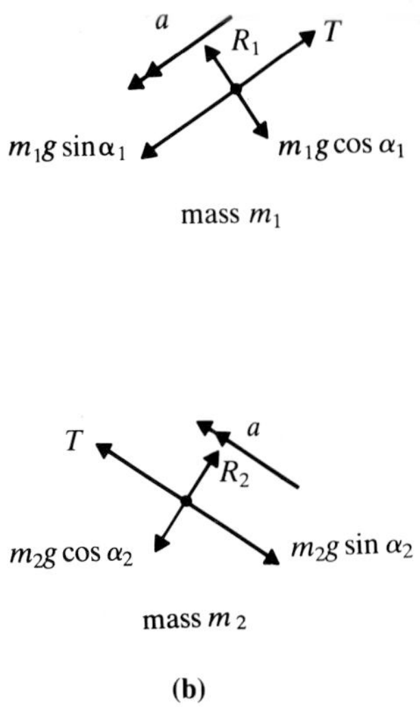

Figure 3.43 shows two trucks of mass m_1 and m_2, which are held at rest on either side of a fixed smooth wedge, whose sides are inclined at angles α_1 and α_2 to the horizontal. They are joined by a light inextensible string which passes over a smooth peg at the vertex of the wedge. Assuming that $m_1 > m_2$ and $\alpha_1 > \alpha_2$, with what acceleration does the system initially move, if it is released from rest, and what is the tension in the string at that instant?

The forces acting on each truck are shown in figure 3.43b, and are:

a) the tension $\boldsymbol{T}$ in the string,
b) the normal contact forces $\boldsymbol{R}_1$ and $\boldsymbol{R}_2$,
c) the weight forces $m_1\boldsymbol{g}$ and $m_2\boldsymbol{g}$, with components $m_1 g \sin \alpha_1$ and $m_2 g \sin \alpha_2$ along the slopes.

Applying N2 along the slopes:

on m_1 $$m_1 g \sin \alpha_1 - T = m_1 a, \quad \textbf{(13)}$$

on m_2 $$T - m_2 g \sin \alpha_2 = m_2 a, \quad \textbf{(14)}$$

where a is the acceleration of the system, as shown in figure 3.43a. Adding equations (13) and (14)

$$m_1 g \sin \alpha_1 - m_2 g \sin \alpha_2 = m_1 a + m_2 a.$$

Rearranging, $$a = \frac{m_1 \sin \alpha_1 - m_2 \sin \alpha_2}{m_1 + m_2} g$$

We can substitute this into equations (13) or (14) to obtain an expression for the tension T:

$$T = \frac{m_1 m_2 (\sin \alpha_1 - \sin \alpha_2) g}{m_1 + m_2}.$$

EXERCISE 3H

Take g as 10 m s^{-2}, where necessary.

1. Particles of mass 3 kg and 4 kg are connected by a light inextensible string which passes over a smooth pulley, and hang vertically. Find the acceleration with which the 4 kg particle descends. What is the tension in the string?

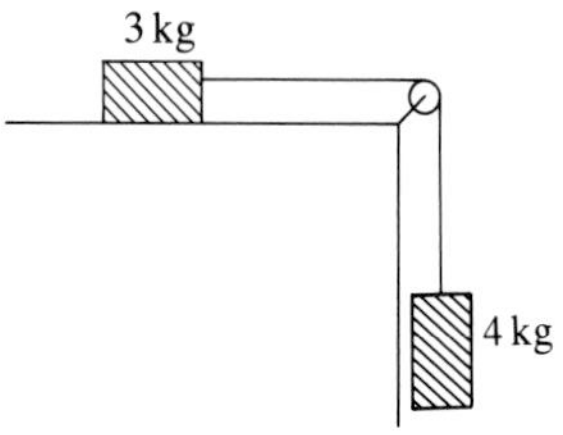

Figure 3.44

2. The two particles of question 1 are connected as shown in figure 3.44. Contact between the 3 kg mass and the table is smooth. What are the acceleration of the 4 kg mass and the tension in the string?

3. The two particles in question 1 are now connected as shown in figure 3.45. Contact between the particles and the wedge is smooth. What is the acceleration of the 4 kg particle and the tension in the string? If the angle of the 40° slope were fixed, how would the angle of the other slope have to be adjusted to keep the system in equilibrium?

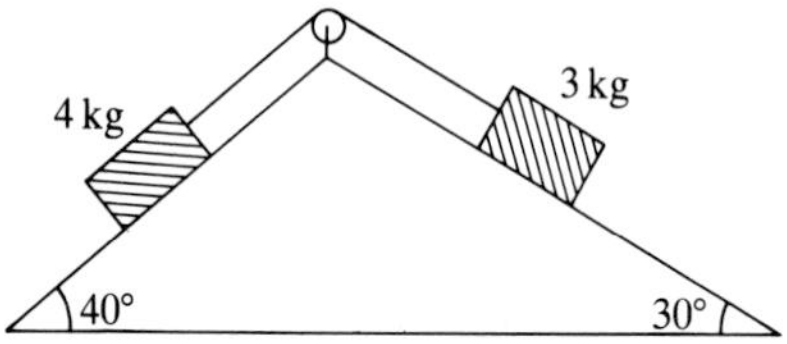

Figure 3.45

4. Two particles of mass m_1 and m_2 are hanging vertically and are connected by a light inextensible string which passes over a smooth pulley. Find the tension in the string and the acceleration of each particle. Assume $m_1 > m_2$.

5. A particle of mass 100 g is attached to one end of a light string which passes over a smooth fixed light pulley. To the other end is attached a mass of 60 g. Find (a) the acceleration of each particle, (b) the tension in the string and (c) the force supporting the pulley.

6. A particle A of mass 5 kg is hanging vertically by a string which passes over a smooth pulley attached to the top of a wedge, as in

figure 3.46. To the other end of the string is attached a mass B of 4 kg which is lying on the smooth slope of the wedge. Find the acceleration of A and the tension in the string, if the slope is inclined at 45° to the horizontal.

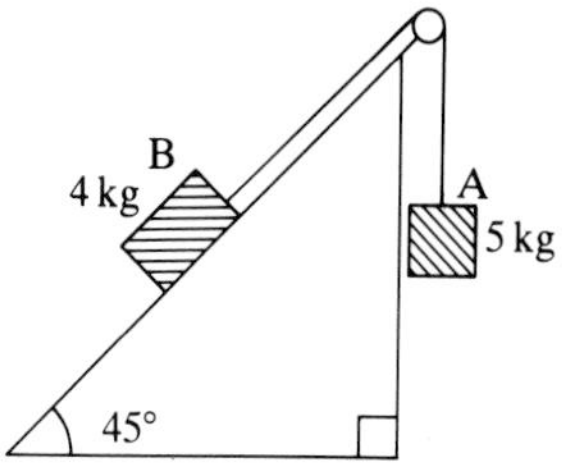

Figure 3.46

7. Three particles are lying on a wedge in the shape of an isosceles trapezium, as shown in figure 3.47. The strings joining them are light and inextensible. Find the tensions in the strings and the acceleration of the system.

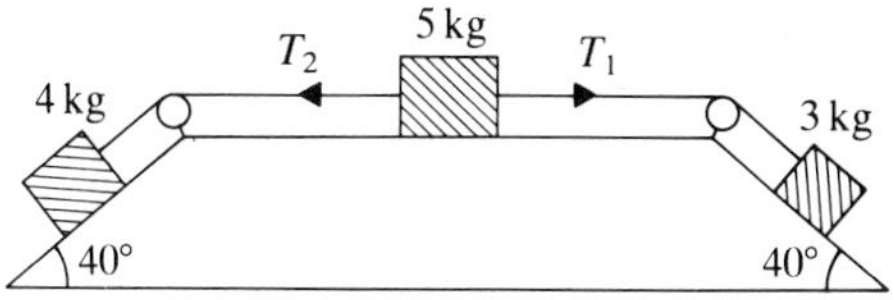

Figure 3.47

8. Two particles of mass 3 kg and 4 kg are lying on the smooth faces of a wedge, as shown in figure 3.48. Find the tension in the light inextensible string which joins them, and find the acceleration of the 4 kg mass.

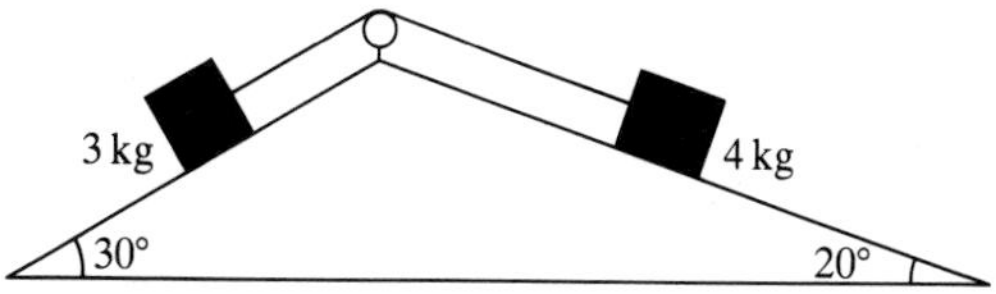

Figure 3.48

9. A particle of mass M is lying on a smooth table. It is attached by light inextensible strings to two particles of masses m_1 and m_2 ($m_1 > m_2$) which hang over the edges of the table, as shown in figure 3.49. What is the acceleration of the system?

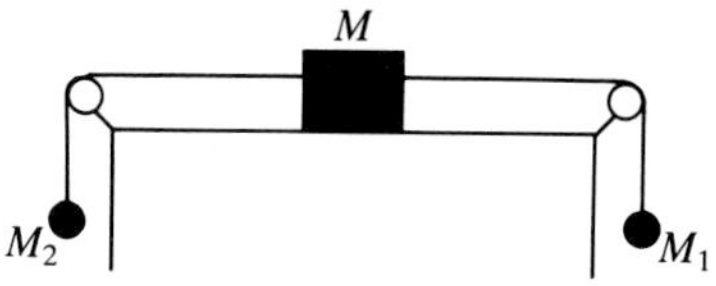

Figure 3.49

10. Three particles are connected to two light smooth pulleys as shown in figure 3.50. Find: (a) the accelerations of the particles, and (b) the tensions in the strings T_1, T_2 and T_3.

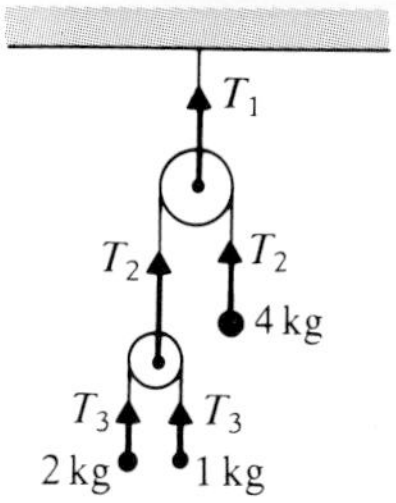

Figure 3.50

11. A light inextensible string is attached to a fixed point A and passes over two pulleys B and C. The mass of the pulley B is 3 kg and the pulley C is fixed. To the other end of the string is attached a mass of 1 kg at D, as shown in figure 3.51. What are the tension in the string and the accelerations of B and D?

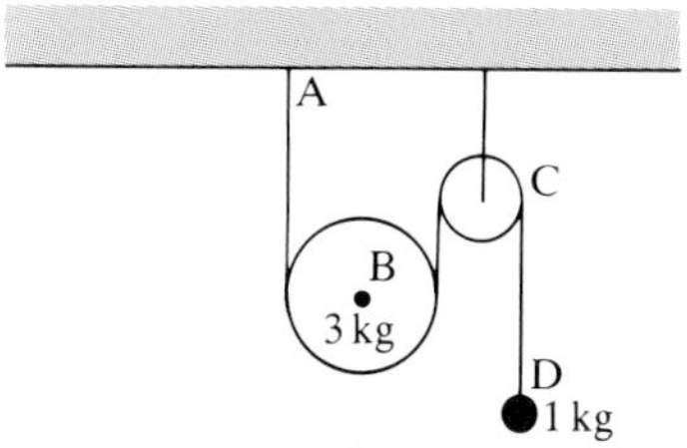

Figure 3.51

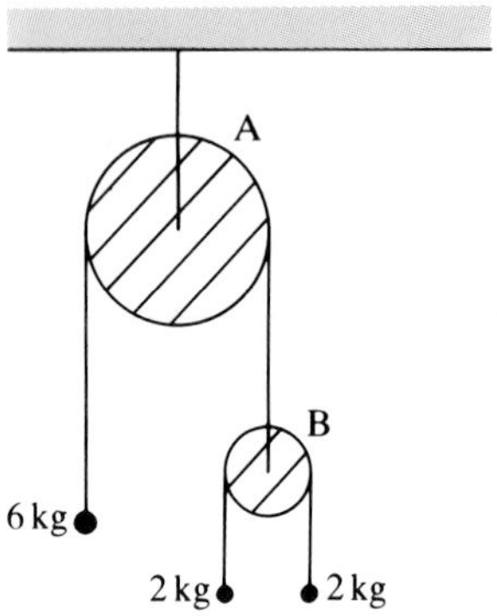

Figure 3.52

12. In figure 3.52 A is a fixed pulley and B is a light pulley which is free to move.

    a) Find the acceleration of B and the tensions in the strings.

    b) If one of the 2 kg masses is replaced by a 3 kg mass, what are the accelerations of each of the masses?

13.* The smooth wedge of mass M in figure 3.53 rests on a smooth table and is free to move. If the masses m_1 and m_2 are released and the pulley at P is light and smooth, prove that the initial acceleration of the wedge is

$$\frac{(m_1 - m_2)g \sin 2\alpha}{2M + (m_1 + m_2)(1 - \cos 2\alpha)}.$$

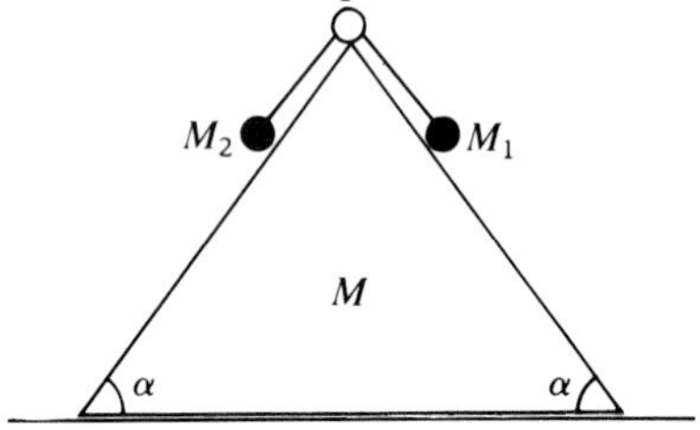

Figure 3.53

3.9 Motion in a circle

As the motor cyclists take the bend they are moving on part of a circle and they must lean into the turn to avoid overbalancing. Why is this?

a) Uniform motion

The kinematics of uniform motion in a circle was discussed in section 2.5. A particle P, moving in a circle of radius r with constant angular velocity ω, has its velocity and acceleration at any instant given by

$v = r\omega$ along the tangent,

$a = r\omega^2 = v^2/r$ towards the centre.

Thus, by N2, the acceleration towards the centre will require a force to cause it, and, if the mass of the particle is m, the force $\boldsymbol{F}$ which must be supplied is

$$\begin{aligned} \boldsymbol{F} &= m\boldsymbol{a} \\ &= -mr\omega^2\hat{\boldsymbol{r}} = -m\frac{v^2}{r}\hat{\boldsymbol{r}}, \end{aligned}$$

where $\hat{\boldsymbol{r}}$ is the unit vector along the outward radius.
We have considered circular motion in several situations.

1 Particles on the end of strings or wires, e.g. a conker on a string, where the inward force is provided by the tension in the string.

2 Planets which orbit about the Sun, where the central force is provided by gravitational attraction.

We now consider, by means of an example, a third type of circular motion.

EXAMPLE 1

A car is going around a circular roundabout of radius 20 m at a steady speed of $10\,\mathrm{m\,s^{-1}}$. In the boot is a tool-kit of mass 20 kg which is not sliding on the floor. Draw a diagram showing the forces on the tool-kit and find the horizontal force acting. How is this produced? Take g as $10\,\mathrm{m\,s^{-2}}$.

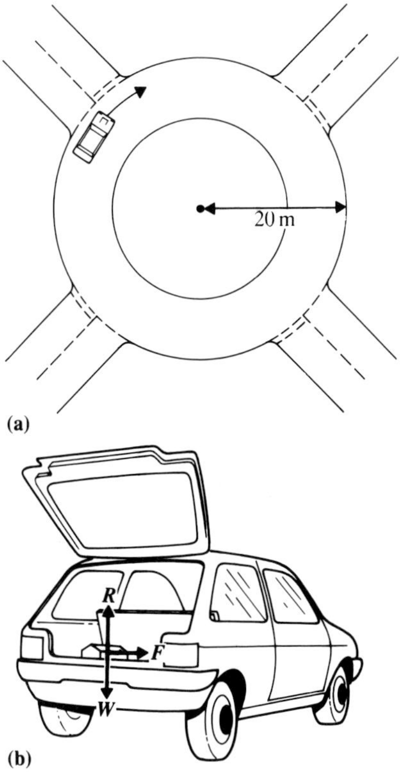

Figure 3.54

Figure 3.54 shows a plan and side view of the car at a particular instant. Treating the tool-kit as a particle, we can show all the forces on it as in figure 3.54b.
Now $a = v^2/r = 5$, giving the acceleration as $5\,\mathrm{m\,s^{-2}}$.
Applying N2 horizontally, taking the positive direction towards the centre of the roundabout,

$$F = 20 \times 5 = 100.$$

This force of 100 N is clearly provided by the friction between the box and the floor of the boot.

□□□□□

We have shown that, for a particle in uniform circular motion, there is an inward force acting. This is sometimes a cause for confusion as the following example will illustrate.

Suppose there is a toy monkey hanging by a string from the back window of a car as it goes round a roundabout at a steady speed. The monkey will not hang vertically, but will be at a fixed angle to the vertical, if the speed is kept constant.
The forces acting on the monkey are shown in figure 3.55 and are

a) its weight force, $m\boldsymbol{g}$,

b) the tension $\boldsymbol{T}$ in the string.

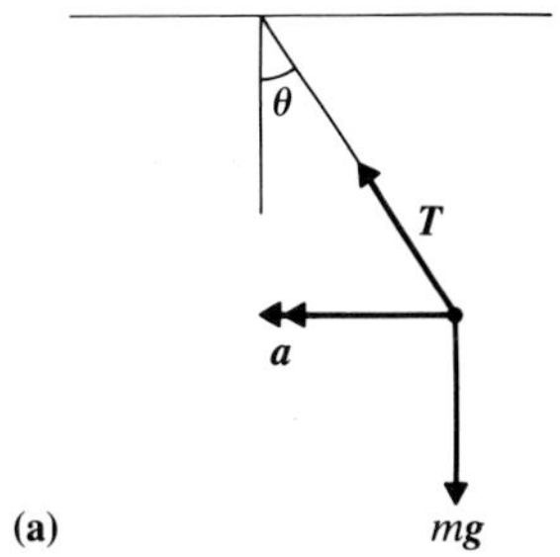

Figure 3.55

In addition we know it will have an acceleration towards the centre of the roundabout.

As the car goes around, the weight force remains vertical, and so the inward force necessary for the circular motion must come from the

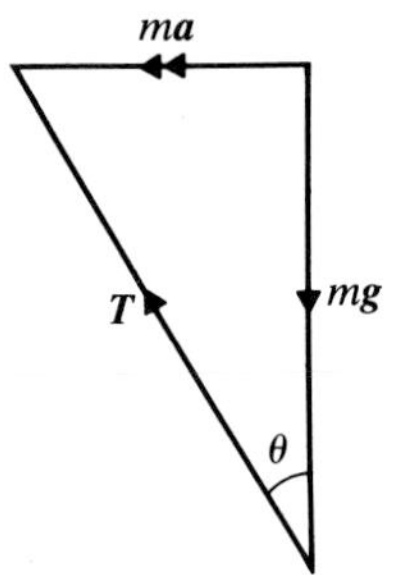

(b)

tension in the string. Thus, the tension must have a horizontal component inwards, and so the string must be inclined outwards, as in figure 3.55b. So the monkey will move outward from its initial position.

In the case of a person seated in a car, he tends to rotate about his seat, since the force required for circular motion only acts through friction in the seat. The washing in a spin drier appears to move outwards because it tends to move in a straight line until it is constrained in circular motion through contact with the drum. A small object placed on a rotating record tends to fly outwards because the frictional force between it and the record is insufficient to keep it moving in a circle.

EXAMPLE 2

A cyclist is moving in a horizontal circle of radius 150 m on a track which is banked at 10° to the horizontal. The mass of the cyclist and his bicycle is 100 kg. What is the speed at which he must travel if there is no tendency for him to sideslip on a smooth track? Take g as 10 m s^{-2}.

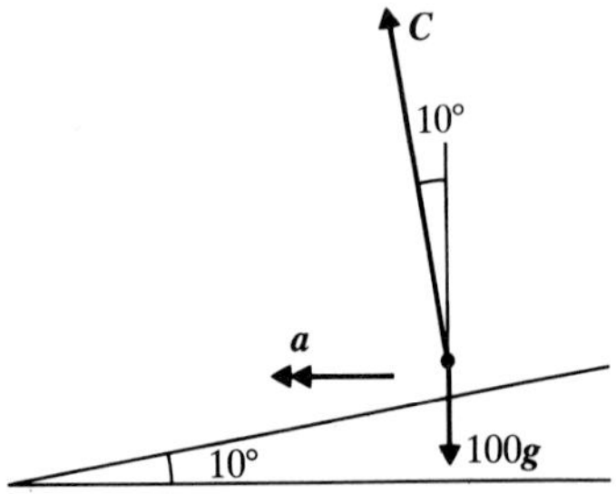

Figure 3.56

Figure 3.56 shows the forces acting on the man and the cycle. Note that the man will have to lean inwards towards the centre to avoid overbalancing. Applying N2 on the man:

vertically $\quad C \cos 10° - 100g = 100 \times 0,$

$$C = 1015, \qquad \textbf{(15)}$$

where $\boldsymbol{C}$ is the normal contact force between the cycle and the ground,

horizontally $\quad C \sin 10° = 100a, \qquad$ **(16)**

where $a = v^2/r = v^2/150$. Thus, from equations (15) and (16), $v^2 = 265$, giving v as 16.2 m s^{-1}.

Alternatively, we could draw a triangle of forces, as shown in figure 3.57. The resultant force,

$$ma = 100g \tan 10° = 176.$$

Since $m = 100$ and $a = v^2/150$

$$v^2 = \frac{176 \times 150}{100}$$

giving v as 16.2 m s^{-1}.

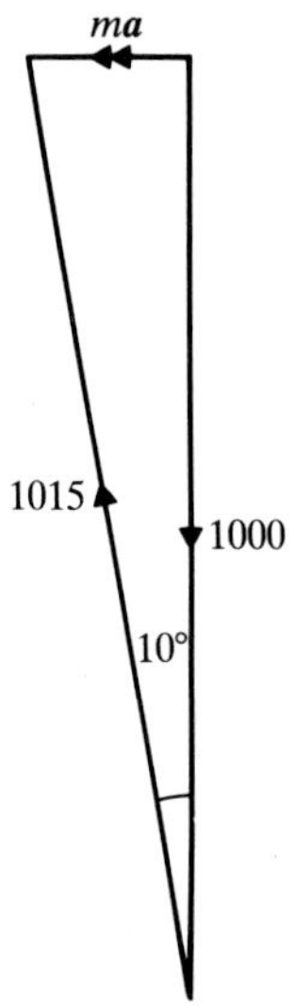

Figure 3.57

EXAMPLE 3 The conical pendulum

A particle of mass m is attached to one end of a light inelastic string of length l, the other end of which is fixed at O, as in figure 3.58. The particle is set rotating in a horizontal circle whose centre C is on the vertical line through O. The string makes an angle α with the line OC. Find (a) the angular velocity of the particle, and (b) the time for one complete revolution.

Let the tension in the string be S and the angular velocity be ω. Applying N2 horizontally towards C

$$S \sin \alpha = mr\,\omega^2$$

$$= m(l \sin \alpha)\omega^2,$$

$$S = lm\omega^2. \qquad (17)$$

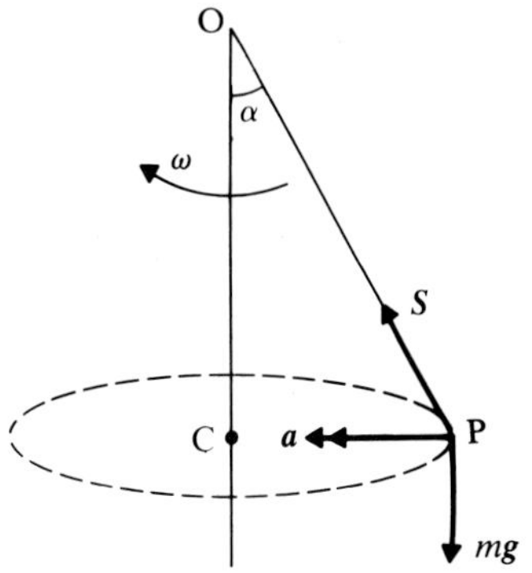

Figure 3.58

Applying N2 vertically upwards

$$S \cos \alpha - mg = 0,$$

$$S = \frac{mg}{\cos \alpha}. \qquad (18)$$

Eliminating S from equations (17) and (18)

$$\omega^2 = \frac{g}{l \cos \alpha} \quad \Rightarrow \quad \omega = \sqrt{\frac{g}{l \cos \alpha}}.$$

The time for one revolution is given by

$$T = \frac{2\pi}{\omega} = 2\pi \sqrt{\frac{l \cos \alpha}{g}}.$$

This system is known as a conical pendulum since the string traces out a cone as it rotates.

EXAMPLE 4

A string of length 50 cm is attached to two points A and B, where B is 40 cm below A. A small smooth ring C of mass 500 g can slide on the string, and is projected so as to rotate in a horizontal circle about the line AB. Given that AC = 30 cm, find the tension in the string and the angular velocity of the ring. Take g as $10\ \text{m s}^{-2}$.

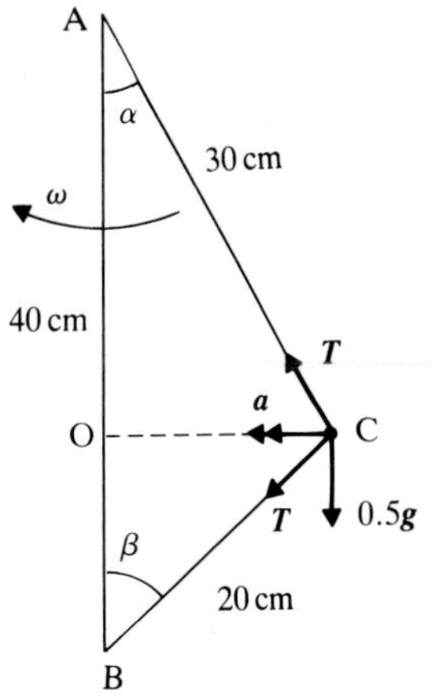

Figure 3.59

In figure 3.59 let $B\hat{A}C = \alpha$, $A\hat{B}C = \beta$, the angular velocity be ω and the inwards acceleration $a = r\omega^2$. Applying N2 towards O

$$T \sin \alpha + T \sin \beta = mr\omega^2.$$

But $r = 0.3 \sin \alpha$ $T(\sin \alpha + \sin \beta) = 0.3m\omega^2 \sin \alpha$.

Also $0.3 \sin \alpha = 0.2\ \beta$ $T(\sin \alpha + \frac{3}{2} \sin \alpha) = 0.3m\omega^2 \sin \alpha$.

Hence $\omega^2 = 16.7T$. Applying N2 vertically upwards

$$T \cos \alpha = T \cos \beta + 0.5g,$$

$$T = \frac{5}{\cos \alpha - \cos \beta}.$$

By the cosine rule, $\cos \alpha = 0.875$ and $\cos \beta = 0.6875$

$$T = \frac{5}{0.875 - 0.6875} = 26.7,$$

so that $\omega^2 = 16.7 \times 26.7 = 446$, so ω is 21 rad s^{-1}.

b) Non-uniform motion

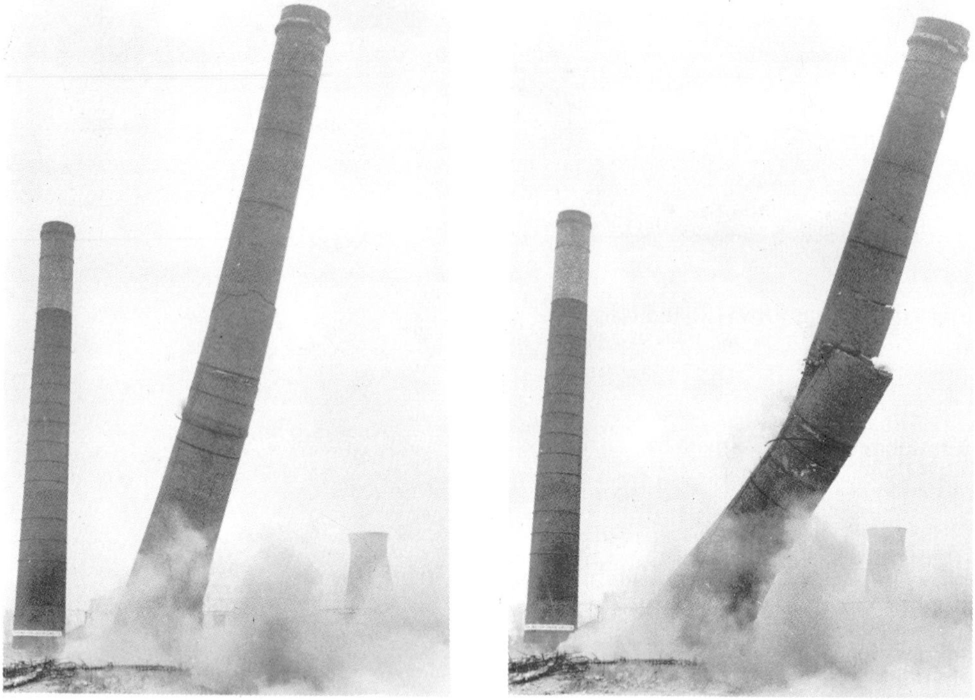

As the chimney falls, the top part would have less angular velocity than the bottom, were it not for internal stress in the chimney. It can be shown that this is maximum about halfway along the chimney, so this is where the break is most likely to occur.

A moment's thought will convince us that there are many cases of circular motion in which the speed is not constant.

EXAMPLE 5

Suppose a conker is attached by a light string to a fixed point, and is released from rest at a position so that the string, which is taut, makes an angle of 45° with the downward vertical. As the conker falls its speed will increase and it will move on the arc of a circle. Firstly, we recall from section 2.5, that the acceleration $\boldsymbol{a}$ has two components:

$r\ddot{\theta}$ along the tangent,
$r\dot{\theta}^2$ towards the centre.

We now examine the acceleration and forces acting in three positions.

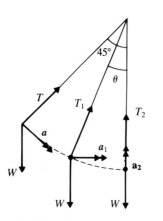

Figure 3.60

1. Immediately after 'letting go'

As shown in figure 3.60 the two forces acting on the conker are $\boldsymbol{W}$, its weight force, and $\boldsymbol{T}$, the tension in the string. Since $u = 0$, the conker starts to move in the direction of the initial acceleration, and so the latter, $\boldsymbol{a}$, will be at a tangent to the circle. In fact, using N2,

towards the centre $\quad T - W\cos 45° = mr\dot{\theta}^2,$

along the tangent $\quad - W\sin 45° = mr\ddot{\theta}.$

At the instant of release, $\dot{\theta} = 0$, and so there is no acceleration inwards.

2. At an angle of θ to the vertical ($45^\circ > \theta > 0^\circ$)

There are still two forces acting, $\boldsymbol{W}$ and $\boldsymbol{T}_1$. T_1 is possibly different from the original tension T, as shown in figure 3.60. Using N2,

towards the centre O, $T_1 - W\cos\theta = mr\dot{\theta}^2$,

along the tangent $-W\sin\theta = mr\ddot{\theta}$.

At this stage $\dot{\theta}^2 > 0$ and so the acceleration, does have a component towards O. Also $W\sin\theta < W\sin 45^\circ$, so $r\ddot{\theta}$ is less than its value in part 1. The acceleration vector will therefore have changed to a position roughly as shown by the vector $\boldsymbol{a}_1$.

3. At the bottom of the swing

There is now no tangential component of the force on the particle and so the acceleration vector is solely inwards, as shown by the vector $\boldsymbol{a}_2$.

□□□□□

The above illustrations should convince us that it is only with uniform motion in a circle that we can say the acceleration vector is directed towards the centre. A more detailed analysis of motion in a vertical circle is given in section 6.3.

EXERCISE 3I

Take g as 10 m s^{-2}, where necessary.

1. A car of mass 1000 kg moves in a horizontal circle of radius 500 m at 45 km h^{-1}. What is the force acting on it towards the centre of the circle?

2. A car of mass 800 kg is travelling at a steady speed of 30 m s^{-1} on a banked surface of a circular track of radius 300 m. At what angle to the horizontal is the surface to be banked if there is no tendency to sideslip?

3. A cyclist and her bicycle have a total mass of 65 kg. What is the maximum speed she can travel on a circular track of radius 100 m, which is banked at 20°, if there is no tendency to sideslip?

4. An aircraft of mass 30 t is flying in a vertical circle of radius 800 m at a speed of 200 m s^{-1}. What is its acceleration at the top of the circle? What is the reaction between a pilot of mass 70 kg and his seat at the top and at the bottom, if he is not harnessed to his seat?

5. An aircraft of mass 10^5 kg is flying at a constant speed around a circle of radius 3 km. The plane is banked at 20° to the horizontal. If there is no tendency for the plane to sideslip, what is the speed of the plane, and what is the lift force on the plane, assumed to be at right angles to the wings?

6. A particle of mass 0.5 kg is attached to a fixed point O by a light inextensible string of length 0.25 m and describes a horizontal

circle of radius 0.15 m with a uniform speed of $5\,\mathrm{m\,s^{-1}}$, in a horizontal plane below O. What is the angular speed with which the particle moves?

7. A particle of mass 15 g is attached to a string of length 50 cm, the other end of which is fixed, and is rotating at $6\,\mathrm{rad\,s^{-1}}$ in a horizontal circle, to form a conical pendulum.
   Find (a) the tension in the string, and (b) the angle the string makes with the downward vertical.

8. A smooth hemispherical bowl of radius 15 cm is fixed with its open end upwards. A particle is projected so that it is rotating at an angular speed of $12\,\mathrm{rad\,s^{-1}}$ in a horizontal circle. Find the distance below the top of the bowl of the centre of this circle.

9. A particle of mass 100 g is attached to one end of a string of length 16 cm and hangs vertically at rest. The string passes through a smooth fixed ring 12 cm above the mass. To the other end of the string is attached a particle of mass 50 g which rotates in a horizontal circle about the vertical part of the string. Find the distance below the ring of the centre of this circle and the angular velocity of the 50 g mass.

10. A conker on the end of a string of length 0.5 m is swung so that it 'just' performs vertical circles. What is the speed at the top of the circle?

11. The photograph shows a gymnast swinging in a vertical circle on the higher of a pair of asymmetric bars. Suppose we can model the motion of the girl by that of a particle of mass 40 kg concentrated at a distance of 0.9 m from the bar. Calculate the tension or thrust in each of her arms given that her angular velocity at the top of the circle is: (a) $0.4\,\mathrm{rad\,s^{-1}}$, (b) $1\,\mathrm{rad\,s^{-1}}$.
    What would the tension in each arm be at the bottom of the swing if her angular velocity there were $5\,\mathrm{rad\,s^{-1}}$?

12. One end of a light inelastic string is attached to a fixed point O. Particles of mass m and $2m$ are attached to the string at A and B, respectively. The string OAB lies in a vertical plane which rotates about the vertical through O with constant angular speed $\sqrt{(g/a)}$. The particles at A and B move in horizontal circles of radius a and 2a, respectively. Find the inclinations to the horizontal of OA and AB.

13. Figure 3.61a shows a hand-driven roundabout used at a school fête. Describe the motion of a child in a chair as the roundabout is wound up from rest. Figure 3.61b shows a model of the situation, with the child and chair replaced by a particle. If the angular velocity of the roundabout is a constant ω and the inclination of AB is a constant angle θ, derive an expression connecting ω and θ.

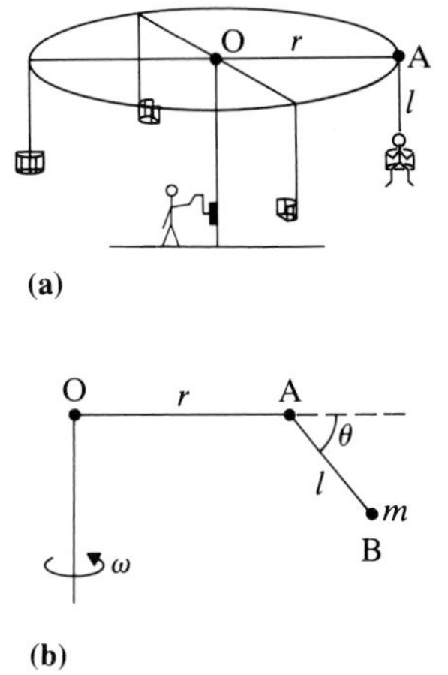

Figure 3.61

14. A skier hits a hump in the shape of an arc of a circle of radius 3 m. What is the maximum speed of the skier at the top, if she does not take off there.
Will she take off at some point on the far side of the hump?

15.* A car is rounding a bend in a race track, as shown in figure 3.62. The mass of the car is 1 t. Assume that there is no air resistance. The car brakes uniformly from $60\,\mathrm{m\,s^{-1}}$ at A to $20\,\mathrm{m\,s^{-1}}$ at B, and then accelerates uniformly to $60\,\mathrm{m\,s^{-1}}$ at C.

a) Calculate the average acceleration of the car from A to C.

b) Calculate the average force on the car. How is this provided?

c) Show the horizontal force on the car immediately after passing A. Calculate the magnitude and direction of the resultant.

d) Repeat (c) when the car is about to pass C.

e) Discuss, without detailed calculation, what happens at B.

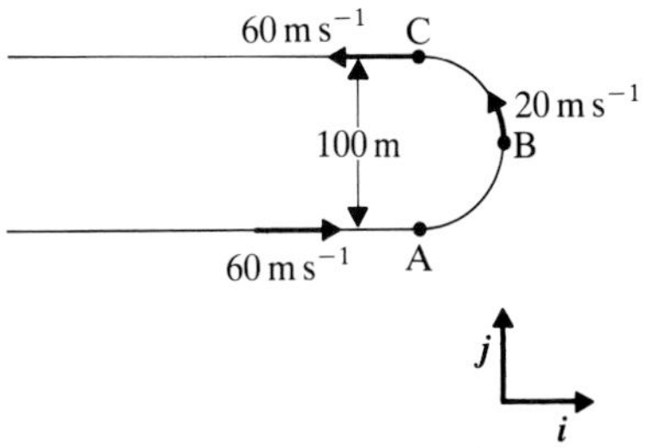

Figure 3.62

16.* Figure 3.63 shows a water skier being pulled by a boat in still water. The skier moves in a circle relative to the boat. The rope is taut and of fixed length. The length of the rope is 50 m and the angular velocity is $0.4\,\mathrm{rad\,s^{-1}}$. At a particular instant $\theta = 30°$ and the boat is travelling at $20\,\mathrm{m\,s^{-1}}$ with an acceleration of $1\,\mathrm{m\,s^{-2}}$. Calculate: a) the velocity of the skier relative to the water, b) the acceleration of the skier. c) the horizontal force if her mass is 45 kg. How is this force provided?

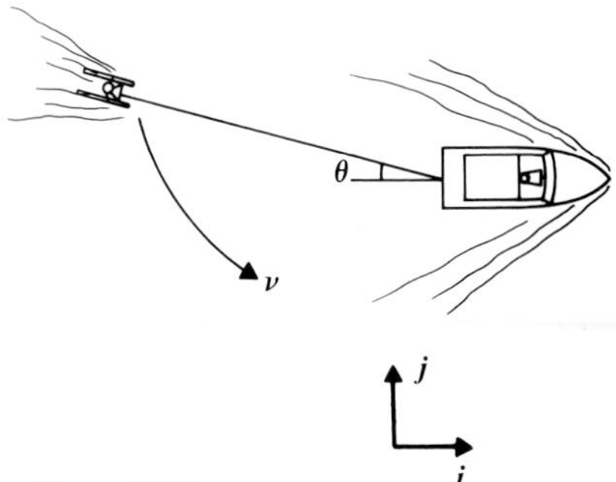

Figure 3.63

17. A particle of mass m is attached by a light inextensible string of length l to the vertex of a cone of semi-vertical angle α. The cone is fixed to a horizontal table, and the particle moves as a conical pendulum on the smooth surface of the cone with angular velocity ω.

a) Find in terms of m, g, α, l and ω the tension T in the string and the normal contact force R between the particle and the cone.

b) Show that the particle will stay in contact with the cone provided $\omega^2 < g/(l \cos \alpha)$.

Summary

Newton's laws

N1 Any body will move with a constant speed in a straight line unless there is a resultant external force acting on it.

N2 The acceleration of a body is proportional to the resultant external force acting on it, and takes place in the direction of the force. In SI units $\boldsymbol{F} = m\boldsymbol{a}$.

N3 If A and B interact and A exerts a force $\boldsymbol{F}$ on B then B exerts a force $-\boldsymbol{F}$ on A.

Newton's law of gravitation

The force of gravitational attraction between two bodies of masses m_1 and m_2 a distance d apart has magnitude F given by:

$$F = \frac{Gm_1m_2}{d^2}.$$

Acceleration due to gravity

All bodies falling freely near the surface of the Earth are subject to a constant acceleration due to gravity whose magnitude g is given by:

$$g = \frac{GM}{R^2},$$

where M is the mass of the Earth and R is its radius.

Weight

This is the force of attraction on a body due to the Earth, whose magnitude W in newtons is given by:

$$W = mg,$$

where m is the mass of the body is kilograms.

Motion in a circle

When a particle moves in a circle with constant speed v, the force on it towards the centre of the circle has magnitude F given by:

$$F = \frac{mv^2}{r},$$

where m is the mass of the body and r is the radius of the circle.

MOTION IN A STRAIGHT LINE

4

Introduction 4.1

In the discussion of Newton's second law (N2) it was stressed that this is a vector equation which can be written in the form $\boldsymbol{F} = m\boldsymbol{a}$.

From the relations between $\boldsymbol{a}$, $\boldsymbol{v}$ and $\boldsymbol{r}$ developed in chapter 2, we have been able to analyse the motion of a particle under the action of a resultant external force $\boldsymbol{F}$ under certain circumstances; or, alternatively, to deduce the force required to make a particle move along a certain path. Two important cases were discussed.

a) The action of a constant resultant force

If $\boldsymbol{F}$, and hence $\boldsymbol{a}$, are constant we have seen that there are two possible types of motion.

i) if the body is initially moving in a direction parallel to the resultant force, it will continue to move in the original straight line. If the origin of reference is on that line, the vectors $\boldsymbol{r}$, $\boldsymbol{v}$ and $\boldsymbol{a}$ will all be parallel, and their magnitudes will be related by the equations of constant acceleration in a straight line (see sections 2.3 and 3.5–3.8).

ii) If the initial velocity of the body is not parallel to the force, the path will be a parabola. A particular case of this is the motion of projectiles, which was discussed in section 2.4.

b) Uniform motion in a circle

In section 2.5 we saw that, when a particle moves in a circle with constant speed, the velocity and acceleration have constant magnitude, but changing direction, figure 4.1. Thus the force needed to produce this motion will also have constant magnitude and changing direction (see section 3.9).

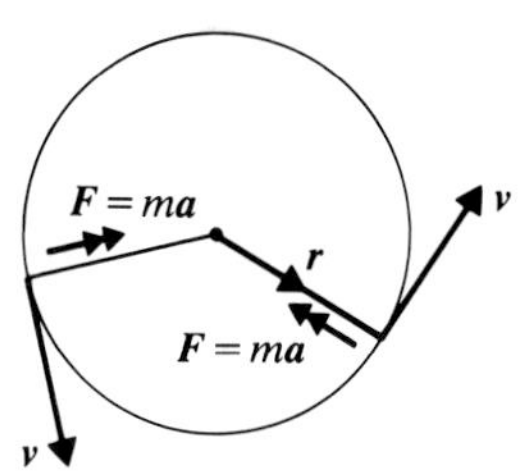

Figure 4.1

A third particularly important special case occurs when $\boldsymbol{F}$ acts in a constant direction, but has variable magnitude. In the case when motion takes place in a straight line we may write $F = ma$ and use the relations between a, v, x (or s) and t to analyse the motion of this particle given the way in which the magnitude of F varies. The most general case of a force varying in both magnitude and direction will be discussed in later chapters.

4.2 The equation of motion

The equation

$$F = ma \tag{1}$$

is a differential equation and can be written in several forms using the standard variables t, x, v, and a. We recall that

$$v = \frac{dx}{dt} \quad \text{and} \quad a = \frac{dv}{dt} = \frac{d^2x}{dt^2}.$$

Thus equation (1) can be written immediately in the following alternative ways:

$$F = m\frac{dv}{dt}, \tag{2}$$

$$F = m\frac{d^2x}{dt^2}. \tag{3}$$

There is a fourth important alternative form which is derived by use of the chain rule, as follows. From equation (2)

$$F = m\frac{dv}{dt} = m\frac{dv}{dx} \times \frac{dx}{dt}.$$

So that

$$F = mv\frac{dv}{dx}.$$

We can proceed a stage further if we note (using the chain rule again) that

$$\frac{d}{dx}\left(\frac{v^2}{2}\right) = \frac{d}{dv}\left(\frac{v^2}{2}\right) \times \frac{dv}{dx} = v\frac{dv}{dx}.$$

Thus (4) can be written as

$$F = m\frac{d}{dx}\left(\frac{v^2}{2}\right). \tag{5}$$

All of the forms (2)–(5) are derived from equation (1) and are useful in different situations, some of which we discuss now, and all of which will be referred to in later chapters.

4.3 Constant forces and accelerations over different intervals

We shall study this topic by means of worked examples.

EXAMPLE 1

A man is running for a bus. He accelerates from rest at $2\ \text{m s}^{-2}$ for the first 3 s, maintains a constant speed for 2 s, and then decelerates at $1\ \text{m s}^{-2}$ for a further 2 s. How far does the man run in the 7 s?

There are three different stages of motion corresponding to the time intervals 0–3, 3–5, and 5–7 s, and we must examine them separately.

Method 1.

In each stage the acceleration is constant so the standard formulae of section 2.3 may be used.

Stage 1. We have $u = 0, t = 3, a = 2$.

Using $s = ut + \frac{1}{2}at^2$, $\quad s = 0 + \frac{1}{2} \times 2 \times 9 = 9$.

Using $v = u + at$, $\quad v = 0 + 2 \times 3 = 6$.

Stage 2. We have $u = 6, t = 2, a = 0$.

Using $s = ut + \frac{1}{2}at^2$, $\quad s = 6 \times 2 + 2 + 0 = 12$.

Stage 3. We have $u = 6$, $t = 2$, $a = -1$ (a deceleration is a negative acceleration).

Using $s = ut + \frac{1}{2}at^2$, $\quad s = 6 \times 2 + \frac{1}{2} \times -1 \times 4 = 10$.

The total distance is 31 m.

Method 2.

We can use a (t, v) graph.

a) Since $a = \mathrm{d}v/\mathrm{d}t$, the gradient of the (t, v) graph gives the acceleration.

b) Since $v = \mathrm{d}s/\mathrm{d}t$, $s = \int v\mathrm{d}t$, and so the area under the (t, v) graph gives the distance travelled.

The (t, v) graph is shown in figure 4.2. Note that at A and B there is a sudden change in the gradient, corresponding to a sudden change in the acceleration.

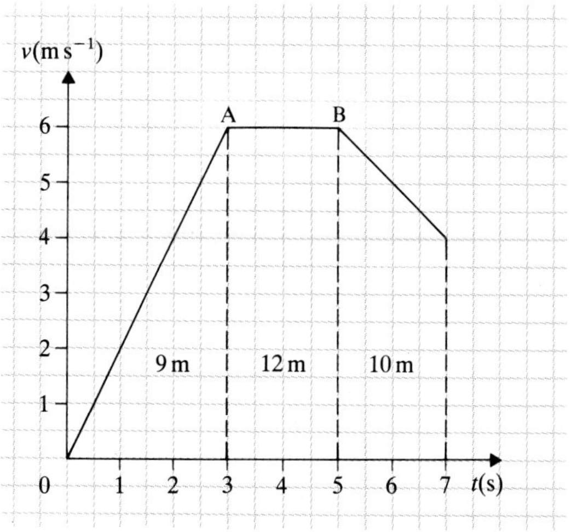

Figure 4.2

EXAMPLE 2

A train starts from rest with constant acceleration a, until it reaches a speed w. It then travels at a constant speed w before it decelerates uniformly to rest, the retardation having magnitude f. The average speed for the whole journey is $\frac{5}{8}w$.

a) Show that the train travels at a constant speed for one quarter of the total time.

b) Find what fraction of the journey is covered at constant speed. The (t, v) graph is shown in figure 4.3.

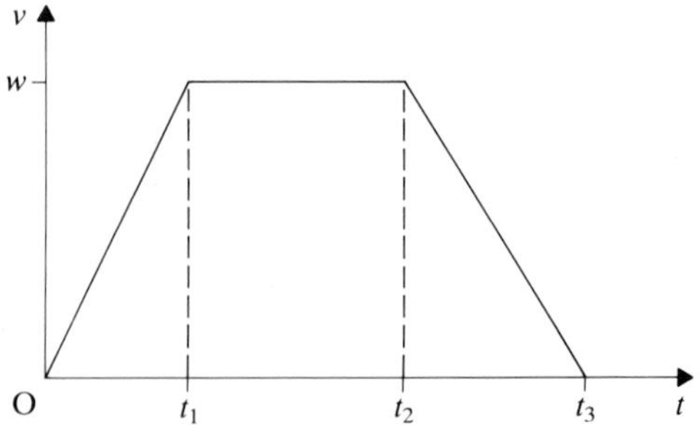

Figure 4.3

a) The distance travelled, s, is given by the area under this graph.

$$s = \tfrac{1}{2}wt_1 + w(t_2 - t_1) + \tfrac{1}{2}w(t_3 - t_2)$$
$$= \tfrac{1}{2}wt_3 + \tfrac{1}{2}w(t_2 - t_1).$$

Since the average speed is $\frac{5}{8}w$, s is also given by $s = \frac{5}{8}wt_3$. Hence

$$\tfrac{5}{8}wt_3 = \tfrac{1}{2}wt_3 + \tfrac{1}{2}w(t_2 - t_1),$$
$$\tfrac{1}{4}t_3 = t_2 - t_1.$$

Now t_3 is the total time of the journey and $t_2 - t_1$ is the time spent at constant speed, which gives the required result.

b) The distance covered at constant speed is

$$w(t_2 - t_1) = \tfrac{1}{4}wt_3.$$

The total distance covered is $\frac{5}{8}wt_3$. The fraction covered at constant speed is $\frac{1}{4} \times \frac{8}{5} = \frac{2}{5}$. Notice that these answers are independent of a and f.

□□□□□

The previous two examples illustrate constant acceleration over given time intervals, and we now consider a case where the force, and hence the acceleration, is fixed over a given distance.

EXAMPLE 3

A driver on a motorway is travelling in a car of total mass 1 t at a constant speed of 40 m s^{-1}. In order to turn off at a junction she begins braking at the first distance marker A for the exit, as shown in figure 4.4, and the net retarding force on the car over the next 300 m is as shown in the table.

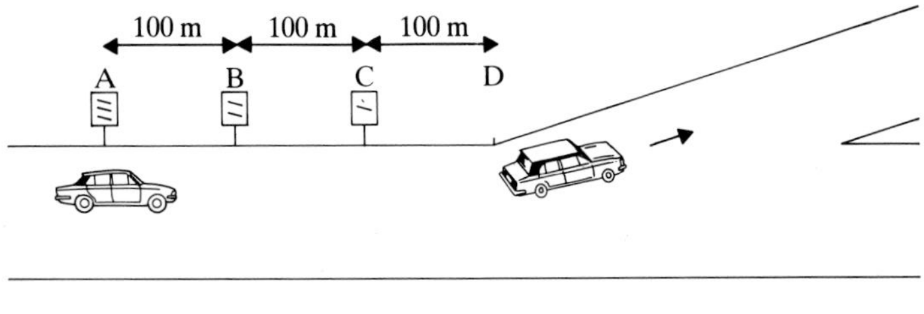

Figure 4.4

Distance after braking started (m)	Resultant retarding force (N)
0–100	3000
100–200	4000
200–300	500

a) What is the speed of the car at the point D on the figure?

b) For how long did braking take place?

There are three different stages of motion corresponding to the distance intervals 0–100, 100–200 and 200–300 m, and we must examine them separately.

Method 1 By calculation

Stage 1 (A *to* B). We have $u = 40$, $s = 100$ and $a = F/m = -3000/1000 = -3$.

Using $v^2 = u^2 + 2as$, $v^2 = 1600 - 600 = 1000$,

$$v = 31.6.$$

Using $s = \frac{1}{2}(v + u)t$, $t = 2.79$.

Stage 2 (B *to* C). We have $u^2 = 1000$, $s = 100$ and $a = -4$.

Using $v^2 = u^2 + 2as$, $v^2 = 1000 - 800 = 200$,

$$v = 14.1.$$

Using $s = \frac{1}{2}(v + u)t$, $t = 4.37$.

Stage 3 (C *to* D). We have $u^2 = 200$, $s = 100$ and $a = -0.5$.

Using $v^2 = u^2 + 2as$, $v^2 = 200 - 100 = 100$,

$$v = 10.$$

Using $s = \frac{1}{2}(v + u)t$, $t = 8.3$.

Thus the car's speed at D is 10 m s^{-1} and the total braking time is 15.5 s.

Method 2 Use of graphs

Equation (5) of section 4.2 gives

$$F = m\frac{\mathrm{d}}{\mathrm{d}s}(\tfrac{1}{2}v^2),$$

and since $F = ma$, we write

$$a = \frac{\mathrm{d}}{\mathrm{d}s}(\tfrac{1}{2}v^2).$$

Integrating this with respect to s gives

$$\tfrac{1}{2}v^2 = \int a \, \mathrm{d}s.$$

Thus the change in $\frac{1}{2}v^2$ is equal to the area under the distance–acceleration (s, a) graph.

The (s, a) graph for the motorway driver is shown in figure 4.5. From the graph, the total change in $\frac{1}{2}v^2$ is -750. Thus

$$\tfrac{1}{2}v^2 = \tfrac{1}{2} \times 1600 - 750.$$

Hence the speed is $10\ \mathrm{m\,s^{-1}}$.

□□□□□

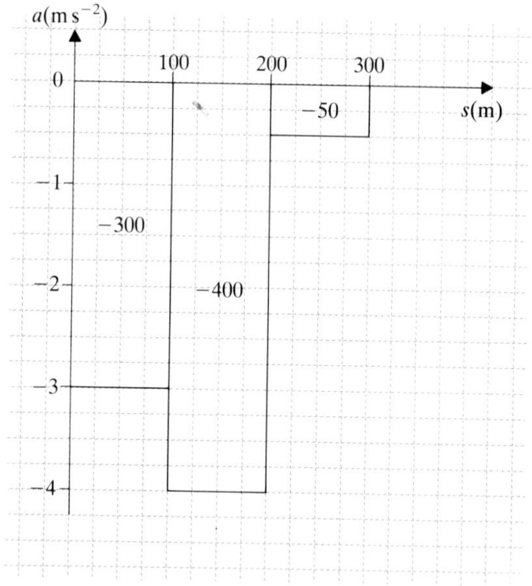

Figure 4.5

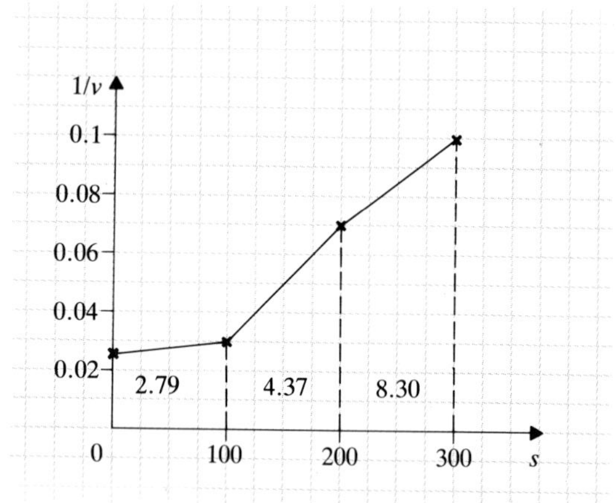

Figure 4.6

Since $v = ds/dt$, $1/v = dt/ds$, so that $t = \int (1/v)\, ds$. Using the values of v obtained in method 1, or by using figure 4.5, we can construct the following table.

s	0	100	200	300
v	40	31.6	14.1	10
$1/v$	0.025	0.032	0.071	0.1

The graph of $1/v$ against s is shown in figure 4.6. The total braking time is given by the area under the graph.

EXERCISE 4A

1. The velocity of a particle at points along a straight line from a fixed point are given in the table.

s (m)	0	10	20	30	40	50
v ($\mathrm{m\,s^{-1}}$)	10	6.7	5	4	3.3	2.86

Show that the graph of $1/v$ against s is approximately a straight line and estimate the time taken to cover 50 m.

2. A lift descends with uniform acceleration a, followed by uniform retardation $2a$. If it begins and ends at rest, descending a distance s in time t, prove that $s = \frac{1}{3}at^2$.

3. A tube train takes 40 s between two stops 500 m apart. On starting it is uniformly accelerated up to a speed of 20 m s^{-1} and maintains this speed until it is brought to rest by a constant retardation. If the time occupied in accelerating is twice that in retarding, calculate the acceleration and the distance travelled at full speed.

4. A man sees a bus 100 m away, starting from rest with uniform acceleration. He runs after it at constant speed and just catches it in 1 min (i.e. the man and the bus have the same speed at this time). Calculate the speed of the man and the acceleration of the bus. If the speed of the man is 3 m s^{-1} instead, find the nearest distance the man can get to the bus and when this occurs.

5. A man pushes a car of mass 1 t with a force of 200 N for 5 s, then with a force 150 N for 3 s and finally with a force of 100 N for 2 s. What is the final speed of the car, assuming a constant resistance to motion of 50 N?

6. A lift cage descends from rest with an acceleration of 2 m s^{-2} for 8 s, and then decelerates to rest. The distance dropped is 120 m. Find the time of descent and the magnitude of the deceleration.

7. A car accelerates from rest as shown in the table.

Time (s)	Gear	Acceleration (m s^{-2})
0–2	1	5
2–3	change	−1
3–5	2	4
5–6	change	−1
6–8	3	3
8–9	change	−1
9–10	4	2

Calculate the speed and the distance travelled in the 10 s.

8. A train starting from rest moves with constant acceleration a until it reaches a speed v. It then travels at a constant speed until it comes to rest with a uniform deceleration a. If the average speed is $\frac{5}{6}v$, show that the train is moving at constant speed for $\frac{2}{3}$ of the time. What fraction of the distance is covered at constant speed?

9. A man rows a boat with 2 oars. He exerts a force of 200 N on each oar for the 3 s they are in the water during a stroke. Water resisttance is a constant 230 N, and the combined mass of the man and the boat is 100 kg. Find the speed of the man after 2 strokes, if a complete stroke takes 5 s.

10. The maximum acceleration of a car is 2 m s^{-2} and the maximum retardation is 8 m s^{-2}. What is the least time it takes to travel 1 km, beginning and ending at rest?

4.4 Time-dependent forces and accelerations

If F is a function of time we use equation (2) of section 4.2:

$$F(t) = m\frac{dv}{dt}$$

and integrate to obtain

$$mv = \int F(t)\, dt.$$

This enables us to find v in terms of t. We can then find x, the distance travelled, from the relation $v = dx/dt$, to give

$$x = \int v\, dt.$$

EXAMPLE 1

A particle accelerates from rest in a straight line in two stages. For the first 10 s the acceleration a is given by

$$a = (100 - 6t).$$

For the next 10 s, a is given by

$$a = 4t.$$

Calculate the distance and the speed of the particle after 20 s.

Stage 1. $a = dv/dt = 100 - 6t$.
Integrating with respect to t, $v = 100t - 3t^2 + c_1$.
Now $v = 0$ when $t = 0$, so $c_1 = 0$ and hence

$$v = dx/dt = 100t - 3t^2.$$

Integrating again, $x = 50t^2 - t^3 + k_1$.
Now $x = 0$ when $t = 0$, so $k_1 = 0$ and hence

$$x = 50t^2 - t^3.$$

When $t = 10$, $v = 700$ and $x = 4000$.

Stage 2. $a = dv/dt = 4t$.
Integrating, $v = 2t^2 + c_2$.
When $t = 10$, $v = 700$, so $c_2 = 500$ and hence

$$v = dx/dt = 2t^2 + 500.$$

Integrating again, $x = \frac{2}{3}t^3 + 500t + k_2$.
When $t = 10$, $x = 4000$, so $k_2 = -\frac{1}{3} \times 5000$ and hence

$$x = \tfrac{2}{3}t^3 + 500t - \tfrac{1}{3} \times 1500.$$

When $t = 20$, v and x are given by

$$v = 800 + 500 = 1300, \qquad x = \tfrac{1}{3} \times 1600 + 10\,000 - \tfrac{1}{3} \times 5000 = 13\,667.$$

After 20 s the distance travelled by the particle is approximately 13 700 m and its speed is then 1300 m s^{-1}.
The graph of a and v against t are shown in figure 4.7.

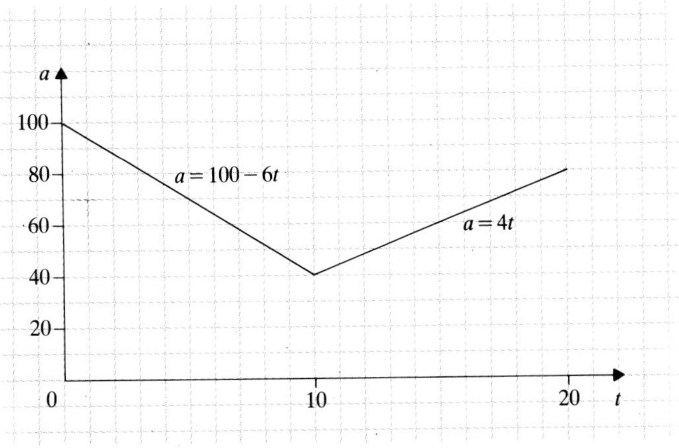

(a)

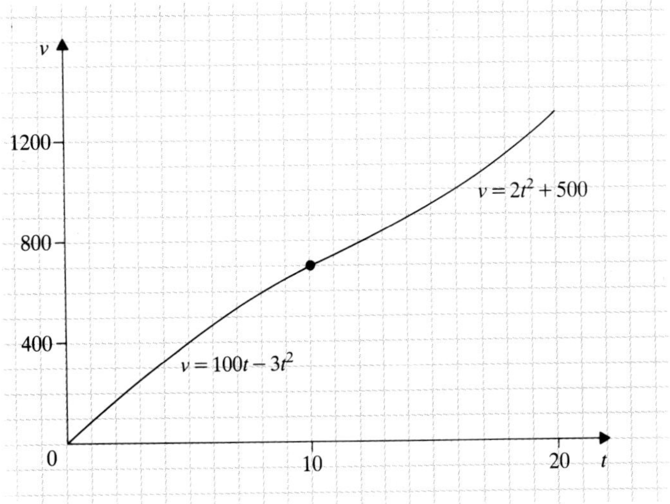

(b)

Figure 4.7

EXAMPLE 2

A particle of unit mass is at the point (4, 0) at time $t = 0$. It has a velocity of $2\,\mathrm{m\,s^{-1}}$ in the positive x-direction, and is acted upon by a force towards O whose magnitude is given by $F = \sin t$. Calculate the distance from O when the particle first comes to rest.

When the particle is at **P**, as in figure 4.8, N2 gives

$$ma = -\sin t,$$

$$\frac{dv}{dt} = -\sin t,$$

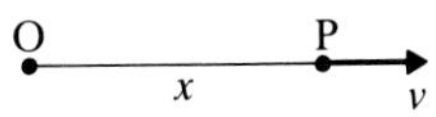

Figure 4.8

since $m = 1$. Integrating with respect to t gives

$$v = \cos t + c.$$

When $t = 0$, $v = 2$, so that $c = 1$, and hence

$$v = \cos t + 1.$$

Now $v = \mathrm{d}x/\mathrm{d}t$, so that integrating v with respect to t,

$$x = \sin t + t + k.$$

When $t = 0$, $x = 4$, so $k = 4$. Thus

$$x = \sin t + t + 4.$$

The particle first comes to rest when $v = 0$. Hence $\cos t + 1 = 0$, so $\cos t = -1$. This occurs for the first time when $t = \pi$. The distance of the particle from O is given by

$$x = \sin \pi + \pi + 4 = (\pi + 4),$$

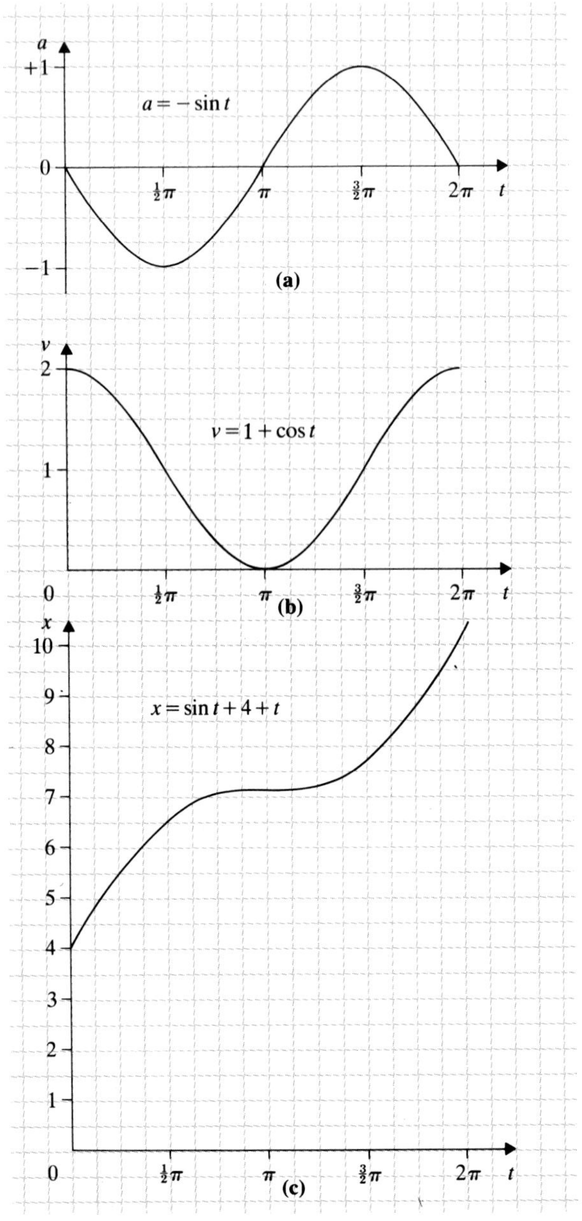

Figure 4.9

So the distance is approximately 7.14 m. The graphs of a, v and x against t are shown in figure 4.9.

□□□□□

The time integral of N2 is very important in mechanics. If the time interval is $t_1 \to t_2$ we obtain from equation (2) of section 4.2

$$[mv]_{t_1}^{t_2} = \int_{t_1}^{t_2} F\,\mathrm{d}t.$$

This equation is called the **impulse momentum equation**, and a further discussion of this, and its extension to more than one dimension will be given in chapter 5.

The quantity mv is called the **linear momentum** of a particle of mass m moving with speed v. The integral $\int_{t_1}^{t_2} F\,\mathrm{d}t$ is called the **impulse** of the force F over the time interval $t_1 \to t_2$.

The original form of N2 can be re-stated as follows:

The force on a body is equal to its rate of change of momentum (what Newton called its 'motion').

This may be written as a differential equation

$$F = \frac{\mathrm{d}}{\mathrm{d}t}(mv).$$

When the mass is constant (as in all the cases we consider), $\mathrm{d}m/\mathrm{d}t = 0$, and we get

$$F = \frac{\mathrm{d}}{\mathrm{d}t}(mv) = m\frac{\mathrm{d}v}{\mathrm{d}t},$$

so that we obtain

$$F = m\frac{\mathrm{d}v}{\mathrm{d}t} = ma,$$

which is the form of N2 given in section 3.2.

EXERCISE 4B

In each of questions 1–5, a particle of mass m starts at O with speed u in the positive x-direction and is acted on by a force F in the positive x-direction. The distance after t is x and the speed is v.

1. $m = \frac{1}{2}$, $F = \sqrt{t}$, $u = 3$, $t = 4$. Calculate v and x.
2. $m = 3$, $F = -9/(2+t)^2$, $u = 19$, $v = 0$. Calculate t and x.
3. $m = 1$, $F = 2t + \sin 2t$, $u = 0$, $t = 2\pi$. Calculate v and x.
4. $m = 3$, $F = -12/(4+t)^{1/2}$, $u = 2$, $v = 0$. Calculate t.
5. $m = 1$, $F = 1/(t+1)^2$, $u = 0$, $t = 9$. Calculate v and x.
6. A particle of unit mass starts at O with a speed of $8\ \mathrm{m\,s^{-1}}$ along the positive x-axis and is acted on by a force of magnitude $4t$ directed towards O. Calculate: (a) the greatest distance of the

particle from O, before returning for the first time. (b) the time taken to return to O.

7. A particle moves along the x-axis with acceleration $(3t+k)^{-2}$ m s^{-2}, where t is the time after leaving O. After 1 s the distance from O is 10 m and after 2 s it is 24 m. Calculate k and the distance from O after 3 s?

8. A woman walks so that her acceleration is $-32/(4+t)^2$ km h^{-2}. a) How far has she walked by the time her speed has been reduced from an initial value of 8 km h^{-1} to 5 km h^{-1}? (b) How long does she take to walk 16 km?

9. A body of mass 1 kg is acted on by a force F in the positive x-direction where:

$$F = \begin{cases} 20 - 2t, & 0 \leqslant t < 9 \text{ s} \\ 6/\sqrt{t}, & 9 \leqslant t \text{ s.} \end{cases}$$

If the body starts at the origin from rest, calculate its speed and distance from O after 16 s.

4.5 Distance-dependent forces

If F is a function of distance we use equation (4) of section 4.2:

$$F(x) = mv\frac{dv}{dx}$$

and integrate by separating the variables to obtain v in terms of x. We can then find x from the relation $v = dx/dt$, to give

$$t = \int \frac{dx}{v}.$$

A particularly important example of a distance-dependent force that we have already met is that due to gravitation (see section 3.4), and another is the force in a stretched or compressed spring. This will be discussed in detail in chapter 8.

EXAMPLE 1

A particle of mass 2 kg is moving along the x-axis under the action of a force in the positive x-direction of magnitude $-3x^2$ N. If the particle starts at the origin with an initial speed of 8 m s^{-1} in the positive x-direction, calculate:

a) the speed of the particle when $x = 2$,

b) where the particle first comes to rest,

c) the speed of the particle on return to the origin.

Using
$$F = mv\frac{dv}{dx},$$

we obtain
$$-3x^2 = 2v\frac{dv}{dx}.$$

Separating the variables,

$$\int 2v\,dv = \int -3x^2\,dx.$$

Integrating, $$v^2 = -x + c$$

When $x = 0$, $v = 8$ and so $c = 64$, giving

$$v^2 = 64 - x^3.$$

a) When $x = 2$, $v^2 = 64 - 8 = 56$, so v is 7.5 m s^{-1}.

b) When $v = 0$, $0 = 64 - x^3$, so x is 4 m.

c) We let $x = 0$ in $v^2 = 64 - x^3$, to give $v^2 = 64$.

So that the speed will be 8 m s^{-1} in the negative x-direction.

EXAMPLE 2

When a stage of a rocket is jettisoned a long way above the surface of the Earth, the acceleration towards the centre of the Earth is given by $a = -gR^2/x^2$, see figure 4.10. (This is the acceleration due to gravitation as in section 3.4.) If the body is at rest relative to the Earth at a height h above the surface, calculate the speed with which it lands.

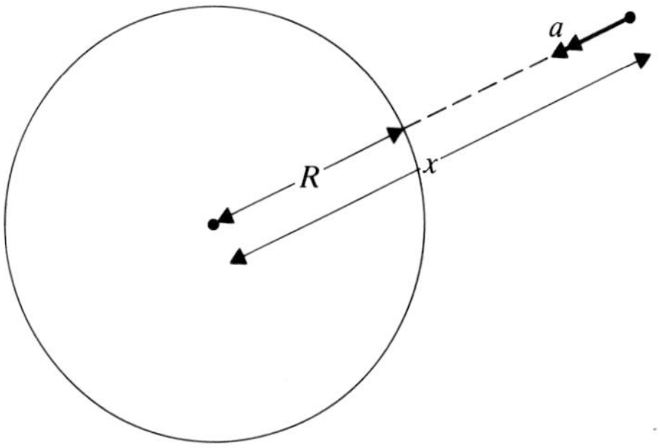

Figure 4.10

We have $$v\frac{dv}{dx} = -\frac{gR^2}{x^2}.$$

Separating the variables $$\int v\,dv = \int -\frac{gR^2}{x^2}\,dx$$

$$\frac{v^2}{2} = \frac{gR^2}{x} + c.$$

When $x = R + h$, $v = 0$, so

$$0 = \frac{gR^2}{R+h} + c.$$

Hence $$\frac{v^2}{2} = \frac{gR^2}{x} - \frac{gR^2}{R+h}.$$

When the body lands, $x = R$, and we obtain

$$\frac{v^2}{2} = \frac{gR^2}{R} - \frac{gR^2}{R+h},$$

$$v^2 = \frac{2ghR}{R+h}.$$

Hence $$v = \left(\frac{2ghR}{R+h}\right)^{1/2}.$$

Two particular cases are of interest.

a) If h is large, i.e. $h \gg R$, we obtain

$$v \to (2gR)^{1/2} \quad \text{as } h \to \infty.$$

Clearly, reversing the process, if a rocket were launched with a speed given by $(2gR)^{1/2}$, it would attain an 'infinite' height. This is known as the 'escape velocity' and its value (using data from section 3.4) is approximately 11 km s^{-1}.

b) If h is small, i.e. $h \ll R$, we obtain

$$v \simeq (2gh)^{1/2}.$$

This is the result obtained under the assumption that the acceleration due to gravity is constant near the surface of the Earth (see sections 2.4 and 3.4).

□□□□□

The distance integral of N2 is also very important in mechanics. If the distance interval is $x_1 \to x_2$ we obtain, from equation (4) of section 4.2,

$$\left[\tfrac{1}{2}mv^2\right]_{v_1}^{v_2} = \int_{x_1}^{x_2} F \, \mathrm{d}x.$$

This equation is usually referred to as the **work–energy equation**, and a fuller discussion of this will be given in chapter 6. The quantity $\frac{1}{2}mv^2$ is called the **kinetic energy** of a particle of mass m moving with speed v. The integral $\int_{x_1}^{x_2} F \, \mathrm{d}x$ is defined to be the **work done** by the force F over the distance $x_1 \to x_2$.

EXERCISE 4C

Radius of the Earth = 6.4×10^6 m,

Radius of the Moon = 1.76×10^6 m,

Mass of the Moon = $\frac{1}{81} \times$ mass of the Earth,

Distance between their centres = 3.84×10^8 m.

1. Neglecting air resistance, calculate the launching speed of a moonshot if it is to return to Earth from the Moon with no driving force available after launch.

2. Calculate the escape velocity from the Moon (ignoring the effects of the Earth and the Sun).

3. A particle starts at O with a speed v in the positive x-direction. It is subject to a retardation of cx, where c is a constant. Show that the distance travelled before the particle comes to rest is $v/\sqrt{c}$.

4. A particle starts from rest at O and has an acceleration of $12\sqrt{x}$ in the positive x-direction. Prove that $x = t^4$, where t is the time taken.

5.* A particle starts from rest a distance d from O and moves towards O with an acceleration $k(x + d^4/x^3)$ where x is the distance of the particle from O. Show that the time taken to reach O is $\pi/4\sqrt{k}$ and find the time taken to reach a point $d/\sqrt{2}$ from O.

6. A particle of mass $\frac{1}{3}$ kg is acted on by a force $(x^2 - 4x)$ N towards O. It starts from O with a speed of 16 m s^{-1} in the positive x-direction. Show that it travels 8 m before coming to rest.

Velocity-dependent forces **4.6**

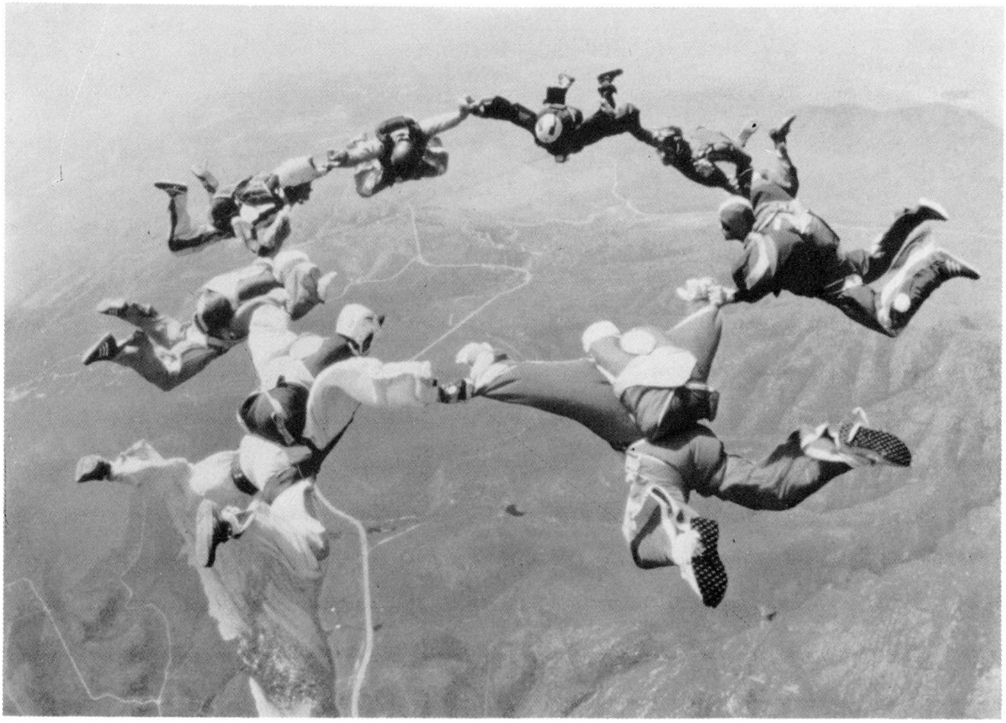

When the sky divers link hands they are moving at approximately terminal velocity.

(This section requires more advanced techniques of integration and may be omitted on first reading.)

When a body moves in a resisting medium, motion is opposed by the medium. Thus when a cricket ball is hit in the air, it does not move under the effect of gravity alone, since it is slowed down by air resistance. In some cases this effect is small and the work in section 2.4 is a reasonable approximation. However, if an engine were to fall off an aeroplane, it would not accelerate at about $10\ \mathrm{m\,s^{-2}}$ (g) downwards until it hit the ground, but would reach a 'terminal' velocity of about $50\ \mathrm{m\,s^{-1}}$.

So far our discussions have ignored the effect of air resistance. This is not negligible under many conditions, and is not a constant force. For low speeds the resisting force is often taken as proportional to the speed. At higher speeds the magnitude of the force is taken to be proportional to the square of the speed.

EXAMPLE 1

In conditions of free fall (as in the photograph above), a sky diver of mass 100 kg, including his pack, reaches a terminal velocity of $50\ \mathrm{m\,s^{-1}}$. If the resistance is proportional to v^2, the square of his speed at any instant, calculate:

a) the constant of proportionality,

b) the distance fallen before he reaches half his terminal velocity,

c) the time taken to reach half the terminal velocity.

The forces on the diver are the weight force and the resistance, which acts vertically upwards. Suppose that after t seconds his speed downwards is v and his acceleration downwards is a.

a) Applying N2 vertically to the man,

$$mg - kv^2 = ma, \tag{6}$$

where k is the constant of proportionality. The terminal velocity is reached when $a = 0$. Hence

$$100 \times 10 = k \times 50^2,$$

which gives $k = 0.4$.

b) While the diver is accelerating, we obtain from equation (6)

$$100v\frac{dv}{dx} = 100 \times 10 - 0.4v^2.$$

Thus
$$v\frac{dv}{dx} = 10 - 0.004v^2.$$

Separating the variables and integrating we obtain

$$\int_0^{25} \frac{v\,dv}{10 - 0.004v^2} = \int_0^d dx,$$

$$\left[-\frac{1}{0.008}\ln(10 - 0.004v^2)\right]_0^{25} = d.$$

Hence, the distance travelled in reaching half the terminal velocity is 36 m.

c) To find the time taken, we obtain from (6)

$$100\frac{dv}{dt} = 100 \times 10 - 0.4v^2,$$

$$\frac{dv}{dt} = 10 - 0.004v^2.$$

Separating the variables and integrating

$$\int_0^{25} \frac{dv}{10 - 0.004v^2} = \int_0^T dt,$$

$$\left[\frac{1}{0.004} \times \frac{1}{2 \times 50}\ln\left|\frac{50 + v}{50 - v}\right|\right]_0^{25} = T.$$

Hence, the time taken to reach half the terminal velocity is 2.75 s.

EXAMPLE 2

Repeat example 1 under the assumption that the resistance is proportional to the speed v.

a) In this case the equation of motion becomes

$$mg - kv = ma. \tag{7}$$

When $a = 0$, $100 \times 10 = k \times 50$, so $k = 20$.

b) From equation (7),

$$100v\frac{dv}{dx} = 100 \times 10 - 20v,$$

$$v\frac{dv}{dx} = 10 - 0.2v,$$

Separating the variables and integrating

$$\int_0^{25} \frac{v\,dv}{10 - 0.2v} = \int_0^d dx,$$

$$\int_0^{25} \left(-5 + \frac{50}{10 - 0.2v} \right) dv = d,$$

$$[-5v - 250 \ln|10 - 0.2v|]_0^{25} = d,$$

$$-125 - 250 \ln 5 + 250 \ln 10 = d,$$

$$d = 125\,(2 \ln 2 - 1).$$

Hence the distance travelled is 48 m.

c) To find the time taken we obtain from equation (7),

$$\frac{dv}{dt} = 10 - 0.2v$$

$$\int_0^{25} \frac{dv}{10 - 0.2v} = \int_0^T dt$$

$$[-5 \ln|10 - 0.2v|]_0^{25} = T$$

Hence $T = 5 \ln 2$, so the time taken is 3.47 s.

EXERCISE 4D

1. The resistance of water to a ship's motion is proportional to the cube of the speed. Prove that, from the time the engines are stopped, the velocity v and distance run x are connected by the equation

$$dv/dv = -kv^2,$$

where k is a constant. Deduce that, if the speed was u when the engines were shut off,

$$1/v - 1/u = kx.$$

2. If the retardation caused by the resistances to the motion of a train is $k + cv^2$, where v is the velocity and k and c are constants, show that it will come to rest from a velocity u in a distance d given by:

$$d = \frac{1}{2c} \ln\left(1 + \frac{cu^2}{k}\right).$$

3. A particle of unit mass moves along the x-axis under a constant force of 2 N in the positive x-direction, and a resisting force of $(v^2 - v)$ N, where v is the speed of the particle. The particle is initially at rest at O.

a) Show that the particle tends to a limiting speed of 2 m s^{-1}.

b) Find the time taken to reach a speed of 1 m s^{-1}.

c) Find the distance travelled in this time.

4.* A cricket ball of mass 0.2 kg is thrown vertically upwards with a speed of 30 m s^{-1}. If the only force on it is due to gravity (giving an acceleration downwards of 10 m s^{-2}), how high does it rise and how long is it in the air? If in addition to gravity there is a resistance to motion of $0.002v^2$, calculate

a) how high the ball rises,

b) the time of ascent,

c) the speed of the ball on hitting the ground,

d) the time of descent.

5.* Repeat parts (a) and (b) of question 3 when the resistance to motion is $0.1v$.

6.* A particle of mass m is projected with a speed u in a medium whose resistance is $mk(c^2v + v^3)$, where k and c are positive constants and v is the speed at time t. Ignoring effects due to gravity etc., prove that the particle will not come to rest in a finite time, and it will travel further than $\pi/2kc$.

7.* A particle of unit mass is projected vertically upwards with velocity u. If air resistance is kv, prove that the particle returns to its point of projection with velocity w, where

$$w + u = \frac{g}{k}\ln\left(\frac{g + ku}{g - kw}\right).$$

(Cf. question 4c.)

Summary

Newton's second law, N2, states

$$F = ma,$$

where

$$a = \frac{dv}{dt} = \frac{d^2x}{dt^2} = v\frac{dv}{dx} = \frac{d}{dx}(\tfrac{1}{2}v^2),$$

$$v = \frac{dx}{dt} = \int a\,dt,$$

$$s = \int v\,dt.$$

MOMENTUM AND IMPULSE

5

Introduction 5.1

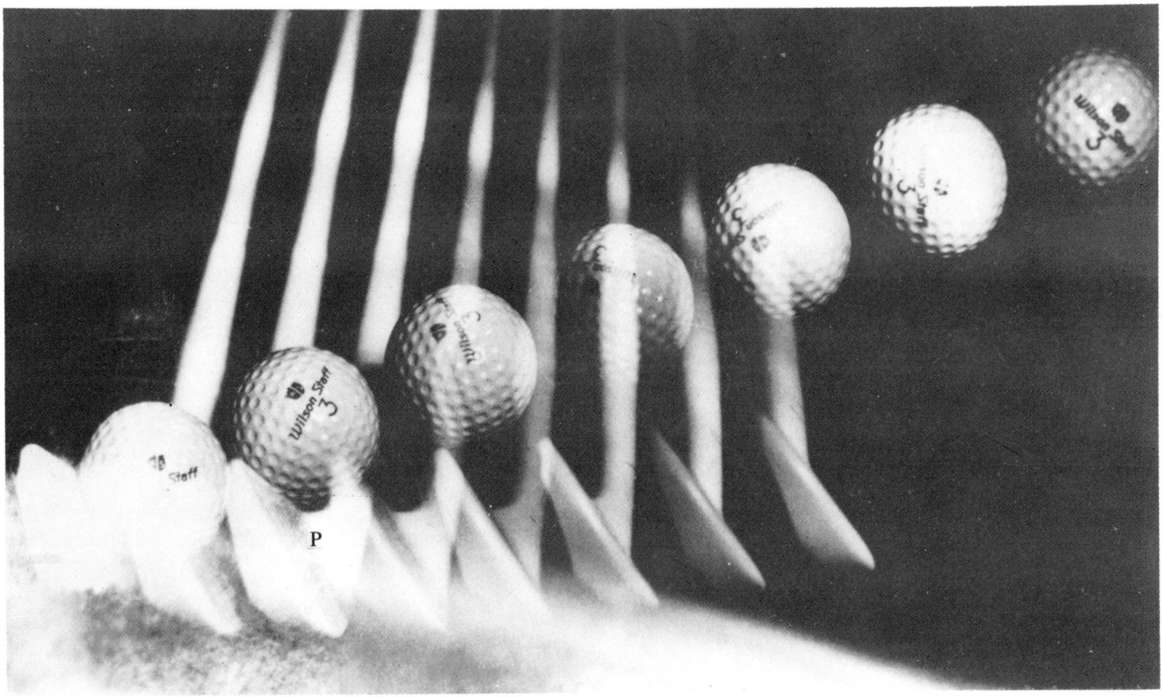

Figure 5.1

The photograph shows a golf ball being struck by a golf club. Once the ball has left the club head (approximately at position P in the photograph) the ball will move under the effect of gravity alone, if we neglect the effects of air resistance, and will therefore move along the arc of a parabola (see section 2.4). During the period of contact with the club, the ball has accelerated and acquired a velocity at P.

The nature of the forces acting during the contact is extremely complicated and the following points are important.

1 The contact force between the club and the ball varies greatly.

2 The time of contact is very small.

3 The ball deforms (changes shape) during contact.

Whenever collisions take place, variable contact forces come into play. These may act over a short time, for example, when two billiard balls collide, or over a relatively long time, for example, as a soccer ball hits the back of the net when a goal is scored.

The time of contact between the ball and net is long, and the ball is not deformed.

The time of contact between baseball bat and the ball is short, during which the ball is considerably deformed.

Although we cannot easily analyse the action of the forces during the impact, we can determine their effects in terms of the changes in velocities produced. The golfer, for example, is concerned mainly with the velocity of the ball at P and its subsequent motion towards the hole, rather than what happens during the impact itself.

5.2 Impulse momentum equation

Suppose the golf ball in figure 5.1, whose mass is 45 g, is replaced on the tee by a cricket ball of mass 150 g. If we assume the golfer can reproduce his swing exactly as in figure 5.1, it is clear that the velocity of the cricket ball at P will be less than that of the golf ball, and will not travel as far subsequently towards the hole.

For a given force, acting on a particle for a given time, we might speculate that the velocity gained is inversely proportional to the mass of the particle, i.e. the product 'mass × velocity' remains constant.

In accordance with this idea we define momentum as follows:

The **momentum** of a particle is the product of its mass, m with its velocity, $\boldsymbol{v}$, namely $m\boldsymbol{v}$, and this is a vector quantity.
The dimensions of momentum are: $[m\boldsymbol{v}] = \mathrm{M\,L\,T^{-1}}$
and the units are kg m s^{-1}.

Suppose that a particle of mass m is acted on by a constant force $\boldsymbol{F}$ for a time t.

From N2, $\boldsymbol{F} = m\boldsymbol{a}$.

Multiplying by t, $t\boldsymbol{F} = mt\boldsymbol{a}$.

Using $\boldsymbol{v} = \boldsymbol{u} + t\boldsymbol{a}$, $t\boldsymbol{F} = m(\boldsymbol{v} - \boldsymbol{u})$,

$$t\boldsymbol{F} = m\boldsymbol{v} - m\boldsymbol{u}. \qquad (1)$$

This is the **impulse momentum equation**. $t\boldsymbol{F}$ is the **impulse** of the force $\boldsymbol{F}$ acting for time t. As noted above, it is often the case when bodies collide, that very large forces come into play for very short times. Such forces are often referred to as blows or impulsive forces. In such situations we may be unable to measure the time of impact and the contact force may vary greatly. We may, however, relate the impulse of a force under these circumstances to the change of momentum it provides. We write equation (1) as

$$\boldsymbol{I} = m\boldsymbol{v} - m\boldsymbol{u}. \qquad (2)$$

Dimensions

From equations (1) and (2), we see that

$$[\boldsymbol{I}] = [t\boldsymbol{F}] = \mathrm{M\,L\,T^{-1}}.$$

The units of impulse are N s, and since the dimensions of impulse and momentum are the same, we use N s as the unit of both ($1\ \mathrm{N\,s} = 1\ \mathrm{kg\,m\,s^{-1}}$).

a) Motion in one dimension

EXAMPLE 1

Suppose a golf ball of mass 45 g leaves a club head with a speed of $60\,\mathrm{m\,s^{-1}}$ at 40° to the horizontal, as in figure 5.2. Find the impulse imparted by the club head to the ball.

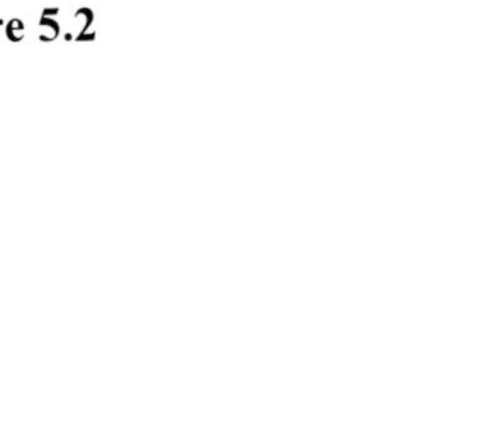

Figure 5.2

We will assume that the ball travels in a straight line over the short distance it is in contact with the club. From equation (2), $\boldsymbol{I}$ is in the same direction as the change in momentum and

$$I = mv - 0,$$

since the initial momentum is zero. Thus

$$I = 45 \times 10^{-3} \times 60 = 2.7.$$

The impulse has a magnitude of 2.7 N s at an angle of 40° to the horizontal.

EXAMPLE 2

A squash ball hits the front wall of a court at right angles at a speed of $40\ \mathrm{m\,s^{-1}}$ and rebounds at $30\ \mathrm{m\,s^{-1}}$. The mass of the ball is 25 g. Find the impulse on the ball.

Once again the motion is in one dimension, but we must be careful to establish the positive coordinate direction. We will take the normal

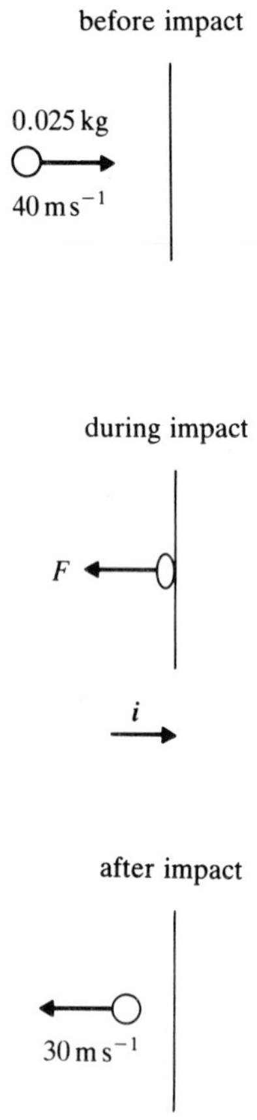

Figure 5.3

towards the wall as positive, as shown in figure 5.3. The impulse momentum equation gives

$$I = mv - mu$$
$$= 0.025 \times -30 - 0.025 \times 40 = -1.75$$

The impulse on the ball is 1.75 N s in the direction away from the wall.

□□□□□

It is often helpful when solving such problems to draw separate sketches showing the three stages of the motion, as in figure 5.3.

b) Motion in more than one dimension.

EXAMPLE 3

Suppose a ball of mass 25 g strikes a wall at an angle of 60° to the wall at a speed of 20 m s^{-1} and rebounds at 30° to the wall. Assume the contact between the ball and the wall is smooth. Calculate: (a) the final speed of the ball, and (b) the magnitude of the impulse on the ball.

There are several possible methods of solution and we will illustrate them in this example.

Method 1 By calculation, using components

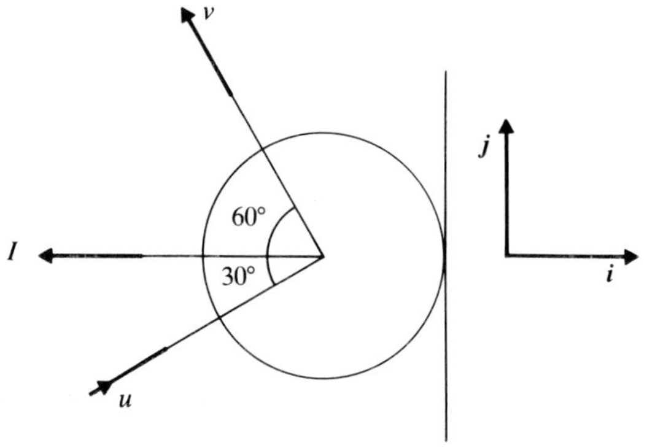

Figure 5.4

Unit vectors $\boldsymbol{i}$ and $\boldsymbol{j}$ are chosen, as in figure 5.4.

The initial velocity $\quad \boldsymbol{u} = 20\begin{pmatrix} \cos 30° \\ \sin 30° \end{pmatrix}.$

The final velocity $\quad \boldsymbol{v} = v\begin{pmatrix} -\cos 60° \\ \sin 60° \end{pmatrix}.$

Suppose that the impulse is $\boldsymbol{I} = \begin{pmatrix} -I \\ 0 \end{pmatrix}.$

Using the impulse momentum equation,

$$\boldsymbol{I} = m\boldsymbol{v} - m\boldsymbol{u}$$

$$\begin{pmatrix} -I \\ 0 \end{pmatrix} = 0.025v\begin{pmatrix} -\cos 60^\circ \\ \sin 60^\circ \end{pmatrix} - 0.025 \times 20\begin{pmatrix} \cos 30^\circ \\ \sin 30^\circ \end{pmatrix}. \qquad (3)$$

Equating components,

$$-I = 0.025(-v\cos 60^\circ - 20\cos 30^\circ),$$
$$0 = 0.025(v\sin 60^\circ - 20\sin 30^\circ).$$

Hence $$v = 20\frac{\sin 30^\circ}{\sin 60^\circ} = 20\sqrt{\tfrac{1}{3}}.$$

Substituting for v,

$$-I = 0.025(-20\sqrt{\tfrac{1}{3}}\cos 60^\circ - 20\cos 30^\circ)$$
$$= 0.025(-10\sqrt{\tfrac{1}{3}} - 10\sqrt{3}) = -\sqrt{\tfrac{1}{3}}$$

The impulse has magnitude 0.577 N s and is directed away from the wall.

Note that equation (3) shows the component of the momentum parallel to the wall as unchanged because there is no impulse in that direction.

Method 2 By vector diagram

Rearranging the impulse momentum equation,

$$\boldsymbol{I} + m\boldsymbol{u} = m\boldsymbol{v}.$$

The vectors $\boldsymbol{I}$, $m\boldsymbol{u}$ and $m\boldsymbol{v}$ form a closed vector triangle. In the vector equation, we know:

a) the length and direction of $m\boldsymbol{u}$

b) the directions of $\boldsymbol{I}$ and $m\boldsymbol{v}$.

We draw a rough sketch of the triangle as follows:

1 In figure 5.5a, a vector representing $m\boldsymbol{u}$ is drawn from the point O.

2 The vector representing the known direction of $\boldsymbol{I}$ is drawn but of an unspecified length.

3 The vector representing the known direction of $m\boldsymbol{v}$ is drawn from O.

The triangle is closed at P, and this determines the lengths of $\boldsymbol{I}$ and $m\boldsymbol{v}$. Figure 5.5b is a scale drawing with $I = 0.58$ and $mv = 0.29$, by measurement.

rough sketch

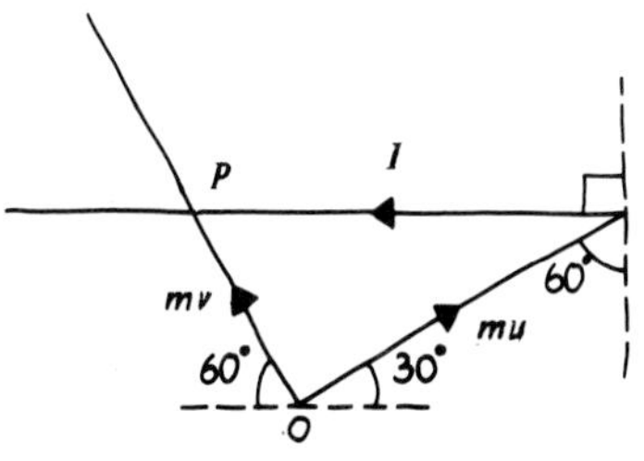

(a)

scale diagram 0.1 N s

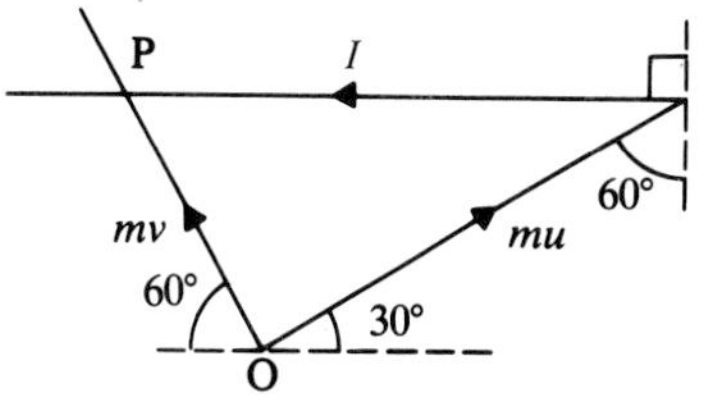

(b)

Figure 5.5

Since in this particular problem there is a right angle at O, we could use elementary trigonometry.
In figure 5.5b we have

$$I = \frac{0.5}{\cos 30^\circ} = 0.577 \quad \text{and} \quad mv = 0.5\tan 30^\circ = 0.5\sqrt{\tfrac{1}{3}}.$$

Thus $$v = \frac{0.5}{0.025\sqrt{3}} = 20\sqrt{\tfrac{1}{3}}$$

EXAMPLE 4

A particle of mass 3 kg is moving with an initial velocity of $\begin{pmatrix} 2 \\ 1 \\ 3 \end{pmatrix}$ m s^{-1}, when it receives an impulse which changes its velocity to $\begin{pmatrix} 4 \\ -1 \\ 2 \end{pmatrix}$ m s^{-1}.

a) Find the impulse on the particle.

b) Find its velocity after a further impulse of $\begin{pmatrix} 3 \\ 1 \\ 9 \end{pmatrix}$ N s.

a) From the impulse momentum equation,

$$\boldsymbol{I} = m\boldsymbol{v} - m\boldsymbol{u}$$

$$= 3\begin{pmatrix} 4 \\ -1 \\ 2 \end{pmatrix} - 3\begin{pmatrix} 2 \\ 1 \\ 3 \end{pmatrix} = \begin{pmatrix} 6 \\ -6 \\ -3 \end{pmatrix}.$$

The impulse on the particle is $\begin{pmatrix} 6 \\ -6 \\ -3 \end{pmatrix}$ N s.

b) Rearranging the above equation, with $\boldsymbol{u} = \begin{pmatrix} 4 \\ -1 \\ 2 \end{pmatrix}$

$$m\boldsymbol{v} = \boldsymbol{I} + m\boldsymbol{u},$$

$$3\boldsymbol{v} = \begin{pmatrix} 3 \\ 1 \\ 9 \end{pmatrix} + 3\begin{pmatrix} 4 \\ -1 \\ 2 \end{pmatrix} = \begin{pmatrix} 15 \\ -2 \\ 15 \end{pmatrix},$$

$$\boldsymbol{v} = \begin{pmatrix} 5 \\ -\frac{2}{3} \\ 5 \end{pmatrix}.$$

The velocity of the particle is $\begin{pmatrix} 5 \\ -\frac{2}{3} \\ 5 \end{pmatrix}$ m s^{-1}.

EXERCISE 5A

1. Calculate the magnitude of momentum, in N s, of:
   a) A car of mass 1.5 t travelling at 80 km h^{-1}.
   b) A dart of mass 30 g travelling at 5 m s^{-1}.
   c) A liner of mass 500000t travelling at 0.2m s^{-1}.
   d) A cricket ball of mass 150 g travelling at 20 m s^{-1}.

2. Calculate the magnitude of the impulse required to stop a car of of mass 1 t travelling at 80 km h^{-1}.

3. A ball of mass 250 g strikes the cushion of a billiard table at right angles with a speed of 3 m s^{-1}. It rebounds with a speed of 1 m s^{-1}. What is the impulse on the ball?

4. A bullet of mass 25 g is fired at a target with a speed of 960 m s^{-1}. It passes through the target, emerging with a speed of 500 m s^{-1}

at an angle of 35° to its original direction. Calculate the magnitude and direction of the impulse on the bullet.

5. A particle of mass 3 kg has a velocity of $(\boldsymbol{i} + 2\boldsymbol{j} + 3\boldsymbol{k})$ m s^{-1}. What impulse is needed to change the velocity to $(3\boldsymbol{i} + 2\boldsymbol{j} + \boldsymbol{k})$ m s^{-1}? A further impulse of $(3\boldsymbol{i} + 3\boldsymbol{k})$ N s is then applied. What will the new velocity be?

6. A ball of mass 50 g has a velocity of $(6\boldsymbol{i} - 4\boldsymbol{j} + 2\boldsymbol{k})$ m s^{-1}. It is struck by a bat, and the velocity immediately after impact is $(-4\boldsymbol{i} + 7\boldsymbol{j} + 5\boldsymbol{k})$ m s^{-1}. Calculate the magnitude of the impulse of the bat on the ball.

7. A hockey ball of mass 150 g is moving at 10 m s^{-1} horizontally across the field. A player wishes to hit the ball directly upfield as shown in figure 5.6. If she exerts an impulse of magnitude 4 N s, calculate:

   a) the direction in which she must aim her shot,

   b) the speed of the ball immediately after impact.

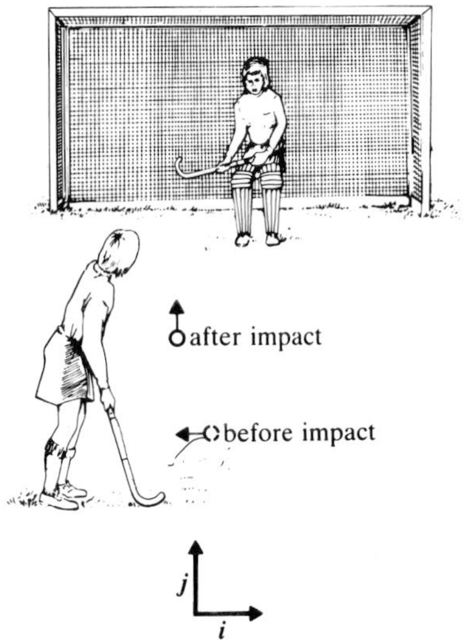

Figure 5.6

8. A pile driver has a block of mass 5 t, which is dropped from a height of 5 m on to a pile. The block rebounds at a speed of 2 m s^{-1} immediately after impact. Calculate the impulse on the pile.

9. An ice puck of mass 0.2 kg travelling horizontally at 20 m s^{-1} strikes the boards of the rink at an angle of 30° to the boards. The puck rebounds with a speed of 15 m s^{-1} at an angle of 40° to the boards. Calculate the magnitude and direction of the impulse on the puck.

10. A ball of mass 0.2 kg is moving at 20 m s^{-1} when it receives an impulse of 10 N s at an angle of 120° to its line of flight. Calculate:

    a) the angle of deflection of the ball,

    b) the speed of the ball after impact.

Impulse 5.3

As we have seen, the impulse of a constant force $\boldsymbol{F}$ acting for a time t is defined as $t\boldsymbol{F}$, and we related the impulse $\boldsymbol{I}$ for a blow to momentum by the impulse momentum equation (p. 115). There may be occasions when we are able to define a variable force $\boldsymbol{F}$ as a function of t. Suppose such a force acts on a particle of mass m. From N2,

$$\boldsymbol{F} = m\boldsymbol{a} = m\frac{\mathrm{d}\boldsymbol{v}}{\mathrm{d}t}.$$

Integrating this with respect to time, we obtain

$$\int_{t_1}^{t_2} \boldsymbol{F}\,\mathrm{d}t = \int_{t_1}^{t_2} m\frac{\mathrm{d}\boldsymbol{v}}{\mathrm{d}t}\,\mathrm{d}t,$$

$$\int_{t_1}^{t_2} \boldsymbol{F}\,\mathrm{d}t = m\boldsymbol{v}(t_2) - m\boldsymbol{v}(t_1).$$

$m\,\boldsymbol{v}(t_2) - m\,\boldsymbol{v}(t_1)$ is the change in momentum of the particle in the time interval $t_1 \to t_2$ and we define $\int_{t_1}^{t_2} \boldsymbol{F}\,\mathrm{d}t$ to be the impulse of the force $\boldsymbol{F}$ over the time interval $t_1 \to t_2$.

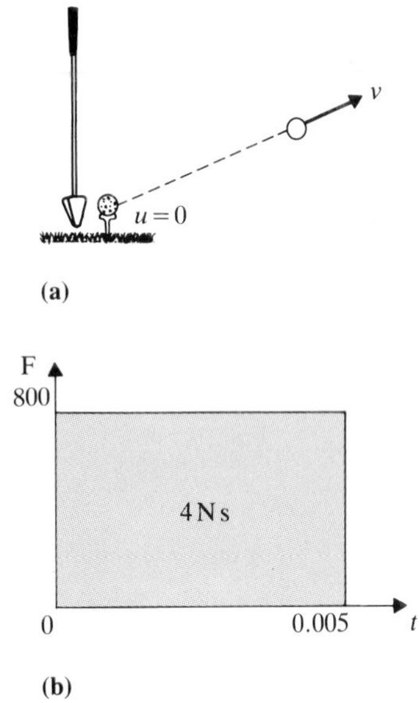

Figure 5.7

EXAMPLE 1

A golf ball of mass 45 g is hit by a club. Find the speed of the ball 0.005 s after impact if:

a) the contact force is a constant 800 N,
b) the contact force t s is given by

$$F = 800 \sin(\pi/0.005)t.$$

In each case sketch a graph of the force F against time t.

The positive coordinate direction is taken along the line of force.

a) Here, the impulse is given by

$$tF = mv - mu$$
$$800 \times 0.005 = 45 \times 10^{-3}v - 0$$

giving v as 89 m s^{-1}. It is important to note that the magnitude of the impulse is 4 N s and is the area under the (t, F) graph in figure 5.7b.

b) In this case, the magnitude of the impulse, I, is

$$I = \int_0^{0.005} F\,\mathrm{d}t$$
$$= 800\frac{0{\cdot}005}{\pi}\left[-\cos\frac{\pi t}{0{\cdot}005}\right]_0^{0.005}$$
$$= \frac{8}{\pi}.$$

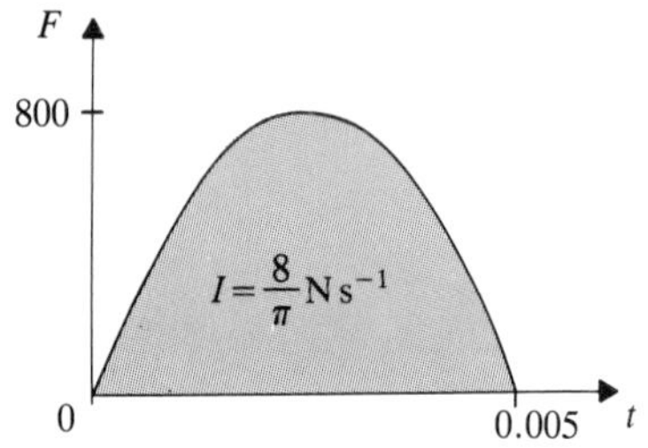

Figure 5.8

Now $\quad I = mv - mu$

$$8/\pi = 45 \times 10^{-3}v - 0$$

giving v as 57 m s^{-1}. Once again the area under the (t, F) graph gives the magnitude of the impulse (figure 5.8).

Note that, $\int_{t_1}^{t_2} F\,\mathrm{d}t/(t_2 - t_1)$ is the average value of F over the interval $t_1 \to t_2$, and so the impulse of a variable force over a given time is equal to the average force × time.

EXAMPLE 2

A particle of mass 0.5 kg is acted on by a force $\boldsymbol{F} = \begin{pmatrix} t^2 \\ \cos 2t \end{pmatrix}$, where t is measured in seconds. If the particle is at rest at $t = 0$, what is the velocity after 3 s?

The impulse is given by

$$\boldsymbol{I} = \int_0^3 \boldsymbol{F}\,\mathrm{d}t = \int_0^3 \begin{pmatrix} t^2 \\ \cos 2t \end{pmatrix} \mathrm{d}t$$
$$= \left[\begin{pmatrix} \tfrac{1}{3}t \\ \tfrac{1}{2}\sin 2t \end{pmatrix}\right]_0^3 = \begin{pmatrix} 9 \\ -0.14 \end{pmatrix}.$$

Hence, by the impulse momentum equation, $\boldsymbol{I} = m\boldsymbol{v} - m\boldsymbol{u}$, so that

$$\begin{pmatrix} 9 \\ -0.14 \end{pmatrix} = 0.5\,\boldsymbol{v} - \boldsymbol{0}.$$

$$\boldsymbol{v} = \begin{pmatrix} 18 \\ -0.28 \end{pmatrix}.$$

□□□□□

We have seen that the impulse momentum equation can be applied in several different situations. In the last two examples, however, where the variation of F with t was known, we could have analysed the motion entirely using Newton's laws (see section 4.4).

The impulse momentum equation is principally useful when sudden 'blows' or 'jerks' are applied to bodies; then very large forces act over very small times, producing effects much greater than those of any other forces which may be acting. In example 1a the impulse from the club head on the golf ball over the contact time had a magnitude of 4 N s. Gravity will be acting on the ball throughout, but the magnitude of its impulse, in N s, during the contact time will be $0.045 \times 10 \times 0.005 = 0.002\,25$. This is negligible compared with the impulse from the club head.

EXERCISE 5B

1. A car of mass 2 t is travelling at 30 m s^{-1}. Braking is applied for 3 s. If the braking force is a constant 2000 N, calculate
   a) the impulse on the car,
   b) the speed of the car at the end of the 3 s period.

2. A cricket ball of mass 150 g is hit vertically in the air at a speed of 20 m s^{-1}.
   a) What is the initial momentum of the ball?
   b) What is the momentum of the ball at the top of the flight?
   c) What impulse destroyed the momentum of the ball? For how long did the impulse act?
   d) Which of the answers in (a)–(c) would have been different if the mass of the ball had been 500 g?

3. Why do cricketers 'gather a ball in' when catching? A cricket ball of mass 150 g is travelling at 20 m s^{-1} when it is caught by a fielder. What is the average force on the fielder's hands if the ball is stopped in: (a) 0.01 s, (b) 0.05 s?

4. Find the impulse of a force of $(6\boldsymbol{i} + 2\boldsymbol{j} + \boldsymbol{k})$ N acting for 1.5 s. If this force acts on a particle of mass 2 kg with an initial velocity of $(-4\boldsymbol{i} + 3\boldsymbol{j} - 2\boldsymbol{k})$ m s^{-1}, calculate the velocity at the end of the period.

5. Calculate the magnitudes of the impulses of the following forces:
   a) 100 N acting for 3 s.
   b) $6t$ N acting from $t = 0$ to $t = 3$ s.
   c) $4t^3$ N acting from $t = 1$ to $t = 3$ s.
   d) $2 \sin t$ N acting between $t = 0$ and $t = \frac{1}{4}\pi$ s.

6. Calculate the impulse of:

   a) a force $(t\boldsymbol{i} + (1 - t)\boldsymbol{j} + 3t^2\boldsymbol{k})$ N acting between $t = 0$ and $t = 2$.

   b) a force $(\sin^2 t\,\boldsymbol{i} + \cos^2 t\,\boldsymbol{j})$ N acting between $t = 0$ and $t = \frac{1}{2}\pi$.

7. A skier of mass 40 kg is skiing at 15 m s^{-1} on horizontal ground. She then runs into a snow bank and is brought to rest in 1.5 s. If the resisting force is in the form $F = k \sin(\frac{1}{3}\pi t)$, calculate the value of k.

8. A cyclist and bicycle have a combined mass of 80 kg. The cyclist starts from rest and pedals for one minute. Calculate the resultant speed in the following situations:

   a) there is a constant effective forward force of 20 N.

   b) the resultant forward force increases linearly to a maximum of 30 N and then decreases linearly to zero. (Does it matter when this maximum is reached, provided it is within one minute?)

   c) the resultant forward force is given by $\frac{1}{60}(60 - t)^2$ N.

9. A particle of mass 2 kg is moving under the influence of a force $(-\cos 3t\,\boldsymbol{i} - \sin 3t\,\boldsymbol{j})$ N. Calculate the impulse over the period $t = 0$ to $\frac{1}{3}\pi$. What is the change in momentum of the particle?

Collisions **5.4**

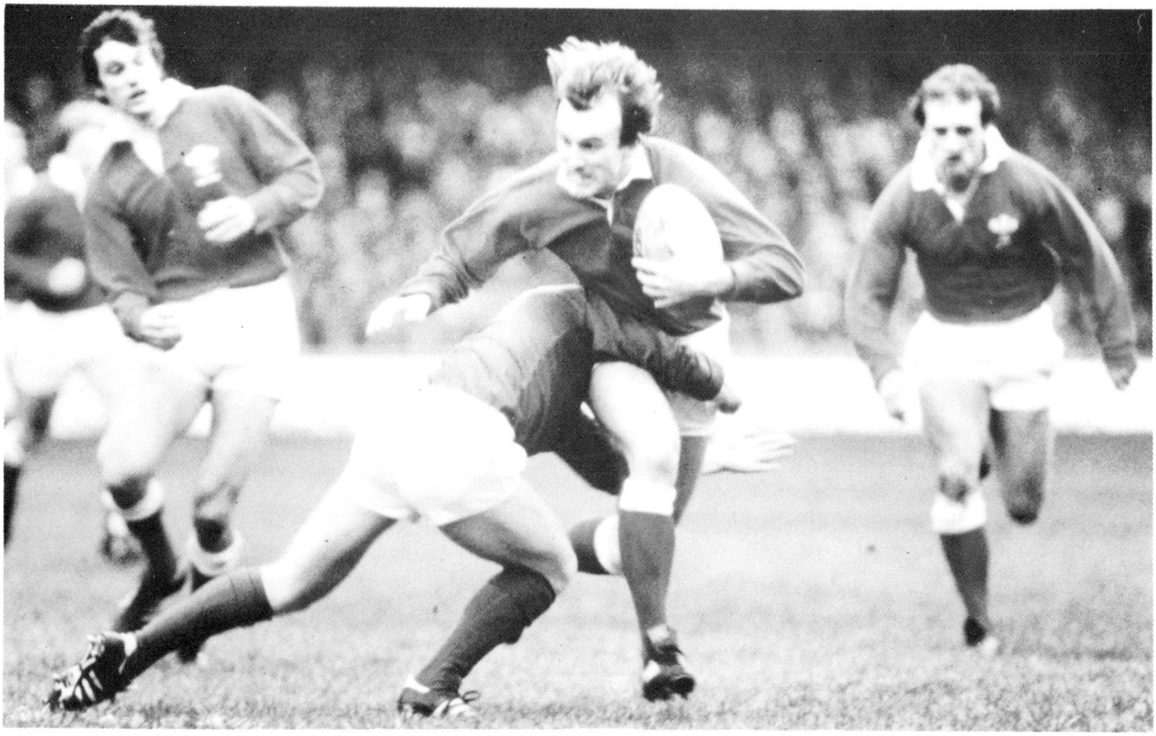

We now extend the use of the impulse momentum equation to two or more moving bodies and will initially consider this with the following example.

EXAMPLE 1

A cue ball A of mass 0.2 kg moving at 3 m s^{-1} strikes a red ball B of the same mass, which is initially at rest. Immediately after the collision the cue ball continues along the same line at a speed of 1 m s^{-1}. Calculate (a) the impulse on the cue ball, (b) the speed of the red ball after impact.

The motion is in one dimension and we take the positive $\boldsymbol{i}$-direction as the initial direction of the cue ball.

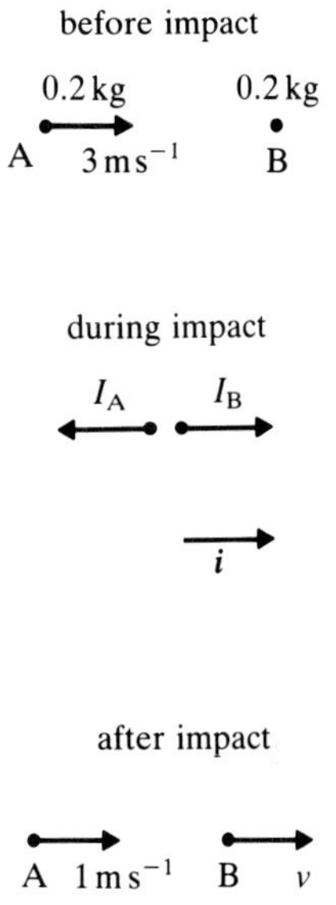

Figure 5.9

a) Let the speed of the red ball be v, as shown in figure 5.9. From the impulse momentum equation,

$$\boldsymbol{I}_A = 0.2(\boldsymbol{i}) - 0.2(3\boldsymbol{i}) = -0.4\boldsymbol{i}.$$

The impulse on the cue ball has magnitude 0.4 N s in the $-\boldsymbol{i}$-direction.

b) Let $\boldsymbol{c}_A$ be the contact force on A at the instant of collision, so the contact force $\boldsymbol{c}_B$ on B is given by N3 as

$$\boldsymbol{c}_A + \boldsymbol{c}_B = 0,$$
$$\boldsymbol{c}_B = -\boldsymbol{c}_A.$$

Hence
$$\int_0^t \boldsymbol{c}_B \, dt = -\int_0^t \boldsymbol{c}_A \, dt,$$
$$\boldsymbol{I}_B = -\boldsymbol{I}_A,$$

i.e. the impulse on ball B is equal in magnitude and opposite in direction to that acting on ball A. Hence

$$\boldsymbol{I}_B = 0.4\mathbf{i}.$$

From the impulse momentum equation,

$$0.4 = 0.2v - 0,$$
$$v = 2.$$

The total momentum before and after the collision is the same. Before the collision, the total momentum is

$$0.2 \times 3\boldsymbol{i} = 0.6\boldsymbol{i}.$$

After the collision, the total momentum is

$$0.2\boldsymbol{i} + 0.2 \times 2\boldsymbol{i} = 0.6\boldsymbol{i}.$$

□□□□□

We now show that, when no external impulse acts, the total momentum of a system is unchanged by a collision. We deal with the most general case, when the motion is not necessarily in a straight line.

Suppose two particles A and B, of mass m_A and m_B, collide. If their velocities before impact are $\boldsymbol{u}_A$ and $\boldsymbol{u}_B$ and after impact are $\boldsymbol{v}_A$ and $\boldsymbol{v}_B$, we seek a relation between these four quantities. The collision is shown schematically in figure 5.10, in which $\boldsymbol{c}_A$ and $\boldsymbol{c}_B$ are the variable contact forces on A and B acting for the same time t.

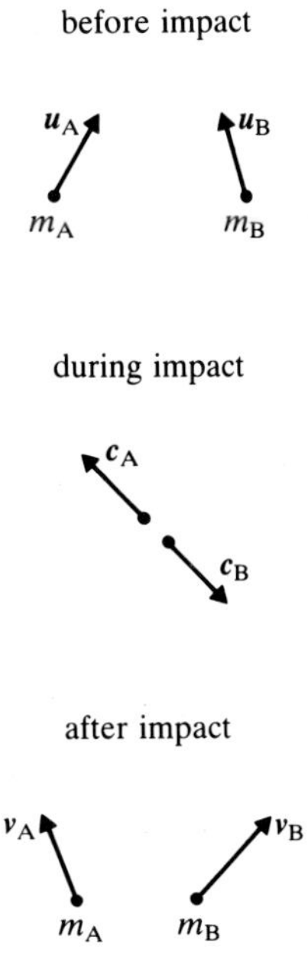

Figure 5.10

Let $\boldsymbol{I}_A$ and $\boldsymbol{I}_B$ be the impulses on A and B. Applying the impulse momentum equation

to A, $$m_A\boldsymbol{v}_A - m_A\boldsymbol{u}_A = \int_0^t \boldsymbol{c}_A \, dt = \boldsymbol{I}_A,$$

to B, $$m_B\boldsymbol{v}_B - m_B\boldsymbol{u}_B = \int_0^t \boldsymbol{c}_B \, dt = \boldsymbol{I}_B.$$

Adding, $$(m_A\boldsymbol{v}_A - m_A\boldsymbol{u}_A) + (m_B\boldsymbol{v}_B - m_B\boldsymbol{u}_B) = \boldsymbol{I}_A + \boldsymbol{I}_B,$$

but N3 gives $\boldsymbol{c}_A = -\boldsymbol{c}_B$, so that $\boldsymbol{I}_A = -\boldsymbol{I}_B$.

Hence $$(m_A\boldsymbol{v}_A - m_A\boldsymbol{u}_A) + (m_B\boldsymbol{v}_B - m_B\boldsymbol{u}_B) = \boldsymbol{0},$$

rearranging $$m_A\boldsymbol{v}_A + m_B\boldsymbol{v}_B = m_A\boldsymbol{u}_A + m_B\boldsymbol{u}_B. \quad (4)$$

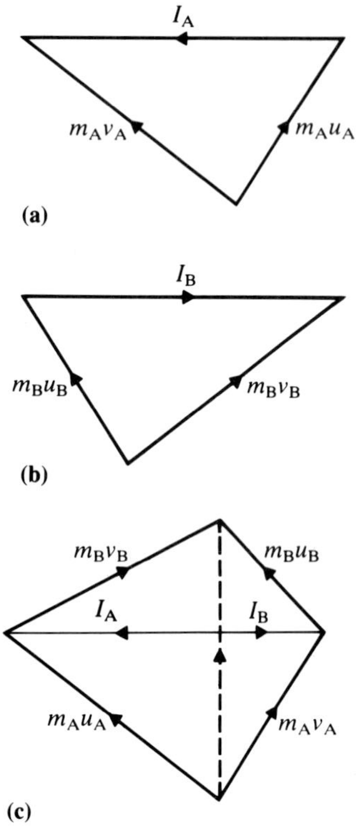

Figure 5.11

The quantity on the LHS of equation (4) is the total momentum of both particles after the collision, and the quantity on the RHS is the total momentum of both particles before the collision.

If we regard the two particles as forming a system, we see that, although both receive an impulse and experience a change in momentum, the total momentum of the system is conserved. This idea can be extended to a system of many particles, and we arrive at a generalised form of equation (4):

$$\sum m_i\boldsymbol{v}_i = \sum m_i\boldsymbol{u}_i,$$

where $\boldsymbol{v}_i$ represents the final velocity and $\boldsymbol{u}_i$ the initial velocity of the mass m_i. This result is known as the **principle of conservation of momentum** and states that:

> When there are no external impulses on a system, the total momentum of the system remains constant.

We can demonstrate the principle for two particles, using vector diagrams. Figure 5.11a and 5.11b illustrate the impulse momentum equation for A and B separately. Figure 5.11c is a superposition of a and b, in which the vector shown with the dotted line represents the total momentum of the system.

The following example illustrates a collision in which an external impulse is present.

EXAMPLE 2

A woman throws a 10 kg turkey down into a loaded supermarket trolley with a speed of 3 m s^{-1} at an angle of 30° to the horizontal. The total mass of the trolley and its contents is 20 kg. The trolley is free to move horizontally and does not tip. The turkey does not rebound on impact. What is the initial combined speed of the trolley and the turkey, and what is the external impulse on the system?

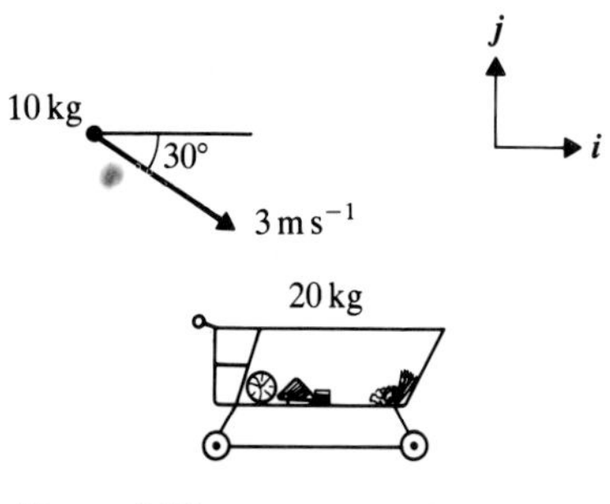

Figure 5.12

Unit vectors $\boldsymbol{i}$ and $\boldsymbol{j}$ are chosen as in figure 5.12. Let V be the combined horizontal speed after impact. Since the trolley is only free to move horizontally, there is an external impulse $\boldsymbol{I}$ which acts vertically.

From the impulse momentum equation

$$10\begin{pmatrix} 3\cos 30^\circ \\ -3\sin 30^\circ \end{pmatrix} + \begin{pmatrix} 0 \\ I \end{pmatrix} = 30\begin{pmatrix} V \\ 0 \end{pmatrix}.$$

Hence $V = \cos 30°$, giving the combined speed as 0.87 m s^{-1}. Also $I = 30 \sin 30°$, so that the external impulse is 15 N s. We note that the horizontal component of the momentum is conserved, since the component of the external impulse in this direction is zero.

In general, when an external impulse $\boldsymbol{I}$ acts on a system, the component of the total momentum of the system in the direction perpendicular to $\boldsymbol{I}$ is conserved.

EXAMPLE 3

After a series of collisions in a game of bowls, a jack of mass 0.2 kg collides with a wood of mass 0.9 kg. The jack has a speed of 4 m s^{-1} and the wood has a speed of 1 m s^{-1}. Their paths converge at an angle of 60° to their line of centres, and the jack is deflected through 90° with its speed reduced to 3 m s^{-1}. Calculate the speed of the wood after the collision, and the angle through which it is deflected.

In this type of question it is essential to draw a sketch showing the situations immediately before and after the collisions, as shown in figure 5.13. We show two methods for solving the problem.

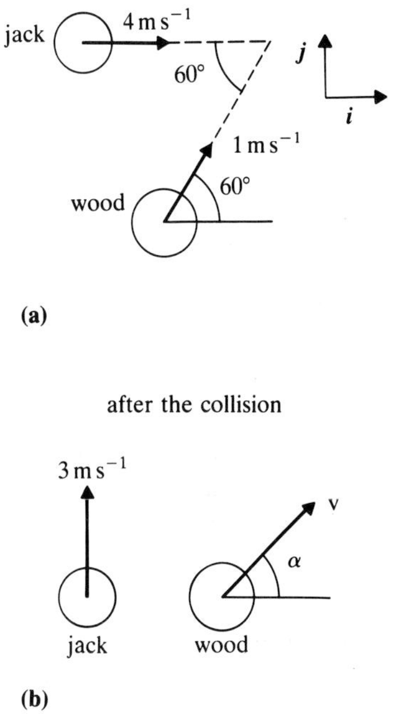

Figure 5.13

a) Solution by calculation

Unit vectors $\boldsymbol{i}$ and $\boldsymbol{j}$ are taken as in the figure.
The total momentum before the collision is

$$0.2\begin{pmatrix}4\\0\end{pmatrix} + 0.9\begin{pmatrix}\cos 60°\\ \sin 60°\end{pmatrix}.$$

The total momentum after the collision is

$$0.2\begin{pmatrix}0\\3\end{pmatrix} + 0.9\begin{pmatrix}v\cos\alpha\\ v\sin\alpha\end{pmatrix}.$$

From the principle of conservation of momentum,

$$0.2\begin{pmatrix}4\\0\end{pmatrix} + 0.9\begin{pmatrix}\cos 60°\\ \sin 60°\end{pmatrix} = 0.2\begin{pmatrix}0\\3\end{pmatrix} + 0.9\begin{pmatrix}v\cos\alpha\\ v\sin\alpha)\end{pmatrix}$$

Equating components we obtain,

$$v\cos\alpha = 1.389,$$
$$v\sin\alpha = 0.199.$$

Hence

$$\tan\alpha = 0.144,$$
$$v^2 = 1.389^2 + 0.199^2.$$

The angle of deflection of the wood is $60 - \alpha = 51.73°$, and the speed is 1.4 m s^{-1}.

b) Solution by drawing

Firstly we draw a rough sketch as in figure 5.14a to establish the total momentum, **OR**, before the collision. The final momentum of the jack, **OQ**, is known, and the final momentum of the wood is given by **QR**. The diagram is then drawn to scale as in figure 5.14b. From figure 5.14b, the angle of deflection is $60° - 8° = 52°$. The final momentum of the wood has magnitude 1.25 N s. The speed of the wood after the collision is 1.4 m s^{-1}.

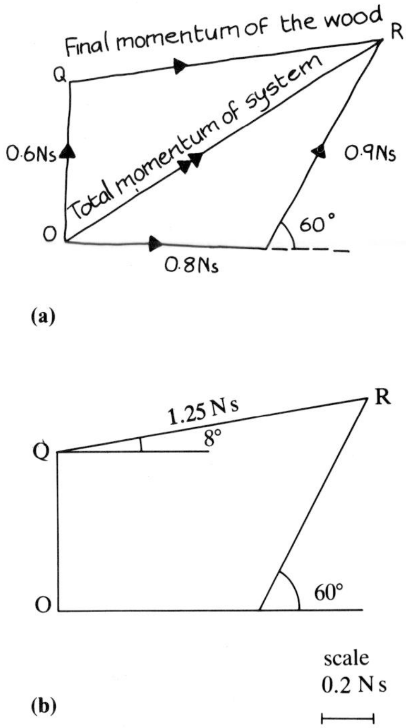

Figure 5.14

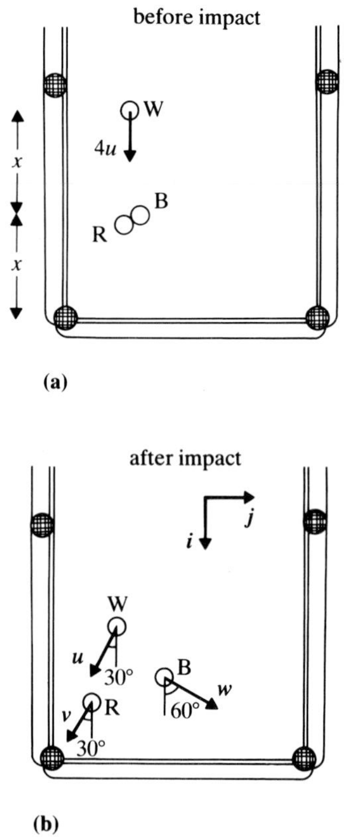

Figure 5.15

EXAMPLE 4

The diagrams in figure 5.15 illustrate a shot performed by a snooker player. There are three balls, white (W), red (R) and blue (B). All the balls have the same mass, m.

Initially the red and blue balls are at rest and the speeds of the white before and after impact are $4u$ and u respectively. Find the order in which the balls drop into the pockets.

Take unit vectors $\boldsymbol{i}$ and $\boldsymbol{j}$ as shown. We apply the principle of conservation of momentum.

$$m\begin{pmatrix}4u\\0\end{pmatrix} = mu\begin{pmatrix}\cos 30^\circ\\-\sin 30^\circ\end{pmatrix} + mv\begin{pmatrix}\cos 30^\circ\\-\sin 30^\circ\end{pmatrix} + mw\begin{pmatrix}\cos 60^\circ\\ \sin 60^\circ\end{pmatrix},$$

where v and w are the speeds after impact of R and B, respectively, which move in the directions shown in figure 5.15b. Equating components,

$$\sqrt{3}(u+v) + w = 8u$$

$$u + v = \sqrt{3}w,$$

Hence $$4w = 8u,$$

$$w = 2u.$$

also $$u + v = 2\sqrt{3}u,$$

$$v = (2\sqrt{3} - 1)u \approx 2.46u.$$

Each ball will drop when it has travelled the same distance in the $\boldsymbol{i}$-direction. Thus the ball to drop first will be the one with the greatest component of velocity in the $\boldsymbol{i}$-direction.

Ball	Component of velocity in the $\boldsymbol{i}$-direction	
B	$w\cos 60^\circ = \sqrt{3}u$	$\approx 1.73u$
R	$v\cos 30^\circ = (3 - \frac{1}{2}\sqrt{3})u$	$\approx 2.13u$
W	$u\cos 30^\circ = \frac{1}{2}\sqrt{3}u$	$\approx 0.866u$

Hence the balls will drop in the order red, blue, white.

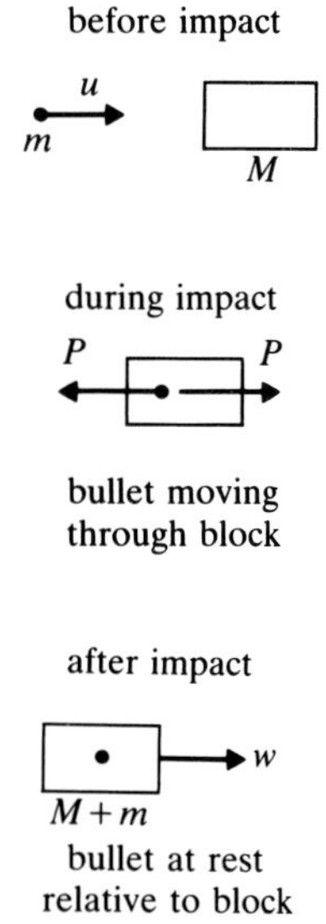

Figure 5.16

EXAMPLE 5

A bullet of mass m is fired horizontally into a block of mass M, which is at rest on a horizontal table. The initial velocity of the bullet is u and the resistance (assumed constant) of the block is P. All units are SI.

a) What is the combined velocity of the block and the bullet?

b) For how long does the bullet move relative to the block?

Figure 5.16 shows the three stages of the motion. Let the final combined velocity be w.

a) By conservation of momentum,

$$mu = (M + m)w,$$

giving
$$w = \frac{mu}{M + m}$$

b) The bullet moves relative to the block for the time the impulse acts, so, using the impulse momentum equation on the block,

$$Pt = Mw,$$

$$t = P\frac{Mmu}{M + m}.$$

□□□□□

The concluding example in this section is not strictly on collisions, but illustrates how the principle of conservation of momentum can be applied to connected particles.

EXAMPLE 6

A breakdown truck of mass 1.5 t is towing a car of mass 1 t, which is initially at rest. If the tow rope becomes taut when the truck is moving at 8 m s^{-1}, find the initial speed of the car. Find also the impulsive tension in the rope. How would the situation change if the car had tried to tow the truck?

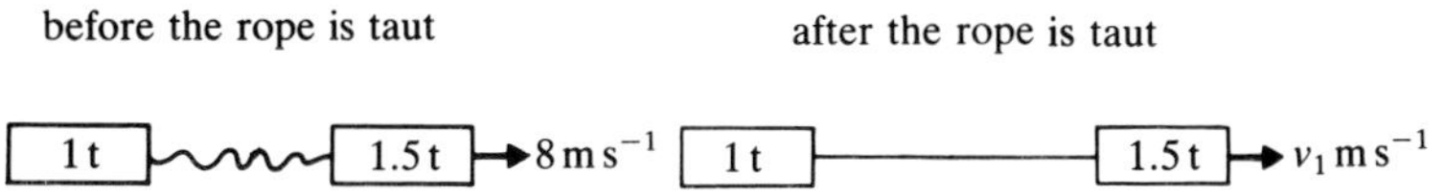

Figure 5.17

Figure 5.17 shows the situation before and after the rope becomes taut. All ropes extend on becoming taut, but we will assume that this rope does not, and so the impulsive tension is used solely to produce the change in momentum on suddenly becoming taut. Since this is an internal impulse, the total momentum of the system is conserved:

$$1000 \times 0 + 1500 \times 8 = (1000 + 1500)v_1,$$

giving v_1, the speed of the car and truck, as 4.8 m s^{-1}. To calculate I, we consider the change in momentum of the car.

$$I = 100 \times 4.8 - 0,$$

giving I as 4800 N s.

If the roles were reversed, we can repeat the calculation. Let the combined speed be v_2, so that by conservation of momentum,

$$1500 \times 0 + 1000 \times 8 = (1000 + 1500)v_2,$$

giving v_2 as 3.2 m s^{-1}. If I is the impulsive tension,

$$I = 1500v_2,$$

giving I as 4800 N s. Although in the second case the combined speed is less, the impulsive tension is the same, whichever vehicle is towing.

EXERCISE 5C

1. A truck of mass 3 t moving at a speed of 6 m s^{-1} collides with a truck of mass 2 t moving at 2 m s^{-1} in the same direction. If the speed of the 3 t truck is reduced to 5 m s^{-1} by the impact, calculate:

   a) the speed of the 2 t truck after the collision,

   b) the impulse on the second truck.

2. A particle of mass 2 kg moving with a velocity $(3\boldsymbol{i} + 5\boldsymbol{j})$ m s^{-1} coalesces with a particle of mass 3 kg moving with a velocity $(\boldsymbol{i} - 2\boldsymbol{j})$ m s^{-1}. Calculate the resulting velocity of the combined mass and the magnitude of the impulse on each mass at the collision.

3. Two satellites of masses 1000 kg and 500 kg are moving with speeds of 10 m s^{-1} and 15 m s^{-1} at 90° to each other. They collide, and after impact move as one body. Calculate:

   a) the speed of the combined body.

   b) the angle through which the 1000 kg satellite is deflected.

4. A 50 kg gazelle leaps with a speed of 20 m s^{-1} at an angle of 50° to the horizontal. At the same instant an 80 kg leopard jumps from directly behind on to the gazelle's back with a speed of 18 m s^{-1} at an angle of 60° to the horizontal, as shown in figure 5.18. Calculate their common speed after impact.

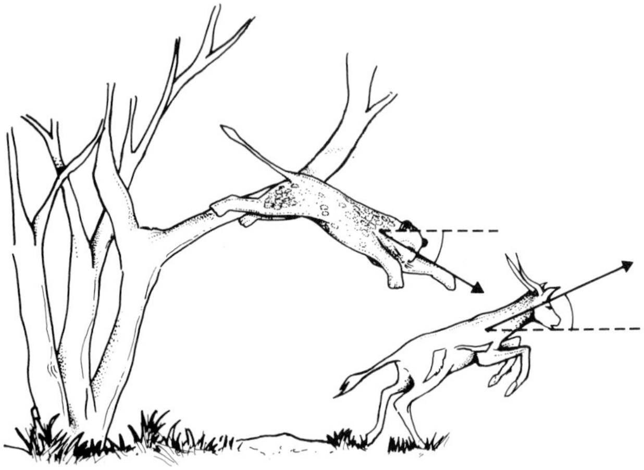

Figure 5.18

5. A proton of mass 1.67×10^{-27} kg moving with a speed of 10^7 m s^{-1} collides with a stationary helium nucleus. The proton rebounds with a speed of 6×10^6 m s^{-1} and the helium nucleus moves forward with a speed of 4×10^6 m s^{-1}. Calculate the mass of the helium nucleus.

6. A seagull of mass 0.9 kg flying horizontally at 5 m s^{-1} is hit from the front by a cricket ball moving towards it at a speed of 10 m s^{-1} at an angle of 30° to the horizontal. After impact, suppose the seagull is deflected through 30° and the ball falls vertically. The

mass of the cricket ball is 150 g. Calculate the speeds of the ball and the bird after impact.

7. A juggler is throwing apples and oranges. After a misthrow an orange of mass 200 g collides with an apple of mass 50 g. The orange has a speed of 3 m s^{-1} and the apple a speed of 1 m s^{-1}. They approach at an angle of 60°, and after the collision the apple is deflected through 90° with its speed doubled. Find the speed of the orange immediately after impact and the angle through which it is deflected.

8. After a ski jump a skier is falling vertically at 5 m s^{-1} when he hits the ground, which is smooth sheet ice and is inclined at an angle of 20° to the horizontal.

   a) What is the speed of the man immediately after landing? (He does not rebound.)

   b) What is the impulse on the man if his mass is 70 kg?

   c) Why do skiers bend their legs when landing in this way?

9. In a game of conkers, a conker of mass $2m$ is at rest on the end of a vertical string. It is struck from above by a conker of mass m moving with speed u at an angle of 30° to the horizontal. The string is inextensible and the lighter conker rebounds at an angle of 30° below the horizontal with speed $\frac{1}{4}u$ as shown in figure 5.19. Find in terms of m and u:

   a) the speed of the heavier conker immediately after impact,

   b) the impulsive tension in the string.

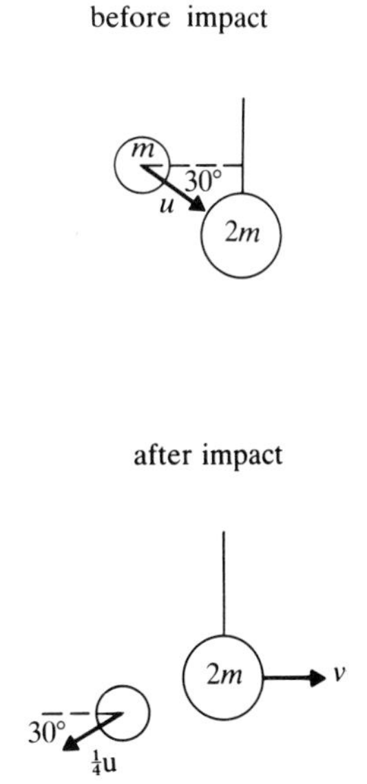

Figure 5.19

10. A trapeze artist of mass 40 kg jumps from one trapeze to another. At the instant she reaches for the second trapeze her speed is 2 m s^{-1} vertically downwards and the second trapeze is at rest with its supports inclined towards her at 30° to the vertical. If she moves on the arc of a circle of radius 4 m immediately after catching hold, calculate:

    a) the impulse on the woman,

    b) the initial speed of the second trapeze if it was instantaneously at rest when the woman caught it.

    How would the answers in (a) and (b) differ if the length of the second trapeze were shortened?

11. A bullet of mass 5 g travelling horizontally at 300 m s^{-1} strikes a block of mass 15 kg which is free to slide without resistance along a horizontal plane. The bullet is moving through the block for 0.01 s. Calculate:

    a) the combined speed of the bullet and the block,

    b) the resistance of the block, assumed uniform.

12. A bullet of mass m is fired at right angles to one face of a cubic block of side d and mass $6m$. The resistance of the block on the bullet is constant and the block is free to move on a smooth horizontal plane. The bullet emerges from the block with a

speed $\frac{3}{4}u$, where u is the speed on impact. Neglecting any rotation of the block, calculate:

a) the final velocity of the block,

b) how long the bullet was in the block,

c) how far the block moved in this time.

13. A bullet of mass m is fired horizontally into a stationary block of mass M. The block provides a constant resistance to the motion of the bullet through it. Show that if the bullet takes T s to come to rest relative to the block when the block is free to move on a smooth horizontal table, it will take $(1 + m/M)T$ s, if the block is held fixed.

5.5 Explosions

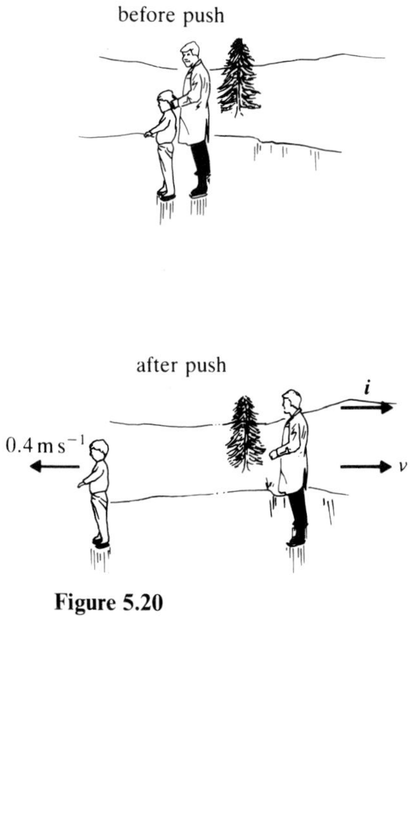

Figure 5.20

Another situation where momentum is conserved occurs when there is an 'explosion' within a system, which causes parts of it to separate. In chemical explosions, there is an internal impulse which is provided by exploding gases. In mathematics, we can consider explosions when any two parts of a system separate. In both cases, provided there is no external impulse, the total momentum of the system is conserved.

EXAMPLE 1

A man of mass 80 kg and his son of mass 50 kg are stuck on very slippery sheet ice. The man can push his son to the edge to go to get help. If the boy moves off at $0.4\ \text{m s}^{-1}$, what is the speed of the man?

Figure 5.20 shows the situation before and after the boy is pushed. The push that the man exerts on the boy is an internal impulse for the system 'man + boy'. Thus, the total momentum of the system is conserved.

Taking the positive coordinate direction from left to right in the figure,

$$0 = 50 \times -0.4 + 80v,$$

so v, the speed of the man, is $0.25\ \text{m s}^{-1}$.

EXAMPLE 2

In an unsuccessful satellite launch the carrier rocket moving vertically upwards at $3000\ \text{m s}^{-1}$ exploded into two parts. The heavier part continued upwards at $40°$ to the vertical with speed $2100\ \text{m s}^{-1}$. If the smaller part is one half the mass of the larger part, find its speed and direction immediately after the explosion.

Figure 5.21 shows the situation before and after the explosion. Unit vectors $\boldsymbol{i}$ and $\boldsymbol{j}$ are taken horizontally and vertically upwards, respectively. Let the mass of the rocket be m and the speed and direction of the smaller fragment be v and α, as shown.

By the principle of conservation of momentum,

$$m\begin{pmatrix}0\\3000\end{pmatrix}=\tfrac{2}{3}m\times 2100\begin{pmatrix}-\sin 40^\circ\\ \cos 40^\circ\end{pmatrix}+\tfrac{1}{3}mv\begin{pmatrix}\sin\alpha\\ \cos\alpha\end{pmatrix}.$$

Equating components,

$$0=-1400\sin 40^\circ+\tfrac{1}{3}v\sin\alpha,$$
$$3000=1400\cos 40^\circ+\tfrac{1}{3}v\cos\alpha,$$

giving
$$\tfrac{1}{3}v\sin\alpha=1400\sin 40^\circ,$$
$$\tfrac{1}{3}v\cos\alpha=-1400\cos 40^\circ+3000.$$

Hence
$$\tan\alpha=\frac{1400\sin 40^\circ}{(-1400\cos 40^\circ+3000)}.$$

Thus
$$\alpha=25^\circ \quad\text{and}\quad v=6388.$$

The speed of the smaller part is 6388 m s^{-1} at an angle of 25° with the vertical.

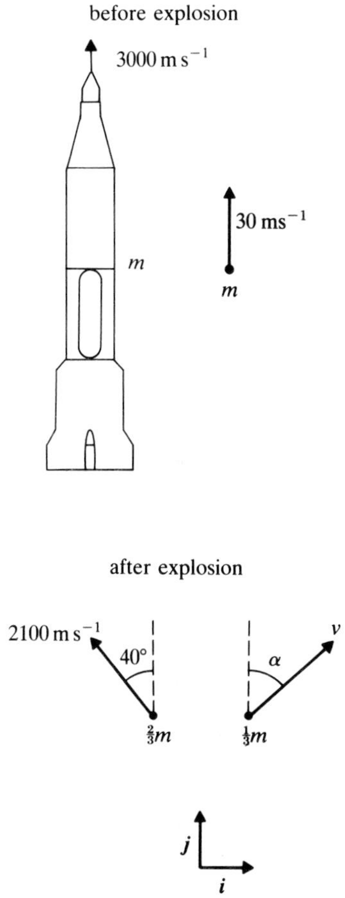

Figure 5.21

EXAMPLE 3

A shell of mass m is fired from a gun of mass M, which can recoil freely on horizontal rails. The angle of elevation of the barrel of the gun is α. Calculate:

a) the initial direction of the shell

b) the impulsive reaction of the ground on the gun in terms of the muzzle velocity of the shell, $\boldsymbol{u}$. (The muzzle velocity of the shell is the velocity of the shell relative to the gun.)

In this example the total momentum is not conserved for the system 'shell + gun', since there is an external impulse provided by the normal contact force from the ground.

Let $\boldsymbol{v}$ be the velocity of the shell relative to the ground, having an inclination of angle θ with the ground, as shown in figure 5.22. Let $\boldsymbol{w}$ be the recoil velocity of the gun and let the impulsive reaction from the ground have magnitude I. Figure 5.23 is a vector diagram showing the velocities from which we obtain the equation:

$$v\begin{pmatrix}\cos\theta\\ \sin\theta\end{pmatrix}=u\begin{pmatrix}\cos\alpha\\ \sin\alpha\end{pmatrix}+\begin{pmatrix}-w\\0\end{pmatrix},$$

Hence
$$\tan\theta=\frac{u\sin\alpha}{u\cos\alpha-w}.$$

Figure 5.22

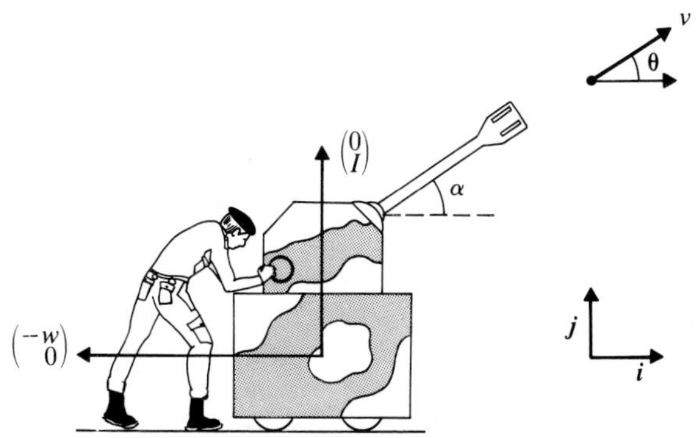

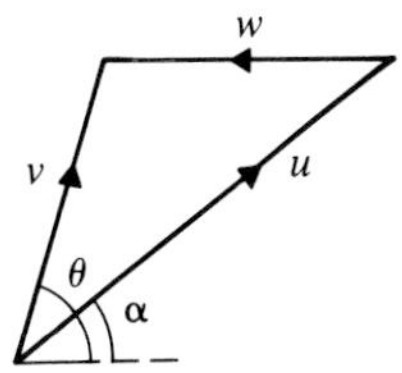

Figure 5.23

The impulse momentum equation gives

$$M\begin{pmatrix} -w \\ 0 \end{pmatrix} + m\begin{pmatrix} u\cos\alpha - w \\ u\sin\alpha \end{pmatrix} = \begin{pmatrix} 0 \\ I \end{pmatrix}.$$

Equating components,

$$-Mw + m(u\cos\alpha - w) = 0,$$

$$mu\sin\alpha = I$$

Hence $\quad u = \dfrac{(M+m)w}{m\cos\alpha} \quad$ and $\quad \tan\theta = \left(1 + \dfrac{m}{M}\right)\tan\alpha$

Hence, the initial direction of the shell is found and the magnitude of the impulsive reaction of the ground is $mu\sin\alpha$.

□□□□□

Although we have seen that momentum is conserved in explosions where there is no external impulse, it is clear that something must have been added to the system. Obviously some form of chemical energy is used up and part of this is converted to mechanical energy. This will be discussed in chapter 6.

EXERCISE 5D

1. A shell of mass $3m$ is moving horizontally with speed u. It splits into fragments of masses $2m$ and m, both still moving along the original horizontal line, with relative velocity $6u$, the smaller fragment moving the faster. Calculate the speed of each fragment.

2. A rocket explodes into three parts. Two parts separate at right angles, a 1 kg piece at 12 m s^{-1} and a 2 kg piece at 8 m s^{-1}. The third piece flies off at 40 m s^{-1}. Calculate the mass of the third piece and the direction in which it flies. Must the three pieces fly off in the same plane?

3. A machine gun is mounted on an armoured car and fires 10 rounds of ammunition each second. Each bullet has a mass of 100 g and a speed of 600 m s^{-1}. Calculate the total impulse on the car during each 10 s burst of fire.

4. If the car in question 3 has a mass of 1.5 t and is free to move horizontally, what is its speed after a 10 s burst of fire straight ahead if it is initially at rest?

5. A pair of ice dancers are moving horizontally at 3 m s^{-1}. The man, whose mass is 70 kg, throws the woman, whose mass is 50 kg, in the air at an angle of 60° to the horizontal and a speed of 8 m s^{-1} through the air. What is the speed of the man after this operation? What is the impulse of the ice on the man?

6. A shell of mass 5 kg is fired from a gun of mass 500 kg. The muzzle speed of the shell is 300 m s^{-1} and the gun is free to recoil horizontally. The angle of elevation of the gun is 60°. Calculate:

   a) the recoil speed of the gun,

   b) the initial angle of elevation of the path of the shell,

   c) the initial speed of the shell.

7. A man of mass 80 kg is sitting in the middle of a frozen lake. He has a gun from which he can fire bullets of mass 25 g at a speed of $1\ \text{km s}^{-1}$. If he fires the gun horizontally and there is no friction between him and the ice, how fast does he move as a result of recoil? He can reload the gun and fire again in 10 s. By repeatedly firing the gun, how soon can he reach the bank, which is 25 m away?

8. The gun of question 6 is at rest on a plane inclined at 20° and is fired horizontally. Calculate:
   a) the recoil speed of the gun up the plane,
   b) the initial angle of elevation of the path of the shell.
   (Consider motion parallel and perpendicular to the inclined plane.)

Newton's law of impact **5.6**

Anyone who has played ball games will have noticed that some balls bounce more than others and that the bounce of a given ball is affected by the surface it is bouncing against. A cricket ball from a fast bowler will not bounce as high on a soggy wicket as it will on a hard one. A squash ball is specially designed so that its bounce is very low when it is cold, but increases rapidly as it warms up during play until it achieves an optimum level.

Consider a 'Newton's cradle', as shown in figure 5.24. Suppose the ball on the left strikes its neighbour with speed v. What happens next?

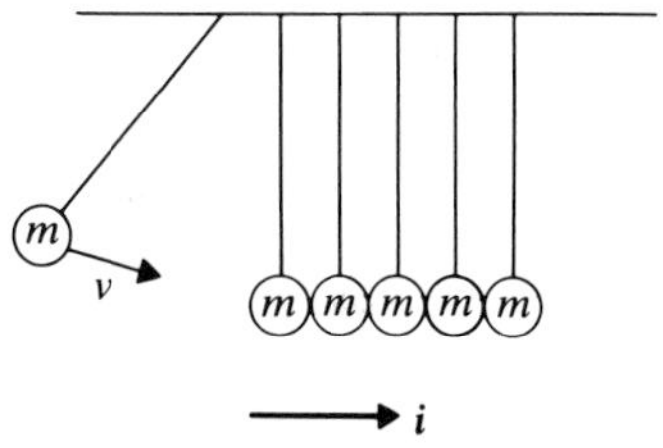

Figure 5.24

We will look at this problem in terms of momentum. The momentum before impact is $mv\boldsymbol{i}$, where the unit vector $\boldsymbol{i}$ is shown in the figure. By the principle of conservation of momentum, the momentum after impact is $mv\boldsymbol{i}$, since there is no external impulse in the horizontal direction. All the diagrams in figure 5.25 appear to be representations of what might happen after impact. In each case the total momentum is $mv\boldsymbol{i}$.

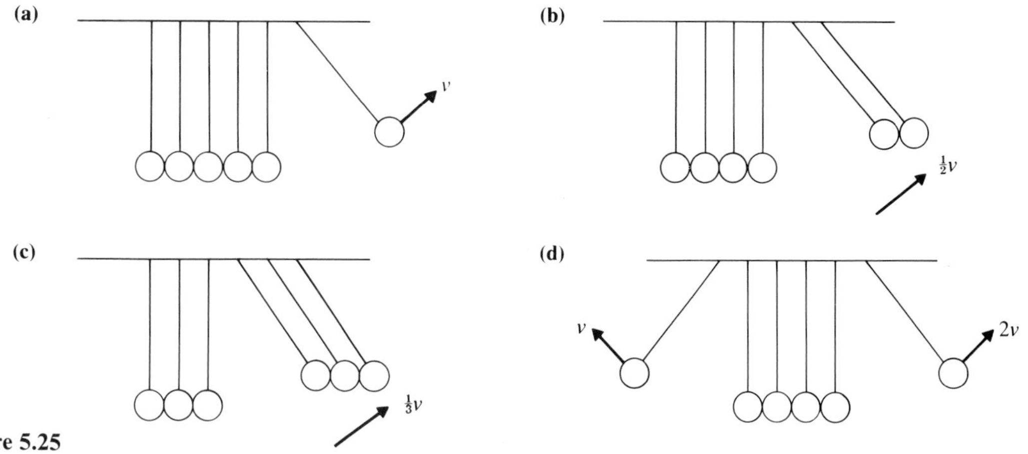

Figure 5.25

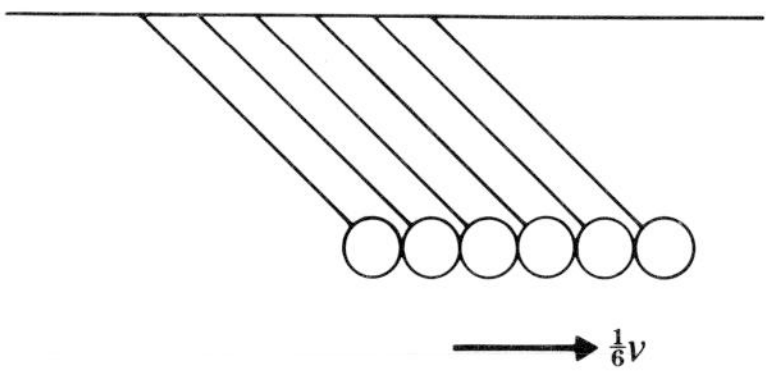

Figure 5.26

The principle of conservation of momentum is not sufficient to determine the motion uniquely. We might expect that the balls will behave as in figure 5.25a, but in order to deduce this we need to know something about the nature of the balls. Suppose for instance that the balls in the cradle were replaced by balls of sticky putty of the same mass. We would quickly agree that the final pattern is not given in figure 5.25, but would be as in figure 5.26.

Newton's experimental law of impact states that:

> When two bodies collide, their relative velocity of separation is proportional to their relative velocity of approach.

This description is not the most useful form of the law, and we will consider its use in two cases of direct and indirect (oblique) impact.

Direct impact

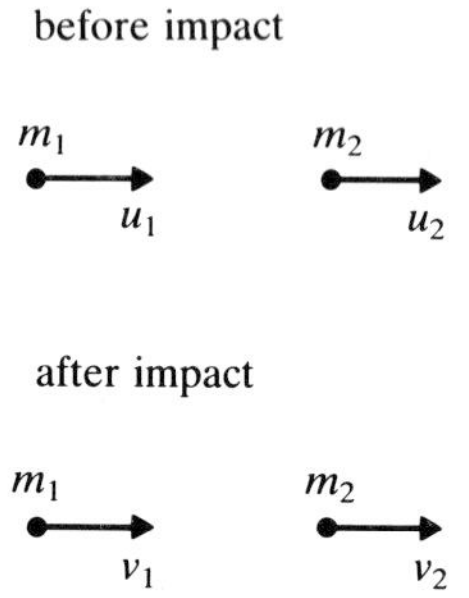

Figure 5.27

Suppose two particles of masses m_1 and m_2 are moving in a straight line with speeds u_1 and u_2 before impact and speeds v_1 and v_2 after impact, in the directions shown in figure 5.27. Newton's law of impact gives

$$v_2 - v_1 = e(u_1 - u_2),$$

where $u_1 - u_2$ is the relative speed with which m_1 approaches m_2 and $v_2 - v_1$ is the relative speed with which m_2 draws away from m_1. There is often confusion over the signs in the equation, and it is convenient to restate it in the form

$$v_2 - v_1 = -e(u_2 - u_1). \qquad \textbf{(5)}$$

Although a negative sign has been introduced, the equation is now symmetrical.

We need another equation to determine v_1 and v_2 in terms of u_1 and u_2, and this is the principle of conservation of momentum:

$$m_1 u_1 + m_2 u_2 = m_1 v_1 + m_2 v_2. \qquad \textbf{(6)}$$

Equations (5) and (6) will enable us to determine the subsequent motion. e is called the **coefficient of restitution** and is a constant for two given particles. The value of e lies between 0 (for two spheres of putty) and 1 (for two 'supaballs'). A collision in which $e = 1$ is called **perfectly elastic**, and when $e = 0$, the collision is **perfectly inelastic**. Knowledge of the coefficient of restitution enables us to determine velocities before and after impact when momentum is not conserved.

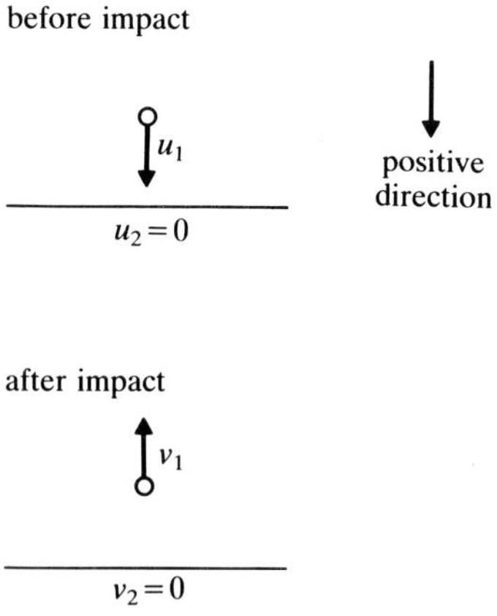

Figure 5.28

For example, if a ball drops on to hard ground, there is a change in momentum of the ball due to the unknown impulsive force of the ground, and hence we cannot use the momentum equation. Newton's law of impact now enables us to calculate the speed with which the ball rebounds in terms of its speed immediately before impact. Applying Newton's law of impact, as in figure 5.28

$$(0 - (-v_1)) = -e(0 - u_1),$$

$$v_1 = eu_1, \qquad (7)$$

where u_1 and v_1 are the speeds of the ball immediately before and after impact, respectively.

EXAMPLE 1

Calculate e for the squash ball and the wall in example 2 of section 5.2.

In this case, the speed before impact $u_1 = 40$ and after impact $v_1 = 30$. Using equation (7) above,

$$30 = 40e$$
$$e = 0.75.$$

EXAMPLE 2

A ball drops from a height h on to the ground. The coefficient of restitution between the ball and the ground is e. Show that the total distance travelled by the ball after many rebounds is given by

$$\frac{1 + e^2}{1 - e^2}h.$$

At the first impact the speed of the ball, using $v^2 = u^2 + 2as$, with $v = u_1$ and $u = 0$, is

$$u_1^2 = 2gh,$$
$$u_1 = \sqrt{2gh}.$$

By Newton's law of impact,

$$v_1 = eu_1 = e\sqrt{2gh},$$

where v_1 is the speed after impact. If h_1 is the height to which the ball rises after the first impact, $v^2 = u^2 + 2as$, with $v = 0$ and $a = -g$, gives

$$2gh_1 = v_1^2,$$

so that
$$h_1 = e^2 h.$$

Similarly, h_2, the height after the second bounce, is given by

$$h_2 = e^2 h_1 = e^4 h.$$

Proceeding in this way, we see that the height after the nth bounce is

$$h_n = e^{2n}h.$$

Thus, the total distance travelled by the ball is

$$\begin{aligned} &h + 2h_1 + 2h_2 + 2h_3 + \cdots + 2h_n + \cdots \\ &= h(1 + 2e^2 + 2e^4 + 2e^6 + \cdots + 2e^{2n} + \cdots) \\ &= h + 2he^2(1 + e^2 + e^4 + e^6 + \cdots), \\ &= h + \frac{2he^2}{1 - e^2} \qquad \text{by summing the series} \\ &= h\frac{1 + e^2}{1 - e^2}, \qquad \text{as required.} \end{aligned}$$

EXAMPLE 3

Three billiard balls A, B and C of mass m are in a line a short distance apart on a table. A is hit towards B with a speed u. The coefficient of restitution for all collisions is e. Prove that there will be three collisions, and there will not be a fourth provided $e > 3 - \sqrt{8}$.

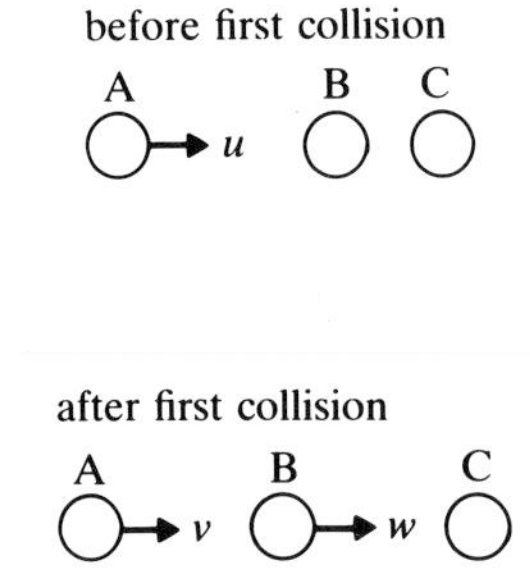

Figure 5.29

We examine each collision separately. Figure 5.29 shows the speeds before and after the first collision. By the conservation of total momentum,

$$mu = mv + mw,$$

$$u = v + w,$$

where v is the speed of A after the impact and w is the speed of B. From Newton's law of impact,

$$eu = w - v.$$

Hence $w = \frac{1}{2}u(1+e)$ and $v = \frac{1}{2}u(1-e)$. Clearly $w > v$, so B will hit C next.

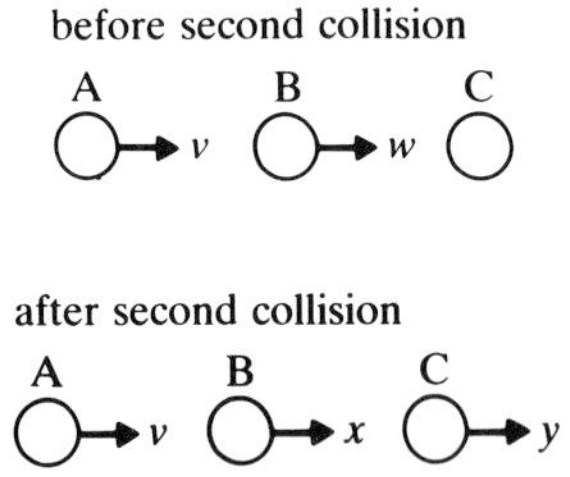

Figure 5.30

Figure 5.30 shows the speeds before and after the second collision between B and C. By the conservation of total momentum,

$$w = x + y,$$

where x and y are the speeds of B and C after the impact. From Newton's law of impact,

$$ew = y - x.$$

Hence $y = \frac{1}{2}w(1+e)$ and $x = \frac{1}{2}w(1-e)$. Now $y > x$ and the third collision will be between A and B provided $v > x$. But

$$\begin{aligned} v - x &= \tfrac{1}{2}u(1-e) - \tfrac{1}{2}w(1-e) \\ &= \tfrac{1}{2}u(1-e)\left[1 - \tfrac{1}{2}(1+e)\right] \\ &= \tfrac{1}{4}u(1-e)^2 > 0. \end{aligned}$$

Hence A does hit B again.

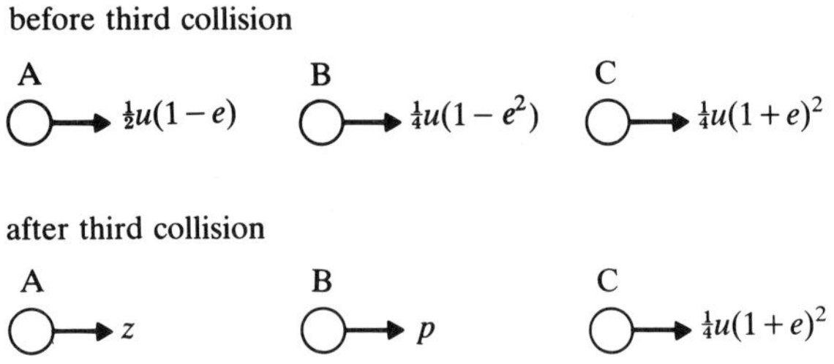

Figure 5.31

Figure 5.31 shows the speeds before and after the third collision. By the conservation of total momentum,

$$v + x = z + p.$$

From Newton's impact law,

$$e(v - x) = p - z > 0.$$

Hence there will be no further collisions unless B hits C. B will not hit C provided $p < y$. Now

$$p = \tfrac{1}{2}v(1+e) + \tfrac{1}{2}x(1-e).$$

Thus, B will not hit C if

$$\tfrac{1}{4}u(1+e)(1-e) + \tfrac{1}{8}u(1-e)^2(1+e) < \tfrac{1}{4}u(1+e)^2,$$

giving

$$2(1-e) + (1-e)^2 < 2(1+e),$$

$$e^2 - 6e + 1 < 0,$$

$$(e - 3 - \sqrt{8})(e - 3 + \sqrt{8}) < 0,$$

$$3 - \sqrt{8} < e < 3 + \sqrt{8}.$$

But $e < 1$, and there will therefore be only three collisions, provided $e > 3 - \sqrt{8}$.

EXERCISE 5E

1. A particle of mass 3 kg is moving at 2 m s^{-1} and strikes a particle of mass 2 kg moving at 1 m s^{-1} in the opposite direction. If the coefficient of restitution is $\frac{1}{2}$, calculate the velocities of the particles after the collision.

2. A particle of mass m moving with speed $2u$ hits a particle of mass $2m$ moving with speed u in the same direction. Prove that the second particle must increase its speed, whatever the value of e.

3. A particle of mass m hits a particle of mass $3m$ which is at rest. After the collision the speeds of the particles are in the ratio 1 : 3. Calculate the coefficient of restitution for the collision.

4. What is the total time taken by the ball in example 2 to come to rest?

5. Two marbles A and B lie in a horizontal circular groove. The groove is smooth and the marbles are initially on opposite ends of a diameter. A is projected along the groove and hits B after time t. Show that the next collision will occur after time $2t/e$, where e is the coefficient of restitution for the collision.

6. Three spheres A, B, C of masses m, $2m$, $4m$ lie in a straight line on a smooth horizontal plane with B between A and C. The coefficient of restitution e is the same for all collisions. A is projected towards B with speed u and C moves with speed $\frac{1}{4}u$ after being struck by B. Prove that A and B are at rest after each collision and find the value of e.

7. A particle A of mass m and speed u strikes a particle B of mass $2m$ which is at rest. The coefficient of restitution for the collision is e. Particle B then strikes a wall at right angles, the coefficient of restitution for this collision being e'. Prove that particle B will subsequently catch up particle A provided:

$$e' > \frac{2e - 1}{e + 1}.$$

8. Two coins of masses $9m$ are at rest on a smooth horizontal table and a coin of mass m is moving along the line of centres between them. If all collisions are perfectly elastic, calculate how many collisions there will be.

9. Three discs A, B, C of masses m, $2m$ and $3m$ lie in a straight line on a smooth horizontal table. The coefficient of restitution for all collisions is $\frac{1}{3}$. If A is projected towards B calculate how many collisions will occur.

10. Two equal spheres of mass m, lying on a smooth horizontal table, are joined by a string of length d. The string is initially taut and A is projected towards B with a speed u. The coefficient of restitution for the collision is e.

    a) Calculate the time before the string becomes taut again.

    b) What is the final speed of both masses?

    c) What is the impulsive tension in the string? (Assume that the string is inextensible.)

5.7 Oblique impact

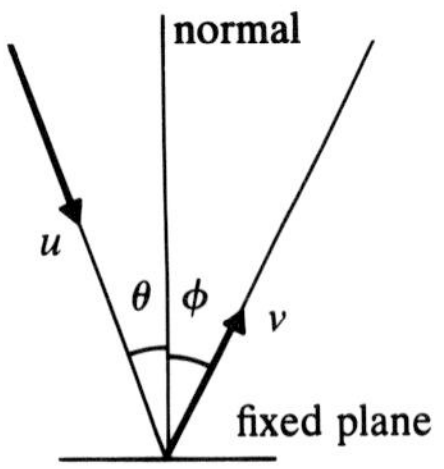

Figure 5.32

When smooth bodies collide the impulsive contact force between them acts along the common normal at the point of contact. In such cases we apply Newton's law of impact to the components of the velocities along the common normal. We consider two situations:

a) when a body strikes a fixed surface at an angle, and

b) when two bodies collide obliquely.

a) Consider a particle which strikes a plane at an angle θ to the normal with speed u and leaves with speed v at an angle ϕ to the normal, as in figure 5.32. Momentum is conserved parallel to the plane so

$$v \sin \phi = u \sin \theta.$$

Newton's law of impact normal to the plane gives

$$v \cos \phi = eu \cos \theta.$$

These two equations will determine the components of v. Also, by dividing, we obtain

$$\tan \theta = e \tan \phi.$$

For the ball and the wall in example 3 of section 5.1, in which the ball hits the wall at 60°, we have $\theta = 30°$ and $\phi = 60°$ (see figure 5.4). Hence $e = \tan 30°/\tan 60° = \frac{1}{3}$.

b) When two smooth discs or spheres collide, as in figure 5.33, we proceed as follows:

Newton's law of impact gives

$$(\boldsymbol{v}_2 - \boldsymbol{v}_1).\boldsymbol{n} = -e(\boldsymbol{u}_2 - \boldsymbol{u}_1).\boldsymbol{n}$$

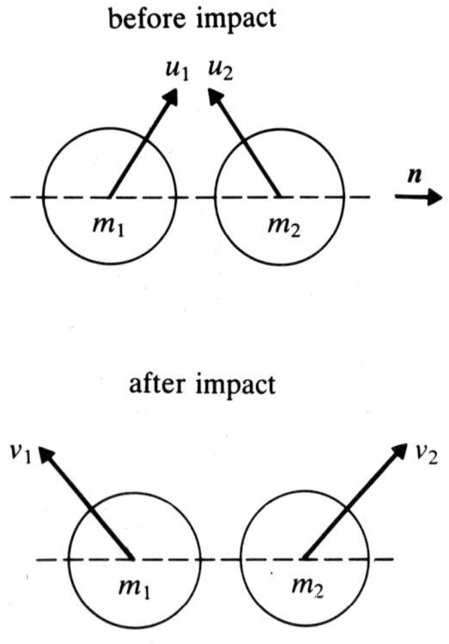

Figure 5.33

where $\boldsymbol{n}$ is a unit normal vector to both spheres at impact. To describe the motion we use the fact that the total momentum is conserved perpendicular to $\boldsymbol{n}$. The following examples will illustrate the method.

EXAMPLE 1

A golf ball is struck with speed V at an angle α with the horizontal ground (as in the photograph). Neglecting air resistance, friction etc., find how far it will travel before it stops bouncing. The coefficient of restitution between the ball and the ground is e.

For the first bounce, the range is

$$\frac{V^2 \sin 2\alpha}{g} \quad \text{(see section 2.4).}$$

It strikes the fairway at an angle α with speed V. Suppose it rebounds with a speed V_1 at an angle θ_1 to the horizontal. Conservation of momentum along the fairway gives the speed V_1 after the first impact.

$$V \cos \alpha = V_1 \cos \theta_1 .$$

Newton's law of impact along the normal to the fairway gives

$$eV \sin \alpha = V_1 \sin \theta_1 .$$

Thus, for the second bounce, the range is

$$\frac{V_1^2 \sin 2\theta_1}{g} = \frac{2V_1 \sin \theta_1 \, V_1 \cos \theta_1}{g} = \frac{2eV \cos \alpha \, V \sin \alpha}{g} = eV^2 \frac{\sin 2\alpha}{g}.$$

Continuing in this way, the range for the third bounce is $e^2 V^2 \sin(2\alpha)/g$ etc. So that the total range is

$$\frac{V^2 \sin 2\alpha}{g}(1 + e + e^2 + e^3 + \cdots) = \frac{V^2 \sin 2\alpha}{g(1-e)}.$$

The above working assumes that the golf ball has bounced an infinite number of times, which it clearly will not do in practice. Provided there is no friction the ball will now slide indefinitely, since the horizontal component of the momentum of the ball is theoretically unchanged.

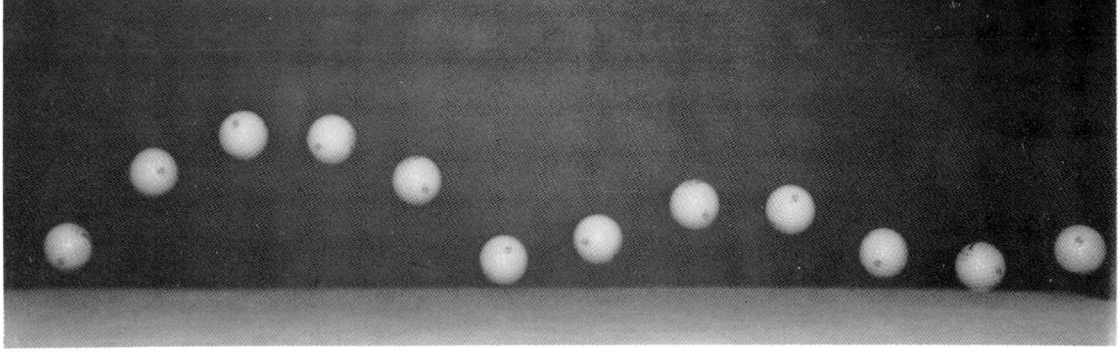

Part of the path of a golf ball as it bounces on a hard surface. Note the reducing height of successive bounces.

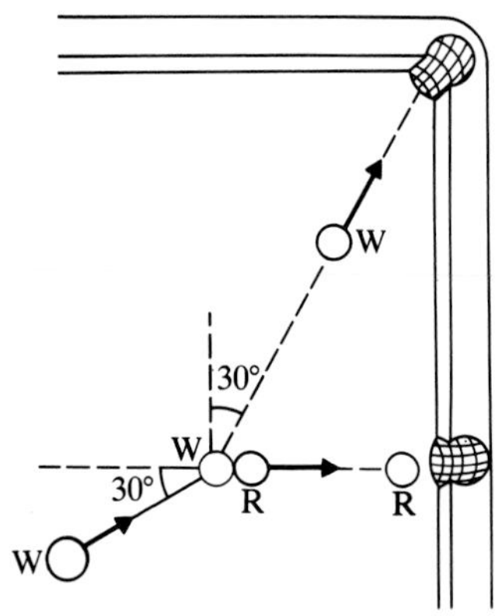

Figure 5.34

EXAMPLE 2

Figure 5.34 shows a shot attempted by a billiards player. He aims to pot the white ball (W) and the red ball (R), as indicated. The balls have identical masses. Determine the coefficient of restitution required for this shot to be possible. Ignore spin etc., and suppose that the balls are smooth.

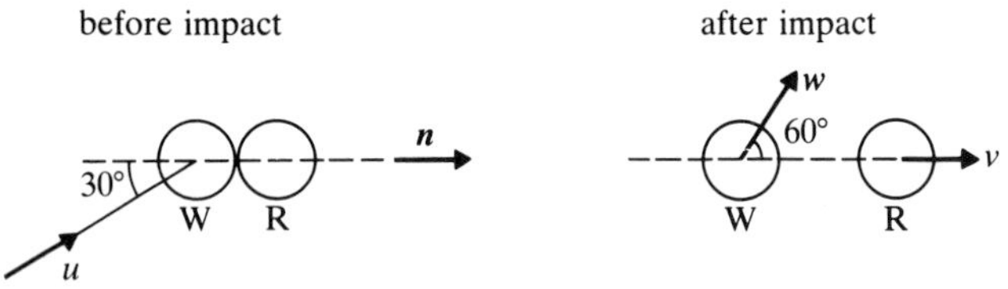

Figure 5.35

Suppose that the situations before and after the impact are as shown in figure 5.35. The momentum of the white ball is unchanged perpendicular to $\boldsymbol{n}$, the unit vector along the line of centres, so that

$$mu \sin 30^\circ = mw \sin 60^\circ,$$

where u is the speed of the white ball before impact, and w and v are the speeds of the white and red balls after impact. Hence

$$u = w\sqrt{3}.$$

The total momentum is conserved along $\boldsymbol{n}$, so

$$mu \cos 30^\circ = mw \cos 60^\circ + mv,$$

$$u\sqrt{3} = w + 2v,$$

Hence $$w = v = u/\sqrt{3}.$$

From Newton's law of impact along the line of centres,

$$v - w \cos 60^\circ = -e(0 - u \cos 30^\circ).$$

Substituting for v and w,

$$u/2\sqrt{3} = eu\tfrac{1}{2}\sqrt{3},$$

giving the coefficient of restitution as $\frac{1}{3}$.

EXAMPLE 3*

A squash player who is knocking up wants to hit the ball so that it will return to him after rebounding from the wall, as shown in figure 5.36. Show that, if e is the coefficient of restitution at the impact between the ball and a smooth wall, then s, the distance from the wall is given by

$$s = \frac{u^2 e \sin 2\alpha}{g(1+e)},$$

where u is the initial speed of the ball and α is the angle it makes with the horizontal.

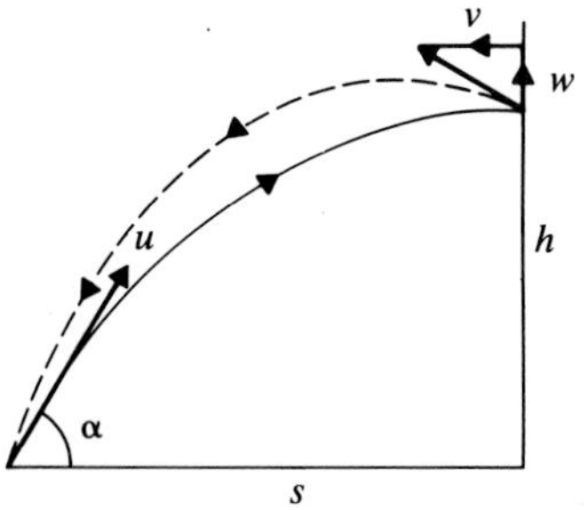

Figure 5.36

We illustrate two possible methods of solution.

a) Suppose that the ball strikes the wall at height h and rebounds with horizontal and vertical components v and w of its velocity, as in figure 5.36. Suppose that the time to reach the wall is t_1, so

$$s = t_1 u \cos\alpha, \qquad h - t_1 u \sin\alpha - \tfrac{1}{2}gt_1^2.$$

Eliminating t_1,

$$h = s \tan\alpha - \tfrac{1}{2}g\frac{s^2}{u^2 \cos^2\alpha},$$

which is the standard expression for the height of a projectile (as in section 2.4). If t_2 is the time taken on the return journey, we have from Newton's law of impact,

$$v = eu \cos\alpha$$

and by the conservation of momentum parallel to the wall

$$\begin{aligned} w &= u \sin\alpha - gt_1 \\ &= u \sin\alpha - \frac{gs}{u \cos\alpha}, \end{aligned}$$

Then $$s = t_2 v = t_2 eu \cos\alpha$$

Vertically, $$-h = wt_2 - \tfrac{1}{2}gt_2^2$$

Eliminating t_2

$$-h = \left(u \sin\alpha - \frac{gs}{u \cos\alpha}\right)\frac{s}{eu \cos\alpha} - \tfrac{1}{2}g\frac{s^2}{e^2u^2\cos^2\alpha}.$$

The two expressions for h give

$$s \tan\alpha - \tfrac{1}{2}g\frac{s^2}{u^2\cos^2\alpha} = \left(u \sin\alpha - \frac{gs}{u\cos\alpha}\right)\frac{s}{eu\cos\alpha} + \tfrac{1}{2}\frac{gs^2}{e^2u^2\cos^2\alpha}.$$

$$s \tan\alpha\left(1 + \frac{1}{e}\right) = \frac{gs^2}{2e^2u^2\cos^2\alpha}(e^2 + 2e + 1)$$

giving $$s = \frac{eu^2 \sin 2\alpha}{g(1+e)}.$$

b) We can neatly avoid finding h as follows. We know that

$$t_1 = \frac{s}{u\cos\alpha}, \qquad t_2 = \frac{s}{eu\cos\alpha}.$$

Hence the total time

$$T = t_1 + t_2 = \frac{s}{u\cos\alpha}\left(\frac{1+e}{e}\right).$$

Now the vertical component of momentum, and hence of velocity, of the ball is unchanged on hitting the wall, and the time of flight is therefore the same as if the wall had not been there. Thus, the total time T is given by

$$0 = Tu \sin \alpha - \tfrac{1}{2}gT^2,$$

where the resultant vertical displacement over the whole path is zero.

$$T = \frac{2u \sin \alpha}{g}.$$

The two expressions for T give

$$\frac{2u \sin \alpha}{g} = \frac{s}{u \cos \alpha}\left(\frac{1 + e}{e}\right).$$

Hence
$$s = \frac{eu^2 \sin 2\alpha}{g(1 + e)}.$$

EXERCISE 5F

1. A billiard ball hits a smooth cushion at an angle θ to the normal. If the coefficient of restitution for the collision is e, prove that the ball turns through a right angle if and only if $\tan \theta = \sqrt{e}$.
2. A sphere of mass m strikes an exactly similar one obliquely. The collision is perfectly elastic. Show that the spheres will now be moving at right angles to each other.
3. A sphere of mass $4m$ strikes an exactly similar one of mass m. The collision is perfectly elastic. Find the maximum deflection of the larger mass.
4. A billiard ball is moving near a corner of a billiard table. Show that after striking two adjacent cushions it will be moving back parallel to its original path. (Assume that the coefficient of restitution is the same for both collisions.)
5. Two coins A and B lie at rest on a smooth shove-halfpenny board. Coin C strikes A and B with speed u perpendicular to the line of centres. After the collision C is at rest. If all the coins are identical, prove that the coefficient of restitution is $\frac{2}{3}$, and find the speeds of A and B.
6. A particle is dropped from a height h above a plane inclined at an angle α to the horizontal. The plane is fixed and the coefficient of restitution for the collision is e. How far down the plane is the next point of impact?
7. Two spheres of mass m and $2m$ are approaching with equal speeds along perpendicular lines. When they meet, the direction of motion of m makes an angle θ with the line of centres. If they move off at right angles after the collision prove that

$$e = \frac{\cos \theta + 4 \sin \theta}{2\,(\cos \theta + \sin \theta)}.$$

8. Two billiard balls A and B have mass m. B is initially at rest on a smooth horizontal table and A moves with a constant speed u until it collides with B. At the instant of collision, the line through the centres of A and B makes an angle of 30° with the direction of motion of A. After the collision, B has speed v and A is deflected through 30°.
   a) Calculate v in terms of u.
   b) Calculate the coefficient of restitution for the collision.
   c) Calculate the magnitude and direction of the impulse on A in the collision.

Summary

Impulse momentum equation

For a constant force:

$$t\boldsymbol{F} = m\boldsymbol{v} - m\boldsymbol{u}.$$

$t\boldsymbol{F}$ is the impulse of the force $\boldsymbol{F}$ acting for time t, $m\boldsymbol{v} - m\boldsymbol{u}$ is the change in momentum of a particle of mass m when its velocity changes from $\boldsymbol{u}$ to $\boldsymbol{v}$.

If $\boldsymbol{F}$ is a known function of t, the impulse of $\boldsymbol{F}$ between t_1 and t_2 is given by the integral

$$\boldsymbol{I} = \int_{t_1}^{t_2} \boldsymbol{F}\,\mathrm{d}t$$

When $\boldsymbol{F}$ is unknown, $\boldsymbol{I}$ can be obtained from the equation

$$\boldsymbol{I} = m\boldsymbol{v} - m\boldsymbol{u}.$$

Principle of conservation of momentum

When there is no resultant external impulse acting on a system, the total momentum of the system remains constant.

If an external impulse acts on a system, the component of the total momentum perpendicular to the impulse will be conserved.

Newton's law of impact

Direct impact:

$$v_2 - v_1 = -e(u_2 - u_1),$$

Oblique impact:

$$(\boldsymbol{v}_2 - \boldsymbol{v}_1)\cdot\boldsymbol{n} = -e(\boldsymbol{u}_2 - \boldsymbol{u}_1)\cdot\boldsymbol{n},$$

where $\boldsymbol{n}$ is a unit vector along the common normal to the bodies in collision.

6 WORK AND ENERGY

6.1 Introduction

In chapter 5 we considered the effects of constant and variable forces acting for given times and saw how the concepts of momentum and impulse were useful. The impulse momentum equation was seen as a time integral of the equation of motion, N2, originally introduced in section 4.4. Also in chapter 4 we produced an integral of N2 over distance and we now study this in greater depth, initially in the case of constant forces with motion in one dimension.

EXAMPLE 1

A car of mass 1000 kg travelling along a straight horizontal road has its brakes applied so that its speed reduces from 25 m s^{-1} to 10 m s^{-1} in a distance of 500 m. Find the braking force, assumed to be constant, given that there is a resistance to motion of 100 N.

Since the braking force is constant, the acceleration will be constant. Using $v^2 = u^2 + 2as$, with $v = 10$, $u = 25$, and $s = 500$, we get

$$100 = 625 + 1000a$$
$$a = -0.525.$$

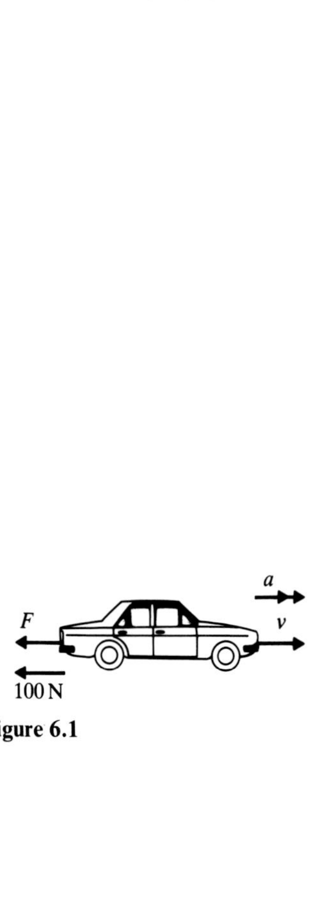

Figure 6.1

By N2, the braking force F is given by

$$-F - 100 = 1000 \times -0.525$$

Thus F is of magnitude 425 N and opposes the motion, as shown in figure 6.1.

□□□□□

This example required us to find the acceleration in order to find the force acting and, as the following more general case shows, we can avoid this step in the calculation.

Suppose a particle of mass m has an initial speed of u and a final speed of v, and is acted upon by a constant force F over a distance s.

By N2, $\quad F = ma.$

Since a is constant $\quad v^2 = u^2 + 2as.$

Rearranging $\quad 2as = v^2 - u^2.$

Now $\quad Fs = mas$

Hence $\quad Fs = \frac{1}{2}mv^2 - \frac{1}{2}mu^2. \quad$ **(1)**

The product Fs in equation (1) is referred to as the **work done** by the constant force F as the body moves through a distance s. The quantity $\frac{1}{2}mv^2$ is called the **kinetic energy** (KE) of the mass m when it is moving with speed v.

Thus, in example 1 we substitute our given values into equation (1) to find F. We find that the work done by the brakes destroys some of the kinetic energy of the car. In fact, as we shall see later, the kinetic energy is converted into other forms of energy. Equation (1) states that the work done by the resultant force on a body equals the change in its kinetic energy, and we shall sometimes refer to this equation as the **work–energy equation.**

Units

The basic unit of the work done by a force is the newton metre (N m). However, in the SI system, it is more usual to call the unit of work the **joule** (J), named after Thomas Joule. The dimensions of both sides of equation (1) are

$$[mv^2] = \mathrm{M\,L^2\,T^{-2}},$$

so that the units are equivalent. Thus, $1\ \mathrm{J} = 1\ \mathrm{kg\,m^2\,s^{-2}}$, and since this is rather clumsy, we will use the joule for both KE and work done.

EXAMPLE 2

A bullet of mass 10 g is fired with a speed of $100\ \mathrm{m\,s^{-1}}$ into a block of wood of thickness 5 cm and emerges with a speed of $50\ \mathrm{m\,s^{-1}}$. What is the average resistance offered by the wood?

We have $s = 0.05$, $v = 50$, $u = 100$, and $m = 0.01$ so that

$$Fs = \tfrac{1}{2}mv^2 - \tfrac{1}{2}mu^2$$

gives $$F \times 0.05 = \tfrac{1}{2} \times 0.01 \times (2500 - 10\,000).$$

F is of magnitude 750 N and is given as a negative force since it opposes the direction of motion of the bullet.

□□□□□

Examples 1 and 2 illustrate the use of work and energy when both the motion and the constant applied force are in the same straight line. We now extend the ideas, by means of an example, to cases where the applied force is not in the same line as the motion.

EXAMPLE 3

A girl is pulling a small toy of mass 3 kg along a horizontal floor by means of a string inclined at 30° to the horizontal. The tension in the string is 5 N and initially the toy is at rest. What is its speed after the girl has walked 2 m? (Neglect frictional and other resistances.)

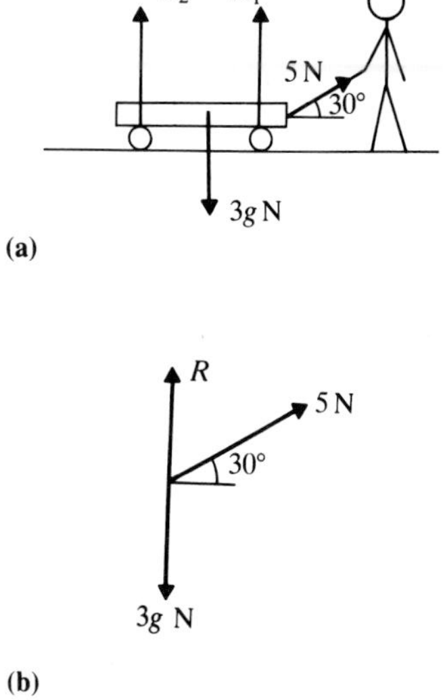

Figure 6.2

Figure 6.2a shows a diagram of the girl and toy and figure 6.2b shows the forces on the toy, treated as a particle. The pulling force has two components, 5 cos 30° N horizontally and 5 sin 30° N vertically. Only the former contributes to the horizontal acceleration and hence to the useful work done on the toy. There is no vertical motion and so the other component does no work.

The work–energy equation in the horizontal direction gives

$$Fs = \tfrac{1}{2}mv^2 - \tfrac{1}{2}mu^2,$$
$$5\cos 30^\circ \times 2 = \tfrac{1}{2} \times 3 \times v^2.$$

This gives the final speed as approximately $2.4\,\mathrm{m\,s^{-1}}$.

□□□□□

The previous example illustrates the idea that the work done by a force in a particular direction is the product of the component of the force in that direction and the distance moved.

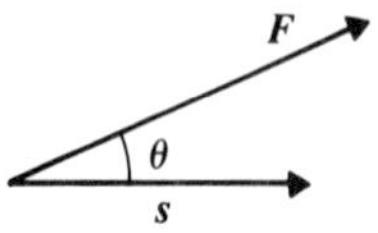

Figure 6.3

In figure 6.3 the work done by $\boldsymbol{F}$ in moving a particle a distance s is $F\cos\theta \times s$. Clearly we can make use of vectors here, since we are dealing with several directions. We state that the work done by a force $\boldsymbol{F}$ in moving a particle through a displacement $\boldsymbol{s}$ is $Fs\cos\theta$ and this is the scalar product of $\boldsymbol{F}$ and $\boldsymbol{s}$, namely

$$\boldsymbol{F}\cdot\boldsymbol{s} = Fs\cos\theta.$$

Indeed, it is convenient to derive the work–energy equation from the vector form of N2.

For a constant force $\boldsymbol{F}$, $\boldsymbol{F} = m\boldsymbol{a}$ and $v^2 = u^2 + 2\boldsymbol{a}\cdot\boldsymbol{s}$ lead to

$$\boldsymbol{F}\cdot\boldsymbol{s} = \tfrac{1}{2}mv^2 - \tfrac{1}{2}mu^2. \qquad \textbf{(2)}$$

It is important to realise that, although we have used vectors, the resulting equation is still a scalar equation and involves speeds rather than velocities.

EXAMPLE 4

A particle of mass 2 kg is moving with velocity $\binom{1}{2}\,\mathrm{m\,s^{-1}}$ when it is acted upon by a constant force $\binom{3}{2}$ N through a displacement $\binom{5}{6}$ m. What is its final speed?

The initial velocity is $\boldsymbol{u} = \binom{1}{2}$, so that the square of its speed

$$u^2 = \boldsymbol{u}\cdot\boldsymbol{u} = 5.$$

Using $\boldsymbol{F}\cdot\boldsymbol{s} = \tfrac{1}{2}mv^2 - \tfrac{1}{2}mu^2$

$$\begin{pmatrix}3\\2\end{pmatrix}\cdot\begin{pmatrix}5\\6\end{pmatrix} = \tfrac{1}{2} \times 2 \times v^2 - \tfrac{1}{2} \times 2 \times 5$$
$$27 = v^2 - 5.$$

The final speed is $\sqrt{32}\,\mathrm{m\,s^{-1}}$.

EXERCISE 6A

1. Calculate the kinetic energy in joules of:
   a) An athlete of mass 70 kg running at $10\ \mathrm{m\,s^{-1}}$.
   b) A ball of mass 200 g travelling at $30\ \mathrm{m\,s^{-1}}$.
   c) A car of mass 1.5 t travelling at $60\ \mathrm{km\,h^{-1}}$.

2. A boy of mass 30 kg rides a bicycle of mass 15 kg along a road at a speed of 5 m s^{-1}. If he halves his speed in 2 s by applying his brakes, calculate

   a) the deceleration, assumed constant, and

   b) the reduction in kinetic energy during braking.

3. A bullet of mass 0.015 kg is moving at 400 m s^{-1} when it hits a block of wood. It comes to rest 2 cm into the wood. Assuming that the block does not move, find the constant resistance of the wood.

4. A bullet of mass 200 g strikes a thick metal plate at 600 m s^{-1} and comes to rest in 2.5 mm. Find the average force exerted on the plate during this penetration.

5. A car of mass 1 t travelling at 15 m s^{-1} comes to rest under braking in a distance of 10 m. If there is a resistance to motion of 100 N, calculate the braking force of the car, assumed constant.

6. A girl of mass 20 kg is sitting on a sledge of mass 10 kg. She is pushed from rest with a force of 50 N against a resistance of 30 N for 12 m. What is her speed after this distance? If she then slows down under the same resistance of 30 N, how far will she travel before coming to rest?

7. A plane of mass 4×10^5 kg accelerates uniformly from rest to a speed of 60 m s^{-1} as it leaves the ground. Assuming that 45% of the mechanical energy output from the engines is used to overcome resistances to motion, find the total mechanical energy output of the engines during this time.

8. Calculate the work done by a force $\boldsymbol{F}$ which moves its point of application in the x–y plane from point A to point B, where:

   a) $\boldsymbol{F} = 3\boldsymbol{i}$, A is (6, 0), B is (0, 6).

   b) $\boldsymbol{F} = 2\boldsymbol{i} + \boldsymbol{j}$, A is (6, 0), B is (−2, 3).

   c) $\boldsymbol{F} = -\boldsymbol{i} + 3\boldsymbol{j}$, A is (0, 0), B is (4, 2).

   d) $\boldsymbol{F} = \boldsymbol{i} + 2\boldsymbol{j} + 3\boldsymbol{k}$, A is (−2, −1), B is (4, 5).

   (Forces are in newtons and distances are in metres.)

9. A woman pulls a large packing case of mass 30 kg across a floor by means of a rope inclined at 30° to the horizontal through a distance of 20 m. If the tension in the rope is 80 N calculate the work done by the woman. If there is a resistance to motion of 25 N, what is the final speed of the case, if it is initially at rest?

10. A loaded sledge of mass 100 kg is pulled by two dogs by means of ropes. The ropes make angles of 40° either side of the direction of motion. The motion and the ropes are horizontal. It starts from rest and is moving at a speed of 5 m s^{-1} after 100 m. Assuming that there is a resistance to motion of 60 N, calculate the tension in each rope.

11. A man pushes a heavy crate along a horizontal floor. The crate has a mass of 50 kg and the man pushes with a force of 200 N

at an angle of 30° to the horizontal. There is a resistance to motion from the floor of 150 N. Find the speed of the crate after it has moved 3 m, if it is initially at rest.

12. A woman pushes a pram of mass 20 kg with a force of 30 N at 60° to the horizontal. If the resistances are 10 N, find the speed of the pram after 2 m, if it is initially at rest.

13. A man pushes a mower of mass 30 kg with a force of 30 N at an angle of 35° to the horizontal against a resistance of 10 N for 5 m. What is the work done by the man and the speed of the mower, if it is initially at rest.

6.2 Motion under gravity

In example 3, section 6.1, we saw that the component of the pulling force at right angles to the path did not contribute to the useful work done on the toy. We now consider other examples where there are forces acting which also do no work.

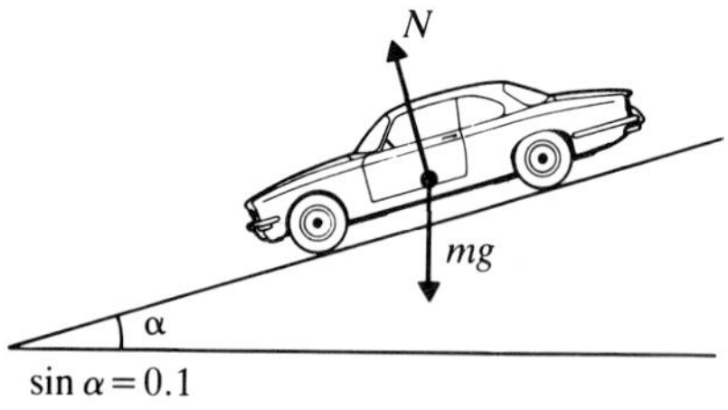

Figure 6.4

EXAMPLE 1

A car of mass 1 t is at rest on a hill of slope $\sin^{-1} 0.1$. If the chocks are removed what is the speed of the car after 15 m ? Assume that the road is icy and that frictional forces and air resistances may be ignored. Take g as 10 m s^{-2}.

The forces acting on the car are $\boldsymbol{N}$, the normal contact force, and $m\boldsymbol{g}$, the weight force, as shown in figure 6.4. The work done by $\boldsymbol{N}$ is zero, since at all points along the path $\boldsymbol{N}\cdot\boldsymbol{s} = 0$. The work done by the weight force is given by

$$m\boldsymbol{g}\cdot\boldsymbol{s} = mgs\cos\theta$$
$$= mgs\sin\alpha.$$

Using the work–energy equation $\boldsymbol{F}\cdot\boldsymbol{s} = \frac{1}{2}mv^2 - \frac{1}{2}mu^2$, with $\boldsymbol{F} = m\boldsymbol{g}$ and $u = 0$, we get

$$1000 \times 10 \times 15 \times 0.1 = \tfrac{1}{2} \times 1000 \times v^2,$$
$$v^2 = 30.$$

The speed of the car after 15 m is approximately 5.48 m s^{-1}.

The work done by the weight force of the car is $mgs\sin\alpha$ and is as a result of gravity. There are two ways in which we can think of this, as illustrated in figure 6.5.

In figure 6.5a

$$mgs\sin\alpha = mg(s\sin\alpha)$$
$$= mgh,$$

where h is the vertical distance fallen as the car moves the distance s down the slope.

In figure 6.5b

$$mgs\sin\alpha = (mg\sin\alpha)s,$$

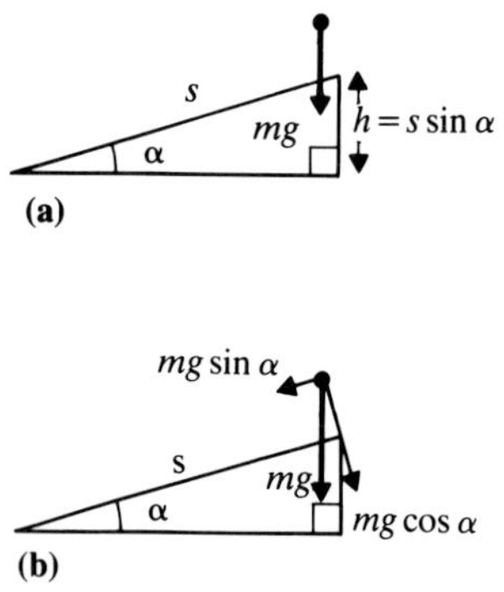

Figure 6.5

which is the work done by the component of mg along the slope moving through the distance s. The other component, $mg \cos \alpha$, does no work along the slope.

We note that the expression mgh is independent of the angle of the slope and depends only on the vertical distance fallen. This idea is useful when we consider paths which are not straight lines, as the following analysis shows.

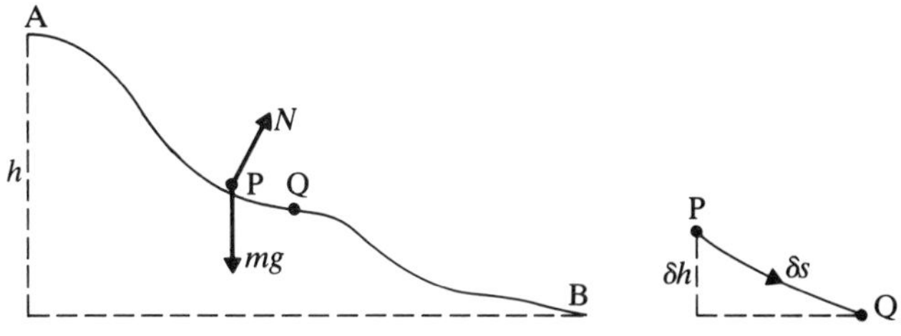

Figure 6.6

Suppose that a particle of mass m moves under gravity from the point A to the point B on a curved path, as in figure 6.6. At a general point P, the forces acting are:

$\mathbf{N}$ – the contact force perpendicular to the path, and

$m\mathbf{g}$ – the weight force acting vertically downwards.

We will neglect all resistances.

Consider a small element of the path from P to Q, written δs. Since $\mathbf{PQ} \approx \delta s$, the work done by each of these forces will be:

(a) The work done by $\mathbf{N} \approx \mathbf{N} \cdot \delta \mathbf{s} = 0$,

since $\mathbf{N}$ is at right angles to the path throughout its length PQ. Over the whole path AB, the total work done by the normal reaction will be zero, by the same argument.

(b) The work done by $m\mathbf{g} \approx mg\, \delta h$,

and so over the whole path the work done is mgh, where h is the total vertical distance between A and B.

EXAMPLE 2

A skier of mass 70 kg is at the top of a smooth slope of length 300 m and height 40 m, as shown in figure 6.7. If he pushes off with a speed of 3 m s^{-1}, what will be his speed at the bottom of the slope, if all resistances are ignored. Take g as 10 m s^{-2}.

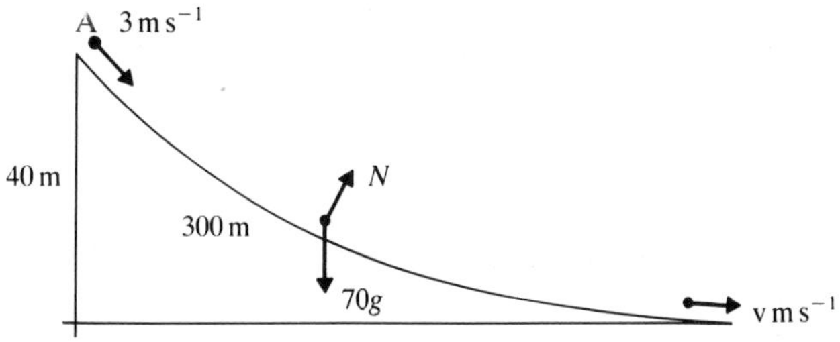

Figure 6.7

Since the slope is smooth, the only forces on the skier are $\boldsymbol{N}$, the normal contact force, and $70\boldsymbol{g}$, his weight force. The work done by $\boldsymbol{N}$ along the path is zero, since the path is smooth and $\boldsymbol{N}$ is perpendicular to it throughout its length. The work done by the weight force is

$$mgh = 70 \times 10 \times 40 = 28\,000\,.$$

The change in kinetic energy is

$$\tfrac{1}{2}mv^2 - \tfrac{1}{2}mu^2 = \tfrac{1}{2} \times 70 \times (v^2 - 3^2).$$

From the work–energy equation, the work done equals the change in KE,

$$28\,000 = 35v^2 - 315$$
$$v^2 = 809,$$

giving the speed at the bottom of the slope as 28.4 m s^{-1}.

Conservative fields

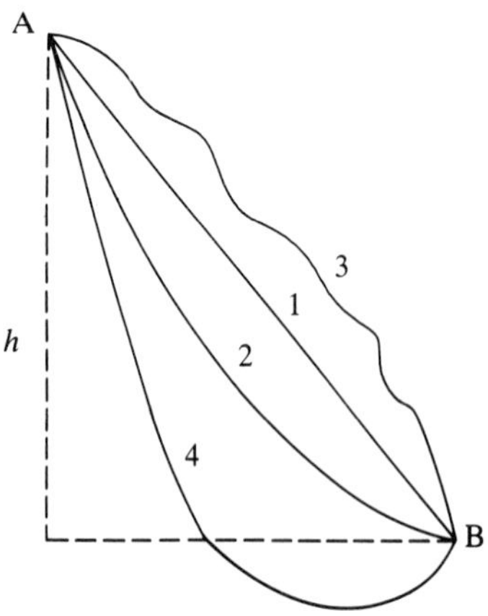

Figure 6.8

We have shown that, when a particle moves from point A to point B, the work done by gravity is independent of the path taken. Thus, in figure 6.8, the work done by gravity on a particle of mass m along the paths labelled 1–4 is constant, and we say that gravity is a conservative field of force.

The work done by gravity along the four paths is mgh. Thus, in the absence of any other forces, the KE gained by the particle between A and B is mgh along all the paths.

In practice, forces such as friction air resistance will affect the kinetic energy lost or gained. For example, if the ski slope in example 2 were not smooth, the skier would reach the bottom at a higher speed from a steeper slope of the same height than from a much flatter one, since the path taken in the former case is shorter and the work done by the frictional force is less.

Gravitational potential energy

In the conservative field of gravity, the work done when an object of mass m falls a distance h is mgh. This expression is called the gravitational potential energy of the mass at height h above some chosen level, which in example 2, above, is the bottom of the ski slope.

Consider a particle of mass m at height x above a chosen zero level moving with speed v vertically upwards, as in figure 6.9a.

By N2 $$F = ma,$$

$$-mg = ma.$$

But $$a = \frac{dv}{dt} = v\frac{dv}{dx} = \frac{d}{dx}(\tfrac{1}{2}v^2),$$

so that $$\frac{d}{dx}(\tfrac{1}{2}mv^2) + mg = 0,$$

i.e. $$\frac{d}{dx}(\tfrac{1}{2}mv^2 + mgx) = 0.$$

Thus $$\tfrac{1}{2}mv^2 + mgx = \text{constant},$$
or $$T + V = \text{constant}. \qquad \textbf{(3)}$$

The term $T = \frac{1}{2}mv^2$ is the **kinetic energy** (KE) of the mass, and $V = mgx$ is the **gravitational potential energy** (GPE). Equation (3) is an example of the work–energy equation for conservative fields, in which the total mechanical energy is conserved. This is known as the **principle of conservation of energy**, or often more briefly as the energy equation. The level chosen for GPE is purely arbitrary.

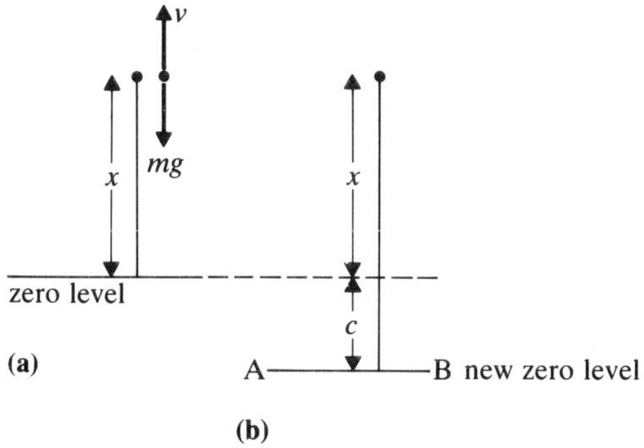

Figure 6.9

Suppose, for example, the position of the particle in figure 6.9b, is measured relative to the line AB, so that the equation

$$\frac{d}{dx}(\tfrac{1}{2}mv^2) + mg = 0$$

becomes $$\frac{d}{dx}(\tfrac{1}{2}mv^2 + mg(x + c)) = 0,$$

giving $$\tfrac{1}{2}mv^2 + mg(x + c) = \text{constant}.$$

Thus, relative to AB, $T + V = \text{constant}$, as before, but the constant now takes a different value. This result can be extended to two dimensions, provided $\boldsymbol{v}$ is the total velocity, and not just the component of the velocity in the vertical direction. We can illustrate this for the skier of example 2, by taking different zero levels. The calculaculations are shown in figure 6.10.

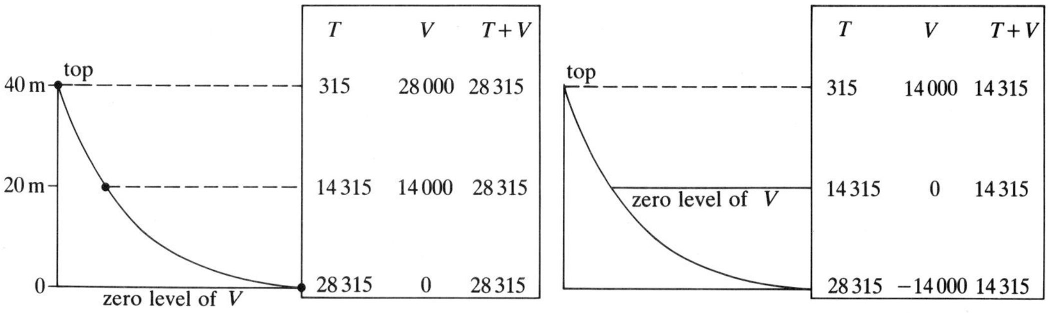

Figure 6.10

EXAMPLE 3

Suppose a ball of mass m is thrown so that at a point P its height is y_P and its velocity is v_P and at a point Q its height is y_Q and its velocity is v_Q, as shown in figure 6.11.

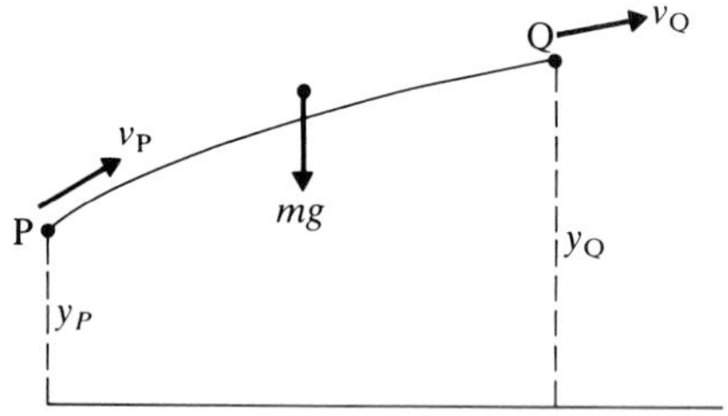

Figure 6.11

Since $T + V = \text{constant}$,

$$T_P + V_P = T_Q + V_Q,$$
$$\tfrac{1}{2}mv_P^2 + mgy_P = \tfrac{1}{2}mv_Q^2 + mgy_Q.$$

Rearranging this we get

$$-mg(y_Q - y_P) = \tfrac{1}{2}mv_Q^2 - \tfrac{1}{2}mv_P^2.$$

The LHS of this equation gives the work done by gravity, and the RHS gives the change in kinetic energy. This agrees with the work–energy equation of section 6.1.

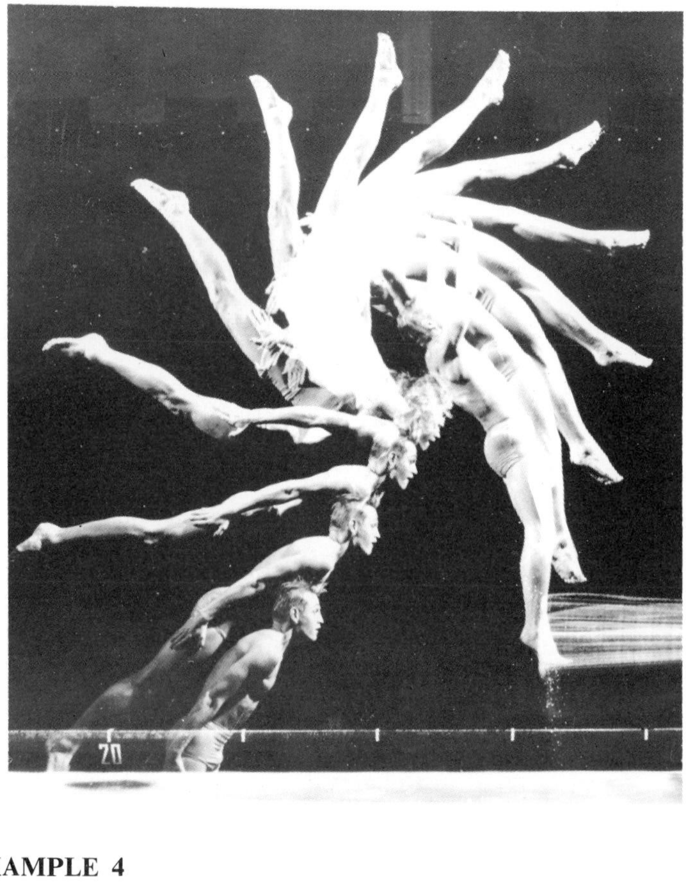

In this multiflash photograph the diver is performing a back dive from the springboard. Describe the energy changes that are occurring.

EXAMPLE 4

Solve example 2 using the principle of conservation of energy, taking the bottom of the slope as the zero level ($g = 10\,\text{m}\,\text{s}^{-2}$).

At the top of the slope,

$$\text{KE} = \tfrac{1}{2}mv^2 = 315, \qquad \text{GPE} = mgh = 28\,000.$$

Thus $$T + V = 28315$$

At the bottom of the slope,

$$\text{KE} = \tfrac{1}{2} \times 70 \times v^2, \qquad \text{GPE} = 0.$$

Thus $$T + V = 35\,v^2$$

$$\text{Since } T + V = \text{constant},$$
$$35v^2 = 28\,315,$$
$$v^2 = 809.$$

The speed at the bottom of the slope is 28.4 m s^{-1}, as before.

□□□□□

There are many other examples of conservative forces, of which a particular example is the tension in a stretched spring, and we shall look at this in chapter 8.

Non-conservative fields

In a non-conservative field, and indeed in many other instances, we do not preserve mechanical energy. It is transformed into heat, electrical, sound and other forms of energy. The following examples illustrate how we deal with problems where mechanical energy is not conserved.

EXAMPLE 5

Suppose that the car in example 1 is subjected to a total constant resistance of 500 N along the slope. What is its speed after travelling a distance of 15 m?

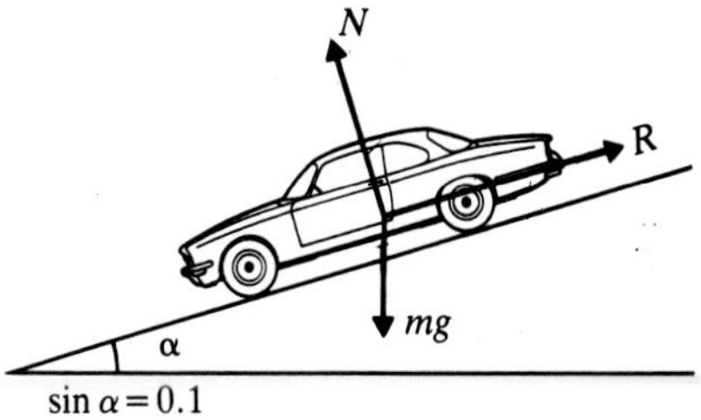

Figure 6.12

The total force, $\boldsymbol{F}$, acting on the car is, from figure 6.12,

$$\boldsymbol{F} = \boldsymbol{N} + \boldsymbol{R} + m\boldsymbol{g},$$

where $\boldsymbol{N}$ is the normal contact force, $\boldsymbol{R}$ is the total resistance and $m\boldsymbol{g}$ is the weight force. Since there is a resistance, the total mechanical energy is not conserved and so we cannot use the energy equation.

Using the work–energy equation, we get

$$(\boldsymbol{N} + \boldsymbol{R} + m\boldsymbol{g})\cdot\boldsymbol{s} = \tfrac{1}{2}mv^2 - \tfrac{1}{2}mu^2.$$

$\boldsymbol{N}\cdot\boldsymbol{s} = 0$, since $\boldsymbol{N}$ is at right angles to the path.

$\boldsymbol{R}\cdot\boldsymbol{s} = R \times$ the distance along the path $= -500 \times 15$.

$m\boldsymbol{g}\cdot\boldsymbol{s} = mgh = 1000 \times 10 \times 15 \sin\alpha$, where h is the distance fallen vertically.

Note that the work done by R is negative, since we take the positive direction to be down the slope. Thus, the work–energy equation reduces to

$$-500 \times 15 + 1000 \times 10 \times 15 \times 0.1 = \tfrac{1}{2} \times 1000 \times v^2 - \tfrac{1}{2} \times 1000 \times 0^2,$$
$$\Rightarrow v^2 = 15,$$

giving the speed as 3.87 m s^{-1}.

EXAMPLE 6

Suppose that, in example 2, there is a resistance of 50 N along the slope. What is the speed of the man at the bottom of the slope in this case?

We consider the work done by the various forces as the man moves down the slope, as given in the table.

Force	Work done	Reason
normal action, N	0	N is at right angles to the slope along its length
weight force mg	$70 \times 10 \times 40$	the man descends 40m and this is his GPE
friction, 50	-50×300	the slope is 300 m long and friction opposes the motion
	Total: 13 000 J	

From the work–energy equation,

$$\text{total work done} = \text{change in KE}$$

$$13\,000 = \tfrac{1}{2} \times 70 \times v^2 - \tfrac{1}{2} \times 70 \times 3^2$$

$$v^2 = 380,$$

hence v is 19.5 m s^{-1}.

EXERCISE 6B

Take g as 10 m s^{-2}, where necessary.

1. A boy of mass 50 kg is sitting at the top of a water chute of length 5 m at a height of 2.5 m above a swimming pool. What is his speed at the bottom of the chute, assuming the chute is smooth?

2. A girl of mass 40 kg is sitting at the top of a slide of length 4 m at a height of 2 m above the ground. What is her speed at the bottom of the slide, assuming a constant resistance to motion of 20 N?

3. A car of mass 1000 kg descends a hill of slope α, where $\sin \alpha = 0.2$. Calculate the constant braking force necessary to bring the car to rest from 80 km h^{-1} in a distance of 100 m, when the resistance to motion is 300 N.

4. A train of mass 300 t is moving down a slope of 1 in 150 at a speed of 50 km h^{-1}. Calculate the total resistance to motion if the train comes to rest in a distance of 60 m after braking.

5. An engine of mass 100t pulls a train of 10 coaches each of mass 25t up a slope of 1 in 100. The resistance to motion is 100 N t^{-1}. If the speed is increased from 24 km h^{-1} to 48 km h^{-1} in 500 m, calculate

   a) the change in kinetic energy of the train,

   b) the total work done by the engine.

6. A girl of mass 40 kg is sitting on a toboggan of mass 3kg and is sliding down a slope of 1 in 8. Her speed from rest after she has done

100 m is 10 m s^{-1}. What is the resistance to motion, assumed constant? What would her speed be on a smooth slope?

7. A car of mass 1 t approaches an upwards slope of 1 in 10 at 100 km h^{-1}. After 500 m its speed has dropped to 50 km h^{-1}. The resistance to motion is 500 N. What is the constant force exerted by the wheels?

8. A cat is seated on the top of an icy roof when it slides down. The mass of the cat is 4 kg and the roof is inclined at 30° to the horizontal. The top of the roof is 3 m above the walls, which are 6 m high. While the cat is sliding down the roof there is a constant resistance to motion of 10 N. With what speed does the cat leave the roof? Where does it land?

9. At the highest point of a roller coaster ride the cars are 35 m above the ground and are moving at 0.5 m s^{-1}. What is the speed of the cars at the bottom of a straight downward slope of 18° to the horizontal, if there is a constant resistance to motion of 0.5 N kg^{-1} against the motion of the cars? Let the total mass of the cars be M kg.

Motion in a vertical circle 6.3

A further example of motion under gravity arises when an object moves on the end of a string in a circular path, e.g. when a child swings on the end of a rope. In chapter 3 we showed that such examples involved non-uniform motion in a circle, since the speed varies along the path, as does the tension in the string. The analysis of such motion can be quite difficult, but using the ideas of energy we can simplify the calculations, because the tension, which is always at right angles to the circular path, does no work during the motion.

EXAMPLE 1

A girl of mass 40 kg swings on the end of a rope of length 5 m which is attached to a tree. Initially the rope is taut and, when the girl is 3 m below the point of suspension of the rope, her speed is 4 m s^{-1}.

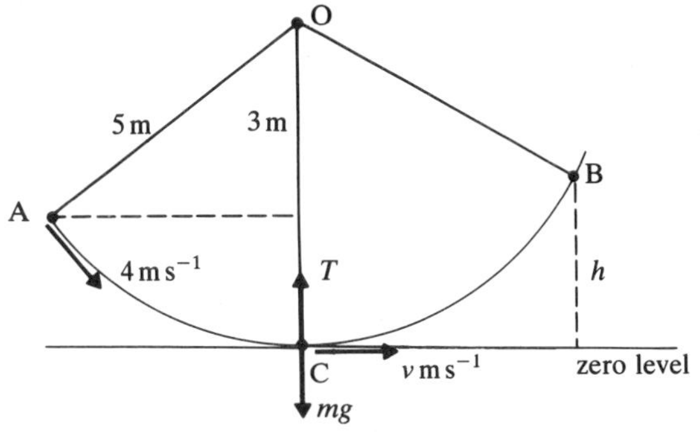

Figure 6.13

Find

a) the maximum height to which she will rise,

b) the tension in the rope when it is vertical.

Take g as 10 m s^{-2}.

We will solve the problem using the principle of conservation of energy, and take the zero level as the lowest point of the swing, as in figure 6.13.

a) When the girl is at A,

$$\text{GPE} = mgh = 40 \times 10 \times 2 = 800,$$
$$\text{KE} = \tfrac{1}{2}mv^2 = \tfrac{1}{2} \times 40 \times 16 = 320.$$

Total energy is 1120 J.

At B, the highest point,

$$\text{GPE} = 40 \times 10 \times h = 400h,$$
$$\text{KE} = 0.$$

Thus $$400h = 1120,$$

Hence she will rise a distance of 2.8 m.

b) When the rope is vertical, the speed at the lowest point is given by the equation:

$$\text{total mechanical energy at A} = \text{KE at C},$$
$$1120 = \tfrac{1}{2} \times 40 \times v^2,$$
$$v^2 = 56.$$

The tension, T, at the bottom is given by N2 towards the centre, O.

$$T - mg = mv^2/r.$$
$$T = 40 \times 10 + \tfrac{1}{5} \times 40 \times 56 = 848,$$

so that when the rope is vertical, the tension is 848 N.

EXAMPLE 2*

A particle of mass m is moving on the end of a light inextensible string of length l in a circular arc, so that, at time t, its position is at θ radians to the downward vertical. At the lowest point the speed is u. Analyse the motion.

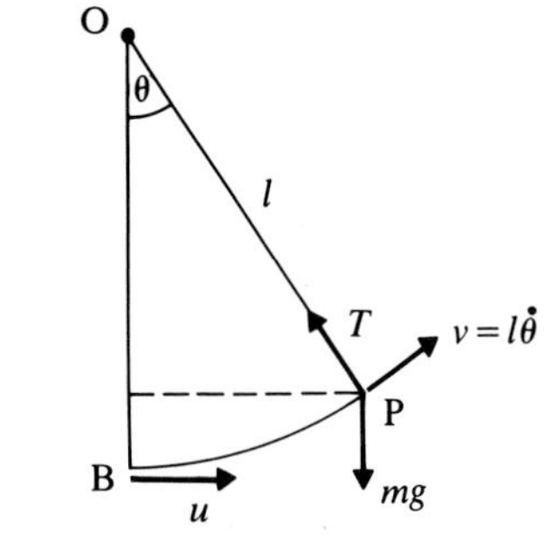

Figure 6.14

Suppose the speed of the particle at time t is v. Since the tension does no work we can apply the principle of conservation of energy:

$$\text{GPE} + \text{KE} = \text{constant}.$$

Referring to figure 6.14,

At B, $\quad \text{KE} = \tfrac{1}{2}mu^2, \quad \text{GPE} = 0.$

At P, $\quad \text{KE} = \tfrac{1}{2}mv^2, \quad \text{GPE} = mgh = mgl(1 - \cos\theta).$

Thus
$$\tfrac{1}{2}mv^2 + mgl(1 - \cos\theta) = \tfrac{1}{2}mu^2,$$
$$v^2 = u^2 - 2gl(1 - \cos\theta). \qquad (4)$$

Applying N2 to the particle at P towards O

$$T - mg\cos\theta = mv^2/l,$$
$$T = mv^2/l + mg\cos\theta. \qquad (5)$$

From (4),
$$T = mu^2/l + mg(3\cos\theta - 2). \qquad (6)$$

We now examine the motion for different values of u.

a) $u^2 \leqslant 2gl$. From (4), $v = 0$ when $u^2 - 2gl(1 - \cos\theta) = 0$:

$$\cos\theta = 1 - \frac{u^2}{2gl}.$$

If $u^2 \leqslant 2gl$, $v = 0$ for $\theta \leqslant \frac{1}{2}\pi$. From (5), $T \geqslant 0$ if $\theta \leqslant \frac{1}{2}\pi$, hence the particle will reach a maximum height for $\theta \leqslant \frac{1}{2}\pi$ and swing to and fro.

b) To find the maximum value required for u for the particle to move in complete vertical circles, we note that T will be a minimum when $\cos\theta$ is a minimum (from (6)). This occurs at the top of the circle when $\cos\theta = -1$. If $T > 0$ when $\cos\theta = -1$, we see, from (6), that

$$u^2/l + g(-5) > 0$$
$$u^2 > 5gl$$

When $u^2 = 5gl$, the speed at the top is given by (4),

$$v^2 = 5gl - 2gl \times 2$$
$$= gl$$
$$> 0.$$

Hence, if $u^2 \geqslant 5gl$, the particle will complete vertical circles.

c) $2gl < u^2 < 5gl$. From (4), $v = 0$ when $u^2 - 2gl(1 - \cos\theta) = 0$:

$$\cos\theta = 1 - u^2/2gl.$$

From (6), $T = 0$ when $u^2 + gl(3\cos\theta - 2) = 0$:

$$\cos\theta = \tfrac{2}{3}(1 - u^2/2gl).$$

Thus, if $2gl < u^2 < 5gl$, T will become zero before v. At this point the particle will begin a free trajectory under gravity until the string becomes taut again, as in figure 6.15.

Noting that $v = l\dot{\theta}$, we may rewrite equation (4) in the form

$$l^2\dot{\theta}^2 = u^2 - 2gl(1 - \cos\theta).$$

Differentiating with respect to t,

$$2l^2\dot{\theta}\ddot{\theta} = -2gl\,\dot{\theta}\sin\theta,$$
$$l\ddot{\theta} = -g\sin\theta,$$
$$ml\ddot{\theta} = -mg\sin\theta.$$

This is N2 applied along the tangent of the circle, and demonstrates that the energy equation is an integral of N2.

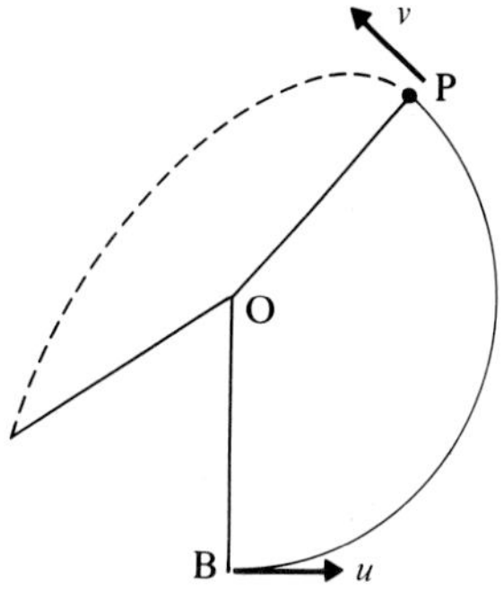

Figure 6.15

EXERCISE 6C

Take g as $10\ \mathrm{m\ s^{-2}}$ throughout.

1. Tarzan, whose mass is 80 kg, is standing in a tree 15 m above the ground and is holding a rope of length 10 m, which is attached to a high branch of another tree at a height of 5 m above him. Keeping the rope taut, he jumps off the branch with a speed of $2\ \mathrm{m\ s^{-1}}$. With what speed will he reach the lowest point of his swing? What is the tension in the rope at that point and how high will he rise on the other side?

2. A child of mass 25 kg is seated on a swing, the ropes of which are 2 m long. She is pulled back by her parents through an angle of $40°$ and pushed off with a speed $2\ \mathrm{m\ s^{-1}}$. What is her speed at the lowest point and how high will she rise on the other side of the swing?

3. The bob of a pendulum of length 4 m is allowed to fall from rest from a point on the same horizontal level as the point of suspension and 2 m away from it. Find the velocity with which it begins to move in a vertical circle when the string becomes taut. Find the height to which it subsequently rises.

4. A bead of mass 100 g is threaded on a smooth wire which forms a vertical circle of radius 0.5 m. The bead is initially at the lowest point of the wire. Describe the subsequent motion if the bead is given an initial speed of (a) $2\ \mathrm{m\ s^{-1}}$, (b) $4\ \mathrm{m\ s^{-1}}$.

5. A particle is hanging from a fixed point by a light string of length 1 m. It is given an initial horizontal speed so that the string slackens when the particle has risen 1.6 m. Through what angle has the string turned, what is the speed of the particle at this point, and how much higher will it rise?

6. A mass of 3 kg is suspended from a point by means of a string of length 3 m. It is pulled aside until it makes an angle of $40°$ with the vertical. It is then released and swings back. What is the speed of the mass at the lowest point and what is the tension in the string at that point?

7. A mass of 0.25 kg is hanging freely on one end of a string of length 2 m, the other end of which is attached to a fixed point. It is projected horizontally with a speed of $2\ \mathrm{m\ s^{-1}}$. What is the greatest angle the string makes with the vertical in the subsequent motion?

8. A string of length 0.5 m is attached to a fixed point and has a mass of 1.5 kg attached to the other end. The mass is held so that the string is horizontal and taut, and is then released to swing. What is its maximum velocity?

9. An eskimo is sitting at the top of an hemispherical igloo of radius 3.5 m when he starts to slide off. What is his speed when he loses contact with the igloo and through what angle will he then have turned? How far from the bottom of the igloo will he hit the ground?

Variable forces which do work **6.4**

In the above examples the forces which do work have all been constant. We now consider variable forces which do work, but our analysis will be restricted to the simplest case of those which act in one dimension.

In chapter 4, the work–energy equation was derived as an integral of N2 as follows:

$$F = ma = m\frac{dv}{dt} = m\frac{dv}{dx}.$$

Integrating with respect to x,

$$\int F\,dx = \int m\,v\frac{dv}{dx}\,dx,$$

$$\int_{x_1}^{x_2} F\,dx = \left[\tfrac{1}{2}mv^2\right]_{v_1}^{v_2}$$

$$= \tfrac{1}{2}mv_2^2 - \tfrac{1}{2}mv_1^2,$$

where x_1 and x_3 are the initial and final positions at which the speeds are v_1 and v_2.

We note that the work done by a force which varies with distance is given by the area under the graph of F against x, as in figure 6.16.

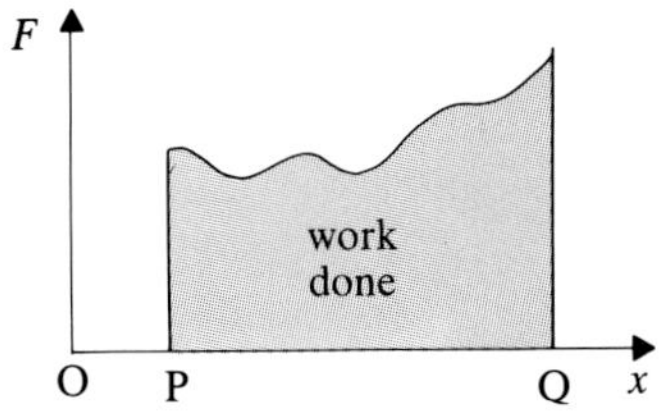

Figure 6.16

EXAMPLE 1

A car of mass 700 kg is initially at rest. It is acted upon by a propulsive force which depends on the distance, x, travelled and is given by $F = 3000 - 15x$. There is a constant frictional force of 500 N opposing the motion. What is the total work done on the car in the first 200 m and what is its speed at that time?

The work done

$$W = \int_0^{200} (F - 500)\,dx$$

$$= \int_0^{200} (3000 - 15\,x - 500)\,dx$$

$$= \left[2500x - 7.5x^2\right]_0^{200}$$

$$= 200\,000.$$

By the work–energy equation,

$$W = \tfrac{1}{2}mv^2 - \tfrac{1}{2}mu^2$$

$$200\,000 = \tfrac{1}{2} \times 700v^2$$

$$v = 23.9.$$

The work done on the car in the first 200 m is 2×10^5 J, and its speed is then 23.9 m s^{-1}.

EXAMPLE 2

The force of repulsion between two electrons is given by

$$F = 2.3 \times 10^{-28} \times x^{-2}\ \text{N},$$

where x is the distance between them in metres. Each electron has a mass of 9.0×10^{-31} kg. If one electron is held fixed, and at an instant the other is moving towards it at a speed of 2×10^{6} m s^{-1} at a distance of 3×10^{-10} m calculate:

a) their closest distance of approach

b) the speed of the free electron when repelled to a distance of 2×10^{-10} m.

a) Suppose the closest distance of approach is X m.
The work done on the free electron is given by:

$$W = \int_{3\times 10^{-10}}^{X} \frac{2.3 \times 10^{-28}}{x^2}\,dx$$
$$= \left[\frac{-2.3 \times 10^{-28}}{x}\right]_{3\times 10^{-10}}^{X}$$

The speed of the free electron at X is zero. By the work–energy equation,

$$W = 0 - \tfrac{1}{2}mu^2,$$

$$2.3 \times 10^{-28}\left[-\frac{1}{X} + \frac{1}{3 \times 10^{-10}}\right] = -\tfrac{1}{2} \times 9 \times 10^{-31} \times 4 \times 10^{12},$$

giving the closest distance of approach as 9×10^{-11} m.

b) The work done in repelling the free electron to a distance of 2×10^{-10} m is given by:

$$W = \int_{9\times 10^{-11}}^{2\times 10^{-10}} \frac{2.3 \times 10^{-28}}{x^2}\,dx.$$

If v is the speed at this point, the work–energy equation gives

$$W = \tfrac{1}{2}mv^2 - 0,$$

$$2.3 \times 10^{-28}\left[\frac{1}{9 \times 10^{-11}} - \frac{1}{2 \times 10^{-10}}\right] = \tfrac{1}{2} \times 9 \times 10^{-31} \times v^2,$$

giving the speed as 1.77×10^{6} m s^{-1}.

□□□□□

It often happens that we do not know how a force varies with distance, or the distance through which it acts. It may still be possible to find the work done under these circumstances by calculating the change in kinetic energy produced. This is analogous to the evaluation of the impulse of an unknown force by equating it with the change in momentum it produces (see section 5.2).

EXAMPLE 3

A tennis ball of mass 60 g is travelling at a speed of $2\ \text{m s}^{-1}$ at 45° below the horizontal when it is hit back by a player with a speed of $5\ \text{m s}^{-1}$ at an angle of 30° above the horizontal. Assuming that the ball remains in the same vertical plane and all resistances can be neglected, find the impulse on the ball and the work done by the player.

We take unit vectors horizontally and vertically, as shown in figure 6.17.

The initial and final velocities $\boldsymbol{u}$ and $\boldsymbol{v}$ are

$$\boldsymbol{u} = \begin{pmatrix} 2\cos 45° \\ -2\sin 45° \end{pmatrix}, \quad \boldsymbol{v} = \begin{pmatrix} -5\cos 30° \\ 5\sin 30° \end{pmatrix}$$

a) The impulse is given by the impulse momentum equation

$$\boldsymbol{I} = m\boldsymbol{v} - m\boldsymbol{u}$$

$$= 0.06\left[\begin{pmatrix} -5\cos 30° \\ 5\sin 30° \end{pmatrix} - \begin{pmatrix} 2\cos 45° \\ -2\sin 45° \end{pmatrix}\right] = \begin{pmatrix} -0.345 \\ 0.235 \end{pmatrix}.$$

The impulse has a magnitude of 0.42 N s and is in the direction 34° above the horizontal.

b) The work done by the player is given by the work–energy equation,

$$W = \tfrac{1}{2}mv^2 - \tfrac{1}{2}mu^2$$
$$= \tfrac{1}{2} \times 0.06 \times (5^2 - 2^2) = 0.63.$$

The work done by the player is 0.63 J.

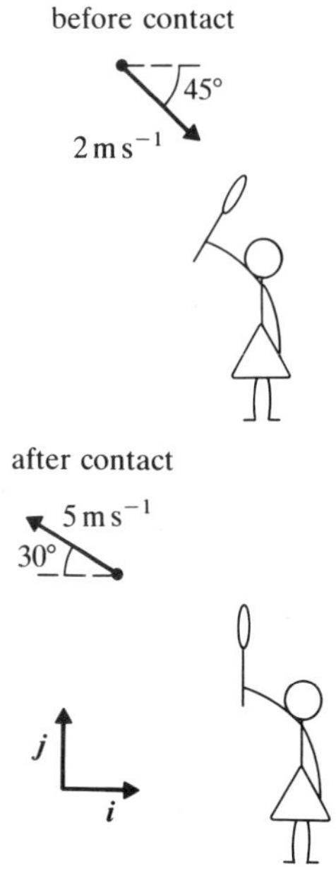

Figure 6.17

EXERCISE 6D

---

1. A woman pulls a bucket of water up a well. The mass of the bucket and water is 8 kg, and she pulls in a series of constant forces, taking up 1 m of rope each time. Her initial pull is 130 N and this reduces by 10 N each pull. Assuming that the bucket does not slow down between pulls, find the speed of the bucket after three pulls, starting from rest.

2. A particle moves in a straight line along the x-axis from O, under the influence of a force kx, directed towards O. The mass of the particle is m. If V is the maximum speed of the particle, prove that it moves to and fro through a distance $2V(m/k)^{1/2}$.

3. A train of mass 200 t moves from rest up an incline of 1 in 150 against a resistance of $10\ \text{N t}^{-1}$. The tractive force, F, at different distances s, is given in the table. Estimate the speed of the train after 300 m.

s (m):	0	50	100	150	200	250	300
F (N × 10^3):	60	62.4	50.4	43.2	36	32.4	30

4. A car of mass 1 t is initially at rest and moves against a resistance of 30 N under the action of a tractive force F N as given in the table. Estimate the speed of the car after 180 m.

s (m):	0	30	60	90	120	150	180
F (N):	300	290	275	260	240	215	200

5. The Earth may be regarded as a sphere of radius R. It exerts an attraction of magnitude mk/x^2 on a particle of mass m at a distance x from the centre of the Earth. If the particle is projected upwards from the surface of the Earth with speed u, use the work–energy equation to show that it will return to the surface provided $u^2 \leqslant 2gR$, where g is the acceleration due to gravity at the surface of the Earth.

6. A particle of mass m is moving along the x-axis under the action of a force F directed towards O, where F is given by:

$$F = \begin{cases} mka^2/x^2, & x > a \\ mkx/a, & x \leqslant a. \end{cases}$$

If the particle starts at rest at $x = 2a$, use the work–energy equation to show that it reaches O with a speed $(2ka)^{1/2}$.

6.5 Collisions and explosions

In chapter 5 we looked at the way in which the total momentum of a system is conserved when two bodies collide in the absence of an external impulse. We now consider changes in the energy of a system after collisions and explosions.

Collisions

EXAMPLE 1

Tarzan is swinging through the trees when he sees Jane in the middle of a clearing about to be attacked by a tiger. He decides to swing down on a creeper to rescue her. The creeper is 15 m long and will just touch the ground at its lowest point. Tarzan is standing on a branch and jumps so that at A, when he is 10 m off the ground, he has a speed of 5 m s^{-1}. The mass of Tarzan is 80 kg and of Jane is 40 kg. The creeper is attached to a point 15 m above Jane at B. Will they reach the safety of a branch of a neighbouring tree which extends to the point C?

Figure 6.18 shows a simplified diagram of the problem. The speed of Tarzan just before he reaches Jane is given by the energy equation:

$$T_A + V_A = T_B + V_B$$

$$\tfrac{1}{2} \times 80 \times 5^2 + 80 \times 10 \times 10 = \tfrac{1}{2} \times 80 \times v^2 + 0,$$

where the zero level of GPE is taken as the lowest point of the swing. This equation leads to $v = 15$.

The momentum of Tarzan before the collision is $80 \times 15 = 1200$. The combined speed of Tarzan and Jane after their collision is given by the conservation of momentum:

$$(80 + 40)v = 1200,$$
$$v = 10.$$

At this point, the total energy is

$$T + V = \tfrac{1}{2} \times 120 \times 10^2 + 0 = 6000.$$

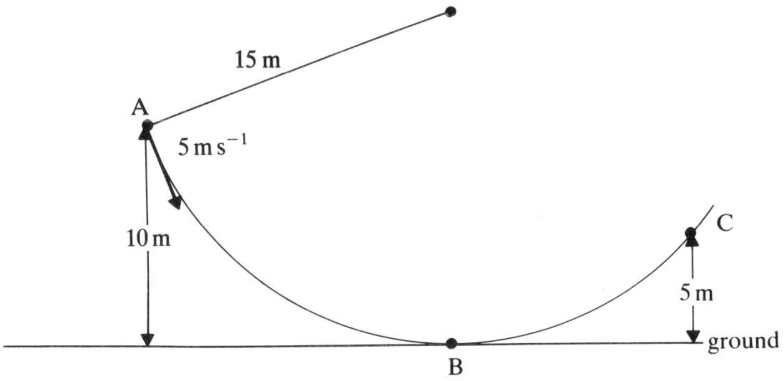

Figure 6.18

By the conservation of energy, they reach the highest point C, when $T_C = 0$.

$$T_C + V_C = 6000,$$
$$0 + 120 \times 10 \times h = 6000,$$
$$h = 5.$$

Thus, they just reach the branch 5 m up the tree with zero speed. Note that the KE of Tarzan just before the collision, when his speed is $15\ \text{m s}^{-1}$, is 9000 J. Thus there is a loss of 3000 J when he collides with Jane. This loss is not due to any external forces, but some of the mechanical energy is transformed into other forms, e.g. heat and sound energy.

We are able to use conservation of energy before the collision, or after it. At the moment of collision we must use conservation of momentum to find the resulting velocity.

The above type of collision is called inelastic, since the bodies do not rebound after collision. In such cases the coefficient of restitution is zero (see section 5.6).

EXAMPLE 2

A pile driver has a block of mass 100 kg which is dropped from a height of 2m on to a pile of mass 1 t. The block does not rebound. The resistance of the Earth is initially 1.5×10^4 N and increases linearly with distance to 4.5×10^4 N in a distance of 1 m. Find the depth of penetration of the pile after 1 blow. Take g as $10\ \text{m s}^{-2}$.

A pile driver.

a) The speed v of the block just before impact is given by conservation of energy.

$$\text{KE just before impact} = \text{PE at the start.}$$
$$\tfrac{1}{2}mv^2 = mgh,$$
$$v^2 = 2 \times 10 \times 2,$$

giving v as 6.32 m s^{-1}.

b) The combined speed V of the pile and block after impact is given by the conservation of momentum:

$$\text{total momentum after impact} = \text{total momentum before impact}$$
$$1100\ V = 100 \times 6.32,$$

giving V as 0.575 m s^{-1}.

c) The resistance at a distance x is

$$R = 1.5 \times 10^4 + x \times 3 \times 10^4 = (1.5 + 3x) \times 10^4.$$

The work done by the resistance in a distance x is

$$W_1 = \int_0^x -(1.5 + 3x) \times 10^4\, dx = -(1.5x + 1.5x^2) \times 10^4,$$

and this is negative since R opposes the motion. The work done by the weight force is

$$W_2 = 1100 \times 10 \times x = 1.1 \times 10^4 \times x.$$

The KE lost in the pile and block coming to rest is

$$\text{KE} = \tfrac{1}{2} \times 1100 \times 0.575^2 = 181.8.$$

Using the work–energy equation, with the positive direction vertically downwards,

$$-(1.5x + 1.5x^2) \times 10^4 + 1.1 \times 10^4 \times x = 0 - 182,$$
$$1.5 \times 10^4 \times x^2 + 0.4 \times 10^4 \times x - 182 = 0.$$

The positive solution of this quadratic equation is found to be $x = 0.0396$.

Note again, that we have not assumed the conservation of energy when a collision occurs. This is also an example of an inelastic collision since, after impact, there is no velocity of separation.

EXAMPLE 3

Two equal masses are moving in a straight line with speeds u_1 and u_2, respectively, as shown in figure 6.19, where $u_1 > u_2$. After they collide they move off with speeds v_1 and v_2, respectively. Discuss the energy loss at collision.

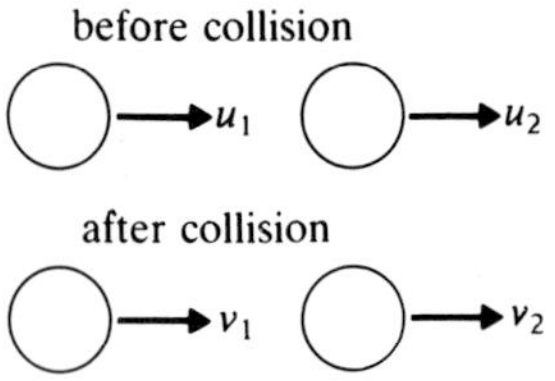

Figure 6.19

By conservation of momentum,

$$v_1 + v_2 = u_1 + u_2.$$

Using the impact equation,

$$v_2 - v_1 = e(u_1 - u_2),$$

where e is the coefficient of restitution. Adding these equations

$$2v_2 = (1+e)u_1 + (1-e)u_2.$$

Subtracting $\quad 2v_1 = (1-e)u_1 + (1+e)u_2,$

Hence $\quad v_1 = \tfrac{1}{2}[(1-e)u_1 + (1+e)u_2],$

$$v_2 = \tfrac{1}{2}[(1+e)u_1 + (1-e)u_2],$$

$$\begin{aligned} v_1^2 + v_2^2 &= \tfrac{1}{4}\{[(1-e)^2 + (1+e)^2](u_1^2 + u_2^2) + 4(1+e)(1-e)u_1u_2\} \\ &= \tfrac{1}{2}(1+e^2)(u_1^2+u_2^2) + (1-e^2)u_1u_2 \\ &= u_1^2 + u_2^2 - \tfrac{1}{2}(1-e^2)(u_1^2+u_2^2) + (1-e^2)u_1u_2 \\ &= u_1^2 + u_2^2 - \tfrac{1}{2}(1-e^2)(u_1-u_2)^2. \end{aligned}$$

The loss of KE is

$$\tfrac{1}{2}m(v_1^2+v_2^2) - \tfrac{1}{2}m(u_1^2+u_2^2) = \tfrac{1}{4}m(1-e^2)(u_1-u_2)^2.$$

We see that the maximum energy loss is for $e = 0$ and that there is no energy loss when $e = 1$. When $e = 1$, $v_2 = u_1$ and $u_1 = v_2$, so that the speeds of the balls are interchanged. When $e = 0$, $v_1 = v_2$ and the balls stick together.

Explosions

Just as with collisions, where mechanical energy may be lost, we can consider explosions, where mechanical energy may be released. In such cases the mechanical energy generated is usually due to the input of chemical energy etc., which causes the explosion.

EXAMPLE 4

A stationary bomb of mass 5 kg explodes into one part, A, of mass 2 kg which flies off with a speed of 60 m s^{-1} and another part, B, of mass 3 kg which flies off with a speed v m s^{-1} in the opposite direction. Find (a) v, the speed of B and (b) the total KE produced by the explosion.

a) Since the explosion is internal, we can apply conservation of total momentum. Taking the direction of v as positive,

$$5 \times 0 = 3v - 2 \times 60$$

The speed of B is 40 m s^{-1}.

b) The initial KE = 0. The final KE is

$$\tfrac{1}{2} \times 3 \times 40^2 + \tfrac{1}{2} \times 2 \times 60^2 = 6000.$$

The total kinetic energy produced by the explosion is 6000 J.

EXAMPLE 5

A stationary bomb of mass 5 kg explodes and breaks into three parts which move off with masses and velocities as shown in figure 6.20. Find (a) the speeds of each part after the explosion, and (b) the gain in KE due to the explosion.

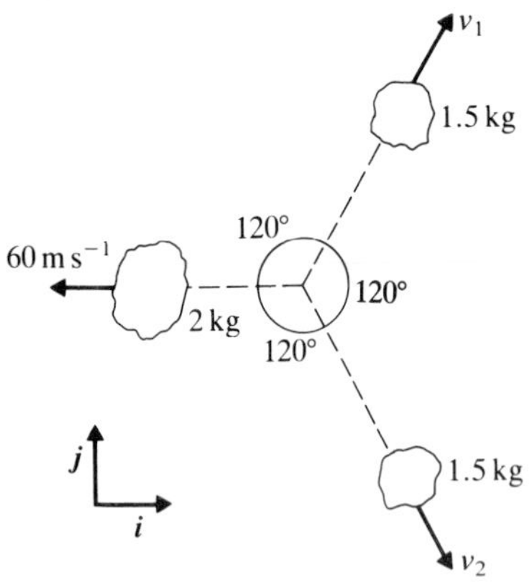

Figure 6.20

a) Taking unit vectors $\boldsymbol{i}$ and $\boldsymbol{j}$ as shown, we apply the principle of conservation of momentum.

$$5\begin{pmatrix}0\\0\end{pmatrix}=2\begin{pmatrix}60\\0\end{pmatrix}+1.5\begin{pmatrix}v_1\cos 60^\circ\\v_1\sin 60^\circ\end{pmatrix}+1.5\begin{pmatrix}v_2\cos 60^\circ\\-v_2\sin 60^\circ\end{pmatrix}.$$

Taking the $\boldsymbol{j}$-component, $\quad v_1=v_2.$

Taking the $\boldsymbol{i}$-component,

$$0=-120+1.5\times 0.5v_1+1.5\times 0.5v_2.$$

Substituting for v_2 $\quad 60=0.75v_1$

Thus $\quad v_1=v_2=\frac{4}{3}\times 60=80.$

Two parts move off with the same speed of 80 m s^{-1}, and the third part with the given speed of 60 m s^{-1}.

b) The energy after the explosion is

$$\tfrac{1}{2}\times 2\times 60^2+\tfrac{1}{2}\times 1.5\times 80^2+\tfrac{1}{2}\times 1.5\times 80^2=13\,200.$$

The energy before the explosion is $\frac{1}{2}\times 5\times 0=0$. The gain in KE is 13 200 J.

EXERCISE 6E

Take g as 10 m s^{-2}, where necessary.

1. A railway truck of mass 4 t is moving at 4 m s^{-1} when it runs into the back of a slower truck of mass 2 t moving at 3 m s^{-1}. After the collision the trucks are coupled together. What is their combined speed after collision? What is the kinetic energy lost at the collision?

2. A ball of mass 2 m is moving at a speed of 2 m s^{-1} towards a ball of mass m which is moving with a speed of 3 m s^{-1} in the opposite direction. The balls collide head on, and the coefficient of restitution for the collision is 1. Calculate the speeds of the balls after impact, and the change in total kinetic energy due to the collision.

3. A man knocks a nail of mass 25 g into a block of wood by delivering a series of 5 blows with a hammer of mass 2 kg. Assuming that the resistance of the wood is uniform and equal to 4000 N and that the speed of the hammer as it hits the nail is 5 m s^{-1}, calculate the depth of penetration after the 5 blows. The nail is vertical and at right angles to the wood, and the hammer and nail remain in contact after each blow.

4. A drop hammer is allowed to fall from rest through a height of 6 m on to a forging. Find the speed of the hammer as it hits the forging. The hammer comes to rest in a distance of 5 cm. Assuming that the resistance is constant, calculate the work done by the forging and the base plate if the mass of the hammer is 500 kg.

5. An apple of mass 0.1 kg is suspended from a tree by a string of length 1 m. Robin Hood shoots an arrow of mass 0.05 kg, with a speed of 10 m s^{-1} at the apple, which it pierces and to which it becomes fixed. Through what angle will the apple swing in the subsequent motion?

6. A pile driver block of mass 0.5 t falls from a height of 2.5 m from rest on to a pile of mass 150 kg. There is no rebound and the pile is driven 10 cm into the ground. Calculate:
   a) the common velocity after impact,
   b) the constant resisting force of the ground in bringing the pile and block to rest.
7. A child of mass 20 kg is sliding down a chute of length 10 m on a slope of angle α where $\sin \alpha = 0.2$. At the bottom of the chute she collides with a stationary child of mass 15 kg and they move off together. Assuming that the chute is smooth, find the speed with which they move off and the distance they travel before they come to rest, if the resistance on the flat is 40 N.
8. A railway truck of mass 15 t moving at 10 km h^{-1} collides with the rear of a second truck of mass 10 t moving at 8 km h^{-1}. After the collision the 10 t truck moves with a speed of 9 km h^{-1} in its original direction. Calculate the speed of the 15 t truck after the collision and the kinetic energy lost in the collision.
9. A projectile of mass 200 g, moving at 500 m s^{-1} hits a pendulum of mass 200 kg which is hanging vertically at rest. If the length of the pendulum is 1 m and the projectile sticks to the bob, calculate the maximum angle to the vertical through which the pendulum will swing.
10. A small 'supaball' of mass m is dropped at the same time, and immediately above a very much larger one of mass M, from a height h above a smooth table. Show that after impact with the ground the large ball will cause the small ball to rebound to a height of approximately $9h$. (Take $e = 1$ for the collisions.)
11. A billiard ball is struck to rebound in turn from each of the four cushions. The coefficient of restitution at each impact is e, and the cushions are smooth. Discuss the motion and the energy loss at each collision.
12. A lump of putty of mass 0.5 kg is thrown with a horizontal speed of 2 m s^{-1} at a circular disc of mass 0.02 kg which hangs vertically from a light string of length 0.5 m. Through what angle will the disc swing, if the putty sticks to the disc. If the putty drops off during the swing, will the disc rise to the same height as before?

Power 6.6

A man of mass 70 kg can run up a flight of 13 stairs each 25 cm high in 6 s, whereas his son of mass 40 kg can run up the same stairs in 3 s. Who is the more powerful on this activity? ($g = 10$ m s^{-2}.)

The work done by the man is given by

$$mgh = 70 \times 10 \times 13 \times 0.25 = 2275,$$

i.e. he does 2275 J of work.

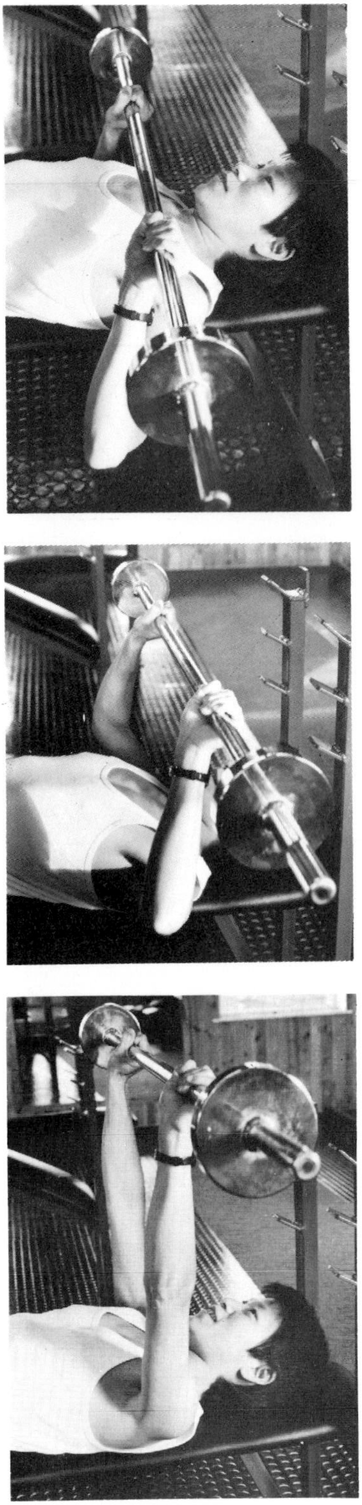

As a further example the rate at which the man can raise the weights gives a measure of his power output.

The work done by the boy is given by

$$mgh = 40 \times 10 \times 13 \times 0.25 = 1300,$$

i.e., he does 1300 J of work. The boy does less work, but he achieves his result in less time than his father.

The man's rate of working is $\frac{1}{6} \times 2275$, i.e. $379\,\mathrm{J\,s^{-1}}$.

The boy's rate of working is $\frac{1}{3} \times 1300$, i.e. $433\,\mathrm{J\,s^{-1}}$.

Thus the boy works at a higher rate than the man and, in this sense, we say the boy is more powerful. That is, he has the capacity for doing work at a higher rate.

There are many instances where we want to know the rate at which work is being done. For example, when manufacturers claim that their cars take various times to reach $100\,\mathrm{km\,h^{-1}}$, they are saying something about the rate at which work can be done by the engines.

We define **power** as the rate of doing work. The units of power are joules per second ($\mathrm{J\,s^{-1}}$), and we define $1\,\mathrm{J\,s^{-1}}$ as 1 **watt** (W), named after James Watt. This is a fairly small unit; it is equivalent to raising a mass of 1 kg through a vertical distance of 10 cm in 1 s; and so we tend to use the kilowatt (kW). For everyday purposes we still sometimes use the unit of **horsepower** (hp), which is equivalent to about 746 W.

It is not always easy to find the work done by a force over a particular distance, because the force might be a function of time rather than of distance. In such cases we proceed as follows.

We write N2 as
$$F = m\frac{\mathrm{d}v}{\mathrm{d}t},$$

multiplying by v
$$Fv = mv\frac{\mathrm{d}v}{\mathrm{d}t}.$$

Integrating with respect to t

$$\int Fv\,\mathrm{d}t = \int mv\frac{\mathrm{d}v}{\mathrm{d}t}\,\mathrm{d}t$$
$$= \tfrac{1}{2}mv^2 - \tfrac{1}{2}mu^2,$$

where u and v are the initial and final speeds. Since the RHS of this equation represents the change in KE, the LHS will be the work done, thus

$$W = \int Fv\,\mathrm{d}t.$$

The power of the force F is

$$P = \mathrm{d}W/\mathrm{d}t$$
$$= \frac{\mathrm{d}}{\mathrm{d}t}\left[\int Fv\,\mathrm{d}t\right]$$
$$= Fv.$$

EXAMPLE 1

A car of mass 1 t is moving at $25\,\mathrm{m\,s^{-1}}$ along a horizontal road with an acceleration of $0.04\,\mathrm{m\,s^{-2}}$. The power output to the driving wheels is 1.6×10^4 W.

a) What is the resistance to the motion of the car at this instant?

b) Whilst travelling at 25 m s^{-1} the car comes to the foot of a hill of slope 1 in 10 when the engine cuts out. If the resistance is the same as before, how far up the hill will the car climb before coming to rest?

a) Let T be the tractive force and R the resistance to motion. Applying N2 horizontally on the car,

$$T - R = ma$$
$$T = R + 1000 \times 0.04$$
$$= R + 40.$$

If P is the power, $P = Tv$:

$$1{\cdot}6 \times 10^4 = (R + 40) \times 25.$$

Hence $$R = 600.$$

So the resistance to motion is 600 N.

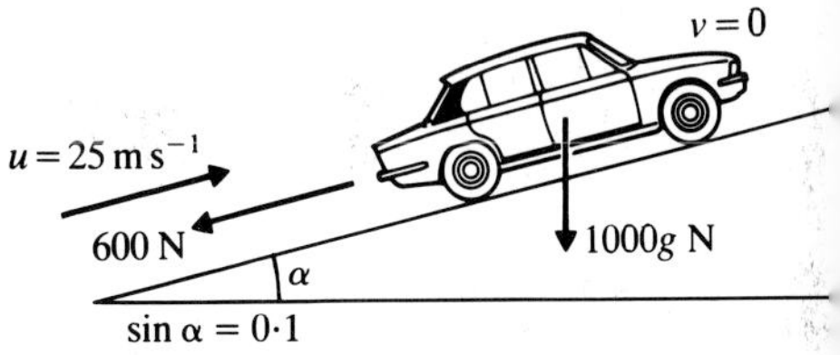

Figure 6.21

b) The situation is illustrated in figure 6.21. In this and other examples, we take the slope of 1 in 10 as an angle given by $\sin^{-1} 0.1$. Suppose the car travels a distance x up the slope before coming to rest. Using the work–energy equation,

work done by resistance + work done by weight force = final KE − initial KE,

$$-600x \quad + -1000 \times 10 \times \tfrac{1}{10} \times x \quad = 0 \quad -\tfrac{1}{2} \times 1000 \times 25^2$$

So the distance x moved up the slope is 195 m.

EXAMPLE 2

The total air and friction resistance on a lorry is of the form $(A + Bv^2)$ N, where $v \text{ m s}^{-1}$ is the speed of the lorry. The mass of the lorry is 10 t, and, on the flat, requires its maximum driving power of 100 kW to maintain a steady speed of 120 km h^{-1}. 40 kW is required to maintain a steady speed of 60 km h^{-1}.

a) Calculate the values of A and B.

b) Show that the lorry can climb a hill inclined at $\sin^{-1} 0.1$ with a constant steady speed of just under 30 km h^{-1}.

a) We convert the speeds to metres per second:

$$120 \text{ km h}^{-1} = 120 \times 10^3/60^2 = 33.3 \text{ m s}^{-1},$$
$$60 \text{ km h}^{-1} = 16.7 \text{ m s}^{-1}.$$

Let the pulling force be F, so that at a steady speed we have, by N2

$$F = A + Bv^2.$$

The power, P, is given by $P = Fv$. Hence $P = (A + Bv^2)v$.

From the data $100 \times 10^3 = (A + B \times 33.3^2) \times 33.3,$

$$40 \times 10^3 = (A + B \times 16.7^2) \times 16.7.$$

Hence $A = 2200$ and $B = 0.72$.

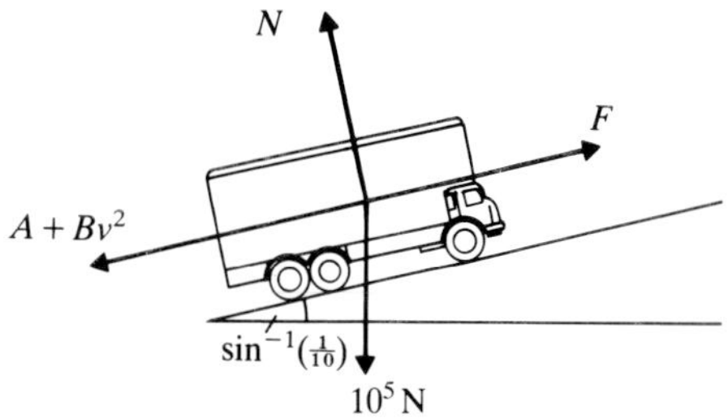

Figure 6.22

b) Suppose that the lorry is going up the slope at a constant speed $v\,\mathrm{m\,s^{-1}}$, as shown in figure 6.22. Applying N2 to the lorry up the slope,

$$F - (A + Bv^2) - 10^5 \times 0.1 = 0.$$

Hence $$Fv = 12\,200v + 0.72v^3$$

Now, $30\,\mathrm{km\,h^{-1}} \approx 8.3\,\mathrm{m\,s^{-1}}$. From the above, when $v = 8.3$, $Fv = 101\,672$. This is just over the maximum 100kW available. Hence the lorry will be able to climb the hill at a speed just under $30\,\mathrm{km\,h^{-1}}$.

□□□□□

Other examples where the idea of power is used, arise when the force is applied at a certain rate. For example, in a hydroelectric plant water falls from a great height, 50 m in the case of Niagara Falls, and the energy released is used to drive water turbines. At the Ffestiniog power station a hydroelectric scheme involves pumping water up a mountain to a lake in 'off-peak' time in order to allow it to descend into turbines later, when the energy is needed at 'peak' times.

The outlet of the lower dam of the Ffestiniog power station. Potential energy of water stored in the upper reservoir is converted to kinetic energy as it falls to the lower reservoir. The kinetic energy is converted to electrical energy by turbines.

EXAMPLE 3

Find the power of a pump which raises water from a lake to a point 10 m higher at a flow rate of $50\,\mathrm{kg\,s^{-1}}$ at a speed of $10\,\mathrm{m\,s^{-1}}$ when (a) the pump is 100% efficient, and (b) when the pump is 60% efficient. Take g as $10\,\mathrm{m\,s^{-2}}$.

a) Since the flow rate is $50\,\mathrm{kg\,s^{-1}}$, the mass of water moved in one second is 50 kg. In that time its increase in energy is

$$\mathrm{PE} = mgh = 50 \times 10 \times 10 = 5000,$$
$$\mathrm{KE} = \tfrac{1}{2}mv^2 = \tfrac{1}{2} \times 50 \times 10^2 = 2500.$$

The total gain in energy in one second is 7500 J, and this is the work done by the pump in one second. The rate at which the pump does work is 7500 J s^{-1}, and this is its power, namely 7.5 kW.

b) The 7.5 kW of effective power is 60% of the actual power of the pump. Thus, the power of the pump is 12.5 kW.

EXAMPLE 4

A man pulls a garden roller of mass 200 kg. The resistance of the ground to motion is 500 N and the man can exert a maximum power of 3 kW.

a) What is the maximum speed he can maintain on the flat?

b) What is the maximum speed he can maintain up an incline of $\sin^{-1} 0.5$?

c) What is the initial acceleration if the slope levels off when the man is pulling the roller at maximum speed?

d)* How long does it take for the man to reach half his maximum speed on the flat, having reached the top of the incline?

e)* How far does the roller travel in this time?

The three stages of the motion are shown in figure 6.23.

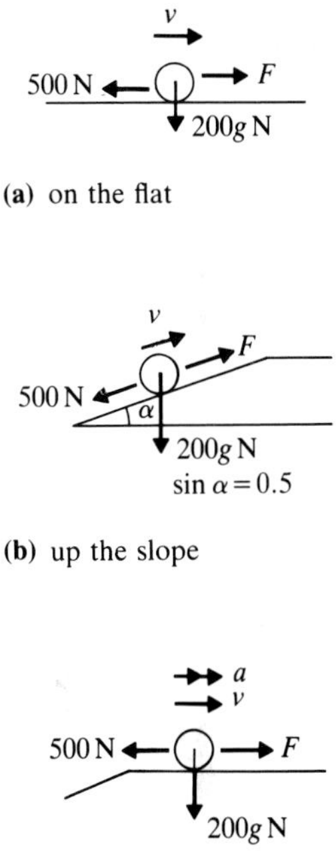

(**a**) on the flat

(**b**) up the slope

(**c**) at top of slope

Figure 6.23

a) On the flat. Let the tractive force on the wheels be F, so that at steady speed, N2 gives

$$F = 500,$$

but at maximum power

$$Fv = 3000 = 500v,$$

so the maximum speed on the flat is 6 m s^{-1}.

b) At steady speed up the slope, N2 gives

$$F - 500 - 200\,g\sin\alpha = 0,$$
$$F = 500 + 200 \times 10 \times 0.5 = 1500,$$

but at maximum power

$$Fv = 3000,$$

so the maximum speed up the slope is 2 m s^{-1}.

c) When the slope levels off, let the initial acceleration be a m s^{-2}. N2 along the path gives

$$F - 500 = 200a,$$
$$F = 500 + 200a,$$

But $\quad Fv = 500v + 200av = 3000.$

Since $v = 2$, $\quad 3000 = 500 \times 2 + 400a,$

giving the initial acceleration as 5 m s^{-2}.

d) In this part a difficulty arises because both F and v vary. But $Fv = 3000$ and, from part (c), $Fv = 500v + 200av$. We write $a = dv/dt$, so the latter equation becomes

$$30 = 5v + 2v\frac{dv}{dt},$$

$$\frac{dv}{dt} = \frac{30 - 5v}{2v}.$$

Separating the variables

$$\int_2^3 \frac{2v}{30 - 5v}\,dv = \int_0^T dt$$

$$\int_2^3 \left[-\frac{2}{5} + \frac{12}{30 - 5v}\right] dv = T,$$

$$\left[-\frac{2}{5}v - \frac{12}{5}\ln|30 - 5v|\right]_3^2 = T$$

$$T = \frac{12}{5}\ln\frac{4}{3} - \frac{2}{5} = 0.284.$$

The man takes 0.284 s to reach half the maximum speed on the flat.

e) As before, $30 = 5v + 2av$, but we now want the distance travelled so we write $a = v\,dv/dx$.

$$30 - 5v = 2v^2\frac{dv}{dx},$$

$$\frac{dv}{dx} = \frac{30 - 5v}{2v^2}.$$

Separating the variables,

$$\int_2^3 \frac{2v^2}{30 - 5v}\,dv = \int_0^X dx,$$

$$\int_2^3 \left[\frac{2}{5}v - \frac{12}{5} + \frac{72}{30 - 5v}\right] dv = X$$

$$X = \frac{72}{5}\ln\frac{4}{3} - \frac{17}{5} = 0.71.$$

The roller moves 0.71 m in this time. Note that the average velocity over this distance is 0.71/0.284 or approximately 2.5 m s^{-1}, as expected.

EXERCISE 6F

Take g as 10 m s^{-2}, where necessary.

1. A lift of mass 500 kg containing a load of mass 700 kg rises through 25 m in 20 s without friction. Calculate the average power output of the motor driving the lift if it is only 60% efficient.

2. A car of mass 1 t can develop 25 kW at a speed of 80 km h^{-1}. Calculate the resistance to motion and, assuming that it varies with the square of the speed, what effective power would be needed for a speed of 90 km h^{-1}?

3. The engine of a light aeroplane develops a power of 800 kW when the machine is cruising at 200 km h^{-1}. Assuming that the resistance is proportional to the square of the speed, find the power developed when it is travelling at 250 km h^{-1} under the same conditions.

4. When a garden hosepipe points vertically upwards, the water reaches a height of 5 m. The pump attached to the pipe delivers water at 30 litres per minute. 1 litre of water has a mass of 1 kg.

   a) With what speed is the water ejected from the pipe?

   b) What is the minimum power of the pump?

   c) How much work does the pump do in 1 min?

   d) If the hosepipe now points horizontally and is placed 1.25 m above the ground, how far will the jet of water travel before it hits the ground?

5. An electric pump raises 10 m^3 of water from a reservoir 5 m below ground to a storage tank above ground. If the outlet of the discharge pipe is 20 m above ground and the whole operation takes 45 min, find the minimum power of the pump if it is 60% efficient.

6. A man lifts a brick of mass 1 kg to a height of 1 m above ground and then throws it with a horizontal speed of 5 m s^{-1}. He repeats this 30 times per minute. What is the average rate in kW at which he is working?

7. A dock 200 m long and 40 m wide contains water to a depth of 12 m. It has to be drained by raising all its water to a height of 1 m above the level of the dock in 5 h. Calculate the power of the engines if they are 60% efficient.

8. The resistance to the motion of a train is $A + Bv$ (in N), where v is the speed in m s^{-1}. The mass of the train is 150 t, A is 3000 N and the total resistance to motion is 4500 N at 30 km h^{-1}. Calculate B and the maximum speed on the flat for a 250 kW engine. In what time will the train come to rest if the power is shut off when the train is travelling at 60 km h^{-1}?

9. The resistance to the motion of a train of mass m (in kg) is $A + Bv$ (in N) where A and B are constants and v is the speed in m s^{-1}.

   a) If the power of the engine is a constant P (in kW) find an expression for the time taken for the train to reach a speed of w (in m s^{-1}), starting from rest.

   b) Find the time taken for a train of mass 200 t to reach 90 km h^{-1} starting from rest, if $A = 2000$, $B = 200$ and P is 200 kW.

10. A Bristol Britannia aircraft has a loaded mass of 82.5 ton and cruises at a speed of 355 mile h^{-1}, powered by four engines each having a power of 4460 hp. What is the air resistance at constant speed if the engines are on full power? (Take 1 ton $\equiv$ 1 tonne, 1 mile $\equiv$ 1.6 km and 1 hp $\equiv$ 0.75 kW.)

Summary

Work and kinetic energy

For a constant force in one dimension, the work done W is given by

$$W = Fs,$$

where F is the force and s is the distance, and the work–energy equation is

$$Fs = \tfrac{1}{2}mv^2 - \tfrac{1}{2}mu^2.$$

For a constant force in one, two or three dimensions,

$$W = \boldsymbol{F}\cdot\boldsymbol{s},$$

and the work–energy equation is

$$\boldsymbol{F}\cdot\boldsymbol{s} = \tfrac{1}{2}mv^2 - \tfrac{1}{2}mu^2.$$

For a variable force in one dimension,

$$W = \int F\,\mathrm{d}x,$$

and the work–energy equation is

$$\int F\,\mathrm{d}x = \int Fv\,\mathrm{d}t = \tfrac{1}{2}mv^2 - \tfrac{1}{2}mu^2.$$

The units of work and kinetic energy are joules (J).

Gravitational potential energy (GPE)

The work done in raising a body of mass m from one level to another a distance h above it against gravity is mgh and this is called its GPE.

Principle of conservation of energy (the energy equation)

In the absence of friction and other non-conservative forces,

$$\text{GPE} + \text{KE} = \text{constant}.$$

Power

$$P = \frac{\mathrm{d}W}{\mathrm{d}t} = Fv.$$

The units of power are:

$$1 \text{ watt (W)} = 1 \text{ J s}^{-1},$$
$$10^3 \text{ W} = 1 \text{ kW}.$$

STATICS

7

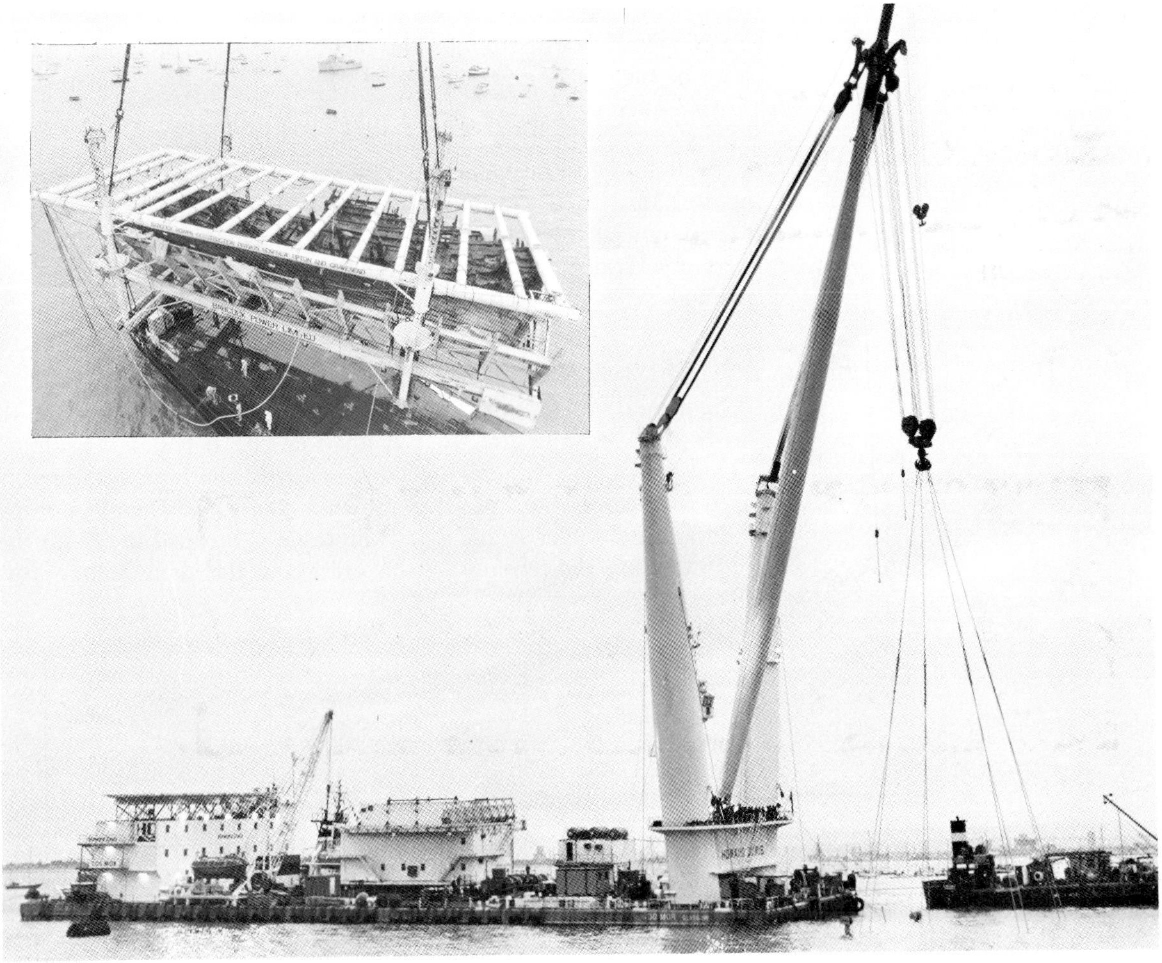

Figure 7.1. *The raising of Henry VIII's flagship, the Mary Rose. Sunk: July 1545. Raised: November 1982.*

When an object remains at rest under the influence of a number of external forces, it is said to be in equilibrium. The study of bodies in equilibrium is known as **statics**.

Equilibrium of a particle **7.1**

We shall review the conditions for a particle to be in equilibrium under the action of a number of forces. Since a particle has no dimensions, all the forces will act at the same point.

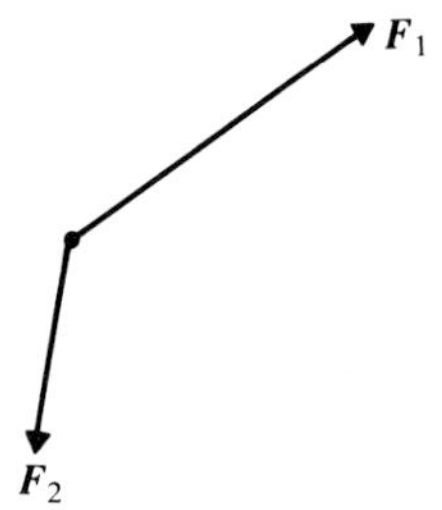

Figure 7.2

a) *One force.* By N1, a particle cannot be in equilibrium when acted upon by a single external force.

b) *Two forces.* A particle will only be in equilibrium under two forces $\boldsymbol{F}_1$ and $\boldsymbol{F}_2$ if $\boldsymbol{F}_1 + \boldsymbol{F}_2 = \mathbf{0}$, i.e. if $\boldsymbol{F}_2 = -\boldsymbol{F}_1$, so that $\boldsymbol{F}_1$ and $\boldsymbol{F}_2$ must be of the same magnitude and be in opposite directions to each other. Thus the particle in figure 7.2 cannot be in equilibrium.

c) *Three forces.* For equilibrium, the forces, as shown in figure 7.3a, must be such that

$$\boldsymbol{F}_1 + \boldsymbol{F}_2 + \boldsymbol{F}_3 = \mathbf{0}.$$

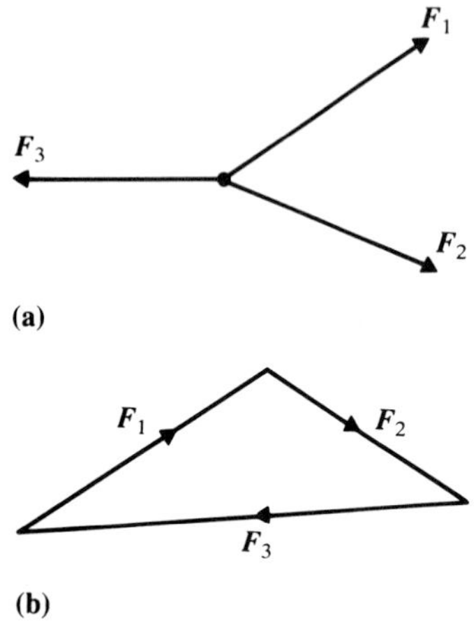

Figure 7.3

The 3 forces must be coplanar and form a closed vector triangle as in figure 7.3b.

Situations involving three forces are very common and in chapter 1 we saw several methods for their solution. We will revise the standard method by means of an example.

EXAMPLE 1

A light bulb is suspended by its cable from the roof of a garage. In order for it to hang directly over a car engine, it is pulled aside by means of a string, which is inclined at 20° to the horizontal and is fixed to a wall of the garage, as shown in figure 7.4. The mass of the bulb and its holder is 200 g and the cable is inclined at 60° to the vertical. Find the tensions in the string and the cable, taking g as $10\ \text{m s}^{-2}$.

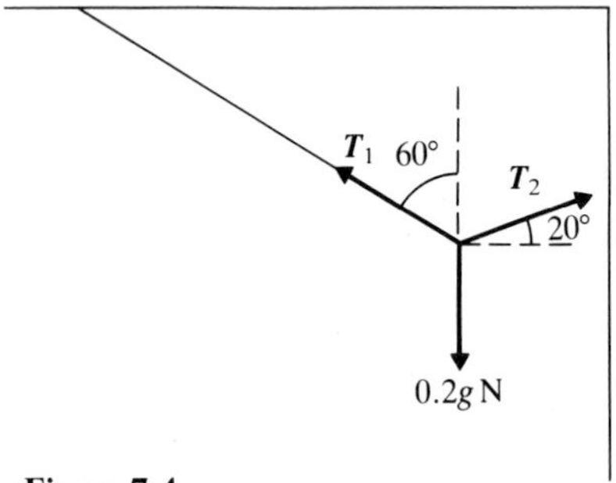

Figure 7.4

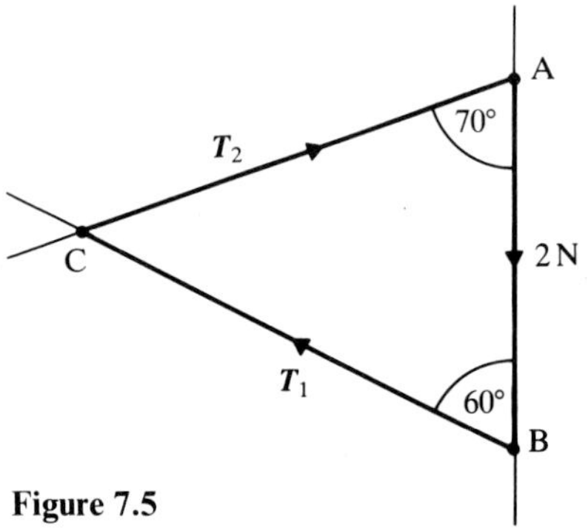

Figure 7.5

The bulb is in equilibrium and so the forces acting upon it form a closed vector triangle, as in figure 7.5. We know the magnitude and direction of **AB**, which represents the weight force, and the directions of **AC** and **BC**, which represent the tensions $\boldsymbol{T}_2$ and $\boldsymbol{T}_1$ in the string and cable, respectively. We are thus able to draw the triangle.
By Lami's theorem,

$$\frac{2}{\sin 50^\circ} = \frac{T_2}{\sin 60^\circ} = \frac{T_1}{\sin 70^\circ},$$

$$T_1 = \frac{2 \sin 70^\circ}{\sin 50^\circ} = 2.45, \qquad T_2 = \frac{2 \sin 60^\circ}{\sin 50^\circ} = 2.26.$$

The tension in the cable is 2.45 N, and in the string the tension is 2.26 N.

d) *Four or more forces in the same plane.* The usual way to solve these problems is to resolve all the forces into two perpendicular directions, as the following example shows.

EXAMPLE 2

Four horizontal wires are attached to a telegraph pole, as in figure 7.6. The magnitudes and directions of the tensions in three of them are shown. Find the tension in the fourth wire, if there is no resultant force on the pole from the wires.

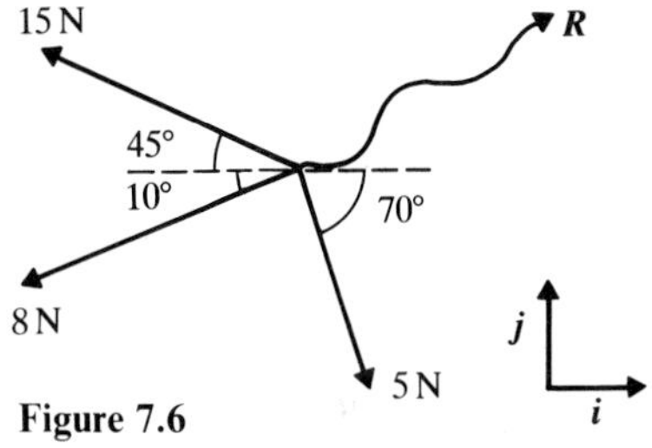

Figure 7.6

We take unit vectors $\boldsymbol{i}$ and $\boldsymbol{j}$ in the directions shown, and let $\boldsymbol{R}$ be the unknown force. Since the pole is in equilibrium, the vector sum of the forces on it is zero:

$$\boldsymbol{R} + \begin{pmatrix} -15\cos 45^\circ \\ 15\sin 45^\circ \end{pmatrix} + \begin{pmatrix} -8\cos 10^\circ \\ -8\sin 10^\circ \end{pmatrix} + \begin{pmatrix} 5\cos 70^\circ \\ -5\sin 70^\circ \end{pmatrix} = \mathbf{0},$$

$$\boldsymbol{R} + \begin{pmatrix} -16.8 \\ 4.52 \end{pmatrix} = \mathbf{0},$$

$$\boldsymbol{R} = \begin{pmatrix} 16.8 \\ -4.52 \end{pmatrix}.$$

The magnitude of the tension,

$$R = \sqrt{\{(16.8)^2 + (-4.52)^2\}} = 17.4,$$

and its direction is given by $\tan^{-1}(-4.52/16.8) = -15^\circ$. The tension has a magnitude of 17.4 N and acts at 15° below the positive $\boldsymbol{i}$-direction.

We could draw a closed polygon, but the solution would involve the use of the cosine rule twice. Alternatively we could draw a scale diagram, although this is subject to inaccuracy in measurement.

□□□□□

In general when four or more forces are in equilibrium they need not be coplanar. They must, however, form a closed polygon. The best method of solution of such problems is to resolve into three mutually perpendicular directions.

EXAMPLE 3

A hot-air balloon of mass 4 t has a lift of 40 400 N when inflated. It is secured 5 m above the ground by four ropes which are attached to four pegs A, B, C and D on the ground and these form a rectangle measuring 12 m by 6 m. The lengths of the ropes are such that OA = OB and OC = OD and the balloon is vertically above the point P, 5 m from AB, as indicated in figure 7.7. Assuming there is no wind, find the tensions in the ropes if the balloon is in equilibrium. Take g as 10 m s^{-2}.

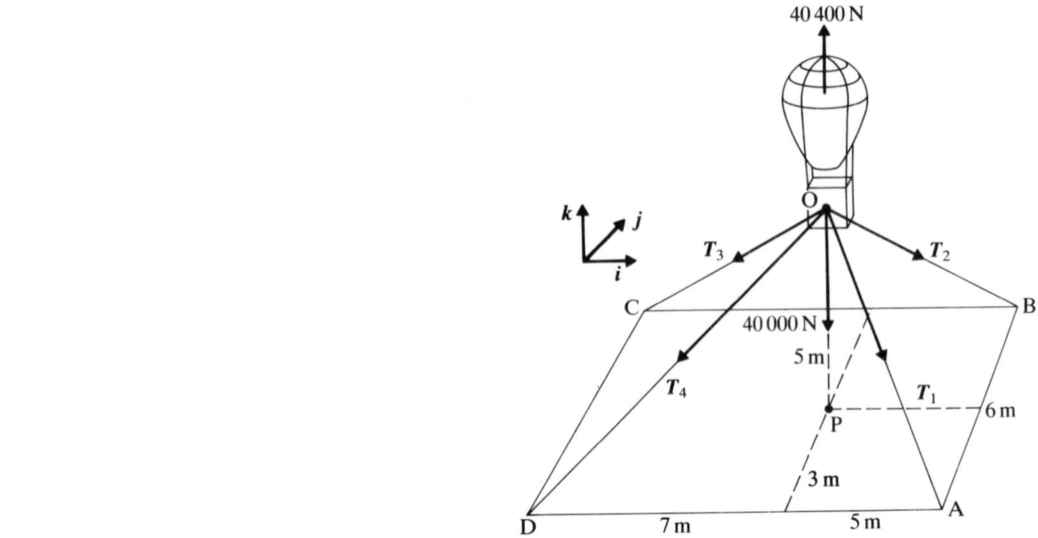

Figure 7.7

We take unit vectors $\boldsymbol{i}, \boldsymbol{j}$ and $\boldsymbol{k}$ with origin O, as shown in figure 7.7. The tensions $\boldsymbol{T}_1$, $\boldsymbol{T}_2$, $\boldsymbol{T}_3$ and $\boldsymbol{T}_4$ act along the vectors **OA**, **OB**, **OC** and **OD**, respectively. By symmetry the magnitudes of $\boldsymbol{T}_1$ and $\boldsymbol{T}_2$ are equal, as are those of $\boldsymbol{T}_3$ and $\boldsymbol{T}_4$. Thus

$$\boldsymbol{T}_1 = s\begin{pmatrix} 5 \\ -3 \\ -5 \end{pmatrix}, \quad \boldsymbol{T}_2 = s\begin{pmatrix} 5 \\ 3 \\ -5 \end{pmatrix}, \quad \boldsymbol{T}_3 = t\begin{pmatrix} -7 \\ 3 \\ -5 \end{pmatrix}, \quad \boldsymbol{T}_4 = t\begin{pmatrix} -7 \\ -3 \\ -5 \end{pmatrix},$$

where s and t are scalars. For equilibrium the vector sum of all the forces on the balloon is zero:

$$s\begin{pmatrix} 5 \\ -3 \\ -5 \end{pmatrix} + s\begin{pmatrix} 5 \\ 3 \\ -5 \end{pmatrix} + t\begin{pmatrix} -7 \\ 3 \\ -5 \end{pmatrix} + t\begin{pmatrix} -7 \\ -3 \\ -5 \end{pmatrix} + \begin{pmatrix} 0 \\ 0 \\ 400 \end{pmatrix} = \begin{pmatrix} 0 \\ 0 \\ 0 \end{pmatrix},$$

where $\begin{pmatrix} 0 \\ 0 \\ 400 \end{pmatrix}$ is the net vertical force due to the weight and the lift.

By comparing components,

$$10s - 14t = 0, \qquad -10s - 10t = -400.$$

Solving these, we get $s = 23.3$ and $t = 16.7$.

Hence
$$\boldsymbol{T}_1 = 23.3\begin{pmatrix} 5 \\ -3 \\ -5 \end{pmatrix},$$

giving $T_1 = 23.3\ (5^2 + (-3)^2 + (-5)^2)^{1/2} \approx 179$ and, by symmetry, $T_2 \approx 179$. Similarly, $T_3 = T_4 \approx 152$.

EXERCISE 7A

Take g as $10\ \text{m s}^{-2}$, where necessary.

1. A particle of mass 20 kg is suspended by two strings of length 1 m and 1.5 m attached to two points 2 m apart on the same horizontal level. What are the tensions in the two strings?

2. A light wire is attached to two points on the same level, 2 m apart. A mass of 5 kg is attached to the middle of the wire, causing it to drop 10 cm below the line joining the two points. What is the tension in the wire?

3. A particle of mass m is at rest on a smooth plane inclined to the horizontal at an angle α. What is the force needed to maintain equilibrium if it acts (a) parallel to the plane, (b) horizontally?

4. A body on a smooth, horizontal table is acted upon by three horizontal forces, as shown in figure 7.8. What is the magnitude and direction of the fourth force needed to keep the body in equilibrium?

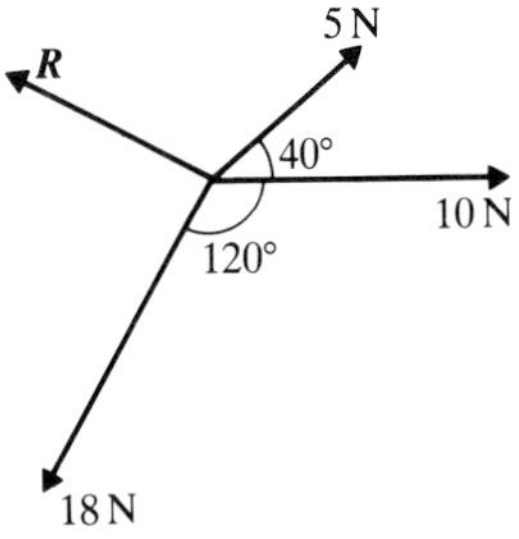

Figure 7.8

5. A particle of mass 1 kg is suspended by a vertical string. What is the horizontal force needed to deflect the string through 40° to the vertical?

6. a) Figure 7.9 shows three masses joined by light wires, passing over smooth pulleys. Calculate the angles between the wires when the system is in equilibrium.

   b) Repeat part (a) if the three masses are replaced by masses of 6 kg, 10 kg and 8 kg, from left to right.

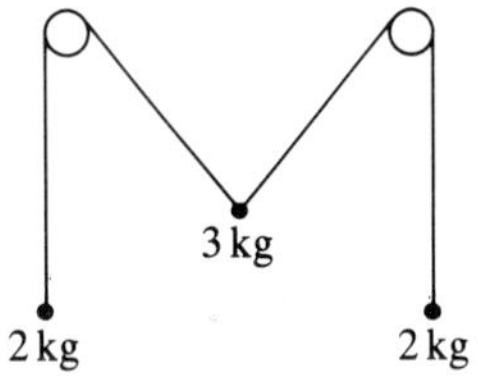

Figure 7.9

7. Figure 7.10 represents a boat and its trailer on a slipway. Two men are holding it by ropes, parallel to the plane and inclined at 20° and 30° to the line of greatest slope. Find the tensions T and S if the boat is in equilibrium.

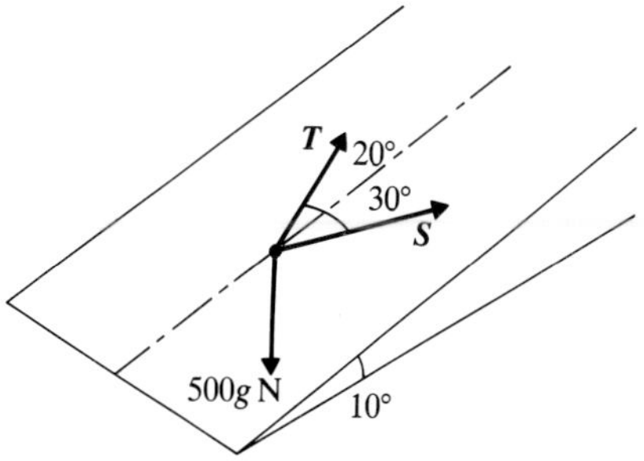

Figure 7.10

8. A vertical flagpole of height 10 m has a number of wires attached to it in the NS and EW lines as shown in figure 7.11. The tensions in the wires are adjusted so that their resultant of 2000 N acts vertically downwards. If $T_4 = 500$ N, calculate the values of T_1, T_2 and T_3.

Figure 11

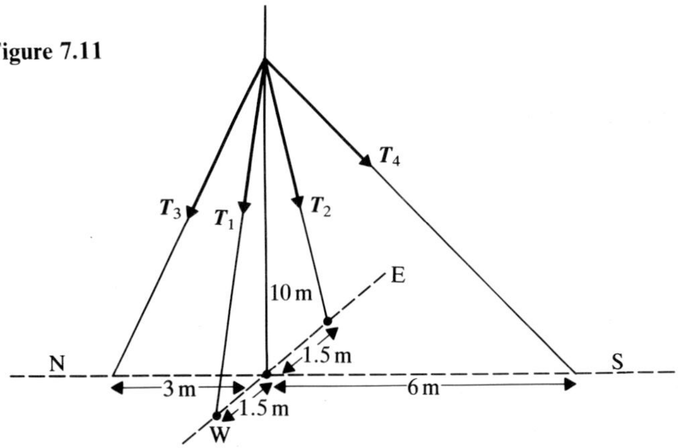

7.2 Friction

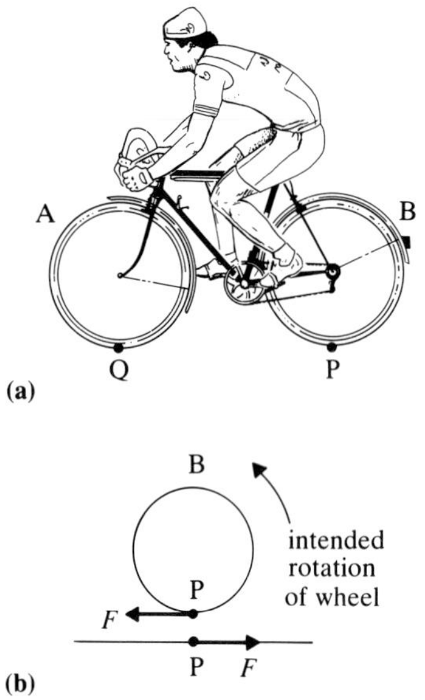

Figure 7.12

Friction is the name given to the force which tends to prevent slipping between surfaces in contact, and we have met this briefly in chapter 3. Whilst there is always some frictional force between slipping surfaces, this is sometimes very small, in which case we neglect it, and say that the contact between the surfaces is *smooth*, e.g. between an ice hockey puck and the ice it moves across.

Surfaces which are not smooth are said to be *rough*. Friction never causes slipping between surfaces in contact, it always opposes it. This is not the same as saying that friction always opposes motion, as the following example shows.

Figure 7.12a shows a cyclist. In order to make the cycle move forward the cyclist presses on the pedals which causes the rear wheel to rotate anticlockwise. If the contact between the wheel and the ground at P were smooth, the cycle would not move forward. Figure 7.12b shows the horizontal forces acting on the wheel and the ground at P. Friction acts to the left on the wheel and, by N3, to the right on the ground. This force will cause the wheel to roll rather than to slip and thus the cyclist will move forward. What are the forces on the front wheel and the ground at Q?

The fundamental properties of the frictional force are as follows:

a) Friction always opposes the relative motion of surfaces in contact and acts at a tangent to the surfaces.

b) Friction is a variable force and when slipping does not take place it is just sufficient to prevent relative motion of the surfaces in contact.

Figure 7.13a shows a man pushing a heavy trunk. Assuming that the trunk does not tip, it will not move until the force the man exerts is large enough to overcome the frictional resistance between the trunk and the floor. All the time the man is failing to move the trunk, the frictional force is just large enough to prevent motion.

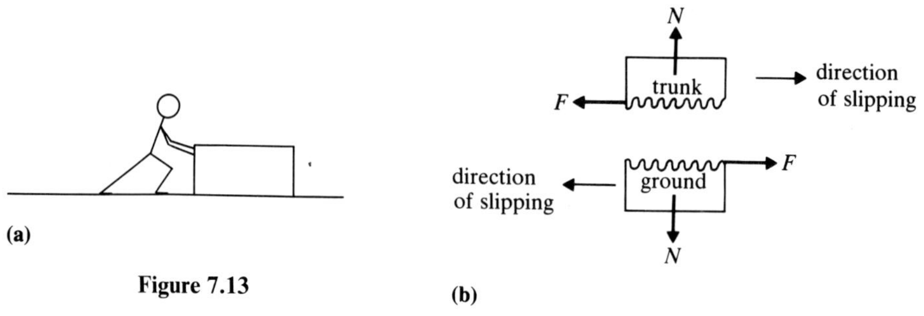

Figure 7.13

c) There is an upper limit to the magnitude of the frictional force, and this is dependent on 2 factors:
(i) the normal contact force between the surfaces,
(ii) the roughness of the surfaces in contact.

This upper limit is reached when sliding is about to occur, and we say that under these circumstances 'friction is limiting'. Experimental observation has led to the formulation of the law

$$F \leqslant \mu N,$$

where F is the frictional force and N the normal contact force as shown in figure 7.13b. When friction is limiting, $F = \mu N$.

μ is a constant which depends on the nature of the surfaces and is called the **coefficient of friction**. For wood on wood, μ lies between 0.2 and 0.5. For metal on metal μ is about 0.2.

When sliding does take place, the frictional force drops very slightly from its limiting value, but we will assume that, under these circumstances, the frictional force takes its limiting value. In order to avoid the complications of tipping and toppling caused by rotation we will confine ourselves to friction between rough planes and particles, or bodies which we can treat as particles. The action of friction on rigid bodies is discussed later.

EXAMPLE 1

A toboggan of mass 10 kg is on level ground. (a) If a horizontal force of 10 N will just move it, find μ. (b) If a boy of mass 30 kg sits on the toboggan, find the least horizontal force needed to move it. Take g as 10 m s^{-2}.

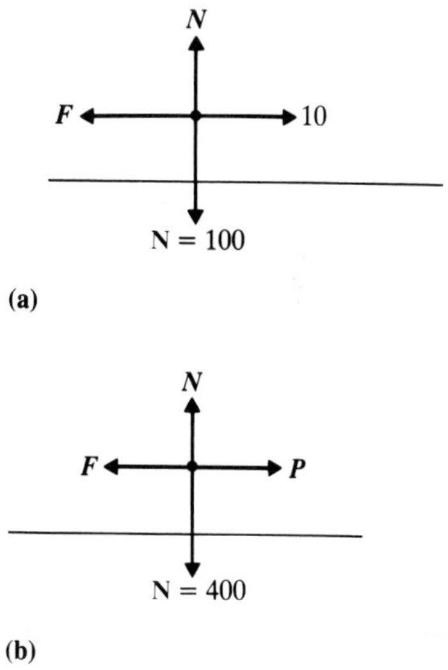

Figure 7.14

a) The forces acting on the toboggan are shown in figure 7.14a. Applying N2 to the toboggan:

vertically $\quad N = 100,$

horizontally $\quad 10 - F = 0, \quad \Rightarrow F = 10.$

Since friction is limiting, $F = \mu N$,

$$10 = 100\mu \quad \Rightarrow \mu = 0.1.$$

b) The forces acting on the toboggan and the boy are shown in figure 7.14b. Applying N2 to this 'particle':

vertically $\quad N = 400,$

horizontally $\quad P - F = 0.$

Since friction is limiting, $F = 0.1 \times 400 = 40.$

Thus $\quad P = 40.$

We note that P is now four times as large as in (a), since N is four times as large.

EXAMPLE 2

A book is lying flat on a horizontal table. One end of the table is raised slowly until the book starts to slide down. If sliding starts when the angle is α, prove that the coefficient of friction between the book and the table is given by $\mu = \tan \alpha$.

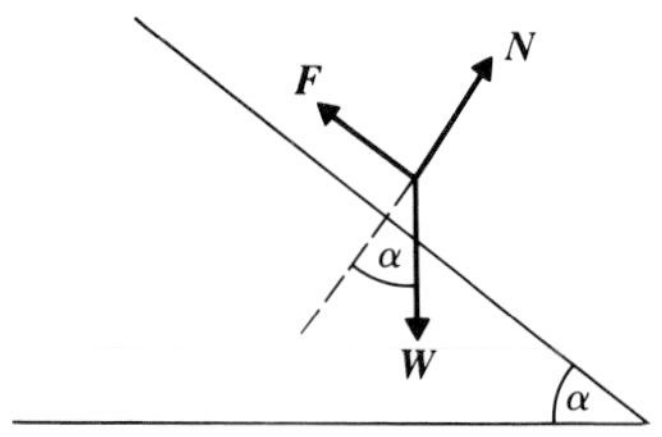

Figure 7.15

Let W be the weight of the book. The forces acting are shown in figure 7.15. Applying N2 to the book:

perpendicular to the plane $\quad N = W\cos\alpha,$

parallel to the plane $\quad W\sin\alpha - F = 0 \qquad$ **(1)**

Friction is limiting and so $F = \mu N = \mu W\cos\alpha$, not μW in this case. From (1)

$$F = W\sin\alpha$$
$$\mu W\cos\alpha = W\sin\alpha,$$
$$\mu = \tan\alpha.$$

EXAMPLE 3

Suppose that the book in example 2 is on a plane inclined at an angle θ to the horizontal, where $\theta > \alpha$. P is the minimum force parallel to the plane needed to prevent the book from sliding down. If this force were to be increased to $2P$ the book would begin to slide up the plane.

a) Find a relation between P, W and θ.

b) Find a relation between μ and θ.

c) If P were removed, prove that the book would slide down the plane with an acceleration given by $a = \frac{2}{3}g\sin\theta$.

a) There are two cases to consider:

i) Figure 7.16a shows the forces on the book when it is about to slide down the plane. In this case friction acts up the plane. Applying N2 to the book:

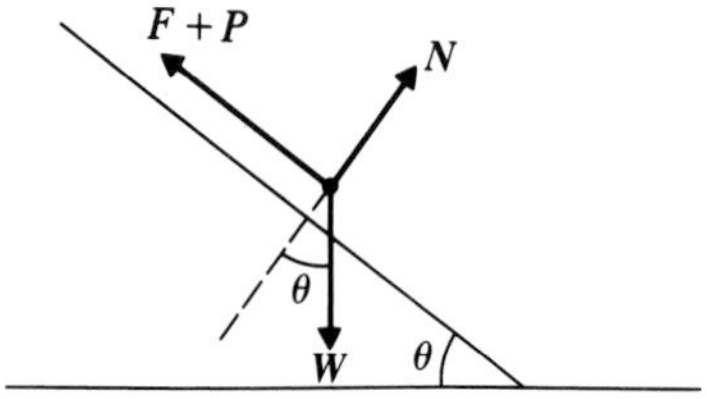

(a)

up the plane $\quad P + F = W\sin\theta,$

perpendicular to the plane $\quad N = W\cos\theta.$

Since friction is limiting, $F = \mu N = \mu W\cos\theta$. Hence

$$P + \mu W\cos\theta = W\sin\theta. \qquad \textbf{(2)}$$

ii) Figure 7.16b shows the forces on the book when it is about to slide up the plane. Friction now acts down the plane. Using N2 and resolving:

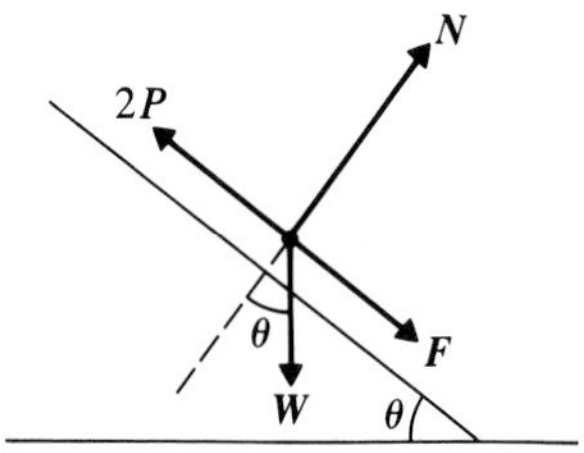

(b)

Figure 7.16

up the plane $\quad 2P - F = W\sin\theta,$

perpendicular to the plane $\quad N = W\cos\theta.$

Since friction is limiting, $F = \mu N = \mu W\cos\theta$. Hence

$$2P - \mu W\cos\theta = W\sin\theta. \qquad \textbf{(3)}$$

Adding equations (2) and (3)

$$3P = 2W\sin\theta,$$
$$P = \tfrac{2}{3}W\sin\theta.$$

b) Substituting in equation (3) for P, we get

$$\tfrac{4}{3}W \sin\theta - \mu W \cos\theta = W \sin\theta,$$
$$\mu = \tfrac{1}{3}\tan\theta,$$
$$\tan\theta = 3\mu.$$

c) With P absent, the forces on the book are as shown in figure 7.16c. If the mass of the book is m, $W = mg$. F clearly acts up the plane and will take its limiting value. Applying N2 to the book:

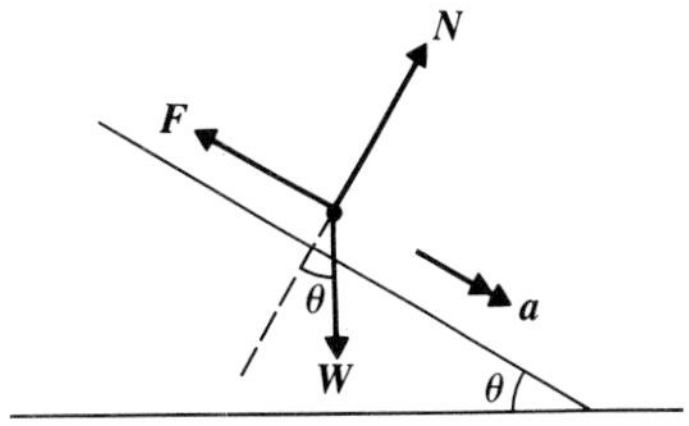

(c)

perpendicular to the plane $N = W\cos\theta$,

down the plane $W\sin\theta - \mathrm{F} = \mathrm{ma}$,

where a is the acceleration. Also

$$F = \mu N = \mu W\cos\theta.$$

Hence, $$W\sin\theta - \mu W\cos\theta = ma$$
$$g(\sin\theta - \mu\cos\theta) = a.$$

Since $\mu = \tfrac{1}{3}\tan\theta$, we obtain

$$g(\sin\theta - \tfrac{1}{3}\sin\theta) = a,$$

giving $$a = \tfrac{2}{3}g\sin\theta.$$

There is sometimes confusion of the variable magnitude and direction of ***F***, and it may be helpful to consider the effect on ***F*** of different applied forces up the line of greatest slope.

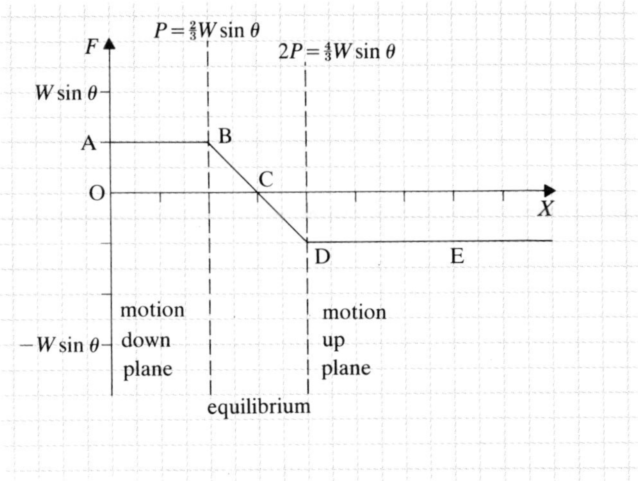

Figure 7.17

Figure 7.17 shows the graph of F against the applied force X where the positive direction is measured up the line of greatest slope.

Point on graph	Applied force	Frictional force	Motion
A	$X = 0$	$F = \frac{1}{3}W \sin\theta$ and limiting	book slides down the plane
B	$X = P = \frac{2}{3}W \sin\theta$	$F = \frac{1}{3}W \sin\theta$ and limiting	book in equilibrium, no motion
C	$X = W \sin\theta$	$F = 0$	X is sufficient to prevent slipping on smooth plane, no friction needed, no motion
D	$X = 2P = \frac{4}{3}W \sin\theta$	$F = -\frac{1}{3}W \sin\theta$ and limiting, acts down the plane.	book just moves up the plane
E	$X = 2W \sin\theta$	as D	book accelerates up the plane,

The table shows the effects of these forces at various points on the graph. Between points B and D, when the book is in equilibrium, the frictional force decreases linearly as X increases.

EXAMPLE 4

A particle of mass m is pulled at constant speed along a rough horizontal floor by a string inclined at an angle θ to the floor. The coefficient of friction between the particle and the floor is μ.

a) Find an expression for the tension, T.

b)* Find the least value of T, and the value of θ for which this occurs.

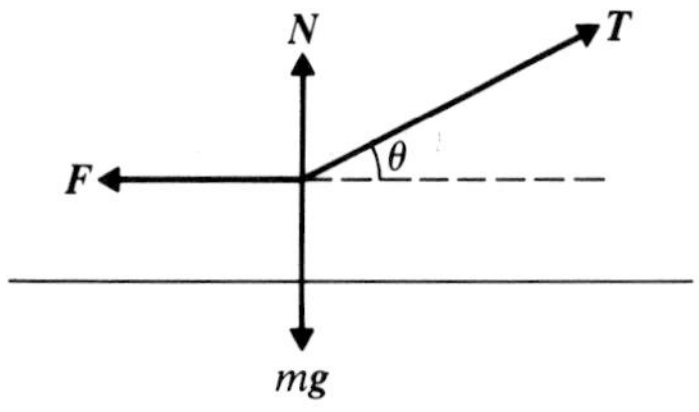

Figure 7.18

a) The forces acting on the particle are as shown in figure 7.18. Applying N2 on the particle:

vertically $\qquad N + T\sin\theta = mg,$

horizontally $\qquad T\cos\theta - F = 0.$

Friction is limiting, so

$$F = \mu N = \mu(mg - T\sin\theta).$$

Hence

$$T\cos\theta = \mu mg - \mu T\sin\theta.$$

$$T(\cos\theta + \mu\sin\theta) = \mu mg,$$

$$T = \frac{\mu mg}{\cos\theta + \mu\sin\theta}. \qquad \textbf{(4)}$$

When $\theta = 0$, $T = F = \mu mg$. When $\theta = 90°$, $T = mg$ and $F = 0$, but the particle does not actually move across the floor.

b) Referring to equation (4), to find the minimum value of T we find the maximum value of $\cos\theta + \mu\sin\theta$.

$$\cos\theta + \mu\sin\theta = \sqrt{(1+\mu^2)}\left[\frac{1}{\sqrt{(1+\mu^2)}}\cos\theta + \frac{\mu}{\sqrt{(1+\mu^2)}}\sin\theta\right]$$

$$= \sqrt{(1+\mu^2)}\cos(\theta - \alpha), \qquad \text{where } \tan\alpha = \mu.$$

Hence $$T = \frac{\mu mg}{\sqrt{(1+\mu^2)}\cos(\theta - \alpha)}.$$

Now T_{min} occurs when $\cos(\theta - \alpha)$ is a maximum, i.e. 1. Thus

$$T_{min} = \frac{\mu mg}{\sqrt{(1+\mu^2)}},$$

when $\theta = \alpha = \tan^{-1}\mu$, as above.

Alternatively this result may be found by differentiation. The graph of T against θ is shown in figure 7.19a. Now

$$F = T\cos\theta = \frac{\mu mg}{(1+\mu\tan\theta)}$$

and the graph of F against θ is shown in figure 7.19b.

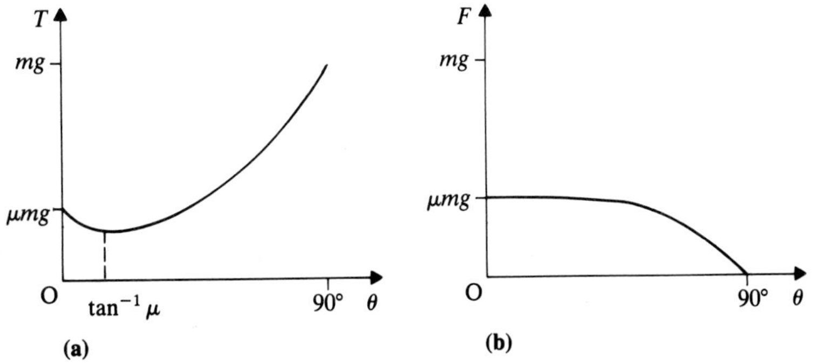

Figure 7.19

EXERCISE 7B

Take g as 10 ms^{-2}, where necessary.

1. A block of mass 5 kg will just move when pushed along a table by a horizontal force of 20 N. Find the coefficient of friction between the block and the table.

2. A trunk of mass 50 kg will just move across a rough floor when dragged by a horizontal rope with a tension of 150 N. What is the coefficient of friction between the trunk and the floor? If the rope is inclined at an angle of 20°, what is the least tension required in it to move the trunk?

3. A gymnast of mass 70 kg is hanging in equilibrium from a vertical climbing rope. The coefficient of friction between his hands and the rope is 0.2. Calculate the total normal force between his hands and the rope.

4. A block of wood is held in a vice, with the sides of the vice vertical. The mass of the block is 2 kg and the coefficient of friction between the wood and metal is 0.3. If the total area of contact between the wood and metal is 0.02 m^2, find the minimum pressure needed to support the block.

5. A particle of mass 8 kg rests on a rough plane inclined at an angle of 30° to the horizontal. The coefficient of friction is 0.2. Find the minimum force required to prevent slipping down the plane if the force is applied (a) up the line of greatest slope, (b) horizontally.

6. A particle of mass 4 kg is on a rough plane inclined at an angle $\sin^{-1}\frac{3}{5}$ to the horizontal. The coefficient of friction is $\frac{1}{2}$. Find the range of values of the applied force P for the particle to remain in equilibrium if P is applied (a) up the line of greatest slope, (b) horizontally.

7. A particle of mass m rests on a rough plane inclined at an angle α above the horizontal. A force P applied up the line of greatest slope will just prevent motion down the slope. If this force is increased to $2P$, motion is about to take place up the slope. Show that, if the coefficient of friction is μ, $3\mu = \tan\alpha$.

8.* Two heavy, identical suitcases are resting on top of one another on a rough plane inclined at an angle α to the horizontal. The coefficient of friction between the two cases is μ_1 and between the lower suitcase and the plane is μ_2. A force P is applied down the line of greatest slope to the middle of the upper suitcase. Given $\mu_1 > \tan\alpha$ and $\mu_2 > \tan\alpha$, show that as P increases, the lower one slips first, provided $2\mu_2 - \mu_1 < \tan\alpha$.

9.* Two masses, m_1 and m_2 are at rest along the line of greatest slope of a rough plane inclined at an angle α to the horizontal, with m_1 the higher. The particles are connected by a light string and $\mu_1 > \tan\alpha > \mu_2$, where μ_1 and μ_2 are the coefficients of friction between the plane and the upper and lower particles, respectively. Show that, if they are both on the point of slipping,

$$\tan\alpha = \frac{\mu_1 m_1 + \mu_2 m_2}{m_1 + m_2}$$

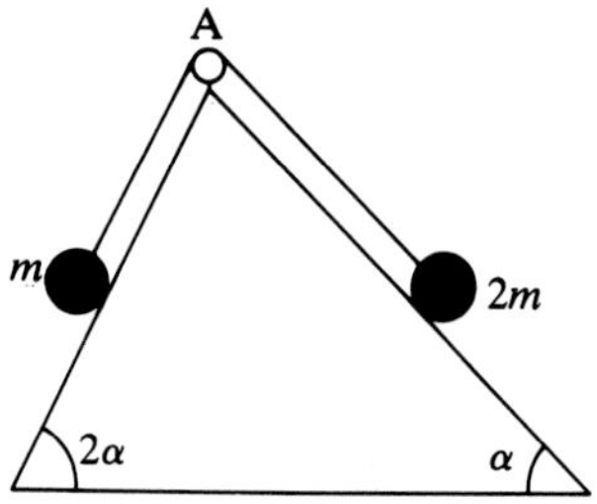

Figure 7.20

10. Figure 7.20 shows two particles on different sides of a fixed wedge, joined by a light inextensible string passing over a fixed smooth pulley at A. The coefficient of friction between both particles and the wedge is μ. Find the least value of μ if the system is to remain in equilibrium.

The angle of friction; rough reaction

The complications involved in determining the least force required to move the particle in example 4 could have been avoided if we could have reduced the number of forces on the particle to three. We can do this if we combine the normal contact force and frictional force to give a resultant which we call the **rough reaction.**

This is illustrated in figure 7.21, where $\boldsymbol{N}$ and $\boldsymbol{F}$ have resultant $\boldsymbol{R}$.

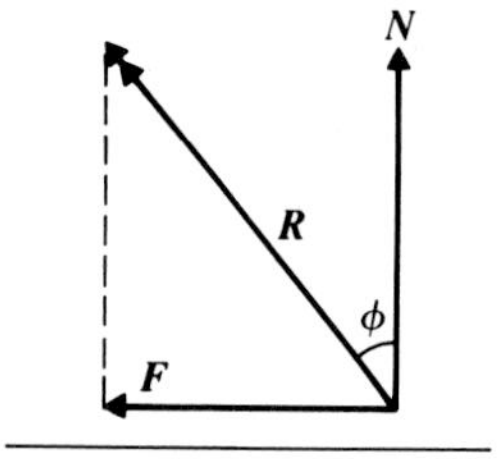

Figure 7.21

Now $\tan \phi = F/N$,

but $F \leqslant \mu N$,

so $F/N \leqslant \mu$.

Hence $\tan \phi \leqslant \mu$.

When friction is limiting, the rough reaction is inclined at its greatest angle to the normal contact force. This angle is usually denoted by λ and is called the **angle of friction**, and we see that λ and μ are connected by the relation

$$\tan \lambda = \mu.$$

We can now solve example 4 much more easily than before. The three forces on the particle are shown in figure 7.22a. When the particle is about to slide, $\phi = \lambda$. Since the forces are in equilibrium, they must form a closed triangle, i.e. $m\boldsymbol{g} + \boldsymbol{R} + \boldsymbol{T} = \boldsymbol{0}$.

Figure 7.22b shows one of many possible triangles. The length of $m\boldsymbol{g}$ is fixed, as is angle λ between $\boldsymbol{R}$ and $m\boldsymbol{g}$. However, T, θ and R are all related variables. The minimum value of T occurs when $\theta = \lambda$ as in figure 7.22c and the tension $\boldsymbol{T}$ is then at right angles to the rough reaction $\boldsymbol{R}$. In this case,

$$T_{\text{min}} = mg \sin \lambda$$

$$= \frac{mg \tan \lambda}{\sec \lambda}$$

$$= \frac{\mu mg}{\sqrt{(1 + \mu^2)}}, \quad \text{as before.}$$

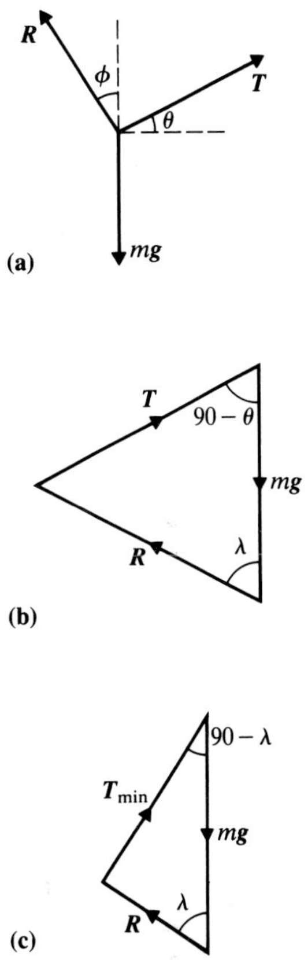

Figure 7.22

Applying Lami's theorem to the triangles in figure 7.22b, we see that, for a general angle θ,

$$\frac{T}{\sin \lambda} = \frac{mg}{\sin (90 + \theta - \lambda)}$$

$$T = \frac{mg \sin \lambda}{\cos (\lambda - \theta)}$$

$$= \frac{mg \sin \lambda}{\cos \lambda \cos \theta + \sin \lambda \sin \theta}$$

$$= \frac{mg \tan \lambda}{\cos \theta + \tan \lambda \sin \theta}$$

$$= \frac{\mu mg}{\cos \theta + \mu \sin \theta}, \quad \text{as before.}$$

EXAMPLE 5

A broom head of mass m attached to a light broom handle is pushed along a rough floor by a force $\boldsymbol{P}$ applied at an angle θ to the horizontal, the coefficient of friction being μ. What is the least force required to push it?

We can think of the broom head as a particle and figure 7.23a shows the forces acting upon it. When friction is limiting, $\phi = \lambda$. The incomplete triangle of forces is shown in figure 7.23b. The minimum

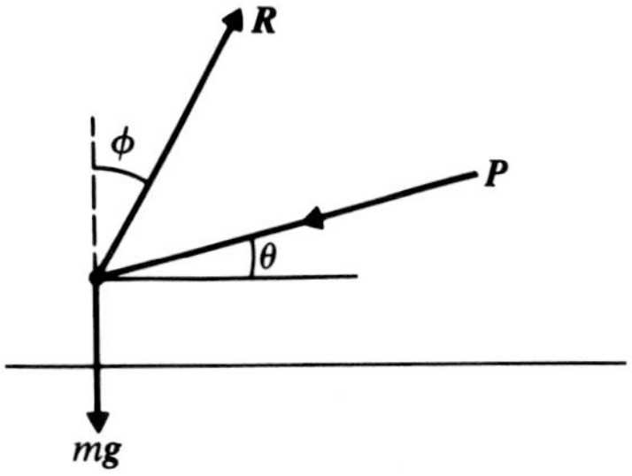

Figure 7.23

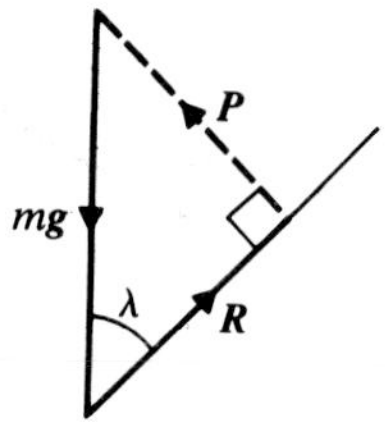

(b)

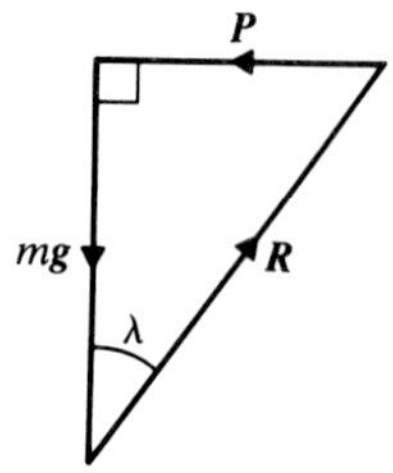

(c)

value of P is shown by the length of the dotted line, but this represents a pull and not a push! The best we can do under the circumstances is to apply $\boldsymbol{P}$ horizontally with $\theta = 0$, as in figure 7.23c, in which we have

$$P_{\text{min}} = mg \tan \lambda \ = \mu mg.$$

□□□□□

A moment's reflection will convince the reader of the difference between a pull and a push in this situation. When 'pulling' at an angle, the component of the pull normal to the surface assists in the decrease of the normal contact force, and hence the frictional force. When 'pushing', the normal component of the push increases the normal contact force and hence the frictional force. It is usually easier to pull a loaded supermarket trolley than to push it.

From example 2 we saw that a particle will rest on a plane inclined at an angle θ provided $\tan \theta \leqslant \mu$, i.e. $\tan \theta \leqslant \tan \lambda$. Hence we see that the particle will rest on a plane inclined at an angle θ provided $\theta \leqslant \lambda$.

EXERCISE 7C

Take g as 10 m s^{-2} throughout.

1. A particle of mass 5 kg is on a rough horizontal plane. A horizontal force of 20 N will just cause it to move.
   a) Find the coefficient of friction between the particle and the plane.
   b) Find the magnitude and direction of the least force required to move the particle along the plane.
2. A particle of mass 4 kg can just be pushed along a rough floor by a force of 20 N acting downwards at 20° to the horizontal.
   a) Find the coefficient of friction between the particle and the floor.
   b) Find the magnitude and direction of the minimum force required to move the particle.
3. A particle of mass 10 kg is on a rough plane inclined at an angle of 30° to the horizontal. The coefficient of friction between the particle and the plane is 0.75.
   a) Will the particle slide down the plane?
   b) What is the least horizontal force which will move the particle up the plane?
   c) Find the magnitude and direction of the minimum force which will move the particle up the plane.
4. A particle of weight W is at rest on a rough plane inclined at angle α to the horizontal. The angle $\alpha > \lambda$, the angle of friction, and the least horizontal force required to prevent slipping down the plane

is W. The least horizontal force to produce motion up the plane is $W\sqrt{3}$. Find α and λ.

5. A particle of mass m will rest in limiting equilibrium on a rough slope inclined at an angle of α to the horizontal ($\alpha < 30^\circ$). If the angle of the slope is increased to 2α, find:
   a) the magnitude and direction of the minimum force required to prevent slipping down the plane,
   b) the magnitude and direction of the minimum force required to move the particle up the plane.

   Discuss the corresponding result if $30^\circ < \alpha < 45^\circ$.

6. A book is on a plane inclined at an angle θ, where $\theta > \lambda$. $\boldsymbol{Q}$ is the minimum force needed to prevent the book from slipping down the plane. When this force is increased to $2\boldsymbol{Q}$, the book is on the point of slipping up the plane. Prove that $\theta = 3\lambda$.

Friction and motion

So far in chapters on dynamics we have referred to frictional resistance as a force of given magnitude without any reference to its nature. We are now able to look at friction in motion in more detail. In all cases, when motion occurs, we will assume friction to be limiting and so $F = \mu N$, where F is the frictional force and N the normal contact force.

EXAMPLE 1

A curling stone is pushed across the ice with an initial speed of 8 m s^{-1}. If the coefficient of friction between the ice and the stone is 0.1, calculate how far the stone travels before coming to rest. Take g as 10 m s^{-2}.

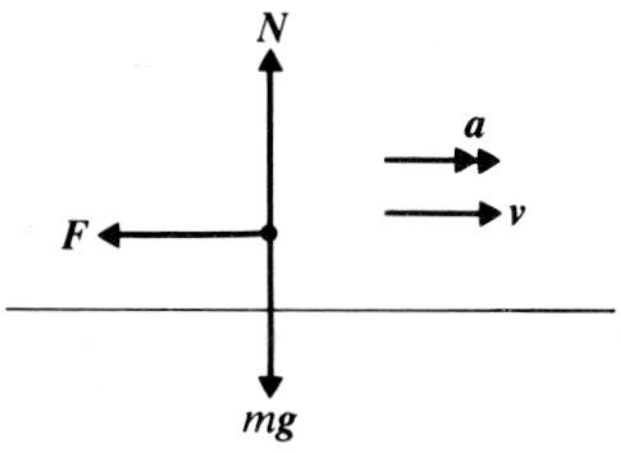

Figure 7.24

Let the mass of the curling stone be m. The forces on the stone are shown in figure 7.24. Applying N2 to the stone:

vertically $\quad N - mg = 0,$

horizontally $\quad -F = ma,$

where a is the acceleration of the stone. Friction is limiting, so

$$F = \mu N = 0.1N.$$

Hence $a = -0.1g$. Since the acceleration is constant, we can apply the equation of constant acceleration. Let v be the speed of the stone after distance s, so that

$$\begin{aligned} v^2 &= u^2 + 2as \\ &= 64 - 0.2gs. \end{aligned}$$

The stone comes to rest when $v = 0$, so $s = 64/0.2g = 32$; the stone travels a distance of 32 m.

EXAMPLE 2

A trunk is pulled up a ramp using a rope. The ramp is inclined at 20° to the horizontal. The tension in the rope, which is parallel to the line of greatest slope, is 400 N. The mass of the trunk is 80 kg and is at rest, but is on the point of moving up the slope so that friction is limiting. If the rope snaps, what is the speed with which the trunk hits the bottom of the ramp?

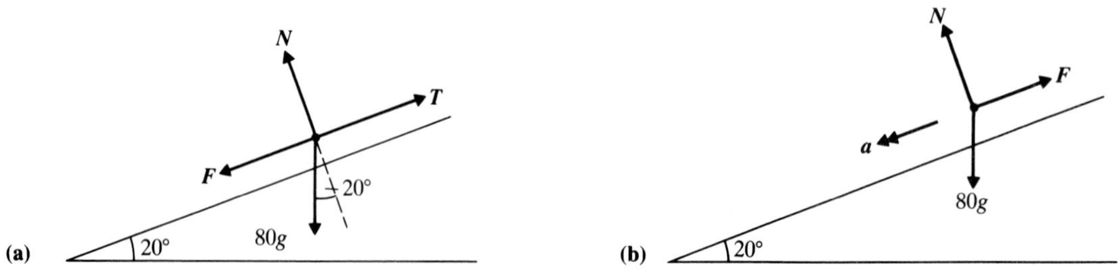

Figure 7.25

Consider the situation just before the rope snaps. Figure 7.25a shows the forces acting on the trunk.
Resolving perpendicular to the slope,

$$N = 80g \cos 20°.$$

Resolving parallel to the slope,

$$400 = F + 80g \sin 20°,$$
$$F = 400 - 80g \sin 20°.$$

Since friction is limiting, $F = \mu N$, so

$$\mu = \frac{400 - 80g \sin 20°}{80g \cos 20°} = 0.17.$$

Consider the motion down the slope, as shown in figure 7.25b. Friction now acts up the slope and takes its limiting value. As before, $N = 80g \cos 20°$ and $F = \mu N$. So

$$F = 0.17 \times 80g \cos 20° = 126.$$

Applying N2 down the slope,

$$80g \sin 20° - F = 80a,$$
$$a = 1.84.$$

From $v^2 = u^2 + 2as$, with the length of the slope 5 m,

$$v^2 = 2 \times 1.84 \times 5,$$

The speed at the bottom of the slope is, therefore, 4.3 m s^{-1}.

EXAMPLE 3

A cyclist is going round a rough banked track at a constant speed v. The angle of banking is α, and the coefficient of friction between the cyclist and the track is μ. Find in terms of μ, α and r (the radius of the circle) (a) the maximum and (b) the minimum values of the speed of the cyclist, if there is no slipping between the cycle and the track.

a) We treat the cyclist as a particle so that figure 7.26a shows the forces acting on the particle when it is about to move up the slope. This will occur when the speed is maximum. Let v be the speed of the particle.

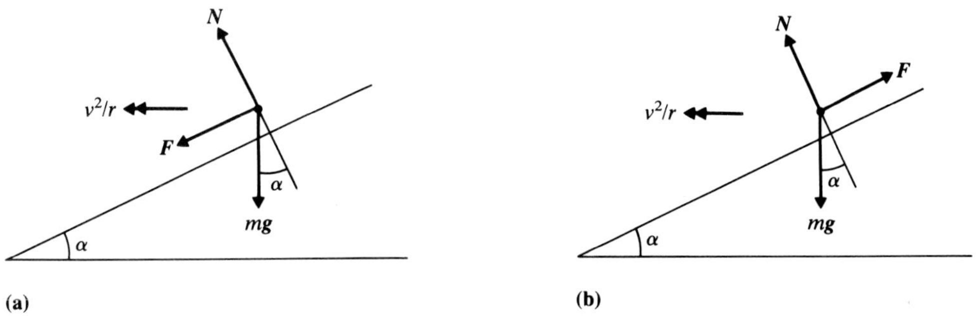

Figure 7.26

Applying N2 to the particle:

vertically $\quad N\cos\alpha = F\sin\alpha + mg, \quad$ **(5)**

horizontally $\quad N\sin\alpha + F\cos\alpha = mv^2/r. \quad$ **(6)**

Friction is limiting, so $F = \mu N$.

In (5) $\quad N(\cos\alpha - \mu\sin\alpha) = mg.$

In (6) $\quad N(\sin\alpha + \mu\cos\alpha) = mv^2/r.$

Dividing
$$\frac{\cos\alpha + \mu\sin\alpha}{\sin\alpha - \mu\cos\alpha} = \frac{v^2}{rg},$$
$$v = \left(rg\frac{\cos\alpha + \mu\sin\alpha}{\sin\alpha - \mu\cos\alpha}\right)^{1/2}.$$

b) Figure 7.26b shows the forces acting on the particle when it is about to slip down the bank. This will occur when the speed is a minimum.

Applying N2 to the particle:

vertically $\quad N\cos\alpha + F\sin\alpha = mg, \quad$ **(7)**

horizontally $\quad N\sin\alpha - F\cos\alpha = mv^2/r. \quad$ **(8)**

Friction is limiting, so $F = \mu N$

In (7) $\quad N(\cos\alpha + \mu\sin\alpha) = mg.$

In (8) $\quad N(\sin\alpha - \mu\cos\alpha) = mv^2/r.$

Dividing
$$\frac{\cos\alpha - \mu\sin\alpha}{\sin\alpha + \mu\cos\alpha} = \frac{v^2}{rg},$$
$$v = \left(rg\frac{\cos\alpha - \mu\sin\alpha}{\sin\alpha + \mu\cos\alpha}\right)^{1/2}.$$

Hence
$$\frac{\cos\alpha - \mu\sin\alpha}{\sin\alpha + \mu\cos\alpha} \leqslant \frac{v^2}{rg} \leqslant \frac{\cos\alpha + \mu\sin\alpha}{\sin\alpha - \mu\cos\alpha}.$$

EXERCISE 7D

Take g as 10 m s^{-2}, where necessary.

1. A particle of mass 5 kg has an acceleration of 0.2 m s^{-2} along a horizontal plane under the action of a horizontal force of 30 N. Calculate the coefficient of friction between the particle and the plane.

2. A particle of mass 8 kg rests on a rough horizontal plane. The coefficient of friction is 0.4. A force of 100 N is applied downwards on to the particle at an angle θ to the horizontal. Find the magnitude of the frictional force and the acceleration of the particle in the cases: (a) $\theta = 0°$, (b) $\theta = 90°$, (c) $\theta = 60°$.

3. A particle of mass m slides down a rough plane inclined at an angle $\tan^{-1}\frac{3}{4}$ to the horizontal. The coefficient of friction between the particle and the plane is $\frac{1}{4}$. Show that the acceleration of the particle is $\frac{2}{5}g$.

4. A particle is projected at 10 m s^{-1} along a rough horizontal surface. The coefficient of friction is 0.4. How far does the particle travel before coming to rest?

5. A particle is projected up the line of greatest slope of a rough plane inclined at an angle 30° to the horizontal. The initial speed of the particle is 10 m s^{-1} and the coefficient of friction is $\frac{1}{2}$. How far above the point of projection does the particle reach?

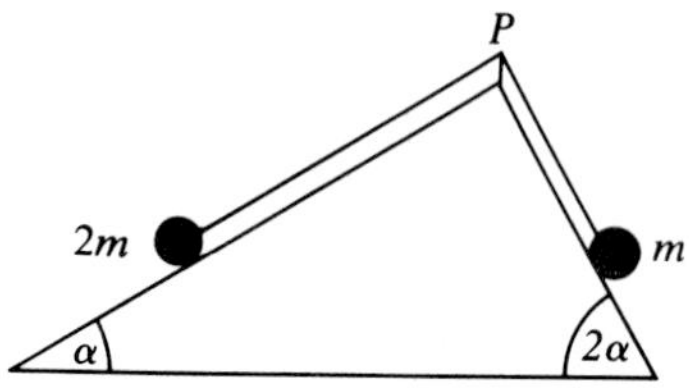

Figure 7.27

6.* Figure 7.27 shows a fixed wedge with a particle on either face, joined by a light wire, passing over a smooth peg at P. The angle of friction between each particle and each inclined face is λ, and $\lambda = \alpha$.

   a) Will the system remain in equilibrium?

   b) Calculate the acceleration of the particles in terms of g and α, when the masses m and $2m$ are interchanged.

7. A spin drier drum of radius 15 cm rotates with angular velocity ω. A wet sock is stuck to the wall of the drum, spinning in a horizontal circle without slipping. If $\mu = 0.7$ for contact between the sock and the wall of the drum, find the minimum value of ω.

8. A particle is projected from a point A with a speed of 20 m s^{-1} up the line of greatest slope of a plane inclined at an angle $\tan^{-1}\frac{3}{4}$ to the horizontal. Between A and B, a point 10 m further up the plane from A, $\mu = \frac{1}{2}$, and above B, $\mu = \frac{3}{5}$. (a) Find how far up the plane the particle travels. (b) Find the time taken to return to A from the top.

9. In a game of shove-halfpenny a coin A collides head on with an identical coin B, which is at rest. Initially coin A is 20 cm from B and is moving towards it at 2 m s^{-1}. If the coefficient of friction between each coin and the table is 0.2 and the coefficient of restitution for the coins is 0.5, calculate how far apart the coins are when they both come to rest.

10.* A particle is projected with speed u up the line of greatest slope of a rough plane inclined at an angle α to the horizontal. The coefficient of friction between the particle and the plane is μ, where $\mu < \tan\alpha$. Prove that the particle returns to its original position with a speed v given by

$$v^2 = u^2\frac{\sin\alpha - \mu\cos\alpha}{\sin\alpha + \mu\cos\alpha}$$

Find also the time taken in terms of u, g, μ and α.

Moments 7.3

Figure 7.28 shows several examples of objects which are initially in equilibrium, but to which a single force P is applied in the directions shown. In each case it is clear from our experience that in addition to possible translational motion caused by the force, there will be a tendency for the objects to rotate. This cannot happen to a particle, but it is possible when we consider a rigid body. A **rigid body** is an object made up of particles all of which are at fixed distances from one another, whether the object is at rest or in motion. Forces may act at different places on a rigid body and will produce different translational and/or rotational motion depending on their lines of action. In each case the applied force may produce a turning effect or **moment**.

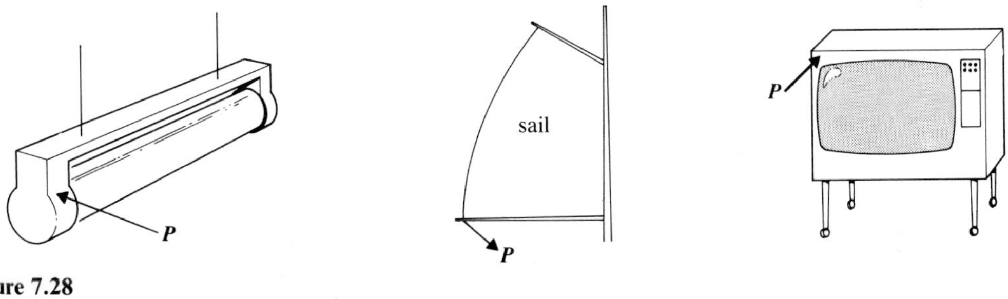

Figure 7.28

The moment of a force

Most people will have experienced the problem of trying to undo a tight nut with a spanner. There is probably a limit to the force which can be applied and often a longer spanner is used, if first attempts fail. Assuming that the applied force, F, has the same magnitude for both spanners, the turning effect for the longer spanner will be greater than for the shorter. Further, the maximum turn from a given force is obtained by pulling at right angles to the spanner rather than obliquely although in practice this is not always possible.

For example, when operating lock gates, we normally walk or push against the bar in a circular path, since in this way we are perpendicular to the bar and achieve the maximum turning effect, as shown in figure 7.29a. However when pulling on the sheet (rope) attached to the mainsail of a sailing dinghy, the helmsman is usually not in a position to pull at right angles to the boom (figure 7.29b).

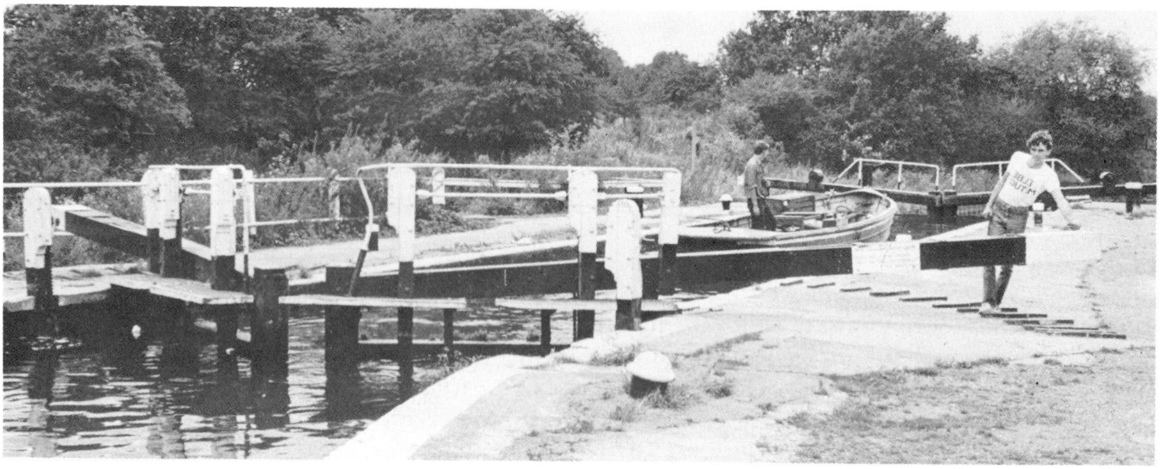

(a) **Figure 7.29**

(b)

Figure 7.30

Figure 7.30 shows a force ***F*** applied at a point P at a distance d from a point O and at right angles to **OP**. The magnitude of the moment of the force ***F*** about the point O is defined to be the product $F \times d$, where d is the perpendicular distance from ***F*** to O. In figure 7.30 we have an anticlockwise moment, which is said to be positive. A clockwise moment is a negative moment.

If, as in figure 7.31a, ***F*** is at an angle θ to the line **OP**, its moment is defined as

$$F \times d \sin \theta,$$

where $d \sin \theta$ is the perpendicular distance of O from the line of action of ***F***.

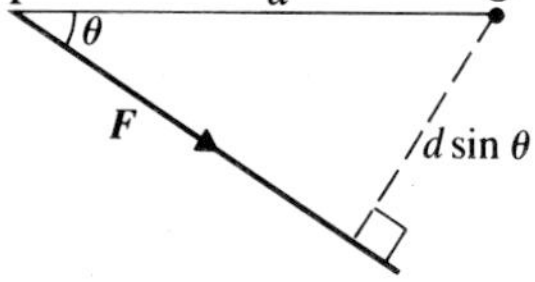

(a)

Figure 7.31

We may also write this expression as

$$F \times d \sin \theta = (F \sin \theta) \times d,$$

which is the component of $\boldsymbol{F}$ perpendicular to **OP** multiplied by d, as in figure 7.31b. In examples, we usually use this form of the moment of a force about a point. The other component, $F \cos \theta$, is in line with O and has no moment about it.

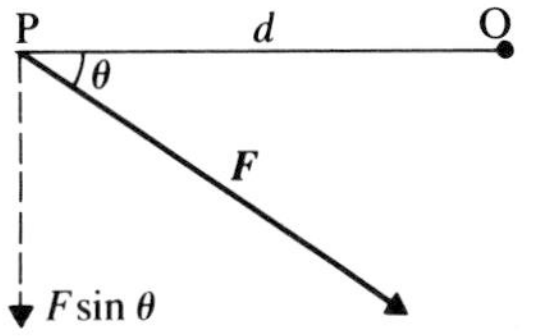

(b)

The unit of moment is the newton metre (N m), and the dimensions are the same as those of work and energy, namely M L^2 T^{-2}.

So far we have regarded force vectors as localised (see section 1.8), but we see that the moment of a force $\boldsymbol{F}$ is unaffected by its point of application, provided the line of action of $\boldsymbol{F}$ is fixed. This is illustrated in figure 7.32.

Figure 7.32

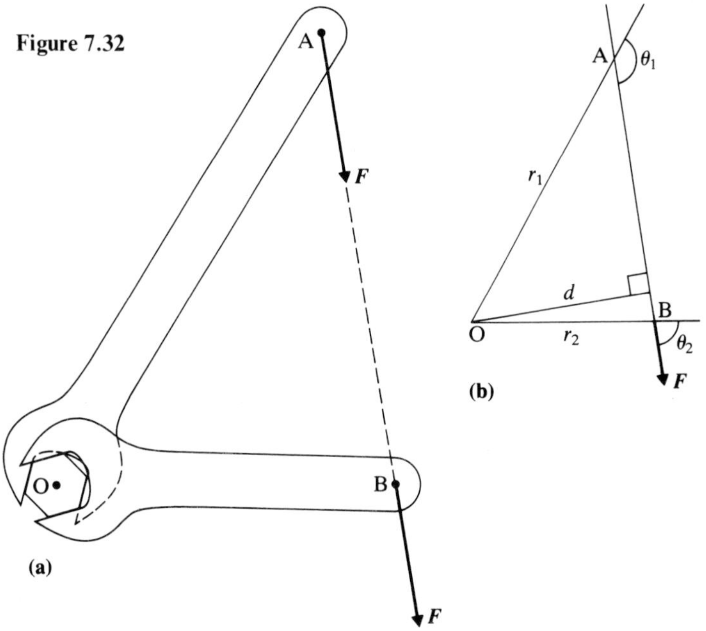

For the long spanner, $\boldsymbol{F}$ is applied at A and its moment about O is

$$Fr_1 \sin \theta_1 = Fd.$$

For the short spanner, $\boldsymbol{F}$ is applied at B and its moment about O is

$$Fr_2 \sin \theta_2 = Fd.$$

Thus we may apply $\boldsymbol{F}$ anywhere along the line AB and it will have the same moment about O

A moment is strictly a vector quantity, since as well as a magnitude it also has a direction associated with it, which is the direction of the axis about which it would cause a rotation. This axis is at right angles to the plane containing the force and its radius vector **OP**, from the point of application to the axis.

Changing the line of action of a force will change its turning effect. For example, if the TV set in figure 7.33 is pushed with the same force $\boldsymbol{F}$ at points A, B, C, the resulting motions will differ.

We can combine the moments of several forces about a given point, as the following example shows.

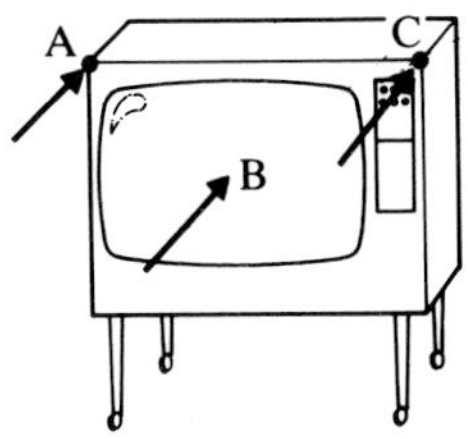

Figure 7.33

EXAMPLE 1

A man and a boy are pushing on the bar of some lock gates, as in figure 7.34. The moment about O of the force applied by the man is

$$100 \times 4 = 400.$$

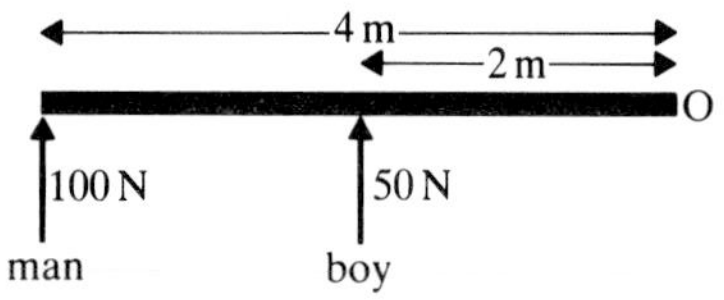

Figure 7.34

The moment about O of the force applied by the boy is $50 \times 2 = 100$. The total moment about O is 500 N m.

If the boy pushes in the opposite direction, we subtract his moment to give the total anticlockwise moment about O as 300 N m.

EXAMPLE 2

A girl of mass 20 kg is seated on a seesaw at a distance of 3 m from its pivot. How far from the pivot should her mother of mass 50 kg sit, in order to keep the seesaw balanced?

The girl will have a clockwise moment about the pivot O of magnitude

$$20g \times 3 = 60g.$$

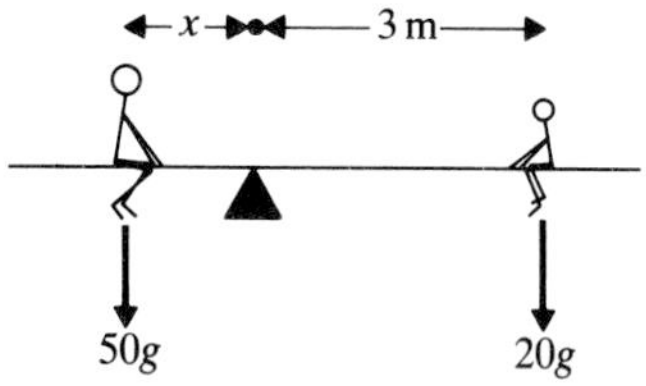

Figure 7.35

The anticlockwise moment of her mother is $50g \times x$, where, as in figure 7.35, x is the distance her mother is from the pivot. These two moments must 'balance', so

$$50g \times x = 60g$$

Thus x is 1.2 m.

□□□□□

This example introduces the idea that for equilibrium it is not sufficient for the reaction at O upwards to equal the total downward weight forces, but also the sum of the turning effects must be zero. This is known as the **principle of moments**, and will be considered in more detail in section 7.5. For simple systems it is often possible to calculate unknown forces by a single application of this principle about a well-chosen point, as the following example shows.

EXAMPLE 3

When the sail is not in place, the boom of a sailing cruiser is held in the horizontal position by a wire attached to its end and to a point higher up the mast, as shown in figure 7.36. The mass of the boom is 3 kg and its length 3 m. Find the tension in the wire if the boom is in equilibrium. Take g as 10 m s^{-2}.

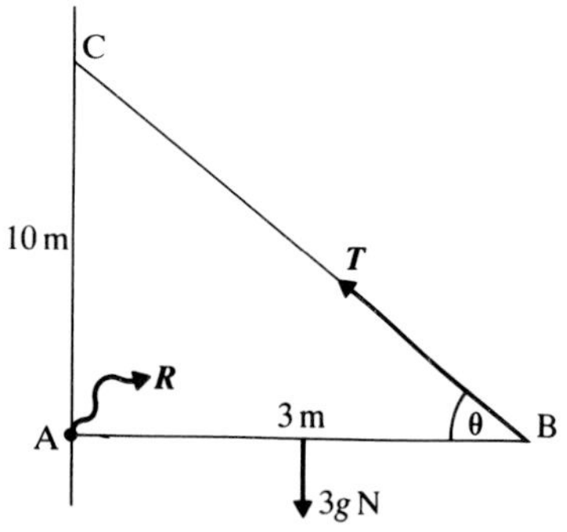

Figure 7.36

The boom is hinged by a universal joint at the mast and the forces acting are rather complicated. We therefore do not resolve the forces to solve the problem.

The unknown and unwanted force R acts through A and so has no moment about A. Taking moments about A,

$$-T \sin\theta \times 3 + 30 \times 1.5 = 0.$$

From Δ ABC, $\sin\theta = 10/\sqrt{109} = 0.958$, Hence the tension is 15.7 N.

Centre of gravity

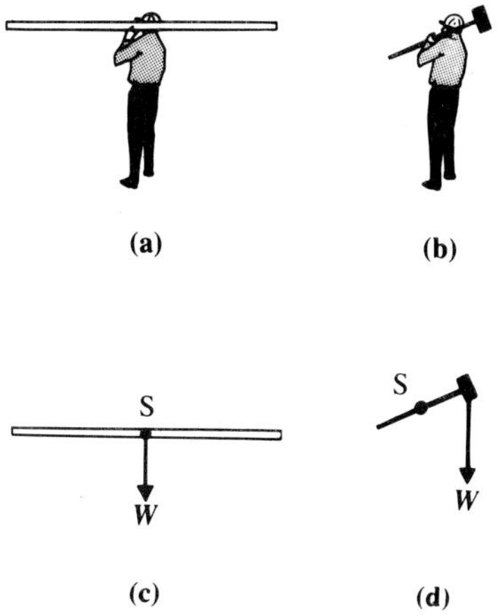

Figure 7.37

We have considered the turning effects of forces acting on simple bodies and now look at the turning effect of the weight force of a rigid body itself.

Figure 7.37 shows a man on a building site carrying on his shoulders a plank and a sledge hammer of approximately equal masses. In each case the man is using his hand and arm to help to balance the mass. In (a) the force required from his arm will be small, whereas in (b) it will require a considerable effort from him to prevent the hammer from slipping back, since the weight force of the hammer has a greater moment about his shoulder, S. The reason for the difference is due to the different positions of the centres of gravity of the bodies. For the plank, as for any uniform rod, the weight force is taken as acting through its geometrical centre, which is approximately at S. For the sledge hammer, the shaft is light compared with the very heavy head, and so the centre of gravity is within the head and is further away from the man's shoulder, S.

The **centre of gravity** of a body is the point where we suppose the weight force to act. If the body were suspended in equilibrium by a string, the line of the string would pass through the centre of gravity. For simple geometrical shapes like rods and discs, the centre of gravity will be at their geometrical centres. These are called **uniform bodies**. For more complicated shapes we will need more careful analysis and this is considered in chapter 9.

We may ignore the weight force due to the shaft of the sledge hammer, since it is very small compared with the weight force from the head. A rod whose weight is negligible is often referred to as a **light rod** (see also section 7.6).

A further mathematical simplification occurs when we have a three-dimensional body whose symmetry allows us to consider it as a two-dimensional flat surface, having the same mass. Such a model is called a **lamina**.

For example, figure 7.38a shows a packet of soap powder placed on a sloping draining board.

Figure 7.38a

Common experience tells us that, placed as on the left, the packet will remain steady, but, if placed as on the right, it is likely to topple over. We cannot reduce the packet to a particle, since it may tip about one edge. However, we can simplify it to a lamina in both situations, as in figure 7.38b. Both the light rod and the lamina are improvements on the particle as approximations to real-life situations, in appropriate circumstances.

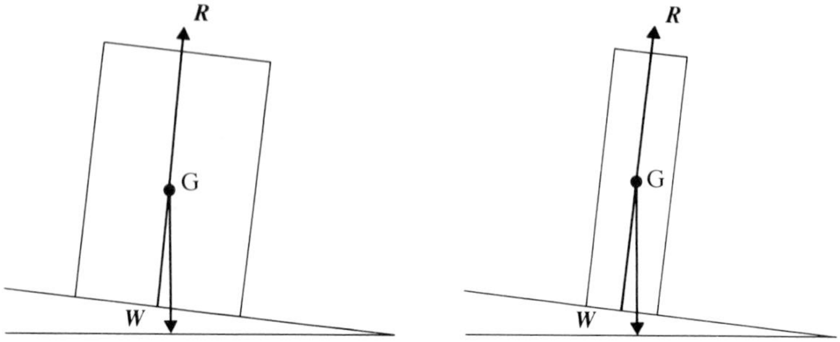

Figure 7.38b

EXERCISE 7E

Take g as $10\ \text{m s}^{-2}$, where necessary.

1. A sledge hammer of length 1 m has a mass 4 kg, with the centre of gravity at one end. A man can exert a force of 15 N vertically downward on the end of the shaft. How far should the heavy end of the hammer be from the man's shoulder for equilibrium?

2. A boy of mass 30 kg sits on the end of a seesaw of length 5 m, pivoted at the centre. Where should a boy of mass 40 kg sit, if the system is to remain in equilibrium?

3.

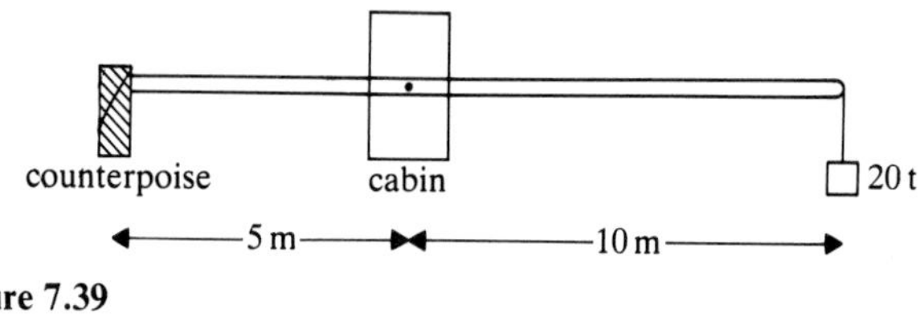

Figure 7.39

Figure 7.39 shows a crane 15 m long, with a mass 20 t at one end, 10 m from the cabin. What is the mass of the counterpoise required if the system is to remain in equilibrium? If the counterpoise remains of fixed mass and the load is doubled, how far in must it be pulled to maintain equilibrium?

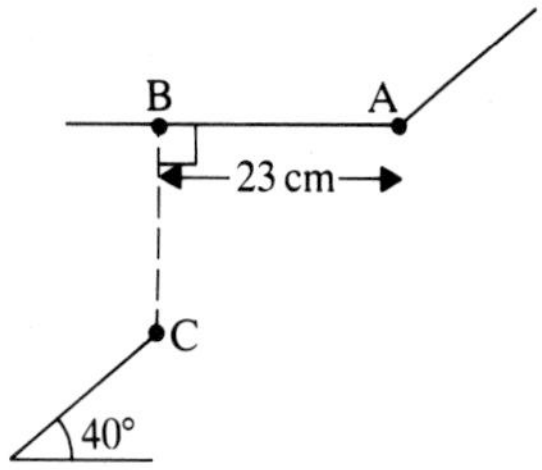

Figure 7.40

4. Figure 7.40 shows a window of length 30 cm of a greenhouse, hinged at A. The mass of the window is 0.25 kg, and it is propped at B, 23 cm from A with the support CB perpendicular to AB. Find the thrust in CB.

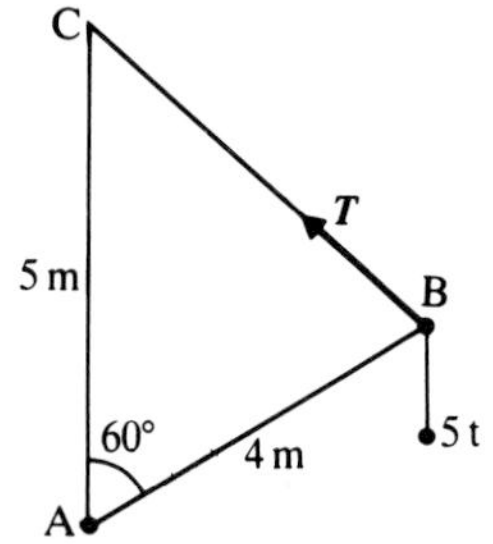

Figure 7.41

5. Figure 7.41 shows a light rod AB, hinged at A. A mass of 5 t is suspended from B. Calculate the tension in the cable BC.

6. With the other details remaining as in question 5, the mass of 5 t is now suspended from a point on AB, 3 m from A. Calculate the new tension in the cable BC.

Figure 7.42

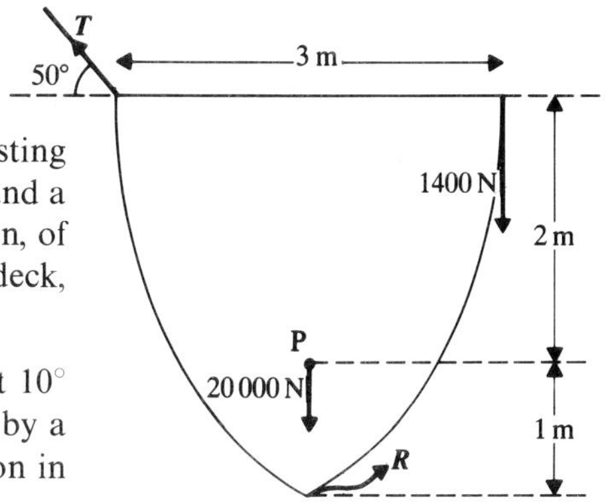

7. Figure 7.42 shows a simplified view of a boat in dry dock, resting on its keel. The centre of mass of the boat is at P, as shown, and a rope is attached to one side at 50° to the horizontal. Two men, of combined mass 140 kg, stand on the opposite edge of the deck, which is 3 m wide. Find the tension T in the rope.

8. A uniform mast of length 10 m and mass 40 kg is inclined at 10° to the vertical. It is hinged at the lower end, and supported by a horizontal rope attached to the top end. Calculate the tension in the rope.

9. A horizontal beam CB, of length 10 m, is supported at A, 1 m from C, and at B. A mass of 1 t is loaded at C, and another of 4 t at D, 3 m from B. The beam is uniform and of mass 2 t. Find the vertical forces on the beam at A and B by taking moments, first about B and then about A.

7.4 Couples and equivalent systems of forces

Couples

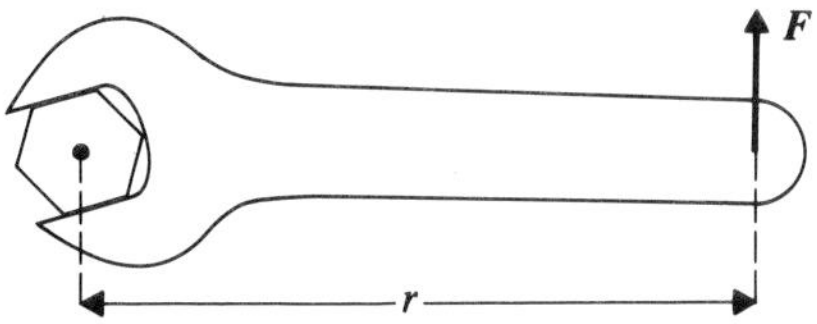

Figure 7.43

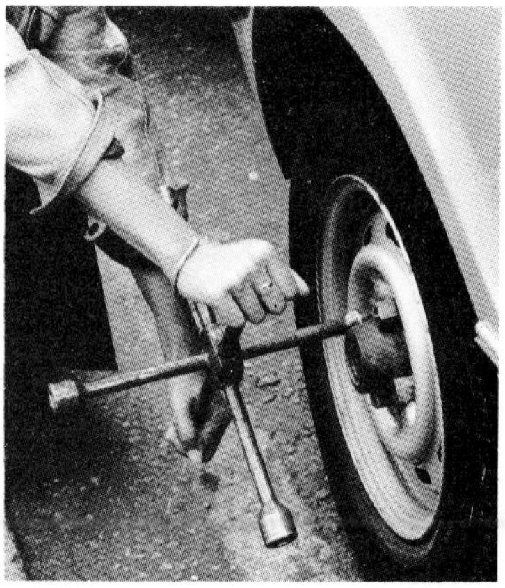

Figure 7.44
A spider wrench.

Consider the spanner shown in figure 7.43. There will be a tendency for the nut to move, as well as rotate, and this movement is prevented by a reaction between the nut and its bolt housing. The nature of this reaction is complicated and will not concern us in any further work. Figure 7.44 shows a special device for undoing wheel nuts, called a spider wrench. When equal and opposite forces are applied, as shown, we see that

a) there is no resultant force and hence no tendency for the nut to translate, and

b) there is a positive moment about the centre of magnitude $2rF$.

Such a system of equal and opposite parallel forces is called a **couple**, and we shall now consider a fundamental property of couples. Consider the two forces $\boldsymbol{F}$ and $-\boldsymbol{F}$ in figure 7.45 where d is the perpendicular distance between their lines of action. Take any point O in the plane and consider positive moments about it:

$$Fr + F(d - r) = Fd.$$

This is independent of the position of O and so the moment of a couple is the same about any point in the plane.

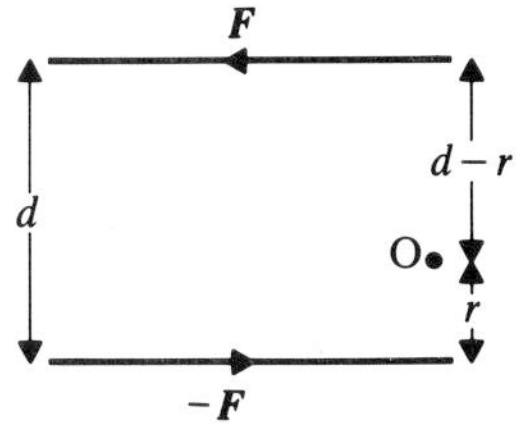

Figure 7.45

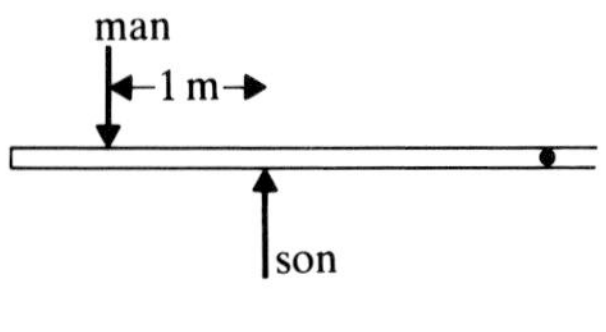

(a)

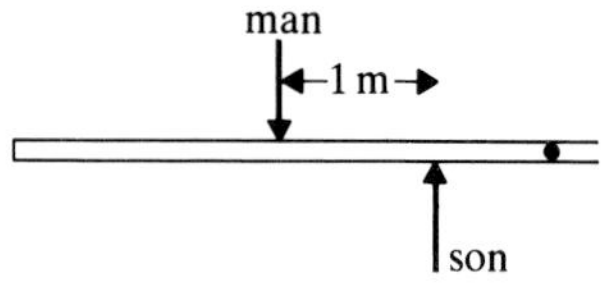

(b)

Figure 7.46

Suppose a man is trying to open a lock gate, but his son is pushing against him with an equal and opposite force of 100 N, as shown in figure 7.46. In both (a) and (b) the magnitude of the moment about the pivot is

$$100 \text{ N} \times 1 \text{ m} = 100 \text{ N m}.$$

Equivalent systems of coplanar forces

When a number of forces act on a particle we have seen in section 7.1 that they can be replaced by a single force, their resultant. We say that the original system is equivalent to the simpler system consisting of a single force (the resultant), since they will have exactly the same effect on the particle.

We would like to be able to reduce systems of forces on rigid bodies in a similar way, in order to determine their motion. However, the situation is much more complicated, since the forces act at different places in the body and can thus cause rotation as well as translation. The study of the dynamics of rigid bodies is beyond the scope of this book, but we can go some way towards seeing how coplanar systems of forces can be replaced by equivalent and simpler ones.

Before dealing with the more general cases we consider a specific example.

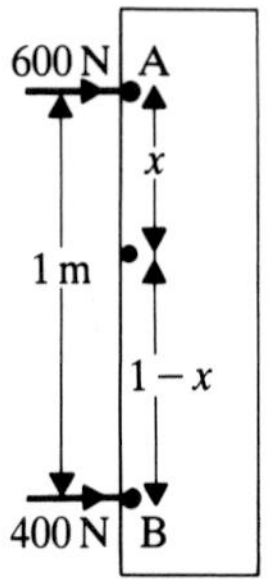

(a)

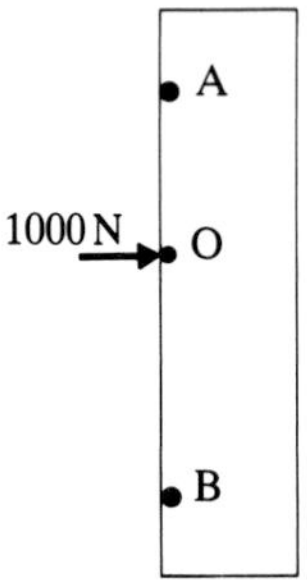

(b)

Figure 7.47

EXAMPLE 1

Two men are pushing a piano as shown in figure 7.47a. Intuitively we see that there will be a tendency for the piano to move to the right and to rotate clockwise, since the man at A is exerting the larger force. Is it possible for one man to produce the same effect as the other two?

He must push with a force of 1000 N, but where must he push to produce the same turning effect? Suppose that the original two forces have zero moment about a point O, x m from A, as in figure 7.47a.

Then $$600x = 400(1 - x),$$
$$1000x = 400,$$

Thus x is 0.4 m.

This suggests that the single man should push at O, which is 0.4 m from A, with a force of 1000 N.

We can check this result by taking moments about B for the two systems.

2 men: $600 \times 1 = 600,$

1 man: $1000 \times 0.6 = 600.$

Thus the system in figure 7.47b is equivalent to the system in figure 7.47a. The point O is called the *centre* of the parallel forces at A and B (see chapter 9 on centre of gravity).

In general, two sets of coplanar forces are said to be equivalent if

a) The vector sum of all forces in both sets is the same.

b) The sum of the magnitudes of the moments for each set is the same about every point in the plane.

We now give two theorems which help us to reduce systems to simpler equivalent ones.

Theorem 1. Any system of coplanar forces can be reduced to a force acting at any given point and a couple.

Consider firstly one force $\boldsymbol{P}$ acting at A, as in figure 7.48a. We wish to replace it by a force at a given point O and a couple. By adding forces $\boldsymbol{P}$ and $-\boldsymbol{P}$ at O, we see that the systems in figure 7.48a and b must be equivalent, since we have effectively added zero force, but the system in figure 7.48b can be thought of as:

a) a force $\boldsymbol{P}$ acting at O, and

b) a couple of moment Pa, resulting from $\boldsymbol{P}$ at A and $-\boldsymbol{P}$ at O.

In figure 7.48b, we see that Pa is the magnitude of the moment of P about O.

We can continue this process for all other forces in the plane, e.g. in figure 7.48c. $\boldsymbol{Q}$ at B can be replaced by (a) $\boldsymbol{Q}$ at O, and (b) a couple of moment Qb. $\boldsymbol{P}$ and $\boldsymbol{Q}$ can now be replaced by (a) a force $\boldsymbol{P}+\boldsymbol{Q}$ acting at O, and (b) a couple of moment $(Pa + Qb)$.

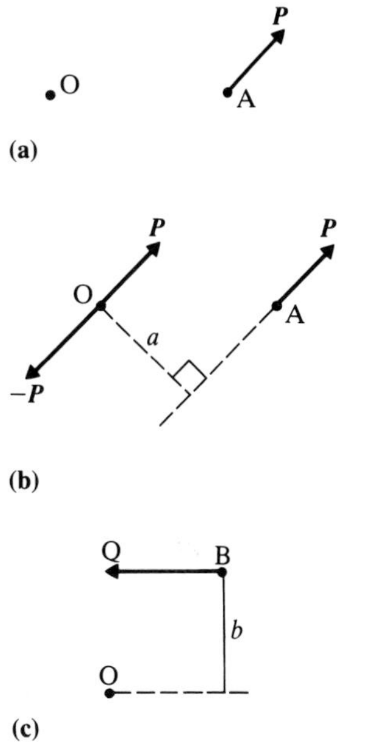

Figure 7.48

In general, any number of forces acting in the plane can be replaced by

a) A single force $\boldsymbol{F}$ equal to the vector sum of all the forces, acting at O.

b) A couple G whose moment is the sum of the moments of all the forces about O.

Note that if $\boldsymbol{F} = \boldsymbol{0}$ and $G = 0$, the system is in equilibrium.

EXAMPLE 2

Reduce the system of forces on the piano in example 1 to a single force $\boldsymbol{F}$ at C and a couple G.

The equivalent force has magnitude, $F = 600 + 400 = 1000$, in the direction shown in figure 7.49a. Taking clockwise moments about C,

$$G = 600 \times 0.5 - 400 \times 0.5 = 100$$

The equivalent system is shown in figure 7.49b and consists of

a) a single force of 1000 N at C, and

b) a clockwise couple of moment 100 N m.

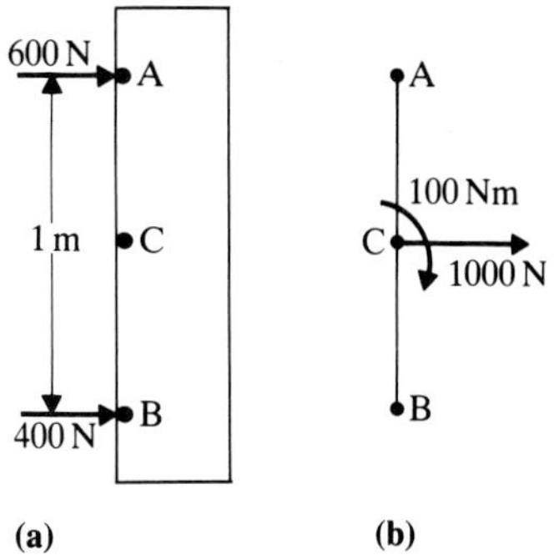

Figure 7.49

EXAMPLE 3

Suppose that three people push the piano of example 1 as shown in figure 7.50. Two of them push with forces of 600 N and 400 N at its back corners E and F, respectively. The third person pushes with a

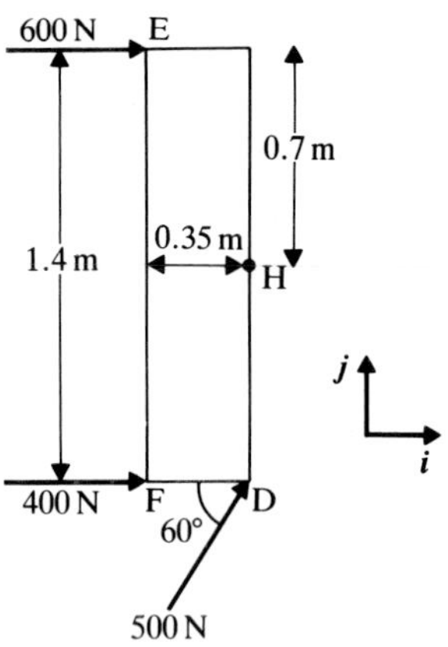

Figure 7.50

force of 500 N at an angle of 60° to one side at a point D, which is 35 cm from the back. Reduce the system to a single force $\boldsymbol{F}$ at the point H shown, and a couple.

We take unit vectors $\boldsymbol{i}$ and $\boldsymbol{j}$, as shown. The total force,

$$\boldsymbol{F} = 600\boldsymbol{i} + 400\boldsymbol{i} + (500 \cos 60^\circ\, \boldsymbol{i} + 500 \sin 60^\circ\, \boldsymbol{j}) = 1250\boldsymbol{i} + 433\boldsymbol{j}$$

The magnitude of $\boldsymbol{F}$ is 1323 N and its direction is given by $\tan^{-1}(433/1250) = 19.1^\circ$, with the $\boldsymbol{i}$-direction. Taking moments about H,

$$G = (400 \times 0.7) + (500 \cos 60^\circ \times 0.7) - (600 \times 0.7) = 35.$$

The total anticlockwise moment about H is 35 N m.

□□□□□

Theorem 1 enables us to reduce a system to a single force $\boldsymbol{F}$ acting at a given point O and a couple of moment G. By moving the line of action of $\boldsymbol{F}$, we can eliminate the couple This is summarised in theorem 2.

Theorem 2 Any system of coplanar forces can be reduced to either

a) a couple,

b) a single force acting along a specific line of action,

c) equilibrium.

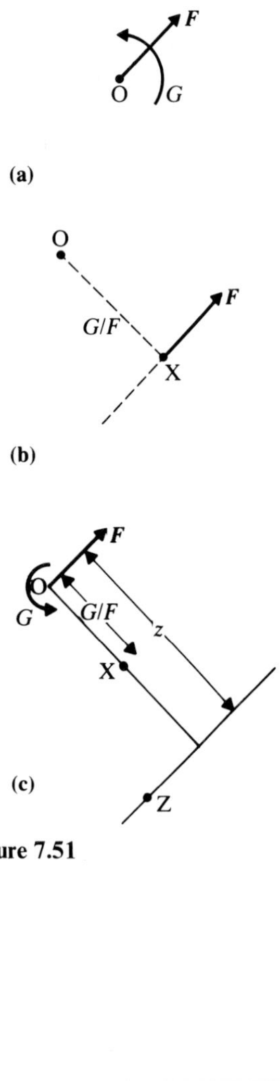

Figure 7.51

From theorem 1, we can replace a system by a single force $\boldsymbol{F}$ acting at O, and a couple of moment G, as shown in figure 7.51a. We call this system 1.

a) If $\boldsymbol{F} = \boldsymbol{0}$, theorem 2 is true, since the system has reduced to a single couple.

b) If, however, $\boldsymbol{F} \neq \boldsymbol{0}$, we take $\boldsymbol{F}$ acting at a point X, a distance G/F from O, as in figure 7.51b, and this is referred to as system 2. The moment of $\boldsymbol{F}$ about O is $F \times (G/F) = G$, as for system 1, but $\boldsymbol{F}$ has no moment about X.

We now show that the moment about any point is the same for both systems. Taking the clockwise moment about any point Z, as in figure 7.51c,

system 1 gives $G - Fz$,

system 2 gives $-F(z - G/F) = -Fz + G$.

Thus, the moment about the arbitrary point Z is the same for both systems, and we conclude that they are equivalent.

c) If $\boldsymbol{F} = \boldsymbol{0}$ and $G = 0$, the system is in equilibrium.

The reader will recognise that we had already anticipated this result when we replaced two men pushing a piano by one man (example 1), although in this case the system we reduced was already quite simple.

EXAMPLE 4

Reduce the system of forces on the piano in example 3 to a single force applied at the back of the piano.

In example 3 we saw how the system could be reduced to a single force of magnitude 1323 N acting at H together with a couple of 35 N m anticlockwise. So the single equivalent force must be of magnitude 1323 N at 19.1° to the $\boldsymbol{i}$-direction and have a moment 35 N m about H. In general we will find it easier to leave the resultant force in component form $(1250\boldsymbol{i} + 433\boldsymbol{j})$. Suppose it acts through a point x m above F, as in figure 7.52a. Taking moments about H,

$$1250(0.7 - x) - 433(0.35) = 35,$$
$$x \approx 0.55.$$

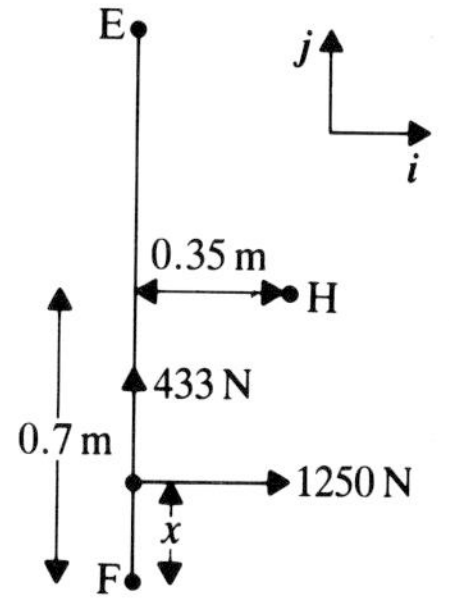

Figure 7.52

The system can be reduced to a single force applied at a point on FE 0.55 m above F. In this case the line of action of the resultant is specified, i.e. fixed. It must pass through the point at 19.1° to the $\boldsymbol{i}$-direction, and has magnitude 1323 N.

□□□□□

Suppose a force $\boldsymbol{F} = a\boldsymbol{i} + b\boldsymbol{j}$ acts at a point $\boldsymbol{r} = x\boldsymbol{i} + y\boldsymbol{j}$, as shown in figure 7.53. The moment of the force about the origin O is given by the expression:

$$G = bx - ay.$$

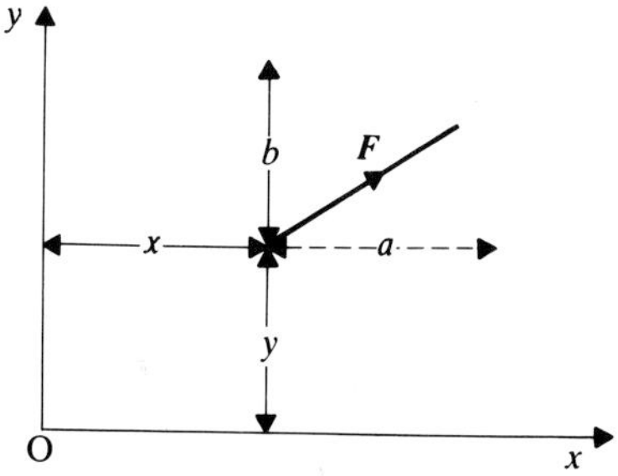

Figure 7.53

This result is useful when moments for more than one force have to be calculated, as the following example shows.

EXAMPLE 5

Two forces $\boldsymbol{F}_1 = \boldsymbol{i} + 3\boldsymbol{j}$ and $\boldsymbol{F}_2 = 2\boldsymbol{i} - \boldsymbol{j}$ act at points (1, − 1) and (2, 3), respectively.

a) Reduce the system to a single force acting at the origin, together with a couple.

b) Reduce the system to a single force, giving its magnitude and line of action.

a) The resultant force $\boldsymbol{F}$ is given by

$$\begin{aligned} \boldsymbol{F} &= \boldsymbol{F}_1 + \boldsymbol{F}_2 \\ &= \boldsymbol{i} + 3\boldsymbol{j} + 2\boldsymbol{i} - \boldsymbol{j} \\ &= 3\boldsymbol{i} + 2\boldsymbol{j}. \end{aligned}$$

The total moment about O can be conveniently calculated from the table.

	a	b	x	y	$bx - ay$
$\boldsymbol{F}_1$	1	3	1	−1	4
$\boldsymbol{F}_2$	2	−1	2	3	−7
					$G = -3$

Thus the system is equivalent to a single force acting at O together with a clockwise couple of magnitude 3 units.

b) The single resultant force is $3\boldsymbol{i} + 2\boldsymbol{j}$ as in (a). Suppose that this force acts through the point (x, y). This must give a couple of magnitude -3 about O. Hence

$$2x - 3y = -3$$
$$y = \tfrac{2}{3}x + 1$$

Thus the system is equivalent to a single force of magnitude $\sqrt{13}$ units acting along the line $y = \tfrac{2}{3}x + 1$.

EXAMPLE 6

OABC is a square of side a, as shown in figure 7.54. Forces of magnitude 1, 3, 5, 7, $8\sqrt{2}$ act along OA, AB, BC, CO and AC, respectively. Find the magnitude of the resultant force and its line of action.

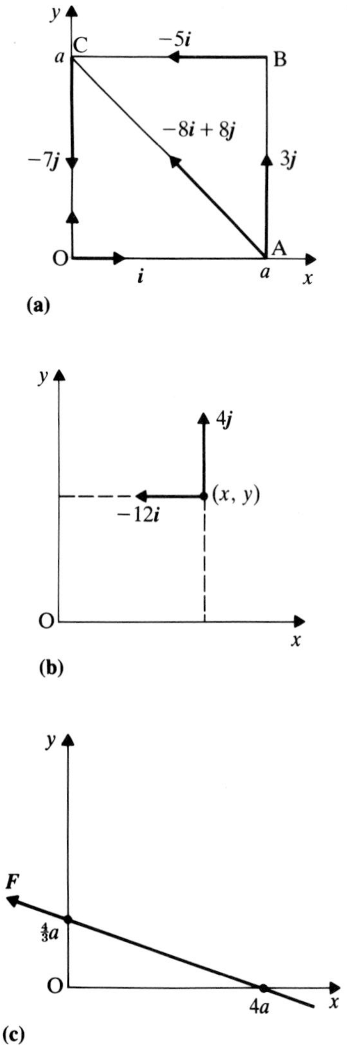

Figure 7.54

The resultant force is given by

$$\boldsymbol{F} = \boldsymbol{i} + 3\boldsymbol{j} - 5\boldsymbol{i} - 7\boldsymbol{j} - 8\boldsymbol{i} + 8\boldsymbol{j}$$
$$= -12\boldsymbol{i} + 4\boldsymbol{j}.$$

The total moment about O is

$$G = 3a + 5a + 8a = 16a$$

Suppose that the resultant $-12\boldsymbol{i} + 4\boldsymbol{j}$ passes through (x, y), as shown in figure 7.54b. The moment of $\boldsymbol{F}$ about O is $12y + 4x$. Since the systems in figures (a) and (b) are equivalent,

$$12y + 4x = 16a,$$
$$x + 3y = 4a.$$

Thus the resultant is $-12\boldsymbol{i} + 4\boldsymbol{j}$, having magnitude $\sqrt{160} \approx 12.6$, and acts along the line with equation $x + 3y = 4a$, as shown in figure 7.54c.

We could have found this line of action by equating moments about any point in the plane. In fact, A would have been most convenient in this case, since three forces in the original system act through it, and therefore have zero moment about it. For the original system, the moment about A is

$$5a + 7a = 12a.$$

For the resultant at (x, y), the moment about A is

$$12y - 4(a - x) = 12y - 4a + 4x.$$

Since the systems are equivalent,

$$12y - 4a + 4x = 12a$$
$$12y + 4x = 16a$$

giving $x + 3y = 4a$, as before.

EXERCISE 7F

In all questions, forces are in newtons and couples are in newton metres.

1. Two forces $\boldsymbol{i} - \boldsymbol{j}$ and $3\boldsymbol{i} + \boldsymbol{j}$ act at points $(1, 1)$ and $(-2, -1)$, respectively. Find the magnitude and line of action of the single equivalent force.

2. Three forces $2\boldsymbol{i}+2\boldsymbol{j}$, $-3\boldsymbol{j}$ and $-2\boldsymbol{i}+\boldsymbol{j}$ act at points with position vectors $2\boldsymbol{j}$, $3\boldsymbol{i}+\boldsymbol{j}$ and $-\boldsymbol{i}-\boldsymbol{j}$, respectively. Show that the system is equivalent to a couple and find the magnitude of the couple.

3. Four forces $3\boldsymbol{i}$, $5\boldsymbol{i}$, $-2\boldsymbol{i}$ and $-4\boldsymbol{i}$ act at points with position vectors $\boldsymbol{i}+2\boldsymbol{j}$, $-\boldsymbol{i}-2\boldsymbol{j}$, $3\boldsymbol{i}-\boldsymbol{j}$ and $2\boldsymbol{i}+\boldsymbol{j}$, respectively. Find the magnitude and line of action of their resultant.

4. Three forces $\boldsymbol{i}+\boldsymbol{j}$, $2\boldsymbol{i}-\boldsymbol{j}$ and $4\boldsymbol{j}$ act at points $(1,2)$, $(3,0)$ and $(-1,-3)$, respectively.

   a) Reduce the system to a single force at O, together with a couple.

   b) Reduce the system to a single force, finding its magnitude and the equation of its line of action.

5. A system consists of two forces $2\boldsymbol{i}+3\boldsymbol{j}$ and $\boldsymbol{i}-5\boldsymbol{j}$ acting at points $(-1, 2)$ and $(1, 1)$, together with a positive couple of magnitude 5.

   a) Reduce the system to a single force at O together with a couple.
   b) Reduce the system to a single force at $(1, 1)$ together with a couple.

   c) Find the magnitude and line of action of the single equivalent force.

6. A force of magnitude 10 acts along the line $3y = 4x + 12$. A second force of $3\boldsymbol{i}-4\boldsymbol{j}$ acts at $(1, 1)$. Find the magnitude and line of action of the resultant.

7. A force of magnitude $3\sqrt{2}$ acts along the line $x + y = 6$ and a force of magnitude $2\sqrt{5}$ acts along the line $y = 2x$. Find the magnitude of the resultant force and the equation of its line of action.

8. Forces $k\mathbf{AB}$, $k\mathbf{BC}$ and $k\mathbf{CA}$ act along the sides of a triangle ABC. Prove that they are equivalent to a couple.
   Forces of magnitude 2, 3, 4 units act along the sides AB, BC, CA of an equilateral triangle. Find the magnitude and line of action of the resultant.

9. ABCD is a square of side a and centre O. Forces of magnitude 1, 2, 3, 4, $6\sqrt{2}$ act along AB, BC, CD, DA, AC.

   a) Reduce the system to a single force at O, together with a couple.

   b) Find the magnitude and line of action of the single equivalent force.

10. ABCD is a square of side a. Forces of magnitude 1, 2, 3, 6 act along the sides AB, BC, CD, DA. Find the magnitudes of the forces which must act along AC and BD in order to reduce the system to a couple. Find the magnitude of the couple.

11. Forces of magnitude 5, x, y, z act along the sides AB, BC, CD, DA of a square ABCD. Find two possible sets of values of x, y, z if the resultant has magnitude $\sqrt{5}$ and whose line of action passes through A and the midpoint of BC.

12. OABCDE is a regular hexagon. Forces of magnitude 1, 2, 3, 4 act along OA, AD, DC, CO, respectively. Taking OA and OD as x- and y-axes, with $OA = a$, find the magnitude and line of action of the resultant.

13. ABCDEF is a regular hexagon with centre O. Forces of magnitude 1, 2, 3, 4, 5 act along AB, BC, CD, DE, EF, respectively. Find three forces acting along the sides of triangle OAF which are equivalent to the given system.

7.5 Equilibrium of a rigid body under coplanar forces

In section 7.4 we saw that any system of coplanar forces not in equilibrium may be reduced to either (a) a single resultant force, or (b) a couple.

If a rigid body is in equilibrium under the action of a system of coplanar forces then

a) the resultant external force must be zero, and
b) the resultant couple must be zero.

In practice, we proceed as follows:

a) We set the sum of the components of the external forces equal to zero, usually in two perpendicular directions.
b) We set the total moment about suitably chosen points to be zero; usually these points are taken as points through which unknown forces act.

We will illustrate the method by means of examples.

One force

As with a particle, a rigid body cannot be in equilibrium under a single non-zero force.

Two forces

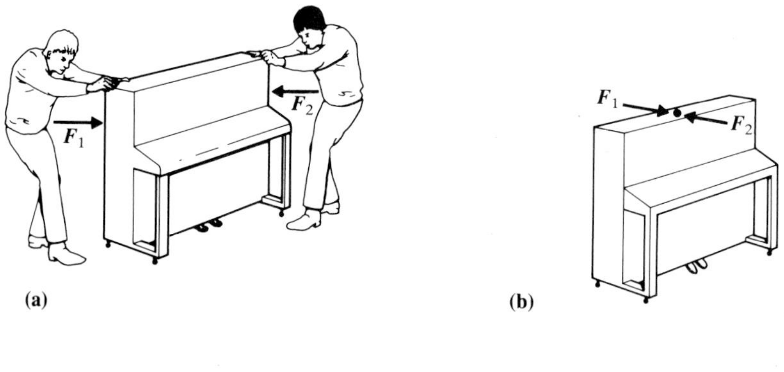

Figure 7.55

Suppose two men A and B are pushing on opposite sides of a piano, as in figure 7.55 with forces $\boldsymbol{F}_1$ and $\boldsymbol{F}_2$. For equilibrium, $\boldsymbol{F}_1 + \boldsymbol{F}_2 = \boldsymbol{0}$, i.e. the forces must be equal in magnitude and opposite in direction. However, to avoid rotation, they must have zero moment about any point O, say, and thus must have the same line of action. Thus, A and B must stand opposite each other.

Three forces

There are three cases to consider.

a) *Parallel forces.* Consider a plan view of the piano, as in figure 7.56, and let three men push it at points A, B and C with forces $\boldsymbol{F}_1$, $\boldsymbol{F}_2$ and $\boldsymbol{F}_3$. For equilibrium,

$$\boldsymbol{F}_1 + \boldsymbol{F}_2 + \boldsymbol{F}_3 = \boldsymbol{0},$$

so that

$$F_3 = F_1 + F_2.$$

The man at B must push with a force equal in magnitude to the sum of the other two. Further, the resultant moment about any point must be zero, so that taking moments about B, say,

$$F_1 a = F_2 b.$$

The position of B is given by the ratio

$$\frac{a}{b} = \frac{F_2}{F_1}.$$

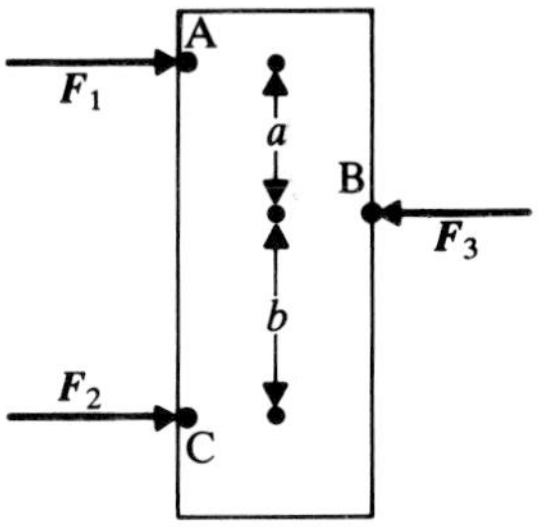

Figure 7.56

b) *Two forces parallel.* This situation is shown in figure 7.57. In this case, we cannot write $\boldsymbol{F}_3$ as a linear combination of $\boldsymbol{F}_1$ and $\boldsymbol{F}_2$, and so the vector sum $\boldsymbol{F}_1 + \boldsymbol{F}_2 + \boldsymbol{F}_3 \neq \boldsymbol{0}$, and thus equilibrium is not possible.

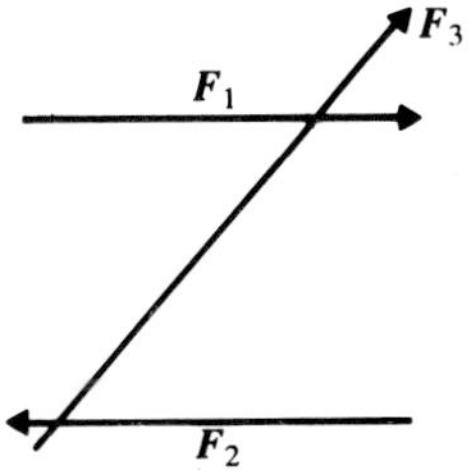

Figure 7.57

c) *Two forces concurrent.* This situation is shown in figure 7.58. For equilibrium, $\boldsymbol{F}_1 + \boldsymbol{F}_2 + \boldsymbol{F}_3 = \boldsymbol{0}$, and the resultant moment about any point must be zero. In particular, $\boldsymbol{F}_1$ and $\boldsymbol{F}_2$ have zero moment about O since they pass through it. Thus the moment of $\boldsymbol{F}_3$ about O must be zero. This is only possible if the line of action of $\boldsymbol{F}_3$ is also through O. This is called the **three–force condition** for equilibrium. It is also called the **concurrency condition**.

For equilibrium three forces must either be parallel or concurrent.

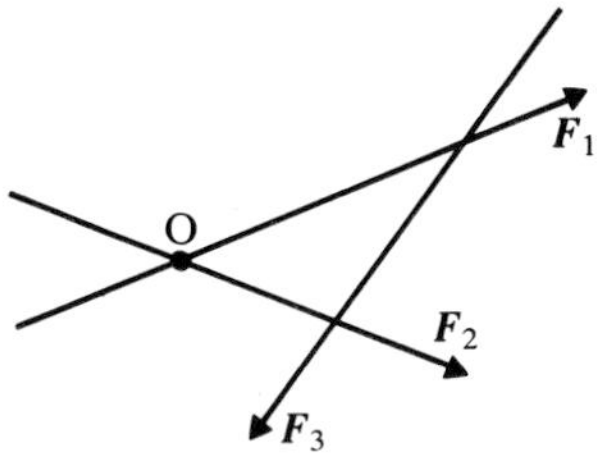

Figure 7.58

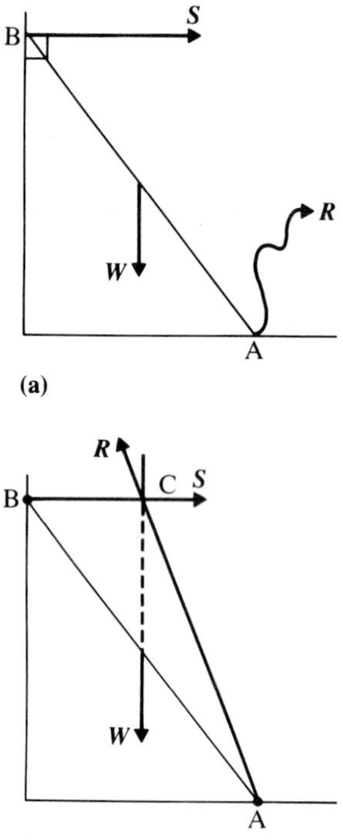

Figure 7.59

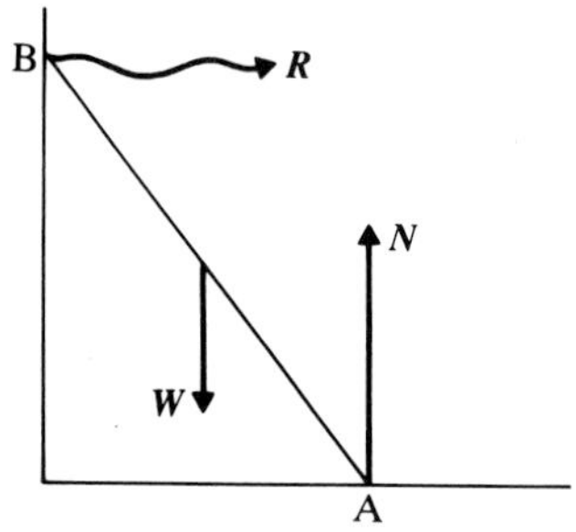

Figure 7.60

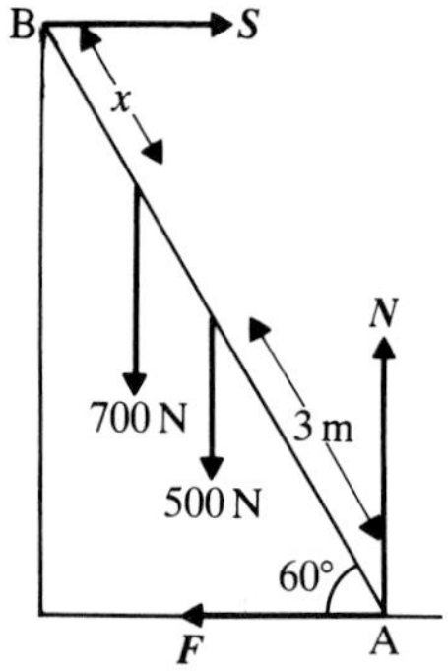

Figure 7.61

EXAMPLE 1

Suppose a ladder of weight W is resting on rough ground at A and against a smooth wall at B, as in figure 7.59. Since the wall is smooth the reaction $\boldsymbol{S}$ is normal to the wall. The direction of the rough reaction $\boldsymbol{R}$ at A is unknown. However, for equilibrium, the three force condition states that the lines of action of $\boldsymbol{S}$, $\boldsymbol{R}$ and $\boldsymbol{W}$ must be concurrent. Thus, the direction of $\boldsymbol{R}$ must pass through the point C, as in figure 7.59b.

EXAMPLE 2

Suppose the ladder in example 1 is resting against a rough wall and on a smooth floor.

The forces acting are shown in figure 7.60. Clearly, since $\boldsymbol{W}$, the weight force, and $\boldsymbol{N}$, the normal action at the floor are parallel, the three forces cannot be concurrent, and hence the system cannot be in equilibrium. The ladder will slide to the ground.

Four or more forces

EXAMPLE 3

A uniform ladder of mass 50 kg and length 6 m is leaning at an angle of 60° to the horizontal against a smooth wall. It is standing on rough ground and the coefficient of friction between it and the ground is 0.4. A man of mass 70 kg climbs the ladder. How far up the ladder will he get before it slips? Take g as 10 ms^{-2}.

The forces on the ladder are as shown in figure 7.61. Suppose the man is x m from the top of the ladder when it slips. Resolving vertically

$$N = 500 + 700 = 1200. \qquad \textbf{(9)}$$

Taking moments about B, since the force S is not required

$$700x \cos 60° + 500 \times 3 \cos 60° + F \times 6 \sin 60° = N \times 6 \cos 60°,$$

$$350x + 750 + 5.20F = 3N. \qquad \textbf{(10)}$$

We have three unknowns F, N and x and so three equations are required. On the point of slipping

$$F = \mu N = 0.4N. \qquad \textbf{(11)}$$

From equations (9)–(11)

$$350x = 3600 - 750 - 0.4 \times 5.20 \times 1200 = 354,$$

$$x = 1.01.$$

The man moves about 5 m up the ladder before it slips.

EXAMPLE 4

A square lamina of side $2a$ and weight W is resting in a vertical plane against a smooth wall at 10° to the horizontal floor. The coefficient of friction between the floor and the lamina is 0.4. What is the minimum weight which can be suspended from the corner D, figure 7.62, to avoid slipping?

Let w be the weight attached at D. At the point of slipping

$$F = 0.4N.$$

Resolving vertically $\quad W + w = N.$

Resolving horizontally $\quad F = S.$

Taking moments about A,

$$W \times a\sqrt{2}\cos 55^\circ = S \times 2a\cos 80^\circ + w \times 2a\cos 80^\circ.$$

Hence $\quad W\sqrt{2}\cos 55^\circ = 2[0.4(W + w) + w]\cos 80^\circ,$

giving
$$w = W\left[\frac{\cos 55^\circ}{\sqrt{2}\cos 80^\circ} - 0.4\right]\Big/1.4$$
$$= 1.383W.$$

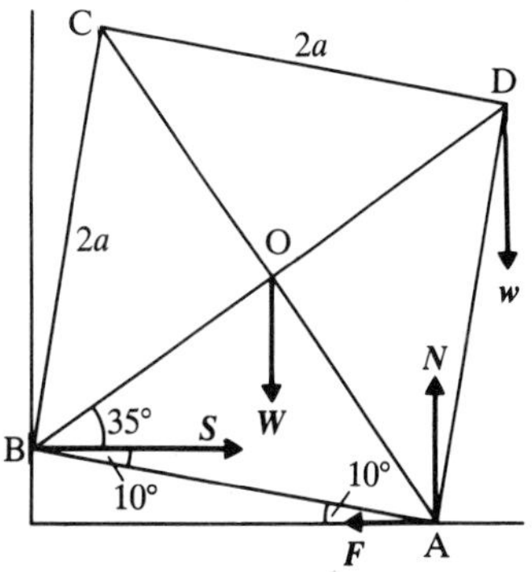

Figure 7.62

EXERCISE 7G

Questions 1–4 refer to a ladder AB of mass 50 kg and length 7 m leaning at an angle of 60° to the horizontal, in contact with the ground at A and a vertical wall at B,

1. If contact at B is smooth, and the coefficient of friction for the contact at A is 0.4, find the reaction between the ladder and the ground.
2. If contact at B is smooth, find the minimum coefficient of friction for contact at A if the ladder is in equilibrium.
3. If the coefficient of friction for contact at B is now 0.2, calculate the minimum coefficient of friction needed at A for equilibrium.
4. If contact at B is smooth and the coefficient of friction at A is 0.4, how far up the ladder can a man of 70 kg climb before slipping occurs?
5. A girder AB of length 10 m and mass 5 t is suspended from a crane by two wires CB and CA of length 6 m and 8 m, respectively. joined together and supported at C. Find the tension in the wires and their inclination to the vertical, when the system is in equilibrium.
6. Repeat question 5 if masses of 1 t and 3 t are attached to the ends A and B respectively.
7. Figure 7.63 shows a square lamina of side $2a$ and weight W leaning in a vertical plane against a smooth wall. The coefficient of friction between the lamina and the ground is 0.5. Find, in terms of W, the minimum weight w that can be suspended from A if the lamina is to remain in equilibrium.
8. Repeat question 7 except that contact between the lamina and the wall is rough, the coefficient of friction being 0.2.

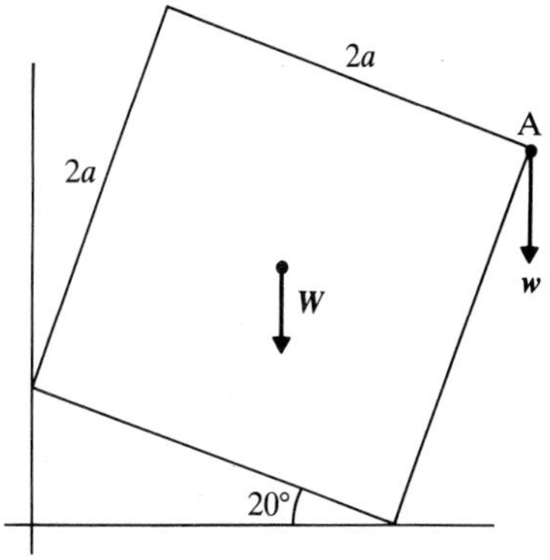

Figure 7.63

9. A uniform plank is at rest with one end on rough ground, making an angle θ with the horizontal, the coefficient of friction being μ. It is supported by a string tied at the upper end, the string being perpendicular to the rod. Find an expression for μ in terms of θ, if the system is in limiting equilibrium.

10. If the rod in question 9 is inclined at 20° to the horizontal, find the minimum coefficient of friction required for equilibrium.

11.* Two smooth planes are inclined at 20° and 40° to the horizontal. A uniform plank rests with one end on each of the planes as shown in figure 7.64. Calculate the inclination of the plank to the horizontal.

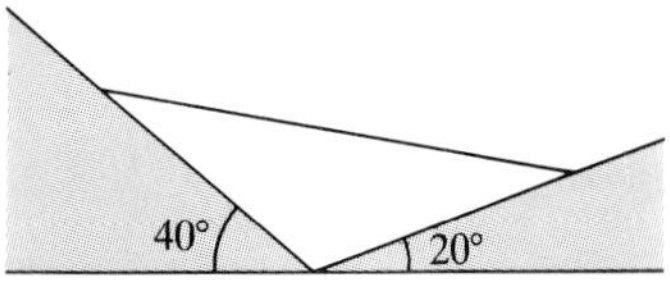

Figure 7.64

7.6 Systems of rigid bodies

In the last section we developed and applied the conditions for equilibrium of a rigid body under the action of external coplanar forces. We now discuss the equilibrium of more than one rigid body in contact.

Rods

A rod can exert forces parallel and perpendicular to its length.

In figure 7.65a the table leg AB exerts a force of magnitude T outwards at its ends; upwards on the table top and downwards on the floor. Such forces are called **thrusts**. The forces on the leg at A and B are inwards. The table leg is said to be in **stress**.

In figure 7.65b the towbar exerts a force F down the slope on the car at A and up the slope on the caravan at B. The forces on the towbar at A and B are both outward and the bar is said to be under **tension**.

In figure 7.65c the beam exerts a force P downwards on the support, perpendicular to its length.

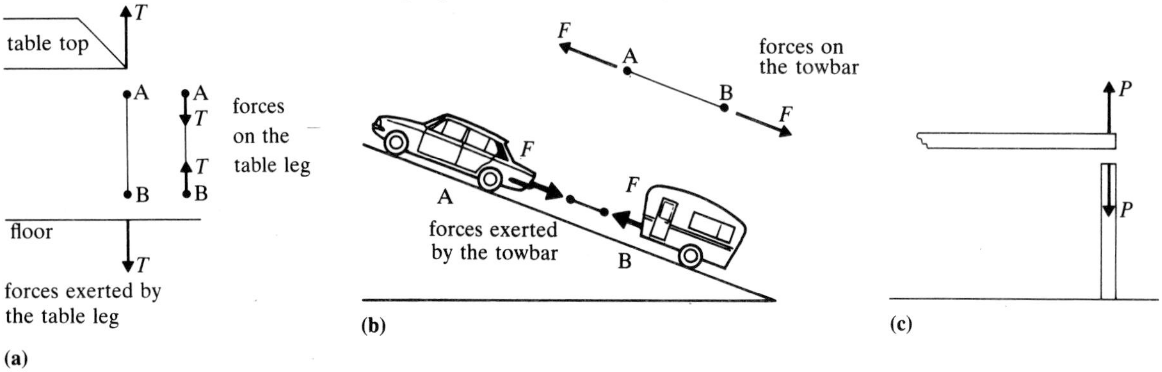

Figure 7.65

Light rods

As we saw in section 7.3, the weight force of a rod is sometimes negligible compared with other forces acting and that under these circumstances the rod is said to be light. For example, the aluminium poles of a large frame tent are rods whose weight is negligible compared with the weight of the canvas and other forces acting.

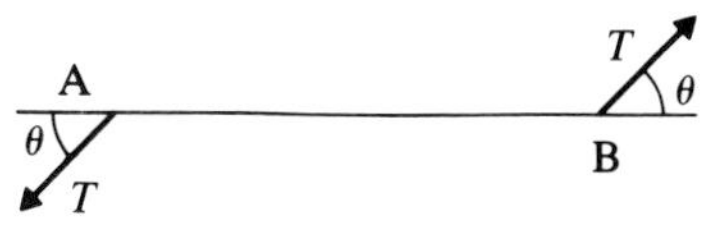

Figure 7.66

If such a rod is in equilibrium under the action of two forces at its ends, the work of section 7.5 indicates that the forces must be equal and opposite and act along the length of the rod. In figure 7.66 the forces acting at the ends of the rod AB are equal in magnitude and opposite in direction, but they are not in equilibrium, since they have a non-zero turning effect, and so the rod will rotate anticlockwise. Thus, for equilibrium, $\theta = 0°$ and the forces must act along the rod.

Figure 7.67

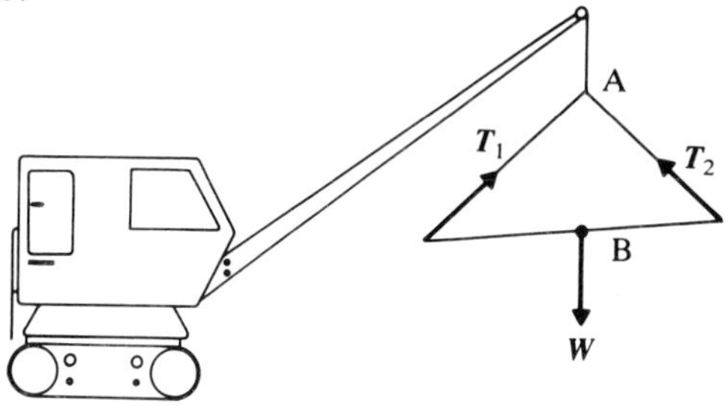

Figure 7.67 shows a heavy girder suspended from a crane. In this case, the forces at the end of the rod are not acting in the line of the rod, but the three forces $\boldsymbol{T}_1$, $\boldsymbol{T}_2$ and $\boldsymbol{W}$ are in equilibrium, and so they satisfy the three–force concurrency condition. In this example this means that the centre of mass, B, must be vertically below A, the point of suspension.

Jointed rods

There are many situations in which rods are jointed or hinged together, e.g. stepladders, cranes and scaffolding. We will model a hinge by a pin at a point on one rod passing through a pinhole in the other rod. The forces on the two hinged bodies must be equal and opposite, according to N3, as shown in figure 7.68.

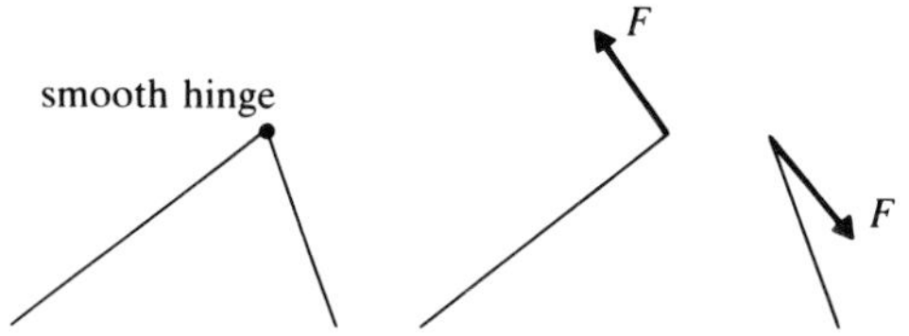

Figure 7.68

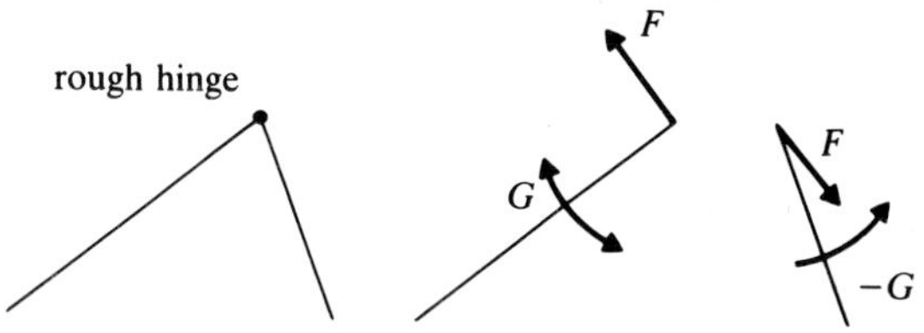

Figure 7.69

When a hinge is rough there may also be a couple acting, as shown in figure 7.69. In this case the couples acting on each rod must be equal and opposite. The following example illustrates the difference between rough and smooth hinges.

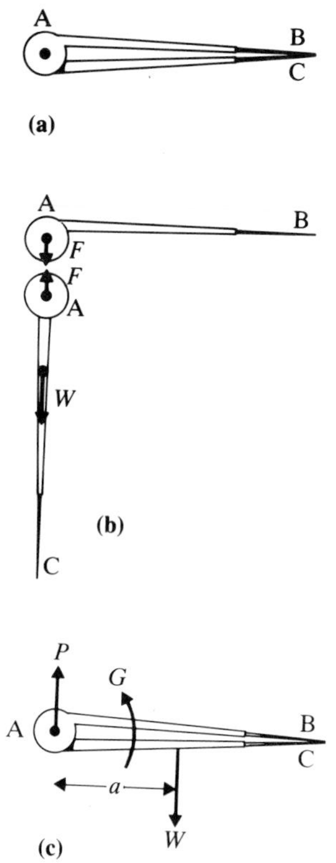

Figure 7.70

Figure 7.70a shows a pair of dividers with arm AB resting on arm AC, the two arms being hinged at A. Suppose the arm AB is held horizontal and lifted up vertically.

If the hinge at A were smooth, arm AC would hang vertically, and the forces at A would then be as shown in figure 7.70b, with $F = W$, which is the weight force on the arm AC.

If the hinge A were rough, the system could remain as in figure 7.70a, in which case the forces on the arm AC, and the couple are as shown in figure 7.70c. In this case, $P = W$ and $G = aW$.

In all subsequent work we will assume that hinges are smooth.

EXAMPLE 1

Figure 7.71a shows a hoist on a boat. AB is a light rod hinged at A. C is a pulley over which a rope passes, the end of which is fixed to the rod at B. The lengths are such that AC = AB = $2a$. A body of weight

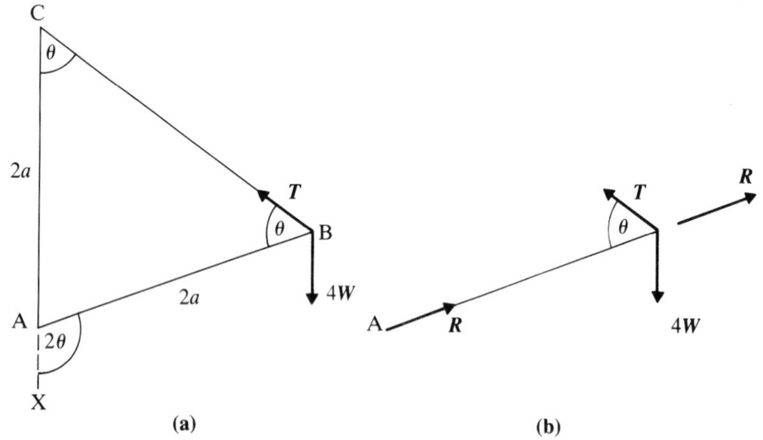

Figure 7.71

$4W$ is suspended from B by a second rope. Find the tension in the rope BC and the reaction at A on the rod in terms of W and θ.

Since Δ ABC is isosceles, $\mathrm{A\hat{C}B} = \theta$ and $\mathrm{X\hat{A}B} = 2\theta$. AB is a light rod so the forces it exerts at its ends must act along its length. Thus there is no resultant force perpendicular to the rod at B. Hence

$$T \sin\theta = 4W \sin 2\theta,$$

$$T = \frac{4W \sin 2\theta}{\sin\theta} = 8W \cos\theta.$$

Let $\boldsymbol{R}$ be the force on the rod at A, as in figure 7.71b. Resolving along the rod,

$$\begin{aligned} R &= T\cos\theta + 4W\cos(180^\circ - 2\theta) \\ &= 8W\cos^2\theta - 4W\cos 2\theta \\ &= 4W. \end{aligned}$$

EXAMPLE 2

Suppose that the light rod in example 1 is replaced by a uniform heavy rod of weight W. If nothing is suspended from B find, in terms of θ and W, the tension in the rope T and the reaction on the rod at A.

We note the following points:

a) Since the rod is not light, the forces at its ends need not act along the line of the rod.

b) Since there are three forces acting on the rod, their lines of action must be concurrent, as shown in figure 7.72a.

From simple geometry we see that $A\hat{P}C = 90°$. The magnitudes R and T are found directly from the triangle of forces shown in figure 7.72b. We see that $R = W \sin\theta$ and $T = W\cos\theta$.

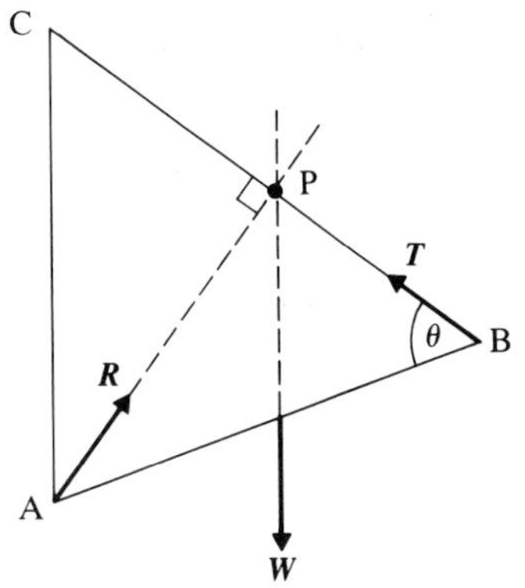

(a)

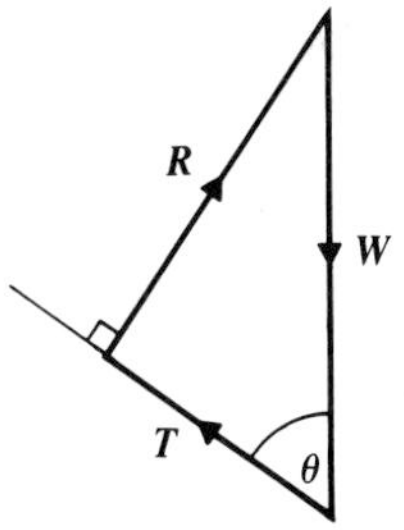

(b)

Figure 7.72

EXAMPLE 3

Suppose that the system of example 2 now supports a body of weight $4W$ at B. Find, in terms of W and θ, the tension in the rope BC and the reaction at A.

Since there are now more than three forces acting on the rod, there is no concurrency condition to enable us to find the direction of the reaction at A. The normal method of approach is to resolve in two perpendicular directions and take moments about one point. There are several ways of doing this and we will illustrate the two most commonly used.

Method 1 Resolving horizontally and vertically

Let the horizontal and vertical components of the forces on the rod at A be X and Y, as shown in figure 7.73a.

Resolving vertically $\quad Y + T\cos\theta = 5W. \qquad$ **(12)**

Resolving horizontally $\quad X = T\sin\theta. \qquad$ **(13)**

Since X and Y act at A they have no moment about A. Thus, taking moments about A will give T directly in terms of W.

$$W \times a\sin 2\theta + 4W \times 2a\sin 2\theta = T \times 2a\sin\theta,$$

$$T = \frac{\sin 2\theta}{2\sin\theta} \times 9W$$

$$= 9W\cos\theta.$$

Hence, from (13)

$$X = 9W\cos\theta\sin\theta$$

$$= \tfrac{9}{2}W\sin 2\theta$$

From (12)

$$Y = 5W - 9W\cos^2\theta$$

$$= 5W - \tfrac{9}{2}W(\cos 2\theta + 1)$$

$$= \tfrac{1}{2}W - \tfrac{9}{2}W\cos 2\theta$$

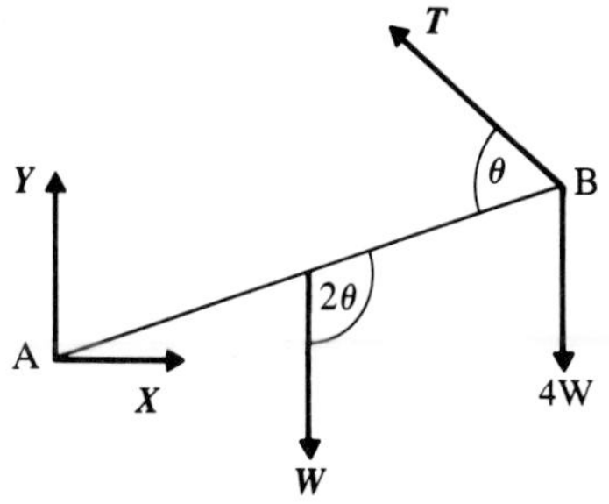

(a)

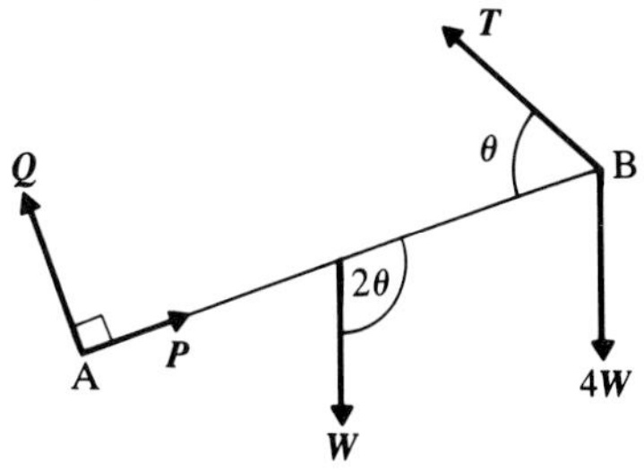

(b)

Figure 7.73

Method 2 Resolving parallel and perpendicular to the rod

In this case let the components of the forces on the rod at B be P and Q, as shown in figure 7.73b.

Resolving along the rod

$$P + 5W\cos 2\theta = T\cos\theta. \qquad \textbf{(14)}$$

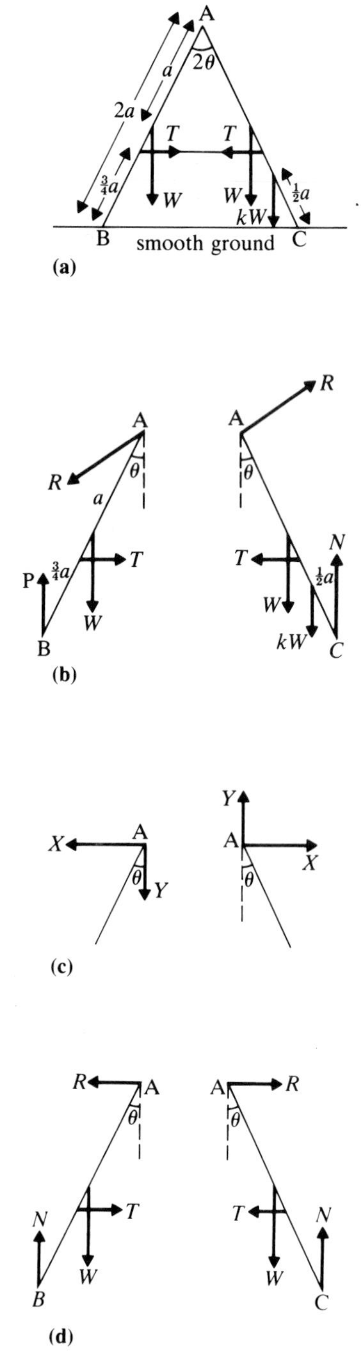

Figure 7.74

Resolving perpendicular to the rod

$$Q + T\sin\theta = 5W\sin 2\theta. \qquad \textbf{(15)}$$

Taking moments about B for the rod AB

$$Q \times 2a = W\sin 2\theta \times a,$$
$$Q = \tfrac{1}{2}W\sin 2\theta.$$

From (15),
$$T\sin\theta = \tfrac{9}{2}W\sin 2\theta.$$
$$T = 9W\cos\theta.$$

From (14),
$$P = 9W\cos^2\theta - 5W\cos 2\theta$$
$$= \tfrac{9}{2}(\cos 2\theta + 1) - 5W\cos 2\theta$$
$$= \tfrac{9}{2}W - \tfrac{1}{2}W\cos 2\theta.$$

In this case, taking moments about B gave Q directly, since both P and T have zero moment about B. Notice

$$X^2 + Y^2 = P^2 + Q^2 = \tfrac{1}{2}W^2(41 - 9\cos 2\theta)$$

Hence the magnitude of the reaction on the rod at A is

$$\sqrt{\tfrac{1}{2}}W\sqrt{(41 - 9\cos 2\theta)}.$$

□□□□□

When analysing the forces in a system of connected bodies, the following points of technique should be remembered.

a) After a preliminary sketch, draw a diagram with points of contact, joints etc., separated with forces on separate components clearly labelled.

For example, figure 7.74a shows someone of weight kW standing on a stepladder of weight $2W$ on smooth ground. Figure 7.74b shows the forces on the two sections of the ladder separately, where $\boldsymbol{R}$ is the reaction at the joint. In order to analyse the forces we can consider the equilibrium of the sections individually, or the whole system. Notice that while $\boldsymbol{R}$ and $\boldsymbol{T}$ are external forces on the separate sections, they are internal forces for the system.

b) It is often convenient to resolve the reaction at the joint into two perpendicular directions. Thus, for the system in figure 7.74a, we might draw the forces at the hinge as in figure 7.74c, which is a modification of figure 7.74b.

c) If the system is symmetrical about the line through a joint, then the reaction at the joint will be perpendicular to the line of symmetry. For the ladder in figure 7.74a, without anyone on it, the forces are acting as in figure 7.74d.

EXAMPLE 4

Find in terms of W and θ the tension in the rope joining the two sections of the stepladder shown in figure 7.74d.

Figure 7.75 shows the forces acting on one section.
Resolving horizontally $R = T$.

Taking moments about B for AB

$$2a \times R\cos\theta = a \times W\sin\theta + T\cos\theta,$$
$$2T\cos\theta = W\sin\theta + \tfrac{3}{4}T\cos\theta,$$
$$\tfrac{5}{4}T\cos\theta = W\sin\theta,$$
$$T = \tfrac{4}{5}W\tan\theta.$$

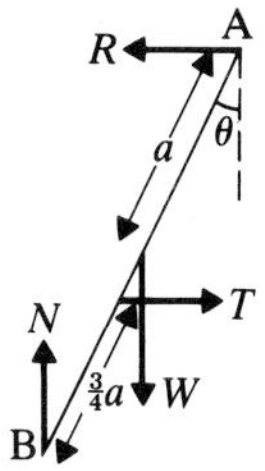

Figure 7.75

EXAMPLE 5

Figure 7.76a shows a man of weight $4W$ standing on a stepladder consisting of two uniform parts each of weight W, smoothly hinged at A. Find the minimum value of the coefficient of friction between the ladder and the ground if the system is in equilibrium.

Figure 7.76b shows the forces acting on AB and AC separately. There are six unknown forces marked, X, Y, N, F, R and S, but we do not require X and Y, so we try to form four equations which do not involve X and Y.

Consider the whole system, for which X and Y are internal forces:

resolving horizontally $\qquad F = S,$ **(16)**

resolving vertically $\qquad R + N = 6W.$ **(17)**

Consider the leg AB, noting that X and Y have no moment about A. Taking moments about A

$$N \times 2a\cos 60^\circ = F \times 2a\sin 60^\circ + W \times a\cos 60^\circ,$$
$$N = \sqrt{3}F + \tfrac{1}{2}W \qquad \textbf{(18)}$$

Consider the leg AC. Taking moments about A

$$R \times 2a\cos 60^\circ = S \times 2a\sin 60^\circ + W \times a\cos 60^\circ + 4W \times \tfrac{1}{2}a\cos 60^\circ,$$
$$R = \sqrt{3}S + \tfrac{3}{2}W. \qquad \textbf{(19)}$$

At this stage we have four equations in the four unknowns N, F, R, S. Substituting from (16), (18) and (19) in (17) we obtain

$$6W = 2\sqrt{3}F + 2W.$$

Hence $\qquad F = 2W/\sqrt{3} = S, \qquad N = \tfrac{5}{2}W, \qquad R = \tfrac{7}{2}W.$

Hence, $\qquad F/N = \dfrac{4}{5\sqrt{3}}, \qquad S/R = \dfrac{4}{7\sqrt{3}}.$

Thus, slipping will occur first at B, since $F/N > S/R$, and this will not occur provided $\mu \geqslant \frac{4}{5\sqrt{3}}$.

Note that, if instead we had been asked to find the reaction at A, then X and Y could be found by taking moments about B and C.

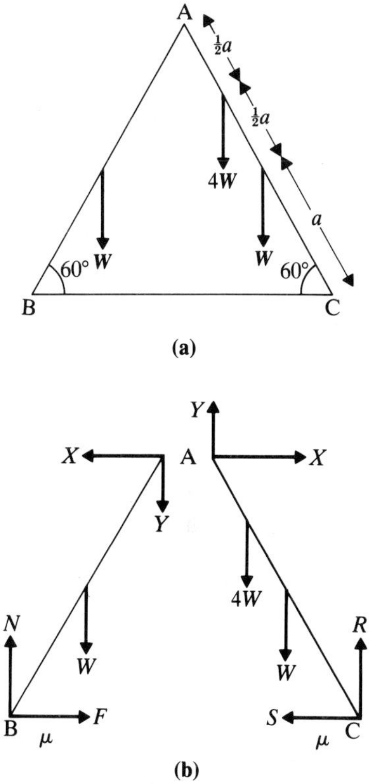

Figure 7.76

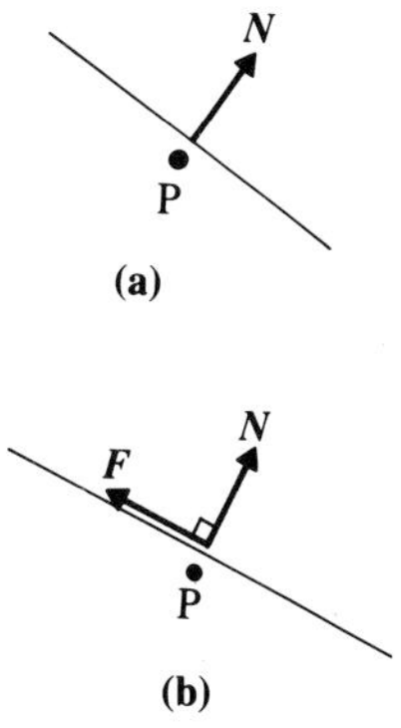

Figure 7.77

Pegs

When a rod rests on a smooth peg, there is a contact force, N, on the rod, perpendicular to the rod, as shown in figure 7.77a. If the peg is not smooth, there may also be frictional forces acting along the rod, as in figure 7.77b.

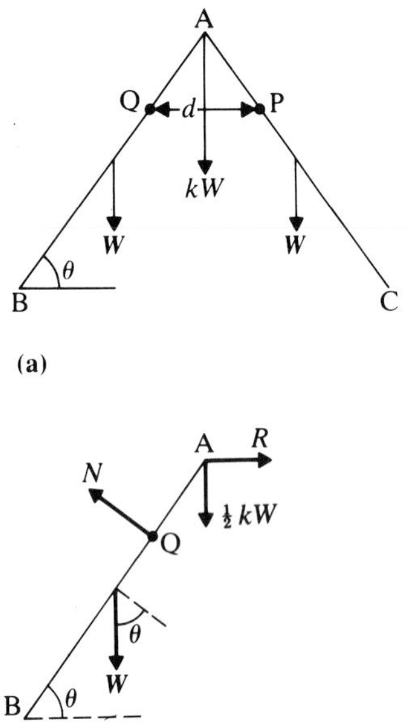

(a)

(b)

Figure 7.78

EXAMPLE 6

Figure 7.78a shows two smoothly jointed uniform rods AB and AC of length a and weight W, resting on two smooth pegs at P and Q. If a weight kW is suspended from A, prove that the angle of inclination of each rod, θ, is given by $\cos^3\theta = d(2+k)/2a$, where d is the distance between the pegs.

The forces on the rod AB are shown in figure 7.78b. Since the system is symmetrical about a vertical line through A, the reaction at A will be horizontal.
For the rod AB, resolving vertically gives

$$N\cos\theta = W + \tfrac{1}{2}kW = \tfrac{1}{2}(2+k). \qquad \textbf{(20)}$$

Taking moments about A, since the unwanted force R has no moment about this point,

$$N \times \mathrm{AQ} = W \times \tfrac{1}{2}a\cos\theta.$$

Now $\mathrm{AQ} = d/2\cos\theta$, hence

$$N = \frac{a}{d}W \times \cos^2\theta. \qquad \textbf{(21)}$$

From equations (20) and (21),

$$\tfrac{1}{2}W(2+k) = \frac{a}{d} \times W\cos^3\theta.$$

This gives $\cos^3\theta = d(2+k)/2a$, as required.

EXAMPLE 7

Figure 7.79a shows a fishing rod with its bottom end in contact with the fisherman's foot at A, and passing over a rough support at B. If the coefficients of friction at A and B are μ_1 and μ_2, respectively, prove that, for equilibrium,

$$\frac{c}{a} \leqslant \frac{\mu_1 + \mu_2}{\mu_2 + \tan\alpha},$$

where $\mathrm{AB} = c$, $\mathrm{AG} = a$, and the rod is inclined at an angle α with the horizontal.

The forces on the rod are shown in figure 7.79b.
Resolving parallel to the rod

$$F_1 + F_2 = W\sin\alpha.$$

Resolving perpendicular to the rod

$$N_1 - N_2 = W\cos\alpha.$$

Taking moments about A

$$N_1 c = W \times a\cos\alpha,$$

$$N_1 = \frac{Wa}{c}\cos\alpha.$$

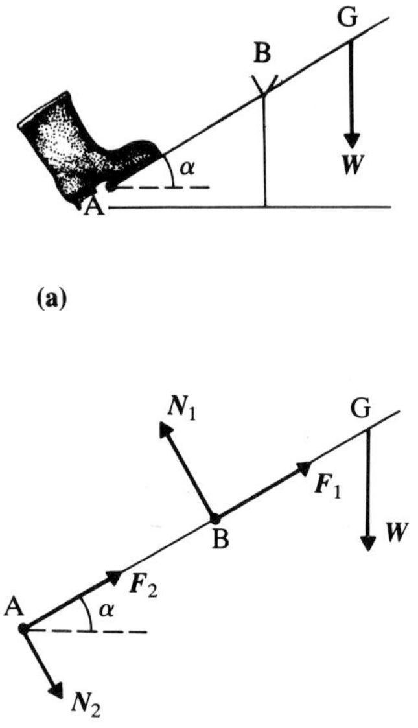

(a)

(b)

Figure 7.79

Hence $$N_2 = -W\cos\alpha + \frac{Wa}{c}\cos\alpha.$$

Now $F_1 \leqslant \mu_1 N_1$ and $F_2 \leqslant \mu_2 N_2$,

hence $$\mu_1 N_1 + \mu_2 N_2 \geqslant W\sin\alpha,$$

$$\Rightarrow \quad \mu_1 W \times \frac{a}{c} \times \cos\alpha + \mu_2 W\left(-\cos\alpha + \frac{a}{c}\cos\alpha\right) \geqslant W\sin\alpha,$$

$$\Rightarrow \quad W\frac{a}{c}\cos\alpha[(\mu_1 + \mu_2)] \geqslant W(\sin\alpha + \mu_2\cos\alpha),$$

hence $$\frac{c}{a} \leqslant \frac{\mu_1 + \mu_2}{\mu_2 + \tan\alpha}.$$

□□□□□

We may apply the preceding methods to other bodies in contact at a single point, as illustrated in the following examples.

EXAMPLE 8

Three logs are resting in contact, as shown in figure 7.80a. They are of exactly the same shape and weight. Find the least value of the coefficient of friction between the upper and lower logs, and between the lower logs and the ground, if the system is in equilibrium.

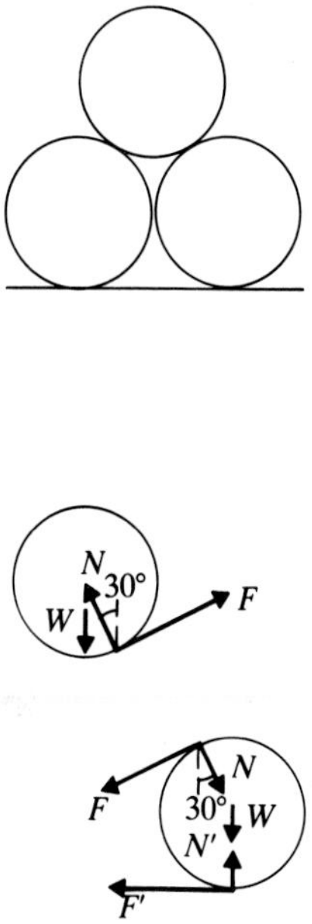

(a)

(b)

Figure 7.80

Let the radii of the logs be a, and weights be W. By symmetry, we only need consider one half of the system, as shown in figure 7.80b Resolving vertically for the whole system

$$2N' = 3W,$$
$$N' = \tfrac{3}{2}W. \qquad (22)$$

Note that $\boldsymbol{F}$ and $\boldsymbol{N}$ are internal forces for the system as a whole. Consider the bottom log.
Taking moments about the centre

$$F = F'. \qquad (23)$$

Resolving vertically

$$N' = W + N\cos 30^\circ + F\sin 30^\circ.$$

Hence $$\tfrac{1}{2}W = N\tfrac{1}{2}\sqrt{3} + \tfrac{1}{2}F$$
$$\sqrt{3}N + F = W \qquad (24)$$

Resolving horizontally

$$F' + \text{F}\cos 30^\circ = N\sin 30^\circ,$$
$$2F' + \sqrt{3}F = N. \qquad (25)$$

Hence

$$F(2+\sqrt{3}) = N \quad \text{and} \quad \mu \geqslant \frac{1}{2+\sqrt{3}},$$

where μ is the coefficient of friction between the upper and lower logs.

From (22)–(24) $\quad \sqrt{3}F'(2+\sqrt{3})+F' = W,$

$$F' = \frac{W}{4+2\sqrt{3}}$$

From (22) and (23),

$$\frac{F'}{N'} = \frac{2}{3(4+2\sqrt{3})} \quad \text{and} \quad \mu' \geqslant \frac{1}{3(2+\sqrt{3})},$$

where μ' is the coefficient of friction between the logs and the ground.

*EXAMPLE 9

A man of weight $4W$ stands in the middle of a plank of weight W resting on rough ground and on a barrel of weight W, as shown in figure 7.81a. If the system is in limiting equilibrium, find the minimum values for the angles of friction λ, μ, and ν for the rough contact at points A, B and C.

Figure 7.81b shows the forces acting on the barrel. Since it is in equilibrium under the action of three non-parallel forces, their lines of action must be concurrent. Hence, the line of action of S must pass through A, and $\mu = \alpha$. From figure 7.81a, $\tan\alpha = \frac{1}{3}$. Hence $\tan\mu = \frac{1}{3}$ and $\mu = 18.4°$. Notice that this value of μ is totally independent of the weight of both the plank and the man.

Without knowing the magnitude of S we cannot determine λ or R, and we therefore consider the forces on the plank. These are shown in figure 7.81c. We could find ν from the concurrency condition since there are three non-parallel forces acting on the plank. However, since we require the magnitude of S, we will use calculation.
Taking moments about C

$$3r \times S\cos\alpha = 2r \times 5W\cos 2\alpha,$$

$$S = \frac{10W\cos 2\alpha}{3\cos\alpha}.$$

Resolving horizontally $\quad T\sin\nu = S\sin\alpha$

Resolving vertically $\quad T\cos\nu + S\cos\alpha = 5W.$

Hence $\quad S\cot\nu\sin\alpha + S\cos\alpha = 5W,$

$$\cot\nu\tan\alpha\cos 2\alpha + \cos 2\alpha = \tfrac{3}{2},$$

$$\cot\nu = \frac{\frac{3}{2} - \cos 2\alpha}{\tan\alpha\cos 2\alpha}$$

$$= \frac{\frac{3}{2} - \frac{4}{5}}{\frac{1}{3} \times \frac{4}{5}}$$

$$= \tfrac{21}{8}.$$

Hence $\tan\nu = \frac{8}{21}$, so $\nu = 20.9°$

Figure 7.81d shows the forces on the barrel.

Taking moments about O $\quad S\sin\alpha = R\sin\lambda.$

Resolving vertically $\quad S\cos\alpha + W = R\cos\lambda.$

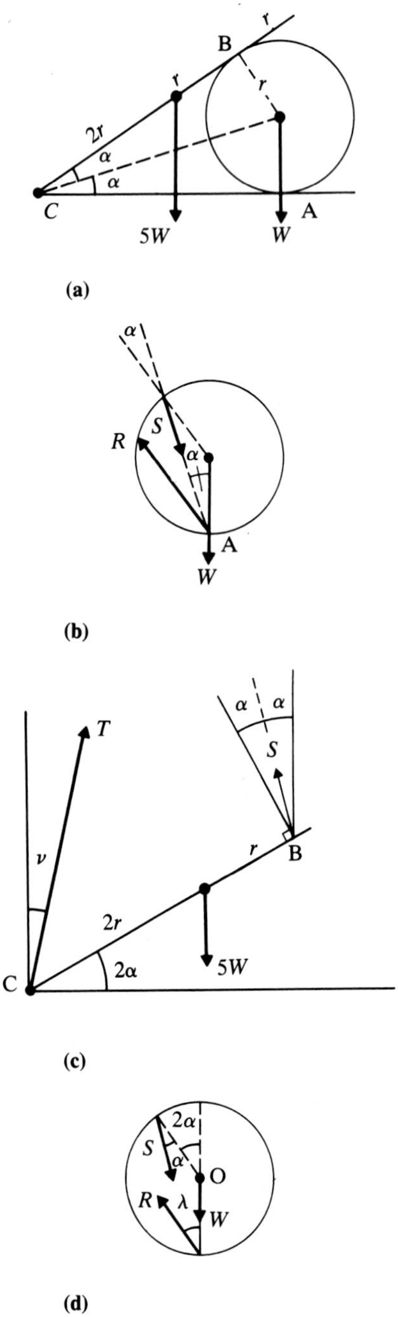

Figure 7.81

Dividing
$$\tan\lambda = \frac{S\sin\alpha}{S\cos\alpha + W}$$
$$= \frac{\frac{10}{3}\tan\alpha\cos 2\alpha}{\frac{10}{3}\cos 2\alpha + 1}$$
$$= \frac{\frac{10}{3}\times\frac{1}{3}\times\frac{4}{5}}{\frac{10}{3}\times\frac{4}{5}+1} = \frac{8}{33}.$$

Hence $\lambda = 13.6°$.

EXERCISE 7H

1. A uniform rod AB of length $2l$ and weight W has one end A on rough horizontal ground, the coefficient of friction being μ. The rod passes over a smooth peg at P, where $AP = a\,(a > l)$. If the rod is in limiting equilibrium, inclined at an angle α to the horizontal, prove that μ is given by
$$\mu = \frac{l\sin\alpha\cos\alpha}{a - l\cos^2\alpha}.$$
If μ is only half this value, find the magnitude of the least horizontal force needed at A to maintain equilibrium.

2. A uniform ladder of weight W rests with end B against a smooth wall and end A on a smooth floor. The ladder is prevented from slipping by a light string attached to the ladder at a point C and to the point O, where the wall joins the floor, where $A\hat{C}O = 90°$. Show that the tension T in the string is given by
$$T = \frac{W\cos\alpha}{2(\sin^2\alpha - \cos^2\alpha)}.$$
Explain why α must be greater than 45°.

3. Two equal rods AB and BC are smoothly jointed at B. The ends A and C are smoothly hinged so that AC is horizontal and both rods hang at an angle α to the horizontal. Both rods are uniform, but the weight of BC is kW and that of AB is W. Find the horizontal and vertical components of the reactions at A and C.

4. A symmetrical stepladder consists of two identical parts of length $4a$ and weight W, smoothly jointed at B. One end A is at rest on a wooden floor and the other end C is at rest on a carpet. The coefficients of friction at A and C are $\frac{1}{5}$ and $\frac{3}{5}$, respectively, and $A\hat{B}C$ is 2θ. A man of weight $5W$ stands on the leg AB a distance a from A. $A\hat{B}C$ is increased until slipping occurs. Does A or C slip first, and what is the corresponding value of θ?

5. A uniform rod AB of mass m is lying on a rough table. A string is attached to end A and is pulled at an angle α above the line of the rod. As the tension in the string is increased, show that the rod begins to slide before it lifts, provided $\mu < \cot\alpha$. Find the corresponding result if a particle of mass m is attached to the rod at A.

6. A uniform rod AB of length $2l$ rests against a smooth sphere of radius a at a point C. The end A of the rod is on rough ground, the coefficient of friction being μ. $AC = 2a$ $(a < l < 2a)$. If the system is in equilibrium, show that $\mu \geqslant 12l/(50a - 9l)$.

7. A uniform rod AB of weight W is smoothly hinged at A. A string BC is attached to the rod at B, with AC horizontal. $C\hat{A}B = \alpha$ and $A\hat{C}B = \beta$. Calculate in terms of W, α and β:
   a) the tension in the string BC,
   b) the horizontal and vertical components of the reaction at the hinge A.

8. Two equal uniform rods AB and AC, each of length $4l$ and weight W, are freely hinged at A. They are placed over a smooth cylinder of radius l, with A vertically above the centre. Show that if $B\hat{A}C = 90°$, the system is in equilibrium.

9. Two equal uniform rods are freely jointed at B and rest in equilibrium with end C on a rough horizontal plane. The end A is held fixed. Prove that if μ is the coefficient of friction for contact at C,

$$\mu \geqslant \frac{2}{\tan\beta - 3\tan\alpha},$$

   where α and β are the angles that BC and AB make with the horizontal, respectively.

10. A stepladder consists of two parts AB and AC of equal length, freely jointed at A and rests in equilibrium on a rough horizontal plane. The weight of each section is W, and a child of weight 2W stands halfway up AB. Show that if the ladder is about to slip, this will occur at C, and that if μ is the coefficient of friction, slipping will occur unless $\mu \geqslant \frac{2}{3}\tan\theta$.

11. A uniform plank AC of length l rests with end A on rough horizontal ground. The plank is also supported at B, a point between A and C, on a semicircular ramp of radius a. If the angle of friction at both points of contact is λ, show that the angle of inclination of the plank to the horizontal, θ, must satisfy the relation

$$\sin^2\theta \leqslant \frac{a}{l}\sin 2\lambda.$$

12. A sphere on a rough slope inclined at θ to the horizontal is kept in equilibrium by a horizontal string fixed to the top of the sphere. If μ is the coefficient of friction find the largest value of θ for equilibrium to be possible.

13. A child is trying to balance a straw AC in a beaker, as shown in figure 7.82. The beaker is held fixed and contact at A and B is smooth. The length of the straw is $2a$ and the radius of the beaker is r. Find θ in terms of a and r when the straw rests in equilibrium.

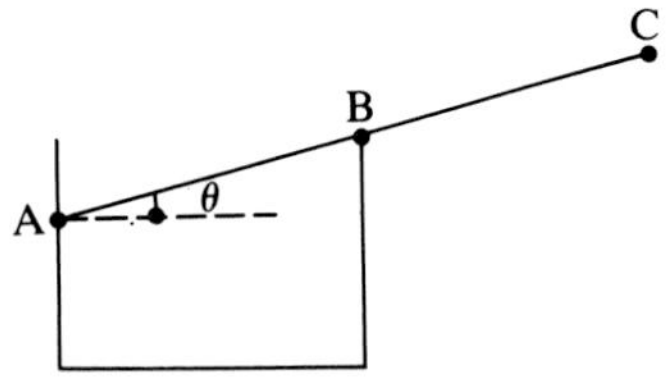

Figure 7.82

14. Figure 7.83 shows three cylinders each of weight W, radius r resting inside a fixed cylinder radius R. Contact between all cylinders is smooth. Show that if the cylinders remain in equilibrium $R < r(1 + 2\sqrt{7})$.

15. Three equal smooth cylinders of weight W rest on a smooth horizontal plane. Horizontal forces of magnitude P are applied to the middle of each of the lower cylinders as shown in figure 7.84. Find the minimum value of P to maintain equilibrium.

16. Figure 7.85 shows a uniform rod AB of length $2a$, weight W resting on a smooth cylinder of radius a. The end B of the rod is fixed to a string which passes over the cylinder and supports a weight W. If θ is the angle of inclination of the rod to the horizontal in the equilibrium position prove: (a) $BC = \frac{1}{2}a$, (b) $\cos\theta = \frac{4}{5}$, (c) the reaction at C is $\frac{8}{5}W$.

17.* A uniform ladder of weight W rests with one end A on the ground and the other end B against a vertical wall. The angle of friction at both points of contact is λ. The rod makes an angle θ with the wall. Prove that equilibrium is possible if $\lambda > \frac{1}{2}\theta$.
If $\lambda < \frac{1}{2}\theta$, a force P is applied horizontally at A. Prove that, in equilibrium with B about to slide down the wall, $P = \frac{1}{2}W \sin(\theta - 2\lambda) \sec\lambda \sec(\theta - \lambda)$. As P is increased, show that B will not slide up the wall provided $\lambda > \frac{1}{2}\pi - \theta$.

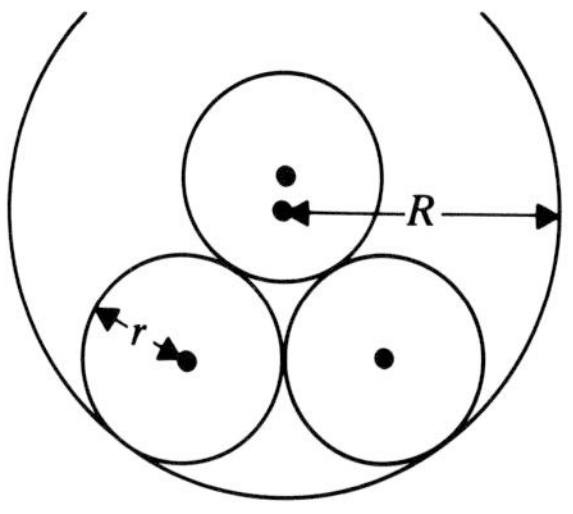

Figure 7.83

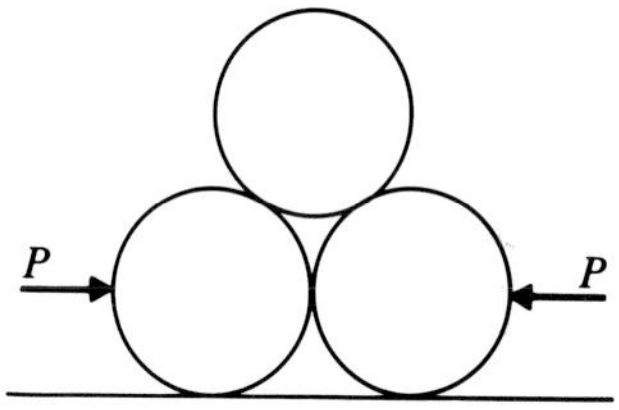

Figure 7.84

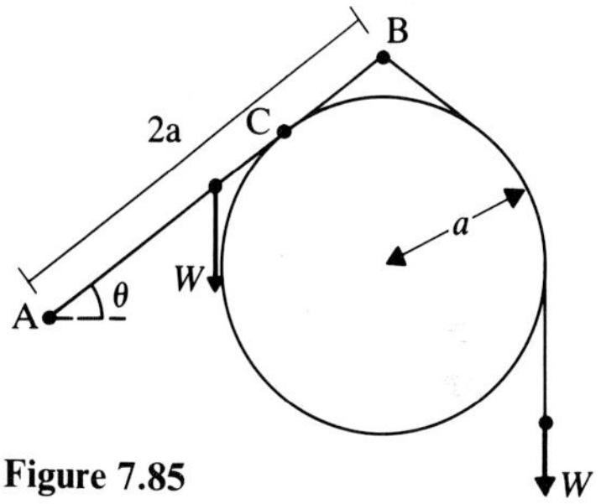

Figure 7.85

Summary

Friction

a) $F \leqslant \mu N$, where μ is the coefficient of friction between surfaces in contact.

b) $\mu = \tan\lambda$ where λ is the angle of friction

Moments

The moment of a force F about a point is Fd where d is the perpendicular distance of the point from the line of action of F.

Conditions for equilibrium of a rigid body

a) The vector sum of the forces is zero.

b) The sum of the moments of the external forces must be zero about any point.

In the special case of the three forces this means that either the forces are parallel or their lines of action are concurrent.

8 ELASTICITY AND SIMPLE HARMONIC MOTION

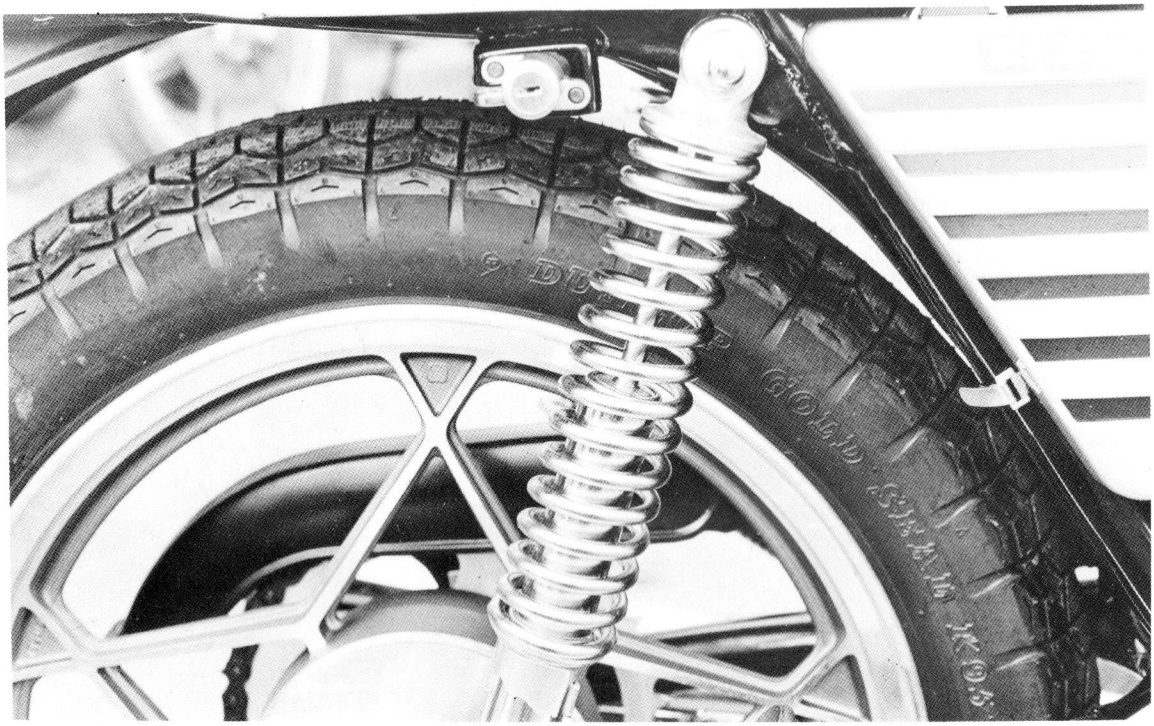

A stiff spring provides part of the rear suspension of a motorcycle

8.1 Hooke's law

In previous chapters we have seen many cases of particles and rigid bodies either accelerating or in equilibrium under the action of various agencies of force. These have included the tension in a string, and as a simplification we have so far assumed all strings to be light (zero mass) and inextensible (fixed length).

There are many situations in which the extension of strings is not negligible, and in this chapter we examine systems involving light strings and springs, where their extension is taken into account.

Elastic string

An elastic string is one which, after being stretched by an external force, will return to its original or natural length after the force is removed. When the string is stretched, it is said to be under tension, and if the string is not stretched, it is said to be slack.

Elastic spring

An elastic spring behaves exactly like an elastic string when extended. However, in order to reduce its length from its original value a force is required inwards on the ends of the spring. The spring is then said to be under compression, and exerts a thrust outwards at its ends.

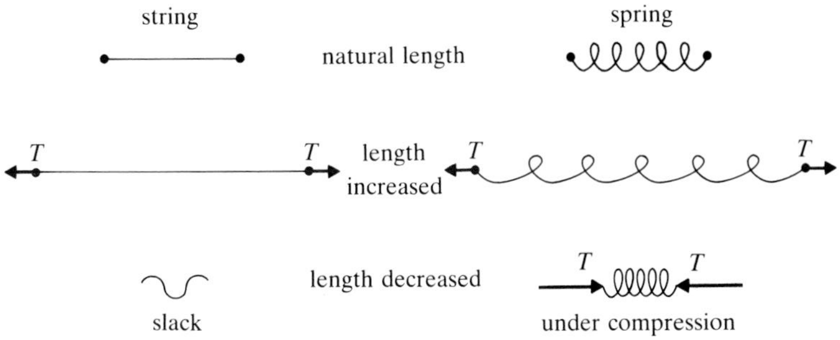

Figure 8.1

Figure 8.1 compares the external forces acting on the ends of a string and a spring in different situations. If a string is overstretched it may break or become permanently deformed. Similarly, if a spring is overstretched or overcompressed its coils may become deformed and it will not return to its natural length when released. The point at which permanent deformation takes place is called the **elastic limit**, and we will assume that this limit is not reached by the strings and springs under consideration here.

Extensions

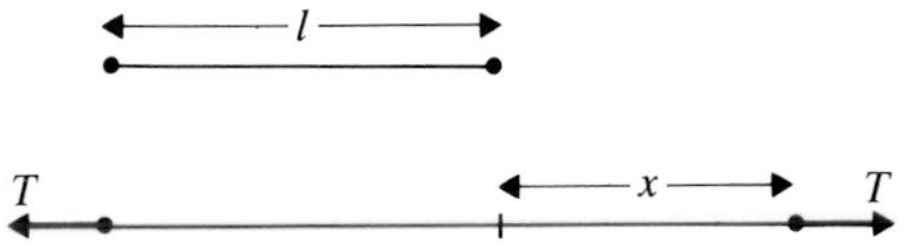

Figure 8.2

Figure 8.2 shows a piece of elastic of natural length l before and after being stretched. It can be shown experimentally that the tension T is related to the extension x by the equation

$$T = kx.$$

This is **Hooke's law**, which states that the tension in an elastic string is proportional to the extension. The result is also applicable to elastic springs.

It is important to remember that the tension in a string is transmitted unchanged throughout its length. The internal forces in the string at some different points are shown in figure 8.3. Notice that, at the ends A and B, the outward forces must be provided by the external agency stretching the string if it is to remain in equilibrium (see section 3.3).

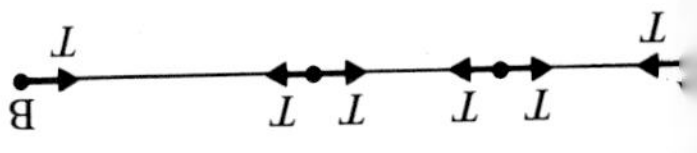

Figure 8.3

Units and dimensions

Since $T = kx$, $$[T] = [k][x],$$

$$[k] = \frac{[T]}{[x]} = \frac{\mathrm{M\,L\,T^{-2}}}{\mathrm{L}} = \mathrm{M\,T^{-2}}.$$

The SI units of k are $\mathrm{N\,m^{-1}}$. k is usually called the **spring constant** and its units are those of force per unit extension.

EXAMPLE 1

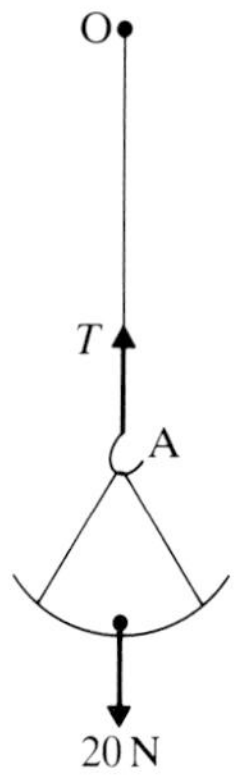

Figure 8.4

Figure 8.4 shows a light spring OA hanging from a fixed point at O. The scale pan and its contents have a weight of 20 N and they extend the spring by 5 cm. Find the spring constant.

The diagram shows the forces acting on the scale pan. Applying N2 vertically to the scale pan,

$$T - 20 = 0, \Rightarrow T = 20.$$

Applying Hooke's law to the spring,

$$T = k \times 0.05,$$

$$k = \frac{20}{0.05}.$$

Hence k is $400\ \mathrm{N\,m^{-1}}$.

□□□□□

Whilst the spring constant is useful, it has one serious disadvantage, as the following example shows.

EXAMPLE 2

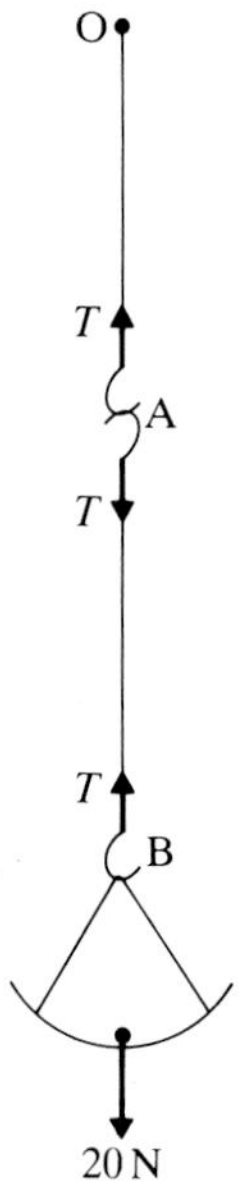

Figure 8.5

Suppose two identical springs OA and AB of the type in example 1 are joined end to end, and the scale pan suspended from the lower one, as shown in figure 8.5. As before $T = 20$. Therefore each spring extends by 5 cm, and the total extension is 10 cm. Applying Hooke's law to the combined spring.

$$20 = k \times 0.1.$$

Hence k is $200\ \mathrm{N\,m^{-1}}$. Thus k depends on the length of the spring: doubling the length has halved the value of k.

□□□□□

It is easy to see that, for three springs, Hooke's law would give

$$20 = k \times 0.15,$$

$$k = \frac{400}{3}.$$

Clearly we could continue to join springs in this manner and deduce that $k \propto 1/l$, where l is the natural length of the spring. We can therefore write

$$k = \frac{\lambda}{l},$$

where λ is called the **modulus of elasticity** (or elastic constant) for the spring. We can now write Hooke's law in the form

$$T = \frac{\lambda x}{l}$$

and this is the form we will generally use in later work.

Rearranging $\lambda = \frac{Tl}{x}$,

hence $[\lambda] = \text{M L T}^{-2}$

Thus the dimensions of λ are those of force and its SI units are newtons. λ is the force required to double the length of the spring, assuming the elastic limit has not been reached.

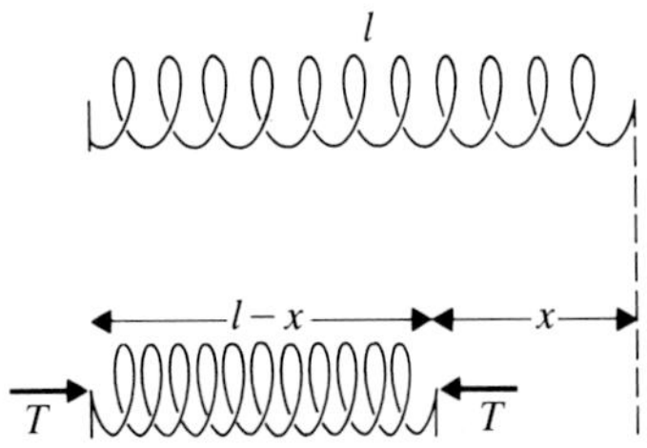

Figure 8.6

Compression of a spring

When a spring is compressed, the magnitude of the thrust it exerts is given by Hooke's law. It can also be seen that for $x < 0$ (corresponding to a compression), the law takes into account the reversed direction of the force exerted by the spring, as shown in figure 8.6.

EXAMPLE 3

Figure 8.7a shows a particle of mass 10 kg suspended between two identical vertical springs each of natural length l, having their ends attached to two fixed points a distance $2l$ apart. When the particle is in equilibrium at X the top spring is extended by $\frac{1}{4}l$ and the lower spring compressed by $\frac{1}{4}l$. Calculate the modulus of elasticity of the springs.

Figure 8.7b shows the external forces acting at X on the particle and on the two springs, where T_1 is the tension in the upper spring and T_2 is the thrust in the lower spring.
Applying N2 vertically to the particle.

$$T_1 + T_2 = 100. \quad \textbf{(1)}$$

We now apply Hooke's law to the upper and lower springs separately. On the upper spring the extension is $\frac{1}{4}l$ and we obtain

$$T_1 = \frac{\lambda \times \frac{1}{4}l}{l},$$

hence $T_1 = \frac{1}{4}\lambda$.

On the lower spring the compression is $\frac{1}{4}l$ and we obtain

$$T_2 = \frac{\lambda \times \frac{1}{4}l}{l},$$

hence $T_2 = \frac{1}{4}\lambda$.

Substituting in equation (1), we obtain

$$\tfrac{1}{2}\lambda = 100,$$

so the modulus is 200 N.

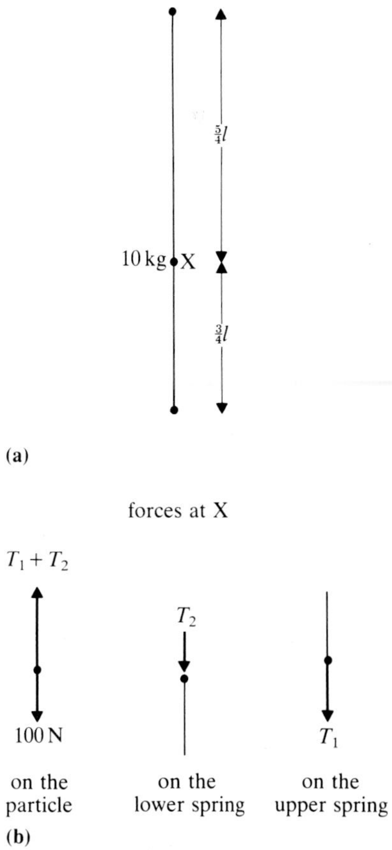

Figure 8.7

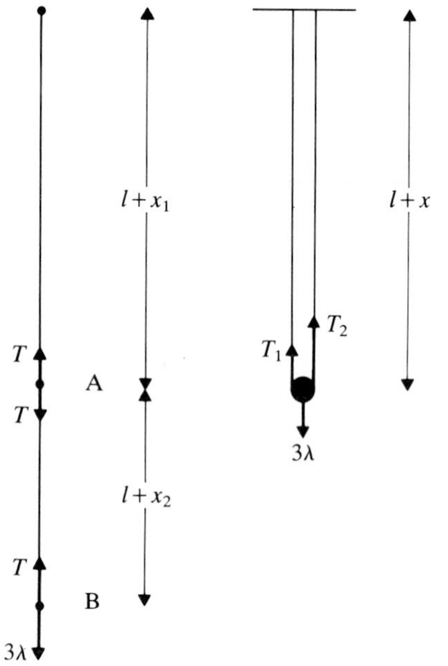

Figure 8.8

EXAMPLE 4

Two light strings of natural length l and modulus of elasticity λ and 2λ, respectively, support a particle of weight 3λ. Find the total extension if the strings are combined (a) end to end (in series), (b) parallel to each other.

a) Let the extension in the top string be x_1 and in the lower string be x_2, as shown in figure 8.8a. Since the strings are light, there must be no resultant force at A and the tension in the two strings must be equal. Applying N2 vertically to the particle at B,

$$T = 3\lambda$$

Applying Hooke's law to:

the upper string $\qquad T = \lambda x_1/l,$

the lower string $\qquad T = 2\lambda x_2/l.$

Hence $x_1 = 3l$, $x_2 = \frac{3}{2}l$, and the total extension is $x_1 + x_2 = \frac{9}{2}l$.

b) Figure 8.8b shows the two strings in parallel. In this case their extensions must be the same, x say, but their tensions will be different. Applying N2 vertically to the particle,

$$T_1 + T_2 = 3\lambda.$$

From Hooke's law,

$$T_1 = \lambda x/l, \qquad T_2 = 2\lambda x/l$$

Hence $3\lambda x/l = 3\lambda$ and the total extension is l.

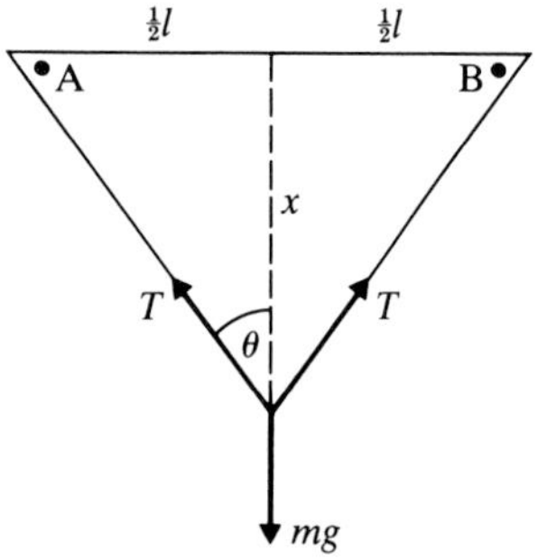

Figure 8.9

EXAMPLE 5

An elastic band of natural length l and modulus of elasticity λ is stretched over two smooth pegs A and B which lie in a horizontal line, a distance l apart. A particle of mass m is attached to the middle of the lower half of the band. Find the depth of the particle below the line AB when the system is in equilibrium.

Let θ be the angle of inclination of the band to the vertical at the point where the mass is attached, as shown in figure 8.9.
Applying N2 vertically to the particle,

$$2T\cos\theta = mg.$$

The extension of the band is

$$l + \frac{l}{\sin\theta} - l = \frac{l}{\sin\theta}.$$

From Hooke's law $\qquad T = \dfrac{\lambda}{\sin\theta}.$

Hence $\qquad 2\lambda\cot\theta = mg,$

Now $\qquad x = \frac{1}{2}l\cot\theta,$

hence the depth below AB is $mgl/4\lambda$.

EXERCISE 8A

1. A piece of elastic trebles in length when under a tension of 50 N. Calculate the modulus of elasticity of the elastic.

2. A mass of 2 kg suspended from a vertical wire of natural length 4 m produces an extension of 0.2 mm. Calculate the modulus of elasticity of the wire.

3. A catapult consists of a piece of rubber of natural length 8 cm attached to two prongs, A and B, 6.5 cm apart. The modulus of elasticity of the rubber is 40 N. What force is required to pull back the rubber until it has doubled in length, if the force is applied to the middle of the rubber, perpendicular to AB?

4. Two elastic springs are joined at P and stretched between horizontal points A and B, where $AB = 6a$. The springs are light. Spring AP has modulus λ and natural length $2a$, and spring PB has modulus 2λ and natural length a. Show that in equilibrium $AP/PB = \frac{11}{4}$.

5. Calculate the ratio AP/PB if the springs in question 4 are compressed in a tube of length $2a$.

6. A set of chest expanders consists of four identical springs in parallel, which can be pulled apart. When the applied force is 200 N, their lengths are 1 m. When the applied force is 300 N, their lengths are 1.2 m. Calculate the natural lengths and elastic constants of the springs.

7. A particle of mass $2m$ is attached to the middle of a light spring of natural length a and modulus of elasticity mg. The ends of the spring are attached to two fixed points A and B, A being at a distance $2a$ vertically above B. Calculate the depth of the particle below A when it is in equilibrium.

8. A particle of mass m is suspended in equilibrium by a light elastic string, which is fixed at its upper end. If a small horizontal force is applied to the particle, will it rise or fall?

9. A light elastic string of natural length l, modulus of elasticity mg, has one end A fixed. A particle of mass m hangs from the other end B, with B vertically below A. A horizontal force $\boldsymbol{P}$ is applied to the particle at B until the string makes an angle of $30°$ to the vertical. Find in terms of m, g and l (a) the magnitude of $\boldsymbol{P}$, and (b) the new length of the string.

10. A bead is threaded on a smooth vertical circular wire of radius a. It is attached to one end of an elastic string of natural length a and modulus of elasticity λ. The other end of the string is attached to the top of the circle. Show that if $\lambda \leqslant 2mg$, the bead will rest in equilibrium at the bottom of the wire. If $\lambda > 2mg$, show that the angle θ between the string and the vertical in equilibrium is given by $\cos\theta = \lambda/2(\lambda - mg)$.

11. A bead of mass m is on a rough horizontal wire. It is connected by an elastic string of natural length l and modulus of elasticity mg

to a point a distance l below the wire. If the string makes an angle θ with the vertical when the bead is in equilibrium, show that

$$\mu \geqslant \tan\theta \frac{1-\cos\theta}{2-\cos\theta},$$

where μ is the coefficient of friction between the bead and the wire.

8.2 Elastic potential energy

When a string is extended, work must be done by the external force which causes the extension. Suppose a string of natural length l and modulus of elasticity λ is extended by an amount e. As the extension increases, the tension T in the string increases and hence the external force must increase. Figure 8.10 illustrates the situation when the extension is x and the string is in equilibrium.

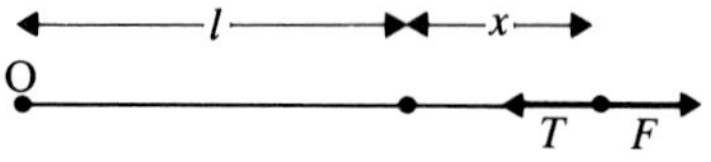

Figure 8.10

Applying N2, $T - F = 0$,

Applying Hooke's law $T = \dfrac{\lambda x}{l}$.

Hence $F = \dfrac{\lambda x}{l}$.

From section 6.4, we see that the work done by F in stretching a total amount e is given by

$$W = \int_0^e F\,dx = \int_0^e \frac{\lambda x}{l}\,dx,$$

giving $W = \dfrac{\lambda e^2}{2l}$.

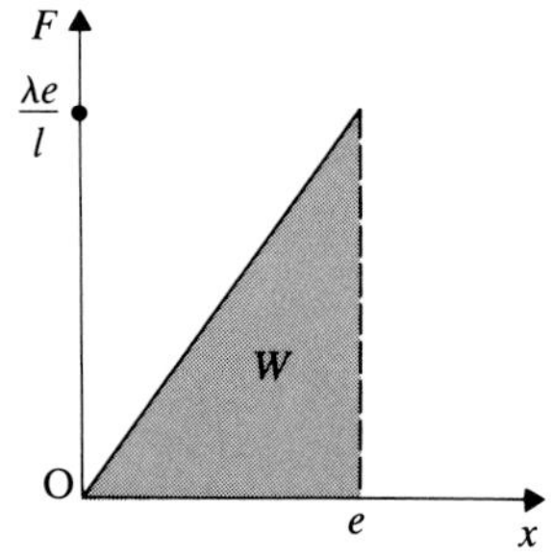

Figure 8.11

Figure 8.11 shows the graph of F against x and the work done, W, is the area under the graph. Notice that

$$W = \tfrac{1}{2} \times \frac{\lambda e}{l} \times e$$

$$= \text{(average force)} \times \text{(extension)}.$$

In terms of the spring constant k, $W = \frac{1}{2}ke^2$. The work done by the string is the work done by T. From the above we see that this is $-W = -\frac{1}{2}(\lambda/l)e^2$. The negative work done by the string means that it has positive energy stored in it. This is referred to as the **elastic potential energy** (EPE) of the string. Thus,

$$\textbf{EPE} = \frac{\lambda e^2}{2l}.$$

This expression also gives the EPE of a compressed spring, in which case e measures the compression, and the external force does work against the outward thrust of the spring. (This is analagous to the situation in section 6.2 where we saw that the GPE of a body is the work in moving it from one level to another against gravity.)

EXAMPLE 1

Figure 8.12 shows part of a horizontal pinball machine. The ball has a mass of 0.02 kg and the spring constant is 800 N m^{-1}. Ignoring friction, calculate the compression needed for the ball to leave the spring with a speed of 10 m s^{-1}.

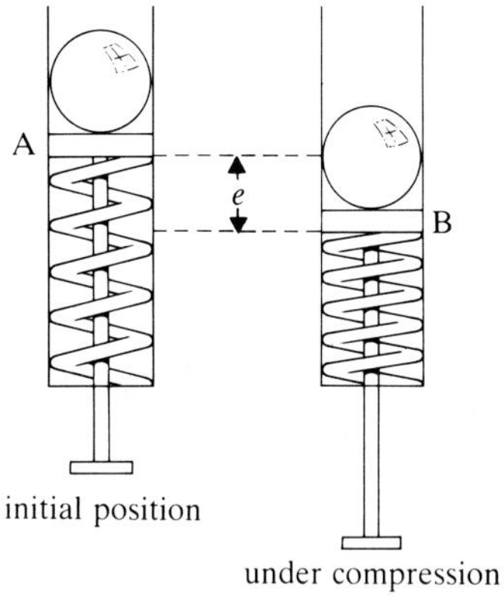

Figure 8.12

Let the required compression be e.

At B, $\quad \text{EPE} = \frac{1}{2} \times 800 \times e^2,$

At A, $\quad \text{EPE} = 0.$

Since there is no friction, the total mechanical energy is conserved, and we may apply the principle of conservation of energy:

$$\text{EPE at A} + \text{KE at A} = \text{EPE at B} + \text{KE at B}$$
$$\tfrac{1}{2} \times 800 \times e^2 + 0 = 0 + \tfrac{1}{2} \times 0.02 \times 10^2$$

Thus $e^2 = 0.0025$, so that e is 0.05 and the required compression is 5 cm.

EXAMPLE 2

Figure 8.13 shows a catapult about to be fired horizontally. The natural length of the elastic is 10 cm and its modulus of elasticity is 100 N. The mass of the small stone to be fired is 30 g and it is pulled back to position B on the figure. Calculate the speed of the stone on release.

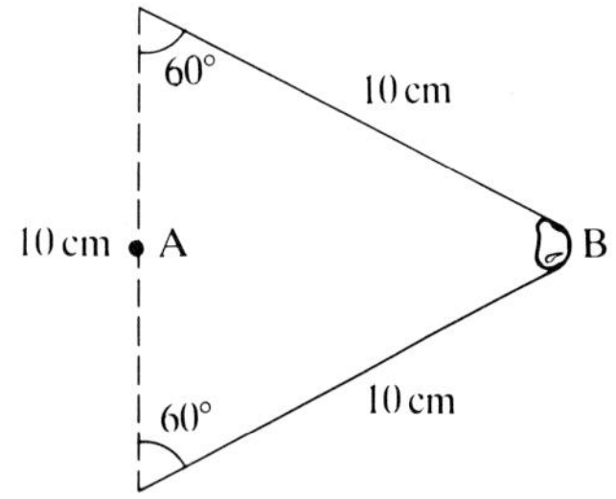

Figure 8.13

At B, $e = 0.1$, $l = 0.1$ and $\lambda = 100$. The EPE at B is given by

$$\tfrac{1}{2} \times \frac{100}{0.1} \times 0.01 = 5.$$

In the absence of friction we may apply the energy equation

$$\text{EPE at B} + \text{KE at B} = \text{EPE at A} + \text{KE at A},$$
$$5 + 0 = 0 + \tfrac{1}{2} \times 0.03 \times v^2,$$

where v is the speed of the stone at A.
Hence $v^2 = 10/0.03$, and so its speed is 18.6 m s^{-1}.

EXAMPLE 3

A particle of mass m hangs from a light string of natural length l attached at the top to a fixed point O. In equilibrium the string is extended by an amount e. The particle is then pulled down a further distance a ($a < e$) and released.

a) Calculate the velocity, v, of the particle at a depth x below the equilibrium position.

b) Calculate the maximum height reached by the particle.

c) Describe the ensuing motion.

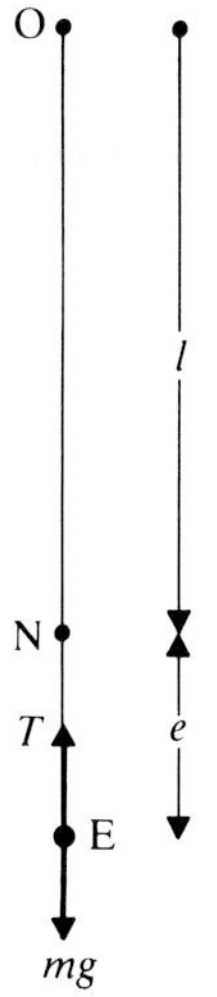

(a)

Figure 8.14

a) Figure 8.14a shows the particle in equilibrium at E.
Applying N2 vertically to the particle,

$$T = mg.$$

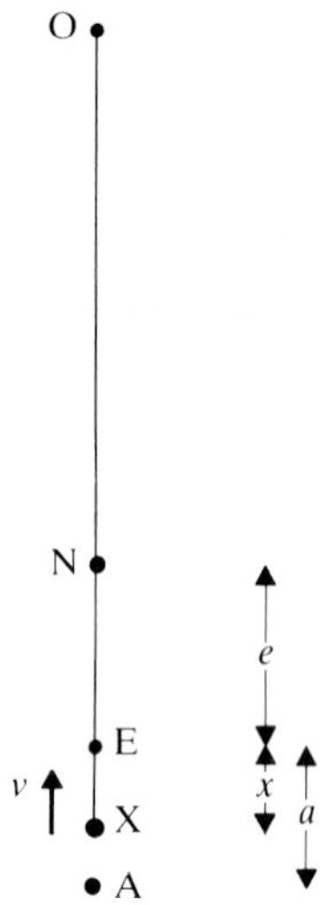

(b)

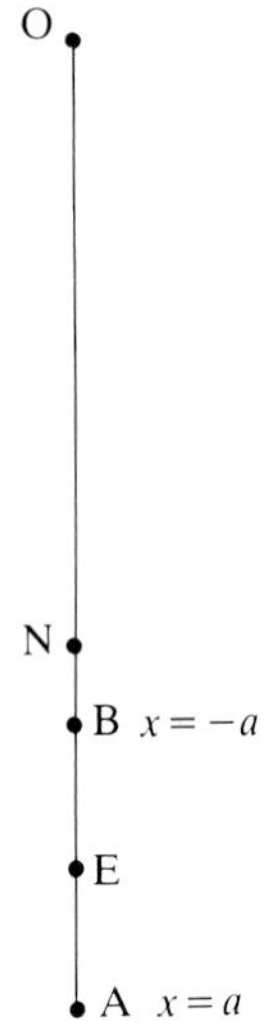

(c)

Applying Hooke's law to the string,

$$T=\frac{\lambda e}{l}.$$

Hence $$\lambda=\frac{mgl}{e}.$$

Figure 8.14b shows the particle at X, distance x below E. A is at a depth a below E. Applying the energy equation,

GPE at A + EPE at A + KE at A = GPE at X + EPE at X + KE at X.

Taking A as the zero level of GPE, we obtain

$$0+\tfrac{1}{2}\frac{\lambda}{l}(e+a)^2+0=mg(a-x)+\tfrac{1}{2}\frac{\lambda}{l}(e+x)^2+\tfrac{1}{2}mv^2.$$

Rearranging,

$$\tfrac{1}{2}mv^2=\frac{\lambda}{2l}\left[(e+a)^2-(e+x)^2\right]-mg(a-x),$$

$$v^2=\frac{g}{e}\left[2ae+a^2-2ex-x^2\right]-2g(a-x).$$

So $$v^2=\frac{g}{e}(a^2-x^2). \qquad \textbf{(2)}$$

We will study equation (2) further in section 8.4.

b) The maximum height will be reached by the particle when $v=0$. This occurs when $x=\pm a$. $x=+a$ corresponds to the point A, and we see that the particle will rise to a point B above E, corresponding to $x=-a$, as shown in figure 8.14c.

c) Applying N2 vertically to the particle at X,

$$mg-T=m\ddot{x}. \qquad \textbf{(3)}$$

Applying Hooke's law to the string,

$$T=\frac{\lambda}{l}(e+x).$$

Hence $$-\frac{\lambda}{l}x=m\ddot{x},$$

giving $$\ddot{x}=-\frac{\lambda}{ml}x.$$

At B, $x=-a$ and

$$\ddot{x}=\frac{\lambda}{ml}a=\frac{g}{e}a>0.$$

Hence the acceleration at B is positive downwards and the particle will descend until it reaches A.
At A, $v=0$ and

$$\ddot{x}=-\frac{g}{e}a<0$$

so the particle will rise.

Thus, in the absence of any energy losses, due to air resistance, etc., the particle will oscillate indefinitely between A and B. Notice that E is midway between A and B. We will return to this in section 8.4.

Note that, whilst equations (2) and (3) were derived for the particle at a depth x below E, it is important to realise that they are valid at points above E provided the string is stretched, i.e. while the particle is below N.

EXAMPLE 4

A particle of mass 1 kg is attached at one end of a string of natural length 2 m with the other end of the string attached to a fixed point. The modulus of elasticity of the string is 10 N. How far will the string be extended if (a) the particle is lowered gradually, and (b) the particle is released from rest at O? Take g as $10\,\mathrm{m\,s^{-2}}$.

a) If the mass is lowered gradually, it does not gain any KE on descent, and equilibrium is reached when the forces on the particle balance. Suppose the extension is then e, as in figure 8.15a.
Applying N2 vertically on the particle,

$$T = g.$$

Applying Hooke's law to the string,

$$T = \frac{\lambda}{l}e.$$

Hence $$e = \frac{gl}{\lambda} = \frac{10 \times 2}{10} = 2.$$

The extension is 2 m.

b) When the particle is released from O it will gain KE on descent. Thus, although the forces balance at E in figure 8.15a, the speed will not be zero and the string will be extended further. We require the point at which the speed of the particle is zero, and this is found using the energy equation. Consider the energy at a point X, distance x below E, as in figure 8.15b. Taking O as the level of zero GPE, we have, from the energy equation

$$\text{GPE at X} + \text{EPE at X} + \text{KE at X} = 0,$$

$$-1 \times 10 \times (x+4) + \tfrac{1}{2} \times \frac{10}{2} \times (x+2)^2 + \tfrac{1}{2} \times 1 \times v^2 = 0. \qquad \textbf{(4)}$$

Notice that the GPE at X is negative since X is below O. The particle comes to rest when $v = 0$, giving

$$4(x+4) - (x+2)^2 = 0,$$
$$x^2 - 12 = 0,$$
$$x = 2\sqrt{3}.$$

Thus the string will be extended by a total amount $2 + 2\sqrt{3}$.

There are two important observations to be made here.
(i) Although the particle is at rest at a depth $2\sqrt{3}$ below E, it is not in

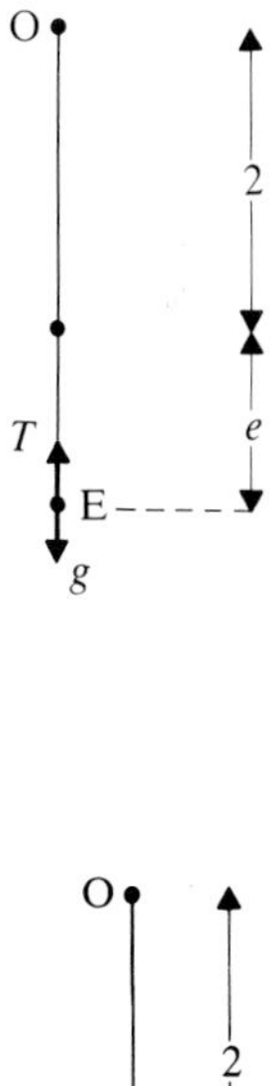

(a)

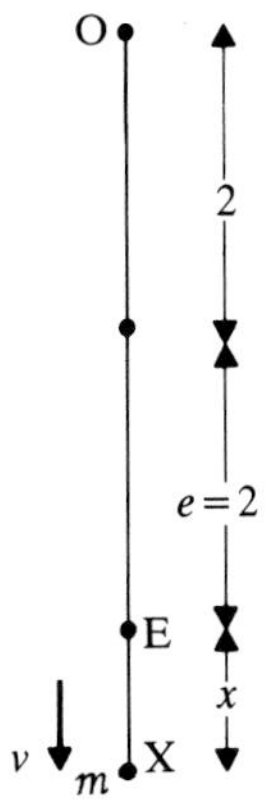

(b)

Figure 8.15

equilibrium. The tension in the string at this point, T, is given by Hooke's law.

$$T = \frac{10}{2}(2 + 2\sqrt{3}) = 27.3,$$

The resultant upward force on the particle is

$$T - g = 17.3.$$

and the particle therefore has an acceleration upwards of $17.3\ \text{m s}^{-2}$. In the absence of air resistance the particle will oscillate between O and the bottom position indefinitely, although common experience tells us that it will slow down and eventually stop. When it does stop its final position will be at E, since there is no resultant force on the particle there.

(ii) Equation (4) enables us to calculate the speed of the particle at any depth below O for $x \geqslant 0$.
Rearranging equation (4) gives

$$v^2 = -5(x+2)^2 + 20(x+4),$$
$$v^2 = 5(12 - x^2).$$

Clearly v is a maximum when $x = 0$, in which case

$$v^2 = 60,$$

so particle has its maximum speed of $7.7\ \text{m s}^{-1}$ in descent at E.

At the bottom of the jump the trampoline is considerably depressed.

EXAMPLE 5

Consider a gymnast on a trampoline. It is of interest to examine the energy changes during the motion.

Clearly there are many problems attached to the real situation that we cannot attempt to solve at this stage including:

a) How is the energy stored in the springs of the trampoline? Can we talk of a spring constant for trampolines?

b) Is mechanical energy conserved? The answer to this is evidently 'No'. Anyone who has watched trampolining will know that gymnasts bend their knees and transmit energy using their leg muscles at the bottom of the motion to compensate for mechanical energy lost during a bounce.

However, as we often do in mechanics, we will model the problem by making a number of major simplifications and see whether our conclusions are reasonable. We will make the following assumptions.

a) The gymnast can be replaced by a particle of mass 50 kg.

b) The trampoline can be replaced by a light spring.

c) No mechanical energy is lost in the motion.

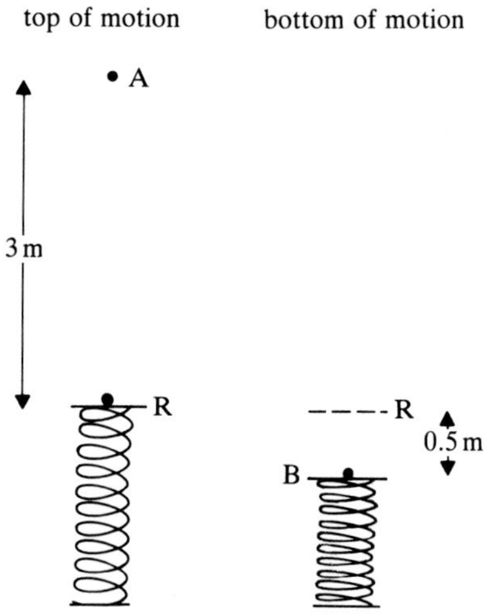

Figure 8.16

Suppose we know that the gymnast can achieve a height of 3 m above the level of the trampoline after it has been depressed by 0.5 m. Figure 8.16 shows the positions at the top and the bottom of the motion. Let R be the top of the trampoline in its natural position. Take the zero level of GPE through R. If C is a point 2 m above R, we can write down the energies at A, C, R and B in a table. For example, at A, the total energy is GPE $= 50 \times 10 \times 3 = 1500$. Note that at each point the total mechanical energy is 1500 J.

Point	GPE	EPE	KE
A	1500	0	0
C	1000	0	500
R	0	0	1500
B	−250	1750	0

Figure 8.17 shows the energy changes throughout the motion. Notice that the maximum speed of the gymnast/particle will occur between B and R. From the table we see that the EPE is 1750 J when the compression is 0.5 m, at B. Hence

$$\tfrac{1}{2} \times k \times (0.5)^2 = 1750,$$
$$k = 14\,000.$$

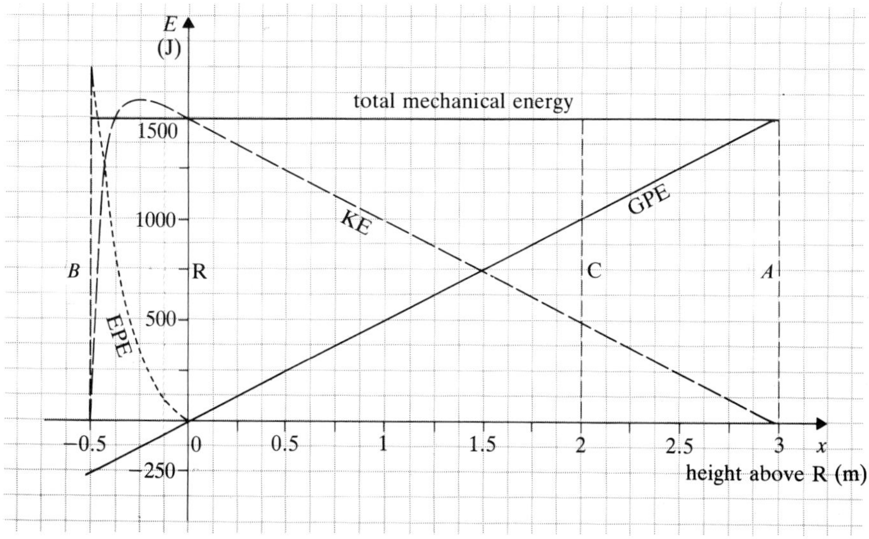

Figure 8.17

Thus, if the gymnast simply stood on the trampoline, it would be compressed by an amount e, given by

$$14\,000\,e = 50 \times 10,$$
$$e = 0.036.$$

The compression is about 3.6 cm.

Further, the work in example 4 indicates that the maximum speed will be at a depth of 3.6 cm below R. This answer does seem to be very low, and leads us to doubt the validity of our model.

EXERCISE 8B

Take g as 10 m s^{-2}, where necessary.

1. An elastic string has natural length 1.6 m and modulus of elasticity 150 N. Calculate the work done in extending it: (a) from 1.6 m to 1.8 m, (b) from 1.8 m to 2.0 m, (c) from 2.4 m to 2.6 m.

2. A child's toy gun fires ping pong balls by compressing a spring. When loaded the compression of the spring is 5 cm and the thrust in the spring is 60 N. What is the energy stored in the spring?

If the mass of a ping pong ball is 10 g, calculate the speed of the ball when it leaves the gun if:

a) all the energy stored in the spring is transmitted to the ball, and

b) 60% of the stored energy is transmitted to the ball.

4. In a car safety test, a car of mass 1 t is driven into a barrier at $20\ \text{m s}^{-1}$. The barrier consists of a spring-controlled buffer as shown in figure 8.18. After impact the maximum compression is 20 cm. Ignoring all resistances calculate the maximum thrust in each spring on compression, and their spring constants. What would the corresponding maximum compression be, if the same car were driven into the barrier at $30\ \text{m s}^{-1}$?

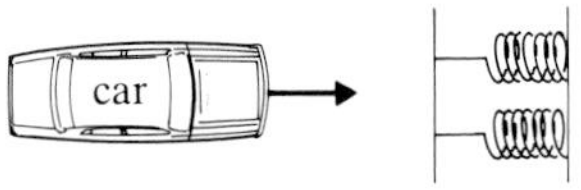

Figure 8.18

4. A catapult consists of a piece of rubber of natural length 8 cm and modulus of elasticity 40 N attached to two prongs 6.5 cm apart. It is in the firing position with the rubber stretched to double its natural length. A shot of mass 50 g is placed at the middle of the rubber. Calculate the speed of the shot on release. Does it make any difference whether the catapult is fired horizontally or vertically?

5. A particle of mass 2 kg is suspended vertically from one end of an elastic string, the other end being attached to a fixed point A. The natural length of the string is 1.2 m, and in equilibrium the string is extended by 0.2 m. The particle is then pulled down a further distance and released. Calculate the distance below A at which the particle comes to rest for the first time if the further extension is: (a) 0.1 m, (b) 0.4 m.

6. Which of the answers to question 5 would be different if the string were replaced by a spring of the same natural length and modulus? Calculate the new answer in this case.

7. A particle of mass 3 kg is attached to one end of an elastic string. The other end of the string is attached to a fixed point O. The natural length of the string is 1 m, and when the particle is released from O it falls to a depth of 1.8 m. Calculate the modulus of elasticity of the string and the maximum speed of the particle during its fall.

8. One end of an elastic string is attached to a fixed point O. The other end is fastened to a particle which doubles the length of the string when hanging in equilibrium. The natural length of the string is l and the particle is released at rest from O. Show that it will fall a distance $(2+\sqrt{3})l$ before coming to instantaneous rest.

9. Figure 8.19 shows a stunt man diving out of a balloon. Attached to his feet are two elastic ropes. The balloon maintains a constant height of 80 m above ground and the natural length of each rope is 50 m. Ultimately the man comes to rest 26 m above ground. Treating the man as a particle of mass 80 kg, and ignoring all resistances in his initial drop estimate the modulus of elasticity of the ropes and determine whether or not the man hits the ground.

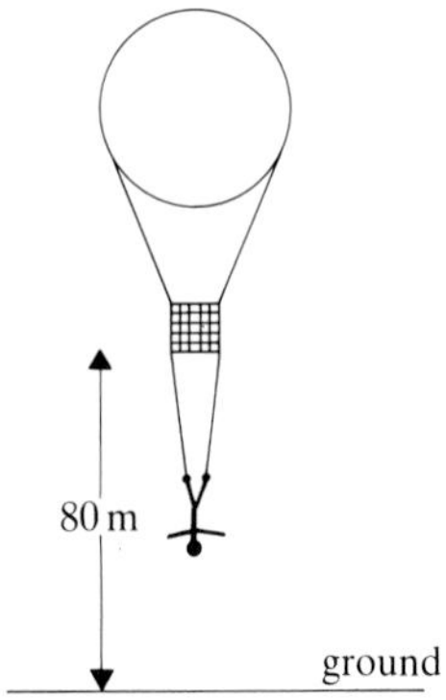

Figure 8.19

10. A particle of mass m is attached to one end of a light elastic string of natural length l and modulus of elasticity mg/c. The other end of the string is attached to a fixed point O. The particle is released from rest at O. Prove that the greatest speed of the particle in the subsequent motion is $\sqrt{\{g(2l + c)\}}$ and find the greatest length of the string.

11. One end of a light elastic string is fixed to a point O and the other end is attached to a particle of mass m. The natural length of the string is l and the modulus of elasticity is mg. The particle is held at a point kl below O and released ($k > 2$). Prove that:
    a) If $k < 2 + \sqrt{5}$ the string will be slack when the particle comes to rest, and the greatest height reached above O is $\frac{1}{2}l(k^2 - 4k + 1)$.
    b) If $k > 2 + \sqrt{5}$ the string is taut when the particle reaches its highest point which is $\frac{1}{2}l(k^2 - 4k)$ above O.

12. Figure 8.20 shows a child's toy. The 'monster' is pressed down so that it is held to the base by suction at the rim C. When the suction fails the spring extends and the monster jumps. In equilibrium the spring has length $\frac{3}{4}l$ and when fully compressed it has length $\frac{1}{4}l$ where l is the natural length of the spring. The mass of the monster is m and the mass of the base is $2m$.
    a) Calculate the maximum extension of the spring if the base is held fixed.
    b) Describe the motion if the base is not held.

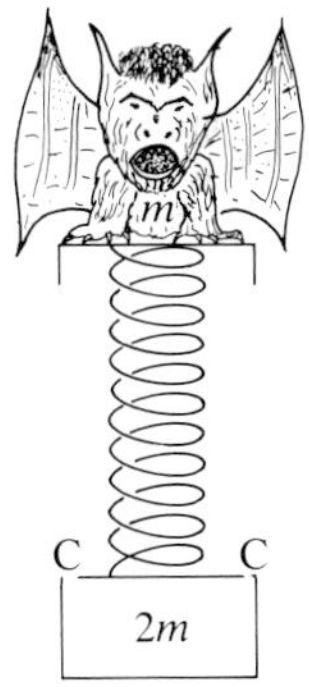

Figure 8.20

Problems involving loss of mechanical energy 8.3

In section 8.2 we saw how the energy equation can be used to analyse motion involving particles attached to strings and springs. We now examine some examples where the total mechanical energy of the system is not conserved. We concentrate on two main types of problem.

a) Problems involving collisions

As we saw in section 6.5, mechanical energy is not generally conserved at collisions. In such cases there are three distinct stages of motion to be analysed separately.

1. *Before collision*: total mechanical energy is constant, so we may apply the energy equation.

2. *At the collision*: mechanical energy is lost. The change of energy may be calculated by use of the impulse momentum and impact equations.

3. *After collision*: total mechanical energy is conserved.

b) Problems involving friction

In this case we cannot apply the energy equation, but instead apply the work–energy equation, the work done by friction being responsible for the loss of total mechanical energy.

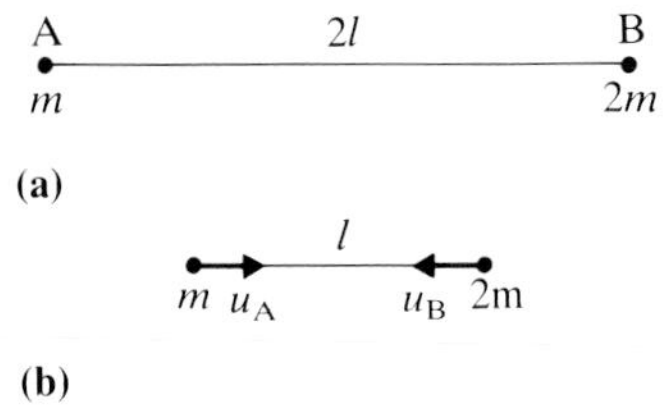

Figure 8.21

EXAMPLE 1

Two particles A and B of masses m and $2m$, respectively, are on a smooth horizontal table where AB $= 2l$, as in figure 8.21a. They are connected by a light string of natural length l and modulus of elasticity λ. The particles are released together. The coefficient of restitution at impact is 0.5. Calculate: (a) the speeds of the particles on impact, (b) the point at which they collide, and (c) the maximum length of the string after the first collision.

a) Before release

$$\text{EPE} = \frac{\lambda l^2}{2l} = \tfrac{1}{2}\lambda l.$$

Let u_A and u_B be the speeds of the particles A and B when the length of the string is l, in the directions indicated in figure 8.21b. Using the energy equation.

$$\tfrac{1}{2}mu_A^2 + \tfrac{1}{2}2mu_B^2 = \tfrac{1}{2}\lambda l,$$

$$u_A^2 + 2u_B^2 = \lambda l/m. \qquad \textbf{(5)}$$

This is insufficient to determine u_A and u_B. By the law of conservation of momentum

$$mu_A = 2mu_B,$$

$$u_A = 2u_B. \qquad \textbf{(6)}$$

From equations (5) and (6) $6u_B^2 = \lambda l/m.$

Hence $u_B = \sqrt{(\lambda l/6m)}, \qquad u_A = 2\sqrt{(\lambda l/6m)}.$

After the string reaches its natural length l, no horizontal forces act on the particles so that their speeds remain constant until the collision.

b) To find the point of collision, we notice that when the string is under tension T, the accelerations of A and B are given by

$$a_A = T/m, \qquad a_B = T/2m.$$

Hence $a_A = 2a_B$. Since they both start at rest this means that the speed of A is twice that of B throughout their motion. We have seen above that in the position of figure 8.21b $u_A = 2u_B$. Thus A must travel twice as far as B before the collision. Hence the collision takes place at G, where AG:GB = 2:1.

c) At impact, mechanical energy is lost. Let v_A and v_B be the speeds of A and B after impact, as shown in figure 8.22. Total momentum is conserved at the collision.

$$mv_A - 2mv_B = 0,$$

$$v_A = 2v_B.$$

From the impact equation,

$$v_B + v_A = \tfrac{1}{2}(u_A + u_B),$$

$$v_B + v_A = \tfrac{3}{2}\sqrt{(\lambda l/6m)}.$$

Hence $3v_B = \tfrac{3}{2}\sqrt{(\lambda l/6m)},$

giving $v_B = \tfrac{1}{2}\sqrt{(\lambda l/6m)}, \qquad v_A = \sqrt{(\lambda l/6m)},$

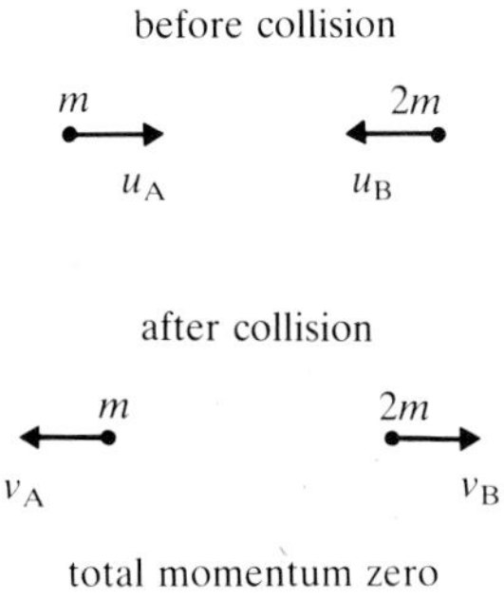

Figure 8.22

The KE after collision is

$$\tfrac{1}{2}mv_A^2 + \tfrac{1}{2}2mv_B^2 = \tfrac{1}{2}m \times (\lambda l/6m)(1 + \tfrac{2}{4})$$
$$= \tfrac{1}{8}\lambda l.$$

When the string is at its maximum length, suppose the extension is e. From the energy equation, the KE after impact = the EPE at the maximum length.

$$\tfrac{1}{8}\lambda l = \frac{\lambda e^2}{2l}$$
$$e^2 = \tfrac{1}{4}l^2.$$

Hence the maximum length of the string after the collision is $\tfrac{3}{2}l$.

EXAMPLE 2

A string of length 2 m and modulus of elasticity 10 N hangs vertically in equilibrium from a fixed point O. A scale pan of mass 1 kg is attached to the lower end, and a piece of putty of mass 1 kg is released from O and sticks to the pan. By how much is the string stretched? Take g as 10 m s^{-2}.

Let x be the extension with the scale pan hanging in equilibrium. Applying N2 vertically on the scale pan,

$$T = mg = 10.$$

Applying Hooke's law to the string,

$$T = \frac{\lambda x}{l} = \tfrac{10}{2}x.$$

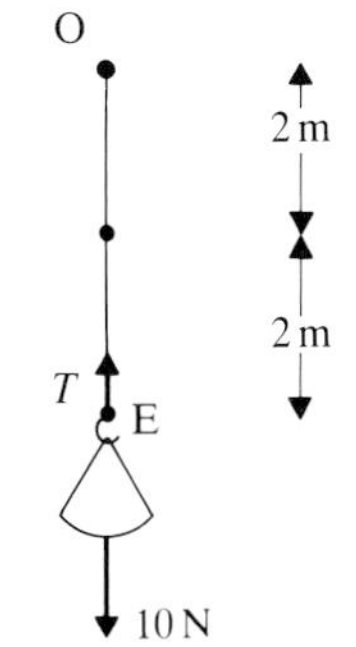

Figure 8.23

Hence x is 2 m. The scale pan hangs at E, as in figure 8.23. We take O as the zero level of GPE. When the putty is dropped from O, its speed, u, at E is given by the energy equation.

$$\text{KE at E} + \text{GPE at E} = 0.$$

Hence
$$\tfrac{1}{2} \times 1 \times u^2 - 1 \times 10 \times 4 = 0,$$
$$u^2 = 80.$$

At the collision, mechanical energy will be lost, since the collision is inelastic. The putty sticks to the pan, so the coefficient of restitution is zero and the putty and the pan will move with the same speed, w. The total momentum is conserved at the collision, since the string is extensible, and does not exert an impulse over the instant of collision. (Compare with an inelastic string, see section 5.4, example 6.) We have $u = 2w$, giving w as $\sqrt{20}$ m s^{-1}.

After the collision the total mechanical energy will maintain its new value. Let the speed of the combined pan and putty be v at a depth x below E, as in figure 8.24. Applying the energy equation

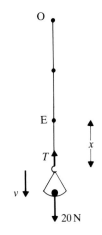

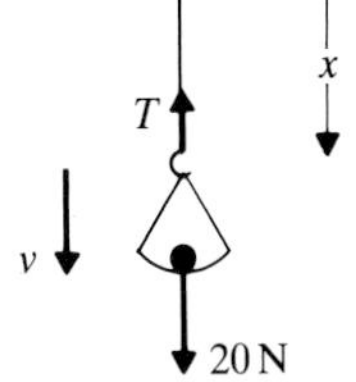

Figure 8.24

$$\text{KE at E} + \text{GPE at E} + \text{EPE at E} = \text{KE at X} + \text{GPE at X} + \text{EPE at X},$$

$$\tfrac{1}{2} \times 2 \times w^2 - 2 \times 10 \times 4 + \tfrac{1}{2} \times \tfrac{10}{2} \times 2^2 = \tfrac{1}{2} \times 2 \times v^2 - 2 \times 10 \times (4 + x) + \tfrac{1}{2} \times \tfrac{10}{2} \times (2 + x)^2.$$

Hence $$v^2 = 20 + 20x + 2.5[2^2 - (2+x)^2]$$
$$= 20 + 10x - 2.5x^2 = 2.5(8 + 4x - x^2).$$

When the string is fully stretched, $v = 0$ and $x^2 - 4x - 8 = 0$, giving $x = 2 + \sqrt{12} = 5.46$.

EXAMPLE 3

A particle of mass m is on a rough horizontal table, the coefficient of friction being μ. The particle is connected to one end of an elastic string of natural length l and modulus of elasticity λ. The other end of the string is attached to a fixed point O on the table. Initially the length of the string is $3l$ and the particle is held at rest. The particle is then released. With what speed does it reach O?

We need to examine the motion in two parts.

a) From B to A, as in figure 8.25, when the string is under tension.
b) From A to O, when the string is slack.

Figure 8.25

a) From B to A. Let the speed at A be u. Since friction is acting, mechanical energy is not conserved. Applying the work–energy equation,

KE at A = work done by string from B to A + work done by friction (negative)

$$\tfrac{1}{2}mu^2 \quad = \quad \tfrac{1}{2}\frac{\lambda}{l}(2l)^2 \quad + \quad -\mu mg2l.$$

Hence $$u^2 = \frac{4\lambda l}{m} - 4\mu lg.$$

b) From A to O. In this case the string is slack, so the only horizontal force acting on the particle is friction. The acceleration towards O, a, is given by

$$ma = -\mu mg,$$
$$a = -\mu g.$$

Hence the acceleration over this part of the motion is constant, and the speed, v, at O may be calculated from the constant acceleration formulae. Thus,

$$v^2 = u^2 - 2\mu gl$$
$$= 4\lambda l/m - 4\mu lg - 2\mu lg = 4\lambda l/m - 6\mu lg.$$

Clearly the particle will stop before reaching O unless $\lambda > \tfrac{3}{2}\mu mg$.

EXERCISE 8C

Take g as 10 m s^{-2}, where necessary.

1. A particle of mass m is fixed to one end of a string of natural length l, modulus of elasticity mg. The other end of the string is attached to a point O on a smooth horizontal table. The particle is projected from O along the table with a speed $2\sqrt{(lg)}$. Calculate: (a) the maximum extension of the string, (b) the speed of the particle on return to O.

2. Repeat question 1, with the smooth table replaced by a rough table, the coefficient of friction being $\tfrac{1}{4}$.

3. A particle of mass 2 kg is on a rough horizontal table attached to one end of an elastic string of natural length 1 m and modulus of elasticity 10 N. The free end of the string is attached to a fixed point O and the particle will rest in limiting equilibrium at a point B on the table where OB = 1.4 m. Calculate the coefficient of friction between the particle and the table. The particle is moved further away from O to a point C and released. Calculate the minimum distance OC if the particle is to reach O.

4. A particle of mass m is fixed to one end of an elastic string of natural length l and modulus of elasticity λ. The other end of the string is fixed to a point O on a rough horizontal table. The coefficient of friction between the particle and the table is $k\lambda/mg$, where $1 > k > \frac{1}{2}$. The string is stretched until the particle is at A, where $OA = 2l$. Prove that the particle will come to rest at B, where $OB = 2kl$.

5. A particle of mass 2 kg is on a rough horizontal table, with coefficient of friction $\frac{1}{2}$. The particle is attached to one end A of an elastic string of natural length 1 m and modulus of elasticity 100 N. The other end of the string is attached to a point O at the base of a vertical wall. Initially OA is of length 2.5 m with the string at right angles to the wall. If collisions between the wall and the particle are perfectly elastic, calculate how many collisions will occur before the particle comes to rest.

6. Repeat question 5 if $e = \frac{1}{2}$ for the collisions between the particle and the wall.

Simple harmonic motion 8.4

In example 3 of section 8.2 we examined the vertical motion of a particle released from a depth a below the equilibrium position. We were able to deduce that, in the absence of loss of energy due to resistance, the particle would oscillate about its equilibrium position, between the points A and B (see figure 8.14c). We obtained a relation for the speed v at depth x below E as

$$v^2 = \frac{g}{e}(a^2 - x^2). \qquad (7)$$

We now use this to find a relation between x and t, the time elapsed after release of the particle.
From equation (7)

$$v = \sqrt{\frac{g}{e}}(a^2 - x^2)^{1/2}$$

Since $v = \mathrm{d}x/\mathrm{d}t$

$$\mathrm{d}x/\mathrm{d}t = \sqrt{\frac{g}{e}}(a^2 - x^2)^{1/2}$$

Separating the variables and integrating,

$$\int \frac{\mathrm{d}x}{(a^2 - x^2)^{1/2}} = \int \sqrt{\frac{g}{e}}\,\mathrm{d}t.$$

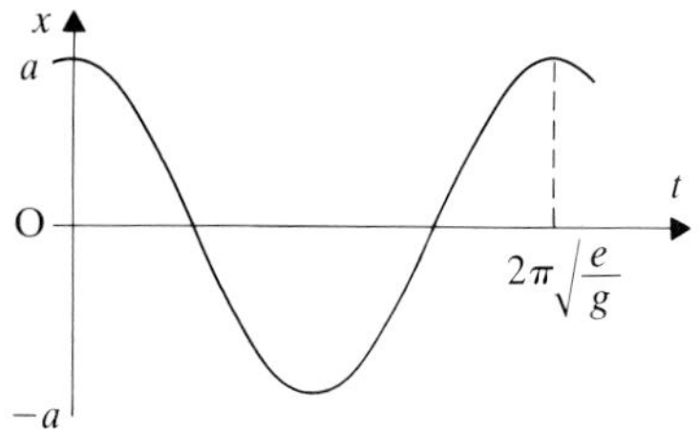

Figure 8.26

Using standard integrals, we obtain

$$\cos^{-1} x/a = \sqrt{g/e}\ t + c.$$

Hence $$x = a\cos[\sqrt{g/e}\ t + c].$$

If we measure t from the instant the particle was released, we obtain $x = a$ when $t = 0$, so $a = a\cos c$ and hence $c = 0$ and $x = a\cos\sqrt{g/e}\,t$. The graph of the depth x against time t is shown in figure 8.26.

When $x = a$, the particle is at A,
$x = -a$, the particle is at B, and
$x = 0$, the particle is at E.

The particle returns to A for the first time after time T, where

$$T = 2\pi\sqrt{g/e}.$$

T is called the **periodic time** of the oscillation. a is called the **amplitude** of the oscillation, and this is a particular example of **simple harmonic motion**.

General simple harmonic motion

There are many physical situations in which oscillatory motion occurs. After making simplifications, most can be reduced to simple harmonic motion (SHM). Although the techniques of modelling real situations are beyond the scope of this book, it is useful to study SHM because the model is simple and the mathematics is identical in all cases. We restrict ourselves for the moment to motion in one dimension.

Definition

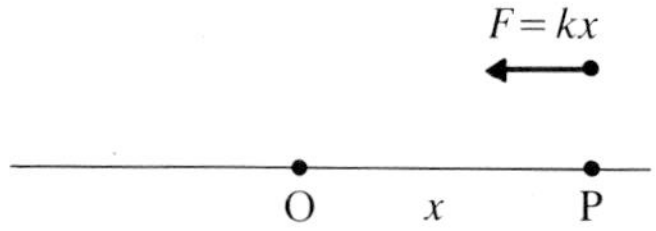

Figure 8.27

SHM occurs when a particle moves in a straight line, under the influence of a force of attraction towards a fixed point, where the magnitude of the force is proportional to the displacement from the fixed point, which is often called the **centre of oscillation**. This is illustrated in figure 8.27.

SHM will occur if $F = kx$, where k is a constant. Suppose the particle has mass m. Applying N2 on the particle

$$m\ddot{x} = -kx,$$

$$\ddot{x} = -\frac{k}{m}x.$$

Writing $k/m = \omega^2$, we obtain

$$\ddot{x} = -\omega^2 x. \qquad \textbf{(8)}$$

Equation (8) is the standard form for SHM.

Now $$\ddot{x} = v\frac{dv}{dx}.$$ (see section 4.2)

Thus, from equation (8) $$v\frac{dv}{dx} = -\omega^2 x.$$

Separating the variables and integrating,

$$\int v\,dv = \int -\omega^2 x\,dx,$$

$$\tfrac{1}{2}v^2 = -\tfrac{1}{2}\omega^2 x^2 + c,$$

where the constant c depends on the initial conditions. Suppose the particle is released from rest at $x = a$, as in figure 8.28, then

$$c = \tfrac{1}{2}\omega^2 a^2, \qquad v^2 = \omega^2(a^2 - x^2). \qquad \textbf{(9)}$$

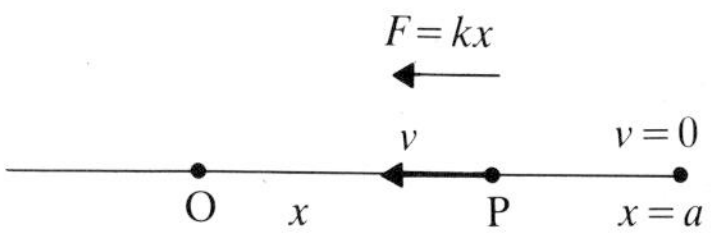

Figure 8.28

Equation (9) is the first integral of equation (8). From equation (9),

$$v = \omega(a^2 - x^2)^{1/2},$$

$$\frac{dx}{dt} = \omega(a^2 - x^2)^{1/2}.$$

Separating the variables and integrating,

$$\int \frac{dx}{(a^2 - x^2)^{1/2}} = \int \omega\,dt.$$

Using standard integrals,

$$\cos^{-1}(x/a) = \omega t + \varepsilon$$

Hence $$x = a\cos(\omega t + \varepsilon). \qquad \textbf{(10)}$$

The initial condition gives $x = a$, $t = 0$, so that $a = a\cos\varepsilon$ and $\varepsilon = 0$.

Thus $$x = a\cos\omega t.$$

The (t, x) graph is shown in figure 8.29. a is called the amplitude of the motion. The time for one complete oscillation is $2\pi/\omega$ and this is called the periodic time.

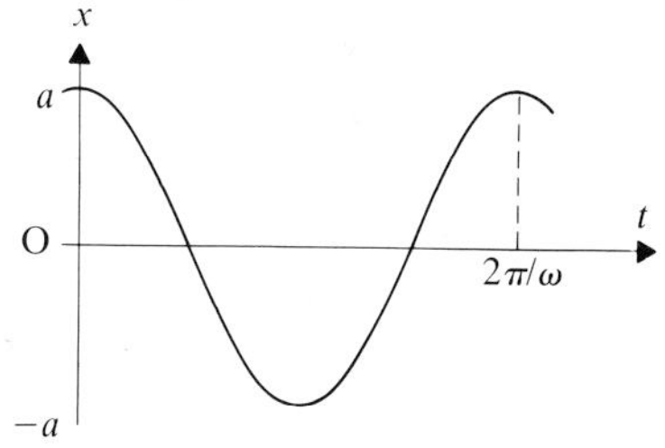

Figure 8.29

Those familiar with solving second-order differential equations will recognise that the solution of equation (8) is of the form

$$x = A\cos\omega t + B\sin\omega t,$$

whereas we have deduced the solution, given by equation (10), using two integrations. We may easily check that $x = A\cos\omega t + B\sin\omega t$ is a solution of equation (8) by direct differentiation, as follows.

$$x = A\cos\omega t + B\sin\omega t,$$

$$\dot{x} = -A\omega\sin\omega t + B\omega\cos\omega t,$$

$$\ddot{x} = -A\omega^2\cos\omega t - Bw^2\sin\omega t,$$

Hence $$\ddot{x} = -\omega^2 x, \qquad \text{as required.}$$

In all the worked examples we will quote the following results:

1. The standard differential equation for simple harmonic motion is

$$\ddot{x} = -\omega^2 x \qquad (8)$$

2. The solution of equation (8) can be written in either of the forms:

a) $$x = a\cos(\omega t + \varepsilon) \quad \text{or} \quad x = a\sin(\omega t + \varepsilon),$$

where a and ε are constants of integration.

b) $$x = A\cos\omega t + B\sin\omega t,$$

where A and B are constants of integration.
All the forms of solution in (a) and (b) are useful.

3. v and x are related by the equation

$$v^2 = \omega^2(a^2 - x^2). \tag{9}$$

The constants of integration will be determined by the initial conditions.

EXAMPLE 1

A particle is moving with SHM along the x-axis with the centre of oscillation at O. At $x = 4$ the speed is 6 m s^{-1} and at $x = 3$ the speed is 8 m s^{-1}. Find the amplitude and period of the motion.

Since we are given values of v and x we use equation (9). Let a be the amplitude and $2\pi/\omega$ be the period. Then

$$v^2 = \omega^2(a^2 - x^2),$$

and we obtain the two equations

$$36 = \omega^2(a^2 - 16), \qquad 64 = \omega^2(a^2 - 9).$$

Rearranging $$\omega^2 = \frac{36}{a^2 - 16} = \frac{64}{a^2 - 9}.$$

Cross-multiplying $36(a^2 - 9) = 64(a^2 - 16)$.
Rearranging $28a^2 = 64 \times 16 - 36 \times 9$.

Hence $a = 5$ and $36 = \omega^2(25 - 16)$, so $\omega = 2$. Thus the amplitude is 5 and the period is π.

EXAMPLE 2

A particle is moving with SHM with period 2 s and amplitude 3 m. Calculate: (a) the maximum speed, (b) the maximum acceleration, (c) the average speed in one oscillation.

In this example $a = 3, 2\pi/\omega = 2$, hence $\omega = \pi$. Thus, from equation (9),

$$v^2 = \pi^2(9 - x^2).$$

a) The maximum speed occurs when $x = 0$, i.e. at the centre of the oscillation. In this case we see that this is $v = 3\pi$.

b) During SHM the acceleration $\ddot{x}$ is given by

$$\ddot{x} = -\omega^2 x.$$

Hence the maximum value of $\ddot{x}$ occurs when x is a maximum, i.e. at the extremes of the oscillation. In this case $|\ddot{x}| = 3\pi^2$.

c) The total distance travelled in one oscillation is $4 \times 3 = 12$ m and since the time for one oscillation is 2 s, the average speed is 6 m s^{-1}. Notice that this is not the same as the magnitude of the average velocity, since the average velocity for one oscillation is zero, (see also section 2.1).

EXAMPLE 3

A particle of unit mass is moving along the x-axis under the action of a force $\boldsymbol{F}$ which is directed towards O and has magnitude $9x$. When $t = 0$, $x = 1$ and the speed is 3, away from O. Find a formula for x in terms of t and sketch the (t, x) graph.

Applying N2 on the particle towards O

$$\ddot{x} = -9x$$

Hence $$x = a\sin(3t + \varepsilon),$$

$$\dot{x} = 3a\cos(3t + \varepsilon).$$

From the initial conditions we obtain,

$$1 = a\sin\varepsilon,$$

$$3 = 3a\cos\varepsilon.$$

Dividing $$1 = \tan\varepsilon.$$

Hence $$\varepsilon = \tfrac{1}{4}\pi,$$

$$1 = a\sin\tfrac{1}{4}\pi,$$

giving $$a = \sqrt{2}.$$

Therefore $$x = \sqrt{2}\sin(3t + \tfrac{1}{4}\pi).$$

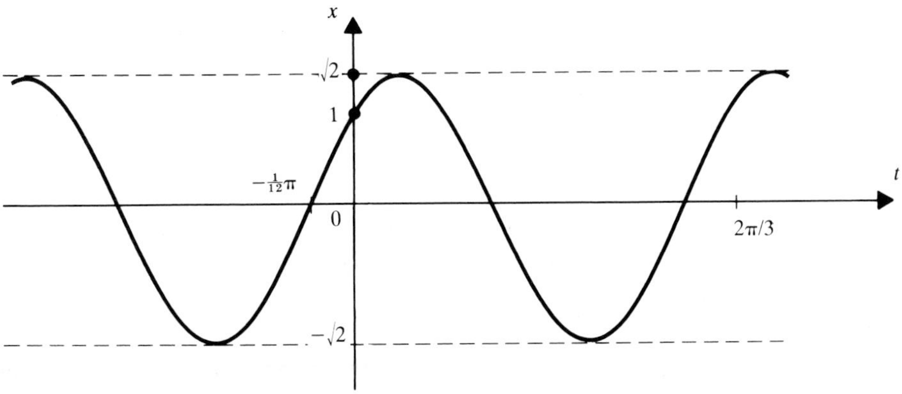

Figure 8.30

The (t, x) graph is shown in figure 8.30. The amplitude is $\sqrt{2}$ and the period is $\frac{2}{3}\pi$. $\frac{1}{4}\pi$ is called the **phase angle** of the oscillation and indicates the position in this oscillation at $t = 0$. Notice that $x = 0$ when $t = -\frac{1}{12}\pi$.

More generally, for an oscillation given by

$$x = a\sin(\omega t + \varepsilon),$$

ε is the phase angle, and $x = 0$ when $t = -\varepsilon/\omega$.

EXAMPLE 4

A particle moves in a straight line and its equation of motion is

$$\ddot{x} = -\omega^2 x$$

where x is the distance of the particle from a fixed point O. It passes through the point P, where $x = b$, with speed u away from O. Prove that it returns to P after time τ given by

$$\tau = \frac{2}{\omega}\tan^{-1}\frac{u}{b\omega}.$$

The motion is SHM and so we can write down the relation between x and t, in the form $x = A\cos\omega t + B\sin\omega t$.
Suppose the particle is at $x = 0$ when $t = 0$ and the amplitude is a, as in figure 8.31. Then $A = 0$, $B = a$ and $x = a\sin\omega t$.

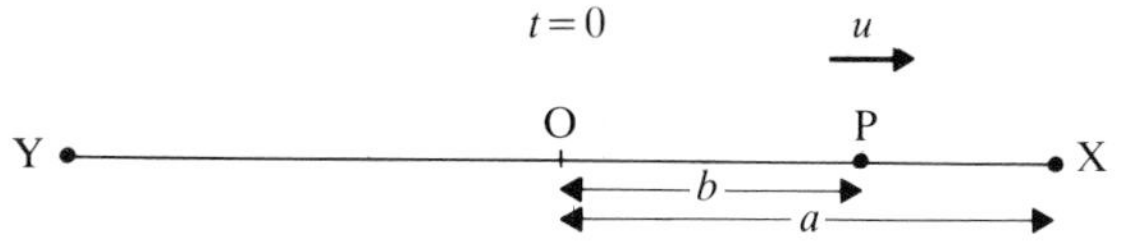

Figure 8.31

Now $\quad \dot{x} = a\omega\cos\omega t.$

Hence $\quad \dot{x}/x = \omega\cot\omega t.$

At P, $\quad u/b = \omega\cot\omega t.$

Hence $\quad t = \dfrac{1}{\omega}\cot^{-1}\dfrac{u}{b\omega}.$

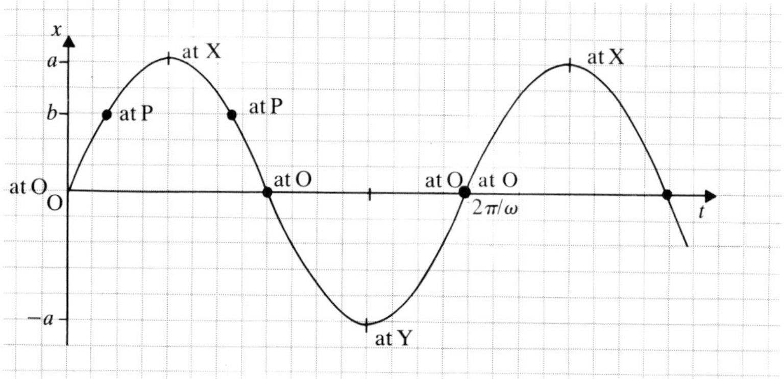

Figure 8.32

Now the motion from O to X is a $\frac{1}{4}$ cycle (as in figure 8.32), taking a time $\frac{1}{4}\times 2\pi/\omega = \pi/2\omega$. Hence the time from P to X is

$$\frac{\pi}{2\omega} - \frac{1}{\omega}\cot^{-1}\frac{u}{b\omega} = \frac{1}{\omega}\left[\tfrac{1}{2}\pi - \cot^{-1}\frac{u}{b\omega}\right] = \frac{1}{\omega}\tan^{-1}\frac{u}{b\omega}.$$

By symmetry $\tau = 2 \times$ (time from P to X), hence

$$\tau = \frac{2}{\omega}\tan^{-1}\frac{u}{b\omega}.$$

EXERCISE 8D

1. A particle performs SHM about O. When the particle is 3 m from O its speed is 8 m s^{-1} and its acceleration is 12 m s^{-2}. Calculate the amplitude, period and maximum speed of the particle.

2. A particle starts from O performing SHM of amplitude a, centre O, and period $2\pi/\omega$. Calculate the time taken: (a) to reach a point $\frac{1}{2}a$ from O, (b) to reduce its speed to half its maximum value.

3. A particle performs SHM at a rate of 3 oscillations per second, and its greatest acceleration is 30 m s^{-2}. Calculate the amplitude of the motion.

4. A particle moves with SHM so that its greatest speed is 4 m s^{-1} and its greatest acceleration is 10 m s^{-2}. Calculate the period and the amplitude of the motion.

5. A particle makes 10 oscillations per second and the amplitude is 5 cm. Calculate the maximum acceleration of the particle.

6. A particle is moving with SHM about a fixed point O. The period is 4π s and it passes through a point A, 3 m from O, with a speed of 3 m s^{-1} away from O. Calculate the time that elapses before it is next at A.

7. A particle performs SHM about O and x is related to t by: $x = \sin \omega t$. Draw graphs of: (a) x against t, (b) the speed v against t, (c) the acceleration a against t, (d) v against x, (e) a against x.

8. Given $x = a\cos(\omega t + \varepsilon)$: (a) Prove by differentiation that $\ddot{x} = -\omega^2 x$. (b) Sketch the (t, x) graph.

9. Draw the (t, x) graph for the following in the range $0 \leqslant t \leqslant 2\pi$ and obtain an equation connecting $\ddot{x}$ and x.
(a) $x = 5 \sin 2t$, (b) $x = 5\sin(2t + 3)$, (c) $x = 3 + 5 \sin 2t$.

10. Solve the equation $\ddot{x} = -9x$, given that $x = 0$, $\dot{x} = 6$ when $t = 0$.

11. Solve the equation $\ddot{x} = -\pi^2 x$, given that $x = -4$, $\dot{x} = 0$ when $t = 0$.

12. A particle moves with SHM along the x-axis. The end points of the motion are at $x = a$ and $x = b$. The maximum speed during the motion is u. Prove that the period is given by $\pi(b - a)/u$.

13. A particle is moving in a straight line under the action of a force $\boldsymbol{F}$ towards a fixed point O. The mass of the particle is m and the magnitude of the force is $F = m\omega^2 x$, where x is the distance from O. If the speed of the particle is zero at $x = a$ use the work–energy equation to deduce the speed of the particle at O.

14. If $a\sin(\omega t + \varepsilon) = A\cos\omega t + B\sin\omega t$, prove that:
(a) $a^2 = A^2 + B^2$, (b) $\tan\varepsilon = A/B$.

15. A particle of unit mass moves along the x-axis under the influence of a force $\boldsymbol{F}$ directed towards O, where $F = \omega^2 x$, and the amplitude of the motion is a. When $x = \frac{1}{2}a\sqrt{3}$ and the particle is moving away from O, it receives an impulse ωa in the positive x-direction. Show that the new motion is SHM about O of amplitude $a\sqrt{3}$.

16. A horizontal shelf is moving vertically in SHM with period one second. If a particle is placed on the shelf show that it will always remain in contact provided that the amplitude of the motion is less than about 0.25 m. If the amplitude is at its critical value, at what point in the motion will the particle be on the point of losing contact with the shelf?

8.5 Oscillatory systems

We now examine the motion of particles on strings or springs in some detail, using the results of section 8.4.

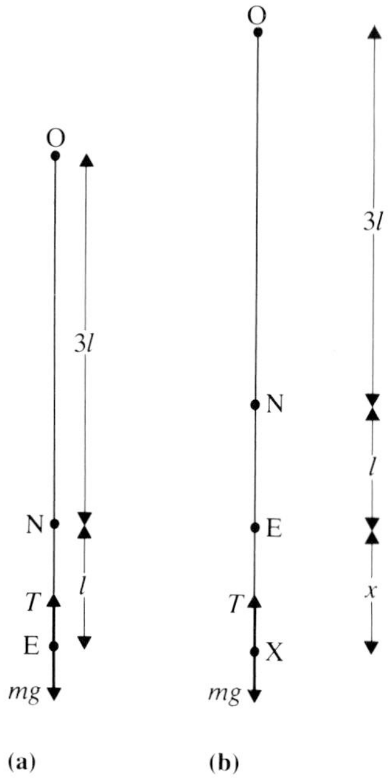

Figure 8.33

EXAMPLE 1

The upper end of an elastic string of natural length $3l$ is attached to a fixed point O. In equilibrium a particle of mass m extends the string by a length l. If the particle is pulled down a further distance $2l$, show that the time taken between release of the particle and the instant when the string becomes slack is $\frac{2}{3}\pi\sqrt{l/g}$.

Figure 8.33a shows the particle hanging in equilibrium at E. Let the modulus of elasticity of the string be λ.
Applying N2 on the particle,

$$T = mg.$$

From Hooke's law

$$T = \lambda \times \frac{l}{3l} = \tfrac{1}{3}\lambda$$

Hence $$\lambda = 3mg.$$

Consider the particle at depth x below E as in figure 8.33b. Applying N2 to the particle,

$$m\ddot{x} = mg - T = mg - \frac{3mg}{3l}(x + l)$$

$$= -\frac{mg}{l}x.$$

Hence $$\ddot{x} = -\frac{g}{l}x.$$

This is SHM and x is given by

$$x = a\cos(\omega t + \varepsilon),$$

where $\omega^2 = g/l$. The initial conditions are $t = 0$, $x = 2l$, $\dot{x} = 0$, leading to $a = 2l$ and $\varepsilon = 0$. Hence

$$x = 2l\cos\omega t.$$

The equation of motion and the given formula for x hold as long as the string is stretched, i.e. provided $x > -l$. When the string becomes slack,

$$-l = 2l\cos\omega t,$$

$$t = \frac{1}{\omega}\cos^{-1}(-\tfrac{1}{2}).$$

Hence the string first becomes slack when

$$t = \frac{1}{\omega}\left[\pi - \tfrac{1}{3}\pi\right] = \tfrac{2}{3}\pi\sqrt{\frac{l}{g}}.$$

EXAMPLE 2

For the particle in example 1, calculate: (a) how high it rises, (b) the time for a complete oscillation.

a) Suppose the particle rises to a point H, as shown in figure 8.34. Since the motion between B and N is SHM, we may apply the equation

$$v^2 = \omega^2(a^2 - x^2),$$

where $a = 2l$ and $\omega^2 = g/l$. At N, $x = -l$ and we obtain $v^2 = 3gl$. The motion from N to H is under constant acceleration due to gravity. Hence $2gh = v^2$, and $h = \frac{3}{2}l$, i.e. the particle rises to a point $\frac{3}{2}l$ above N.

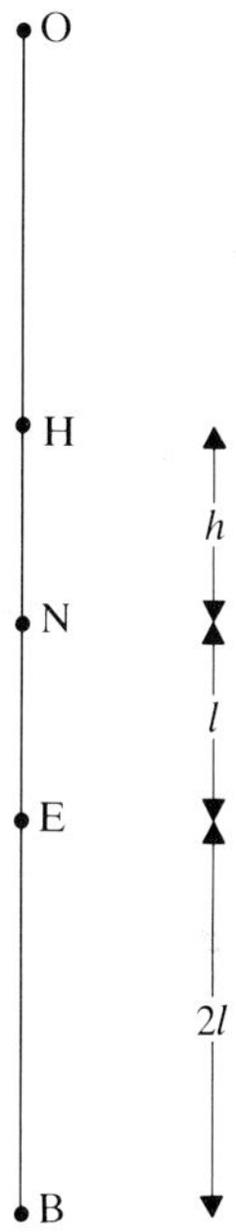

Figure 8.34

b) Since the motion from N to H is under gravity alone, the time for this part is given by

$$0 = \sqrt{3gl} - gt,$$
$$t = \sqrt{3l/g}.$$

The time from B to N is $\frac{2}{3}\pi\sqrt{l/g}$ (from example 1).
Hence the time from B to H is $\sqrt{l/g}\,[\frac{2}{3}\pi + \sqrt{3}]$.
The motion will be symmetrical, so the time for one oscillation is $2\sqrt{l/g}\,[\frac{2}{3}\pi + \sqrt{3}]$

It is of interest to examine the graph showing the position of the particle at various times. Let y be the height *above* E at time t. The (t, y) graph is shown in figure 8.35.

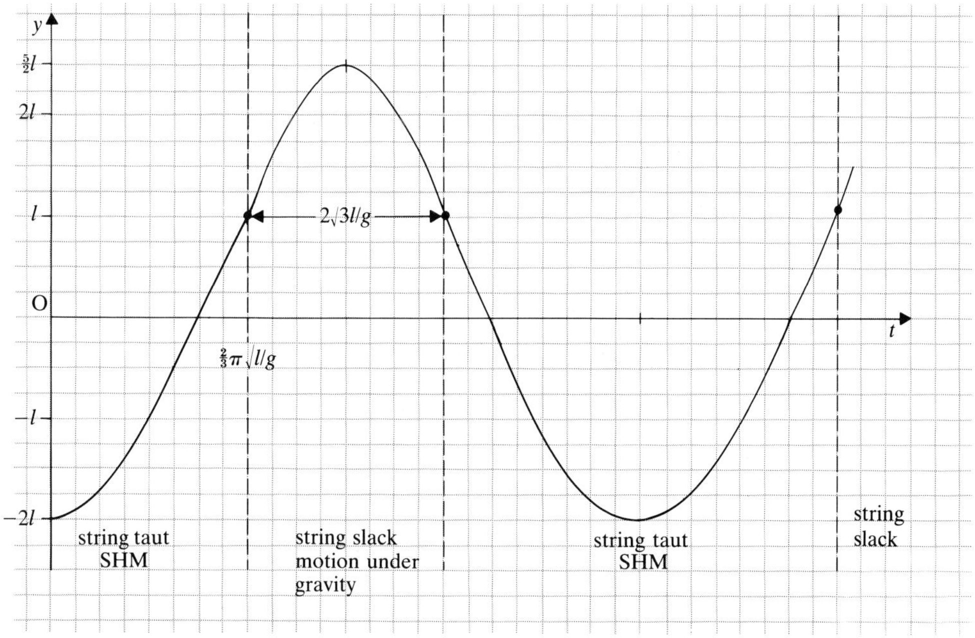

Figure 8.35

EXAMPLE 3

The similar elastic strings each of natural length l and modulus $4mg$ are fastened to a particle of mass m. Their other ends are attached to two fixed points P and Q, $4l$ apart, on a smooth horizontal table. Initially the system is released from rest with the particle at R where OR $= \frac{1}{2}l$, O being the midpoint of PQ.

a) Prove that the motion is SHM with period $\pi\sqrt{l/2g}$.

b) When the particle is at O and moving towards Q, the string OQ is cut. Find how far the particle moves towards Q before it comes to rest.

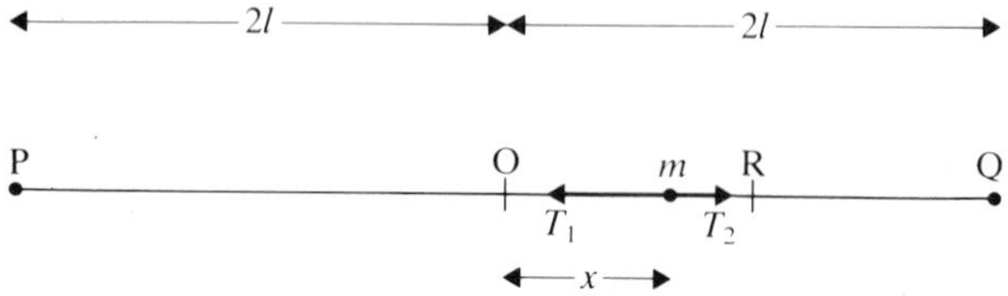

Figure 8.36

a) Let x be the displacement to the right of O at time t as shown in figure 8.36. Applying N2 to the particle, where T_1 and T_2 are the tensions in the strings,

$$m\ddot{x} = T_2 - T_1.$$

Applying Hooke's law to the strings,

$$T_1 = \frac{4mg}{l}(l + x), \qquad T_2 = \frac{4mg}{l}(l - x).$$

Hence
$$m\ddot{x} = -\frac{4mg}{l} \times 2x,$$

$$\ddot{x} = -\frac{8g}{l}x.$$

Since both strings are taut at R, they will remain so throughout the motion, which is SHM

$$x = a\cos(\omega t + \varepsilon), \qquad \omega^2 = 8g/l.$$

The initial conditions are $x = \frac{1}{2}l$, $\dot{x} = 0$ when $t = 0$, giving $a = \frac{1}{2}l$ and $\varepsilon = 0$. Hence

$$x = \tfrac{1}{2}l\cos\omega t.$$

The period is $2\pi/\omega = \pi\sqrt{l/2g}$.

b) If v is the speed at O,

$$\begin{aligned} v &= a\omega \\ &= \tfrac{1}{2}l\sqrt{8g/l} \\ &= \sqrt{2lg}. \end{aligned}$$

After the string OQ is cut, we can find an expression for the speed v at the point X in figure 8.37 using the energy equation.

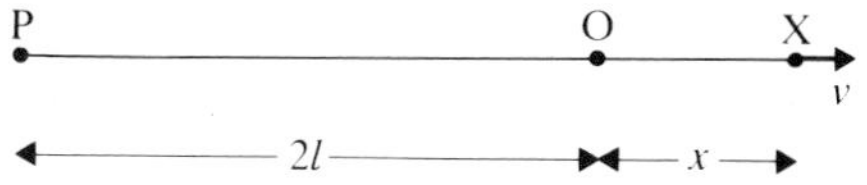

Figure 8.37

KE at O + EPE at O $\quad = $ KE at X + EPE at X,

$$\tfrac{1}{2}\text{m} \times 2lg + \tfrac{1}{2} \times \frac{4mg}{l} \times l^2 = \tfrac{1}{2}mv^2 \quad + \tfrac{1}{2} \times \frac{4mg}{l} \times (l + x)^2.$$

The particle is closest to Q when $v = 0$,

$$lg + 2lg = 0 + \frac{2g}{l}(l + x)^2,$$

$$(l + x)^2 = \tfrac{3}{2}l^2,$$

Hence $\qquad x = l(\sqrt{\tfrac{3}{2}} - 1)$

Approximate SHM

We conclude this chapter by giving two examples in which the motion is approximately simple harmonic. The first of these is important because it provides the basis for more advanced work and is an example in which the motion is not in a straight line.

EXAMPLE 4 The simple pendulum

Consider a particle of mass m suspended on the end of a light inextensible string of length l. We have seen in section 6.3 that under certain conditions the particle will perform vertical circles. Figure 8.38 shows the particle at a general position.

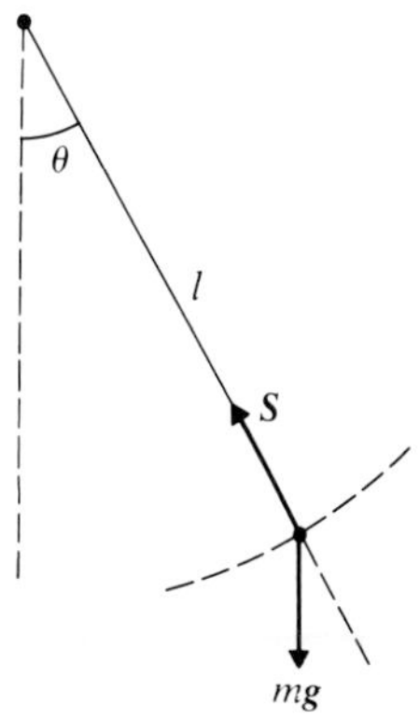

Figure 8.38

Applying N2 to the particle:

towards O $\qquad S - mg \cos \theta = ml\dot{\theta}^2,$

tangentially $\qquad -mg \sin \theta = ml\ddot{\theta}.$

From the tangential equation we obtain

$$\ddot{\theta} = -\frac{g}{l}\sin \theta.$$

When θ is small, $\sin \theta \approx \theta$ and

$$\ddot{\theta} \approx -\frac{g}{l}\theta$$

This is the equation of SHM for θ.

Thus, if the particle were pulled to the side through a small angle and released it would perform SHM with period $2\pi\ (l/g)^{1/2}$. This system is called the simple pendulum.

Notice that the period T is independent of the mass of the particle:

$$T = 2\pi\sqrt{l/g}.$$

Rearranging we obtain $g = 4\pi^2 l/T^2$ and this result provided an early method for calculating the acceleration due to gravity.

When other systems are found to perform SHM they are often described by quoting the length of the equivalent simple pendulum, that is, the simple pendulum having the same period as the given system. Thus, for example 3, the length of the equivalent simple pendulum is $\frac{1}{8}l$.

EXAMPLE 5*

Consider the situation in example 3. Suppose that from O, the particle is pulled a small distance on the table at right angles to PQ and released. Show that the motion is approximately SHM, and prove that the period is $\pi\sqrt{l/g}$.

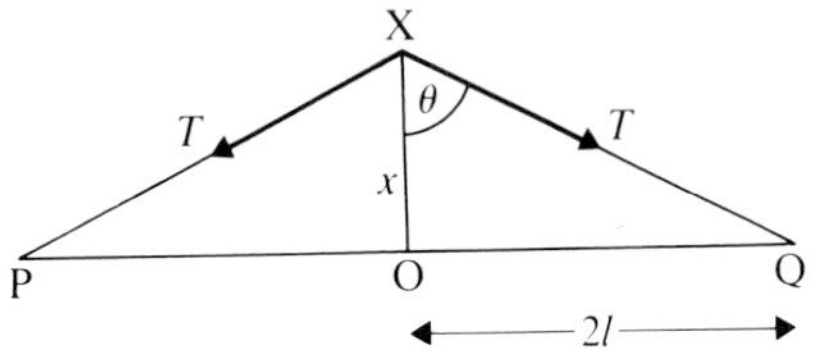

Figure 8.39

Figure 8.39 shows the particle displaced by an amount x from O. Applying N2 to the particle along **OX**

$$m\ddot{x} = -2T\cos\theta,$$

$$\ddot{x} = -\frac{2T}{m}\cos\theta.$$

Now $XQ = XP = (4l^2 + x^2)^{1/2}$ and $\cos\theta = x/(4l^2 + x^2)^{1/2}$. From Hooke's law

$$T = \frac{4mg}{l}[(4l^2 + x^2)^{1/2} - l].$$

Hence
$$\ddot{x} = -\frac{8gx}{l}\left[1 - \frac{l}{(4l^2 + x^2)^{1/2}}\right]$$

$$= -\frac{8gx}{l}\left[1 - \tfrac{1}{2}\left(1 + \frac{x^2}{4l^2}\right)^{-1/2}\right].$$

Now, from the binomial theorem,

$$\left(1 + \frac{x^2}{4l^2}\right)^{-1/2} = 1 + (-\tfrac{1}{2})\left(\frac{x^2}{4l^2}\right) + \frac{(-\frac{1}{2})(-\frac{3}{2})}{2!}\left(\frac{x^2}{4l^2}\right)^2 + \text{higher terms.}$$

If x is small, $|x^n| \ll |x|$ if $n > 1$ and we can neglect all but the first term in this expansion.

Hence
$$\left(1 + \frac{x^2}{4l^2}\right)^{-1/2} \approx 1$$

giving
$$\ddot{x} \approx -\frac{8gx}{l}[1 - \tfrac{1}{2}]$$

$$\approx -\frac{4g}{l}$$

This is SHM with period $2\pi\sqrt{l/4g} = \pi\sqrt{l/g}$.

The vibration in example 4 is called longitudinal while that in example 5 is called transverse.

EXERCISE 8E

Take g as 10 m s^{-2}, where necessary.

1. A particle of mass m is on a smooth horizontal table attached to one end P of an elastic string of natural length a and modulus of elasticity λ. The other end is fixed to a point O on the table, and the particle is released when $OP = b$ $(b > a)$. Find the time taken for the particle to reach O.

2. One end of an elastic string of natural length a is attached to a fixed point. When a particle of mass m is attached to the other end and hangs in equilibrium under gravity the string is stretched by an amount d $(d < a)$.
   a) The particle is pulled down a further distance $\frac{3}{4}d$ and released. Prove that the particle executes SHM and find the period.
   b) If the particle were pulled down a further distance $\frac{5}{4}d$ instead of $\frac{3}{4}d$ describe the motion and find the period.

3. The particle in question 2 is hanging in equilibrium when it is given a blow upwards, the magnitude of the impulse being $2m\sqrt{(gd)}$. Prove that the particle reaches its lowest point after a time $[2\sqrt{3} + \frac{5}{6}\pi]\sqrt{(d/g)}$

4. Figure 8.40 shows a bead of mass m at C on a smooth horizontal wire. It is connected to one end of an elastic string of natural length a, modulus of elasticity λ, which passes through a smooth fixed ring at A to a fixed point O where $OA = a$. Prove that when the bead is released it performs SHM whose period is independent of the length AB.

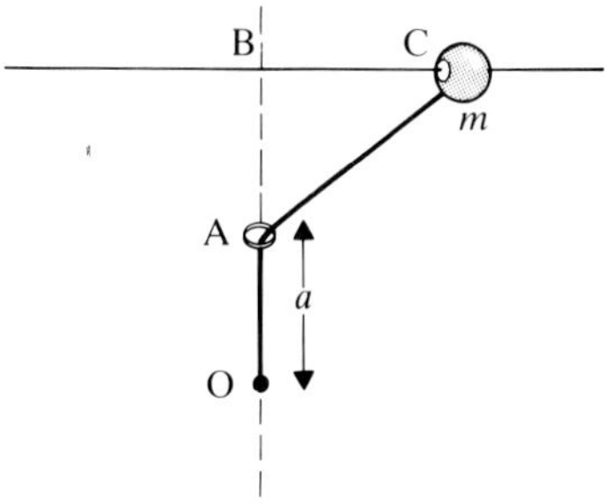

Figure 8.40

5. One end of an elastic string of natural length a, modulus of elasticity λ is fixed to a point O on a smooth horizontal table. The other end is attached to a particle of mass m, which is lying on the table. The particle is pulled to a point P, where $OP = 2a$ and then released from rest. Show that the time taken to return to P is $2(\pi + 2)\sqrt{(am/\lambda)}$.

6. An elastic string of natural length a and modulus of elasticity λ is stretched between two points A and B on a smooth horizontal table, where $AB = 2a$. A particle of mass m is fastened to the middle of the string. It is then pulled towards A to a point P, where $AP = \frac{1}{2}a$, and is then released. Show that the subsequent motion is simple harmonic with period $\pi\sqrt{(ma/\lambda)}$, and find the greatest speed of the particle.

7. A seconds pendulum is one which takes one second for half a complete oscillation. Calculate the length of such a pendulum.

8. Figure 8.41 shows a proposed channel tunnel from Dover to Calais. Neglecting all resistances to motion, show that a car could freewheel from Dover to Calais in approximately $\frac{3}{4}$ hour. Prove that the same time would be taken to freewheel along a sub-Atlantic tunnel between Dover and New York. (The force on a particle inside the Earth is directed towards the centre of the Earth, and has a magnitude kr, where k is a constant and r is the distance from the centre.)

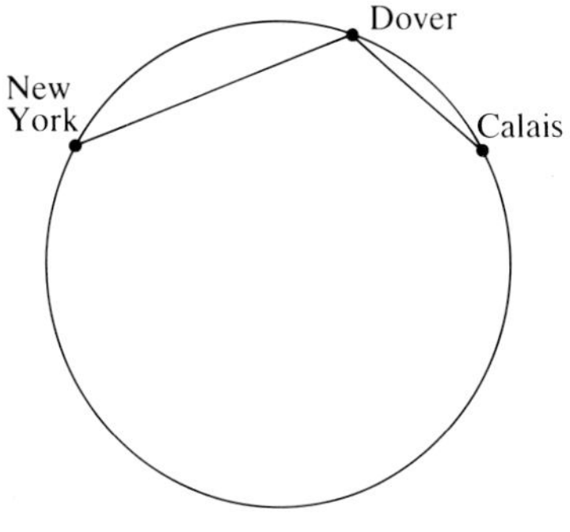

Figure 8.41

9. A smooth circular wire of radius a is fixed in a vertical plane. A light string of natural length a and modulus of elasticity λ has one end fixed to the wire vertically above the centre. A bead of mass m threaded on the wire, is attached to the other end of the string. Show that if $\lambda < 2mg$ the bead will perform approximate SHM about the lowest point of the wire with period $2\pi\sqrt{(2am/(2mg - \lambda))}$.

10. Two particles of mass m and M are joined by a light elastic string, which passes through a hole O in a smooth horizontal table of height h. The natural length of the string is h and the modulus of elasticity is λ. Initially m rests on the table at O and M rests on the ground. m is projected horizontally from O with a speed u. Show that M will not rise if $u < Mg\sqrt{(h/\lambda m)}$, and if this condition is satisfied, find the period and amplitude of the oscillation of m.

11. A particle hanging in equilibrium at the end of a light spring stretches it by a distance d. Prove that for vertical oscillations about the equilibrium position, the length of the equivalent simple pendulum is d.

12. A light elastic band of natural length $2a$, passes over two smooth pegs A and B, stuck in a wall at the same level, a distance a apart. A particle is attached to the middle of the lower portion, and in equilibrium the band is in the shape of an equilateral triangle. Show that if the particle is pulled down a small amount and released it will approximately perform SHM with period $2\pi\sqrt{(\frac{2}{7}a\sqrt{3})}$.

13. One end of an elastic string of natural length a and modulus mg is attached to a fixed point O and the other end is attached to a particle of mass m. The particle is released from rest at a point $\frac{1}{2}a$ below O. Prove that it returns to its initial position after a time $(\frac{3}{2}\pi + 2)\sqrt{(l/g)}$. Prove also that the greatest speed attained is $\sqrt{(2ag)}$.

Summary

Hooke's law

The tension in a stretched string is given by

$$T = \begin{cases} kx, & \text{where } k \text{ is the string constant } (\mathrm{N\,m^{-1}}) \\ \dfrac{\lambda x}{l}, & \text{where } \lambda \text{ is the modulus of elasticity (N),} \end{cases}$$

where x is the extension beyond the natural length l.
The work done in stretching a string by an amount x is given by

$$W = \frac{\lambda x^2}{2l}.$$

Elastic potential energy (EPE)

The energy stored in a stretched string is equal to the work done in stretching it.

Simple harmonic motion (SHM)

Fundamental equation: $\ddot{x} = -\omega^2 x$.

The periodic time: $T = \dfrac{2\pi}{\omega}$.

The general displacement:

$$x = a \sin(\omega t + \varepsilon),$$

where a is the amplitude and ε the phase angle.

The speed is given by: $v^2 = \omega^2(a^2 - x^2)$.

9 CENTRE OF GRAVITY

In section 7.3 we introduced the idea of the centre of gravity as the point where the weight force acts. For a uniform body in a constant gravitational field the centre of gravity coincides with the geometrical centre. We now examine the definition of the centre of gravity in more detail and show how to find its position for various different types of rigid bodies.

9.1 Particles

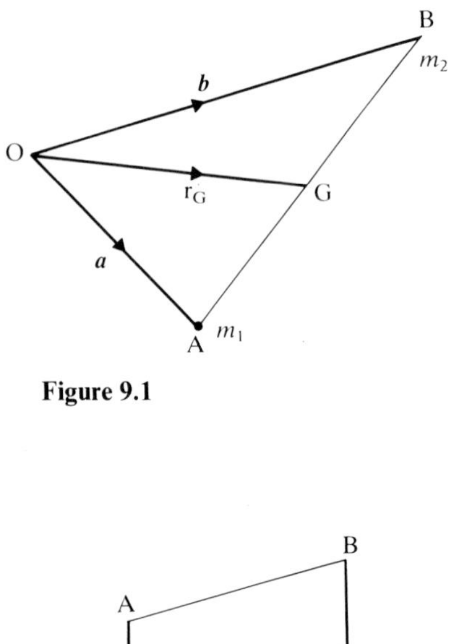

Figure 9.1

Consider two particles A and B of masses m_1 and m_2 with position vectors $\boldsymbol{a}$ and $\boldsymbol{b}$ relative to an origin O, as in figure 9.1. We define the vector $\boldsymbol{r}_G$ as the position vector of the **centre of mass** G by the equation

$$(m_1 + m_2)\boldsymbol{r}_G = m_1\boldsymbol{a} + m_2\boldsymbol{b}$$

$$\boldsymbol{r}_G = \frac{m_1}{m_1 + m_2}\boldsymbol{a} + \frac{m_2}{m_1 + m_2}\boldsymbol{b}$$

From the ratio theorem this indicates that G lies on the line AB and divides it in the ratio $m_2 : m_1$.

Consider the weight forces $\boldsymbol{w}_1$ and $\boldsymbol{w}_2$ on the particles at A and B, respectively. If the distance AB is not large the weight forces will be parallel. From the work in section 7.5, these two forces are equivalent to a single force $\boldsymbol{w}_1 + \boldsymbol{w}_2$ acting through P, a distance x from A, as in figure 9.2. Since $\boldsymbol{w}_1 + \boldsymbol{w}_2$ has no moment about P,

$$w_1 x = w_2(\mathrm{AB} - x),$$

$$x = \frac{w_2}{w_1 + w_2}\mathrm{AB}.$$

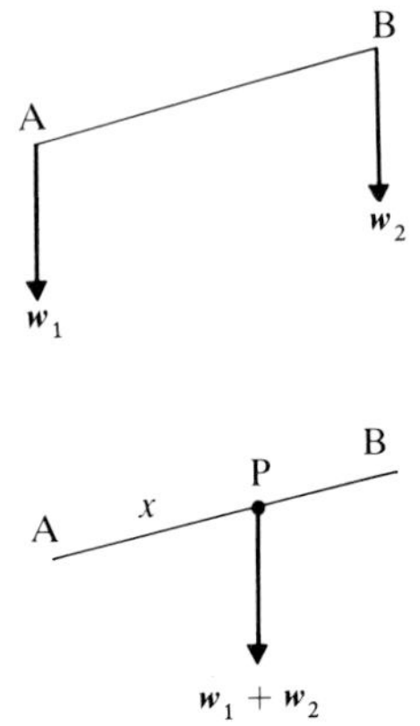

Figure 9.2

Hence

$$\boldsymbol{r}_P = \boldsymbol{a} + \frac{w_2}{w_1 + w_2}(\boldsymbol{b} - \boldsymbol{a})$$

$$= \frac{w_1}{w_1 + w_2}\boldsymbol{a} + \frac{w_2}{w_1 + w_2}\boldsymbol{b}.$$

Now $w_1 = m_1 g$ and $w_2 = m_2 g$, so

$$\boldsymbol{r}_P = \frac{m_1}{m_1 + m_2}\boldsymbol{a} + \frac{m_2}{m_1 + m_2}\boldsymbol{b}$$

$$= \boldsymbol{r}_G.$$

P is called the **centre of gravity** and is the point where the total weight force may be considered to act. It coincides with G, the centre of mass. If we think of the weights as suspended from the ends of a light rod, the centre of gravity is the balance point of the system. We will use the letter G to denote both the centre of mass and the centre of gravity, since we often use either term in examples.

EXAMPLE 1

A light rod of length 2 m has two particles of masses 2 kg and 3 kg attached to its ends. Find the position of the centre of mass.

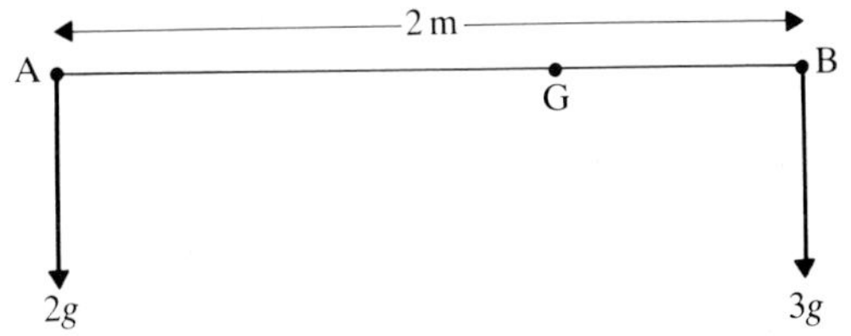

Figure 9.3

Referring to figure 9.3, G is given by

$$\boldsymbol{r}_G = \frac{m_1}{m_1 + m_2}\boldsymbol{a} + \frac{m_2}{m_1 + m_2}\boldsymbol{b}$$

Taking A as the origin and AB as the positive x-direction

$$x_G = \tfrac{2}{5} \times 0 + \tfrac{3}{5} \times 2 = 1.2$$

i.e. G is 1.2 m from A.

□□□□□

We can extend the above ideas to the case where a body is composed of a large number of particles.

Suppose n masses $m_1, m_2, \dots m_i, \dots m_n$ are at points with position vectors $\boldsymbol{r}_1, \boldsymbol{r}_2, \dots \boldsymbol{r}_i, \dots \boldsymbol{r}_n$. The position vector of the centre of mass G is defined by

$$(m_1 + m_2 + \cdots + m_n)\boldsymbol{r}_G = m_1\boldsymbol{r}_1 + m_2\boldsymbol{r}_2 + \cdots m_i\boldsymbol{r}_i + \cdots + m_n\boldsymbol{r}_n,$$

$$\left(\sum_1^n m_i\right)\boldsymbol{r}_G = \sum_1^n m_i\boldsymbol{r}_i$$

$$\boldsymbol{r}_G = \sum_1^n m_i\boldsymbol{r}_i \Bigg/ \sum_1^n m_i,$$

where $\Sigma_1^n m_i = M$, the total mass of the system. (Note that in subsequent work we will write Σ_1^n as Σ.)

From the results of section 7.5 and an analysis similar to the one above, we see that the weight forces on the individual particles are equivalent to a single weight force $M\boldsymbol{g}$ acting at G, provided that the weight forces are all parallel, and tend to produce the same acceleration $\boldsymbol{g}$. This is valid if the distances between individual particles are small compared with the radius of the Earth, which is true for all examples considered in this book.

The equation for $\boldsymbol{r}_G$ is a vector equation and so, for example, in two dimensions, $\boldsymbol{r}_i = x_i\boldsymbol{i} + y_i\boldsymbol{j}$. If $\boldsymbol{r}_G = x_G\boldsymbol{i} + y_G\boldsymbol{j}$, then

$$x_G = \frac{\Sigma m_i x_i}{M}, \qquad y_G = \frac{\Sigma m_i y_i}{M}. \qquad \textbf{(1)}$$

We find it convenient to call $m_i x_i$ the moment of m_i about the y-axis and $m_i y_i$ the moment about the x-axis. This is analagous to the moment of a force about a point. We will use equation (1) as the definition of the x- and y-coordinates of G. It extends in the obvious way to give z_G in a 3-dimensional situation.

EXAMPLE 2

Find the centre of mass of particles of mass m, $2m$, $4m$ and $5m$ placed at the corners of a square lamina of side $2a$, as shown in figure 9.4.

We take O as the origin of the coordinate system. There are three ways in which we can write out the solution.

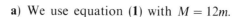

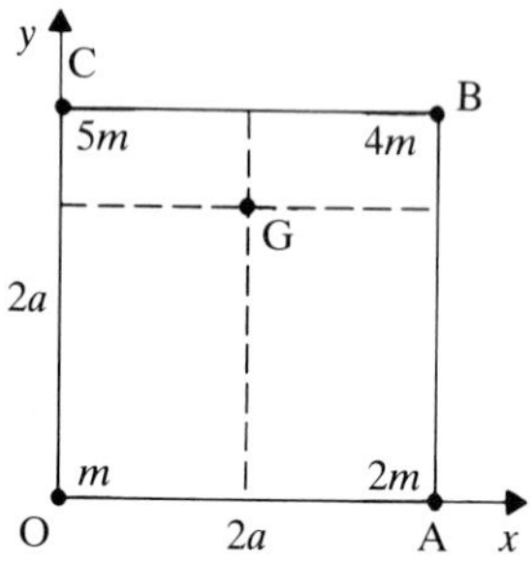

Figure 9.4

a) We use equation (**1**) with $M = 12m$.

$$12mx_G = m \times 0 + 2m \times 2a + 4m \times 2a + 5m \times 0,$$

$$x_G = \frac{12ma}{12m} = a,$$

$$12my_G = m \times 0 + 2m \times 0 + 4m \times 2a + 5m \times 2a,$$

$$y_G = \frac{18ma}{12m} = 1.5a.$$

Thus the centre of gravity is at the point $(a, 1.5a)$, relative to O.

b) We display the calculation in a table:

Point	Mass	Moment about the y-axis	Moment about the x-axis
(x_i, y_i)	m_i	$m_i x_i$	$m_i y_i$
(0, 0)	m	0	0
$(2a, 0)$	$2m$	$4ma$	0
$(2a, 2a)$	$4m$	$8ma$	$8ma$
$(0, 2a)$	$5m$	0	$10ma$
Total	$12m$	$12ma$	$18ma$

Thus
$$x_G = \frac{12ma}{12m} = a, \quad y_G = \frac{18ma}{12m} = 1.5a.$$

c) We use column vectors.

$$12m\boldsymbol{r}_G = m\begin{pmatrix}0\\0\end{pmatrix} + 2m\begin{pmatrix}2a\\0\end{pmatrix} + 4m\begin{pmatrix}2a\\2a\end{pmatrix} + 5m\begin{pmatrix}0\\2a\end{pmatrix}$$

$$= \begin{pmatrix}12ma\\18ma\end{pmatrix}.$$

So
$$\boldsymbol{r}_G = \begin{pmatrix}a\\1.5a\end{pmatrix}.$$

EXERCISE 9A

1. Two particles of mass 2.5 kg and 3.5 kg are placed at the ends of a light rod AB of length 1.5 m. Find the distance of the centre of mass from the 2.5 kg mass.

2. Two particles of mass 0.5 kg and 1.5 kg are placed at the ends of a light rod AB of length 0.5 m. Find the position of a third particle of mass 1.6 kg, if the centre of mass of the whole system is at the centre of the rod.

3. Four masses of 1, 2, 3 and 4 g are placed at the corners A, B, C and D, respectively, of a square of side 0.25 m. Find the position of the centre of mass relative to axes through AB and AD.

4. Masses of 1, 2, 4, 3, 6, and 5 g are placed at the corners A–F, respectively, of a regular hexagon of side 20 cm. Find the position of mass relative to axes OA and OP, where O is the centre of the hexagon and P is the midpoint of BC.

5. Three particles of mass 1.2, 0.5 and 2.3 kg are placed at the corners A, B and C, respectively, of a triangle which is right-angled at A. The side AB = 5 cm and BC = 3 cm. Find the position of the centre of mass relative to the axes AB and AC.

6. Find the position of the centre of mass of particles of mass 2, 3 and 5 kg which are placed at the points with coordinates A(2, 3), B(4, − 1) and C(5, 8), respectively.

7. A particle of mass 2 kg is placed at the point with position vector $2\boldsymbol{i} + \boldsymbol{j}$, and another of mass 3.5 kg is placed at $-2\boldsymbol{j}$. Find the position of a third particle of mass 0.5 kg, if the centre of mass of the system is at the origin.

8. Particles of mass 1.5 kg, 2.3 kg and 3.4 kg are placed at the points (2, − 1), (− 3, 2) and (− 1, 4), respectively. Find the coordinates of the centre of mass.

Continuous mass distributions **9.2**

Simple geometrical shapes

Density The **density** of an object is the ratio of its mass to its length, area or volume. In one dimension, the linear density is the mass per unit length. In two dimensions, the surface density is the mass per unit area, and in three dimensions, the density is the mass per unit volume. All simple bodies in this chapter will have uniform (constant) density.

A rigid body can be considered to be made up of an infinite number of particles, and we cannot use the simple summation formula in equation (1) on p. 255 to determine the position of the centre of mass. In most general cases the summation must be done using techniques of integration, and these are discussed in section 9.5, but we may deduce the position of G for simple geometrical shapes by using symmetry. We now illustrate this argument in a number of cases.

Uniform rod

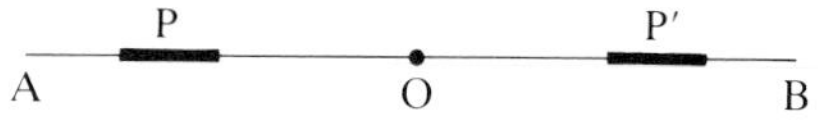

Figure 9.5

We can think of the rod composed of pairs of particles, such as P and P′ of equal mass and equal distance from O, the midpoint of the rod in figure 9.5. They have no total moment about O and hence G will lie at O.

Triangular lamina

We divide the lamina into a series of strips parallel to BC, as in figure 9.6. The centre of mass of each strip is at its midpoint and these points all lie on the median AL. Similarly, by dividing the lamina into strips parallel to the sides AC and AB, we deduce that the centre of mass must lie on all three medians and hence at the **centroid** of the triangle.

Figure 9.6

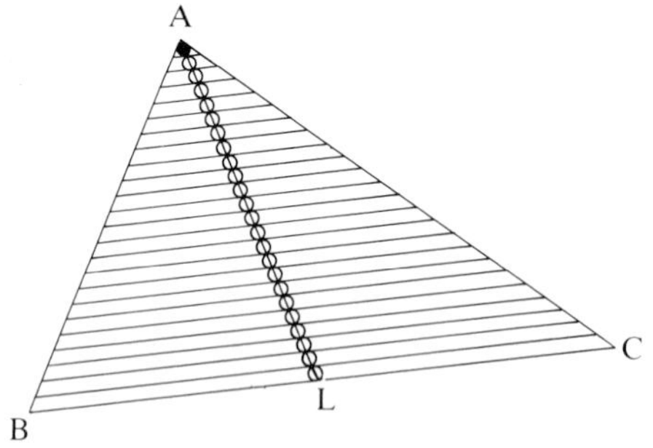

Figure 9.7

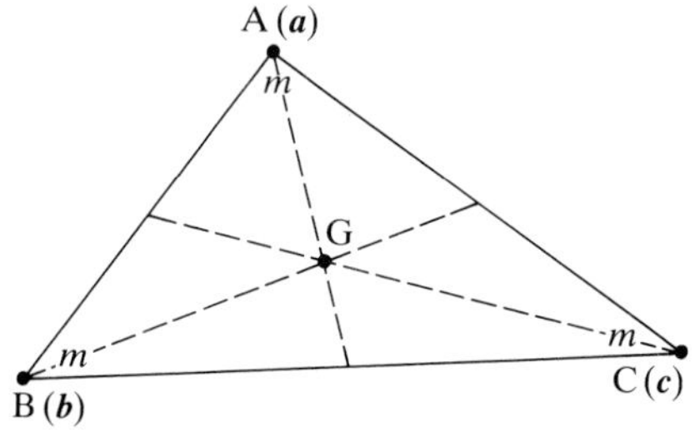

It is of interest to note that this is the same as the centre of mass of three equal particles placed at the vertices of the triangle. In figure 9.7,

$$\boldsymbol{r}_G = \frac{\Sigma m \boldsymbol{r}_i}{\Sigma m} = \frac{m(\boldsymbol{a}+\boldsymbol{b}+\boldsymbol{c})}{3m}$$

$$= \tfrac{1}{3}(\boldsymbol{a}+\boldsymbol{b}+\boldsymbol{c}),$$

where $\boldsymbol{a}$, $\boldsymbol{b}$ and $\boldsymbol{c}$ are the position vectors of the vertices. Here, as in other geometrical shapes, the centroid will locate the centre of mass.

Uniform cuboid

The centre of mass is at its geometrical centre.

Uniform tetrahedron

The centre of mass will be at its centroid which, by extension of the work for the triangular lamina, is at the point given by

$$\boldsymbol{r}_G = \tfrac{1}{4}(\boldsymbol{a} + \boldsymbol{b} + \boldsymbol{c} + \boldsymbol{d}),$$

where $\boldsymbol{a}$, $\boldsymbol{b}$, $\boldsymbol{c}$ and $\boldsymbol{d}$ are the position vectors of its vertices.

We can state, using the ideas of symmetry, the position of the centre of mass of a number of other uniform geometrical shapes.

Shape/object	Position of G
circular hoop	centre of the circle
circular disc	centre of the circle
triangular prism	midpoint of the line joining the centroids of the triangular faces
cylinder	midpoint of the axis of symmetry

The word centroid is generally used when we are dealing with geometrical shapes which have no reference to masses or weights. As above, it locates the same position as the centre of mass or centre of gravity.

Composite bodies

A simple composite body is one which is composed of uniform bodies whose individual centres of mass are known. The combined centre of mass is found by treating the individual parts as point masses concentrated at their mass centres.

Suppose a body consists of two simple bodies A and B of masses m_1 and m_2. The centre of mass is given by

$$\boldsymbol{r}_G = \frac{m_1\boldsymbol{r}_1 + m_2\boldsymbol{r}_2}{m_1 + m_2},$$

where $\boldsymbol{r}_1$ and $\boldsymbol{r}_2$ are the position vectors of the centres of mass of A and B.

Similar expressions hold for weights, areas and volumes, and the result can easily be extended to three or more individual parts.

EXAMPLE 1

A sledge hammer is composed of a head of mass 7 kg in the shape of a cuboid and a cylindrical shaft of mass 0.25 kg. Figure 9.8 shows a cross-section of the hammer through its plane of symmetry and its dimensions are shown. Find the position of the centre of mass.

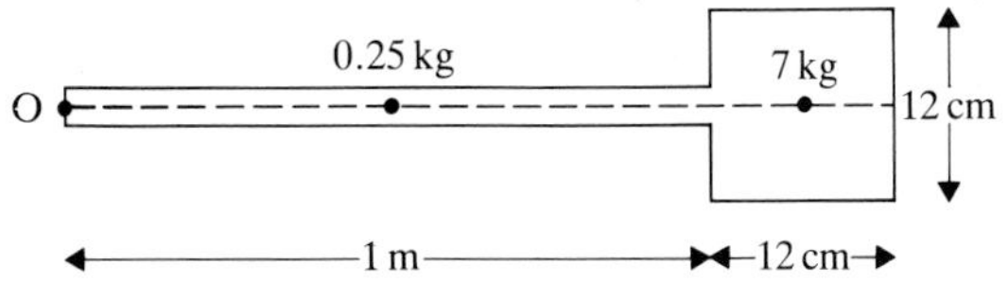

Figure 9.8

We take the origin O at the end of the shaft as in figure 9.8 and let x_G be the distance of the centre of mass from O.

$$Mx_G = \sum m_i x_i.$$
$$7.25x_G = 0.25 \times 0.5 + 7 \times 1.06,$$
$$x_G \approx 1.04,$$

Hence the centre of mass is only 2 cm to the left of the centre of the head.

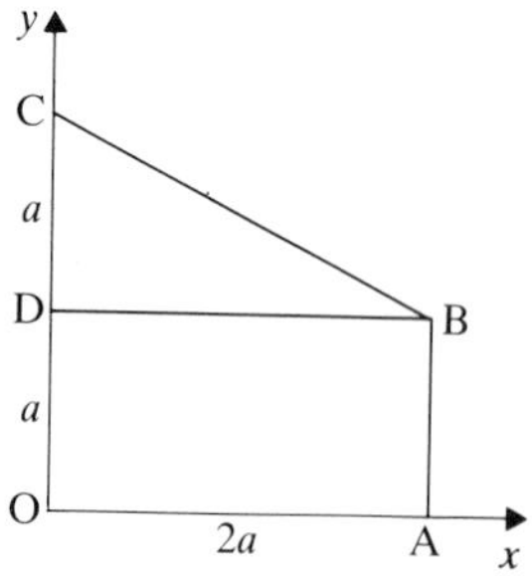

Figure 9.9

EXAMPLE 2

Figure 9.9 shows a rectangular lamina measuring $2a$ by a, joined to a triangular lamina of side $2a$ and height a. Find the position of the centre of mass. Take the origin O at the corner as shown.

Method 1

Let the surface density of the lamina be σ per unit area. We set out the calculation in a table.

Figure	Mass	Coordinates of the centre of mass of the part	
	m_i	x_i	y_i
ABCD	$\sigma 2a^2$	a	$\frac{1}{2}a$
DBC	σa^2	$\frac{1}{3} \times 2a$	$\frac{4}{3} \times a$
Total	$\sigma 3a^2$	x_G	y_G

$$Mx_G = \sum m_i x_i,$$
$$\sigma 3a^2 x_G = \sigma 2a^2 a + \sigma a^2 \tfrac{2}{3}a,$$
$$3x_G = 2a + \tfrac{2}{3}a,$$
$$x_G = \tfrac{8}{9}a;$$
$$My_G = \sum m_i y_i,$$
$$\sigma 3a^2 y_G = \sigma 2a^2 \tfrac{1}{2}a + \sigma a^2 \tfrac{4}{3}a,$$
$$y_G = \tfrac{7}{9}a.$$

Hence, relative to O, the centre of mass is at $(\frac{8}{9}a, \frac{7}{9}a)$.

Method 2 Column vectors

Let $\boldsymbol{r}_1 = \begin{pmatrix} a \\ \frac{1}{2}a \end{pmatrix}$ and $\boldsymbol{r}_2 = \begin{pmatrix} \frac{2}{3}a \\ \frac{4}{3}a \end{pmatrix}$ relative to O, so

$$\boldsymbol{r}_G = (2m\boldsymbol{r}_1 + m\boldsymbol{r}_2)/3m$$
$$= \left[2m\begin{pmatrix} a \\ \frac{1}{2}a \end{pmatrix} + m\begin{pmatrix} \frac{2}{3}a \\ \frac{4}{3}a \end{pmatrix} \right] \Big/ 3m$$
$$= \begin{pmatrix} \frac{8}{9}a \\ \frac{7}{9}a \end{pmatrix}.$$

Note that in method 1 the surface density cancels out in each equation and we are effectively taking moments of areas rather than masses to find the centre of mass or centroid. We may summarise these ideas in the following table:

Information given about a system of composite geometric objects	Appropriate term	Method of calculation
weights of objects	C of G	$\boldsymbol{r}_G = \dfrac{\Sigma w_i \boldsymbol{r}_i}{\Sigma w_i}$, where w_i is the weight and $\boldsymbol{r}_i$ locates the C of G of a part
masses of objects	C of M	$\boldsymbol{r}_G = \dfrac{\Sigma m_i \boldsymbol{r}_i}{\Sigma m_i}$, where m_i is the mass of a part
areas of laminas with surface density σ	centroid	$\boldsymbol{r}_G = \dfrac{\Sigma A_i \boldsymbol{r}_i}{\Sigma A_i}$, where A_i is the area of a part
volumes with density ρ	centroid	$\boldsymbol{r}_G = \dfrac{\Sigma V_i \boldsymbol{r}_i}{\Sigma V_i}$, where V_i is the volume of a part
frameworks with density (mass/unit length) m	centroid	$\boldsymbol{r}_G = \dfrac{\Sigma l_i \boldsymbol{r}_i}{\Sigma l_i}$, where l_i is the length of a part

EXAMPLE 3

A framework is made of a series of rods, as shown in figure 9.10. Find the position of its centre of mass, assuming all the rods are made of the same material, and are the same thickness.

Take the origin of the coordinate system at C as shown. The masses of the rods are proportional to their lengths, since the density is assumed to be constant. Suppose the centre of mass G has coordinates (x_G, y_G). By symmetry $x_G = 0$, which simplifies the problem. We can compile a table, showing the length of each rod and the y-coordinate of its centre of mass relative to O.

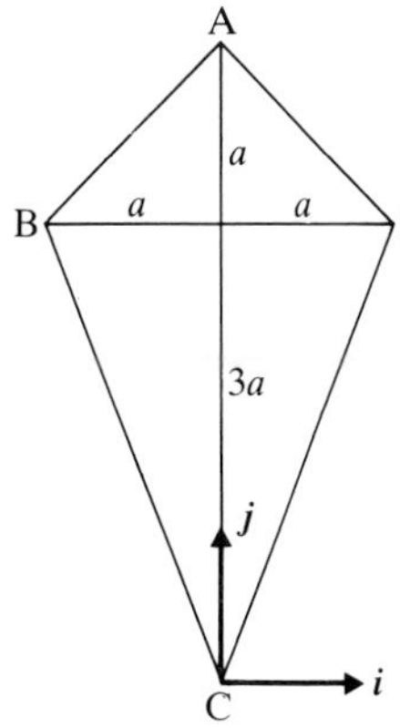

Figure 9.10

Rod	Length	y-coordinate of G
BC	$a\sqrt{10}$	$\frac{3}{2}a$
CD	$a\sqrt{10}$	$\frac{3}{2}a$
CA	$4a$	$2a$
BD	$2a$	$3a$
AB	$a\sqrt{2}$	$\frac{7}{2}a$
AD	$a\sqrt{2}$	$\frac{7}{2}a$

Taking moments about the x-axis,

$$[2(\sqrt{10}+\sqrt{2})+6]ay_G = 2\times\tfrac{3}{2}a\times a\sqrt{10}+4a\times 2a+2a\times 3a$$
$$+2\times a\sqrt{2}\times\tfrac{7}{2}a$$

$$y_G=\frac{(3\sqrt{10}+14+7\sqrt{2})}{(2(\sqrt{10}+\sqrt{2})+6)}a=2.20a$$

The centre of mass is $2.2a$ along CA from C.

EXERCISE 9B

1. A garden spade may be simplified to a shaft of length 1 m and mass 0.25 kg attached to a rectangular metal plate of mass 1.2 kg and length 0.25 m. Find the distance of the centre of mass from the top of the shaft.

2. A 'lollipop' lady carries a stick which consists of a uniform rod of length 1.5 m and mass 0.3 kg, surmounted by a circular disc of radius 0.25 m and mass 0.2 kg. Find the distance of the centre of mass from the end of the stick.

3. A standard lamp consists of a heavy metal base of radius 10 cm, thickness 4 cm and mass 2 kg. Attached to the centre of this is a metal rod of length 1.75 m, radius 2.5 cm and mass 0.25 kg. Locate the centre of mass.

4. A squash racket of mass 200 g and total length 70 cm consists of a handle of mass 150 g whose centre of mass is 20 cm from the end, and a frame whose centre of mass is 55 cm from the end. Find the distance of the centre of mass from the end of the handle.

5. A cricket bat of mass 1 kg and length 85 cm consists of a handle of mass 0.1 kg and length 30 cm. The blade is 55 cm long and its centre of mass is 30 cm from the toe and is on the line of symmetry. Find the distance from the centre of mass of the bat to the toe.

6. A hammer has a uniform shaft 30 cm long of mass 100 g which is attached to a head of mass 1 kg, whose centre of gravity is 3 cm from the end of the shaft. Find the centre of mass of the hammer.

7. A man of mass 70 kg is seated at the top of a mast of height 10 m and mass 250 kg. Find the position of the centre of mass of the man and the mast combined.

8. An isosceles trapezium consists of sides of length 4 cm and 2 cm, which are 2 cm apart. Find the position of its centre of mass.

9. An open rectangular wooden box has external dimensions 6 cm × 4 cm × 3 cm. If the thickness of the box is ignored, find the centre of mass. If the wood is 0.25 cm thick, locate the centre of mass.

10. Four uniform discs of thickness 2 cm and radii 6 cm, 5 cm, 4 cm and 3 cm are placed in order on top of each other with their centres in line. Find the position of the centre of mass.

11. A framework for one end of a greenhouse consists of four pieces in the shape of a trapezium. The two parallel sides are 2 m and 1.5 m high and these are 2 m apart. Find the height of the centre of mass and its distance from the shorter vertical side.

12. A gallows consists of an upright of height 2 m and a horizontal bar of length 1.5 m fixed at one end to its top. A third strut is fixed across the top corner at a distance of 0.5 m from the corner along both bars. Find the approximate position of the centre of mass and its horizontal distance from the upright. (Assume all pieces are made of identical material of negligible thickness.)

Subtraction of moments 9.3

Another set of objects for which we can readily obtain centres of masses are those which are composed of regular objects from which regular objects have been removed. For example, the object in figure 9.11 is irregular, and the position of its centre of mass is not obvious. However, if we think of it as a cuboid from which a cylinder has been removed, we can derive its centre of mass.

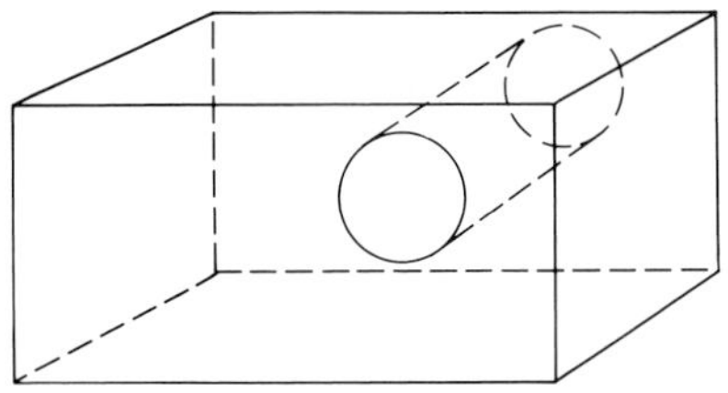

Figure 9.11

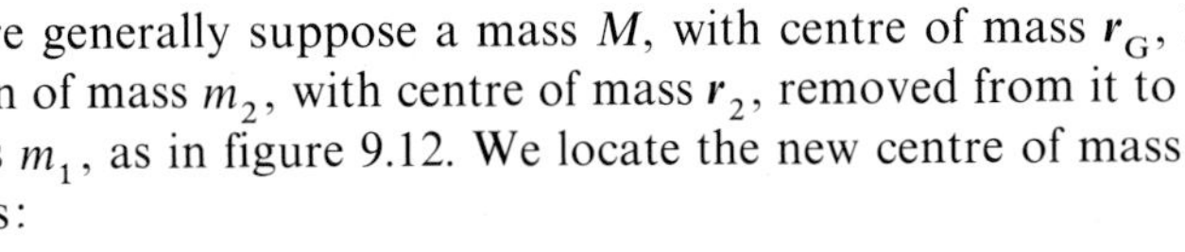

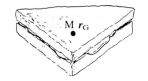

Figure 9.12

More generally suppose a mass M, with centre of mass $\boldsymbol{r}_G$, has a portion of mass m_2, with centre of mass $\boldsymbol{r}_2$, removed from it to leave a mass m_1, as in figure 9.12. We locate the new centre of mass $\boldsymbol{r}_1$ as follows:

For the whole mass, $M\boldsymbol{r}_G = m_1\boldsymbol{r}_1 + m_2\boldsymbol{r}_2$.

Rearranging $m_1\boldsymbol{r}_1 = M\boldsymbol{r}_G - m_2\boldsymbol{r}_2$,

$$\boldsymbol{r}_1 = (M\boldsymbol{r}_G - m_2\boldsymbol{r}_2)/m_1.$$

We will use this result in the following examples.

EXAMPLE 1

A pendant is made from a piece of metal in the shape of a circle of radius 5 cm from which a circle of radius 4 cm has been removed, so that the centre C of the latter circle is 4 cm from the top of the pendant, as shown in figure 9.13. Find the centre of mass.

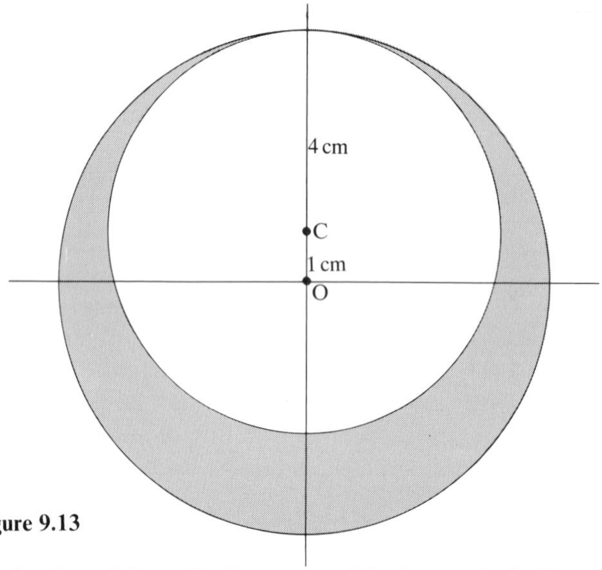

Figure 9.13

Shape	Area	y_i
solid circle	25π	0
hole	16π	1
pendant	9π	y_G

We take the origin at O, the centre of the larger circle. By symmetry $x_G = 0$. We compile a table of moments of the areas about the x-axis.

Thus, $$y_G = \frac{25\pi \times 0 - 16\pi \times 1}{9\pi} = -1.78,$$

i.e. the centre of mass is 1.78 cm below the centre of the large circle.

EXAMPLE 2

Find the centre of mass of the quadrilateral PQRS shown in figure 9.14.

We can think of the quadrilateral as a rectangle OBQA with three triangles removed.

Area PQRS = Area OAQB − Area OSP − Area SAR − Area PQB.

We set out the calculation in a table as follows.

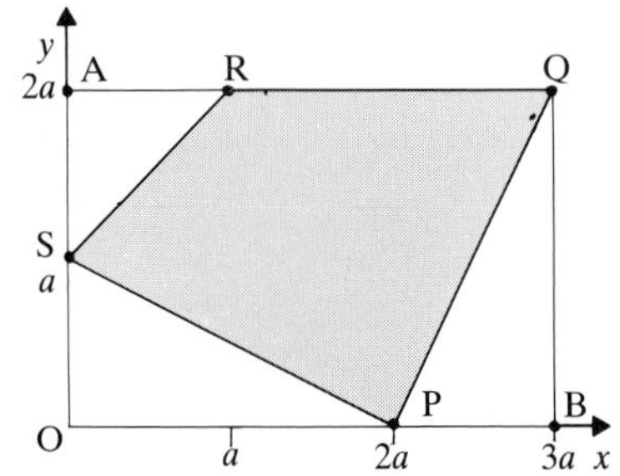

Figure 9.14

Shape	Area A_i	Coordinates of centre of mass x_i	y_i	Moments $A_i x_i$	$A_i y_i$
OAQB	$6a^2$	$\frac{3}{2}a$	a	$9a^3$	$6a^3$
OSP	a^2	$\frac{2}{3}a$	$\frac{1}{3}a$	$\frac{2}{3}a^3$	$\frac{1}{3}a^3$
SAR	$\frac{1}{2}a^2$	$\frac{1}{3}a$	$\frac{5}{3}a$	$\frac{1}{6}a^3$	$\frac{5}{6}a^3$
PBQ	a^2	$\frac{8}{3}a$	$\frac{2}{3}a$	$\frac{8}{3}a^3$	$\frac{2}{3}a^3$
PQRS	$\frac{7}{2}a^2$	x_G	y_G		

Taking moments about the y-axis

$$\tfrac{7}{2}a^2 \times x_G = 9a^3 - \tfrac{2}{3}a^3 - \tfrac{1}{6}a^3 - \tfrac{8}{3}a^3$$
$$= \tfrac{33}{6}a^3,$$
$$x_G = \tfrac{11}{7}a.$$

Taking moments about the x-axis

$$\tfrac{7}{2}a^2 y_G = 6a^3 - \tfrac{1}{3}a^3 - \tfrac{5}{6}a^3 - \tfrac{2}{3}a^3$$
$$= \tfrac{25}{6}a^3,$$
$$y_G = \tfrac{25}{21}a.$$

Hence the centre of mass has coordinates $(\tfrac{11}{7}a, \tfrac{25}{21}a)$.

EXERCISE 9C

1. A letter 'U' is made from a rectangle measuring 6 cm by 9 cm, from which a rectangle measuring 3 cm by 6 cm is removed. Find its centre of mass.

2. A circular metal plate of radius 14 cm has a circular hole of radius 5 cm removed from it. If the centre of the small hole is 3 cm from the centre of the plate, find the centre of mass.

3. A large cube of side $2a$ consists of eight solid cubes of side a.
   a) If one cube is removed from a corner, find the coordinates of the new centre of mass.
   b) If a tetrahedron is removed from one corner, as shown in figure 9.15, find the coordinates of the centre of mass.

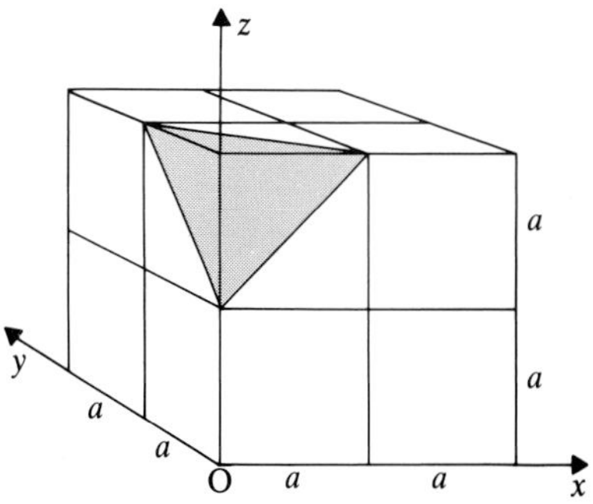

Figure 9.15

4. A rectangular sheet of paper measuring a by $2a$ is folded over as shown in figure 9.16. Find the coordinates of the centre of mass.

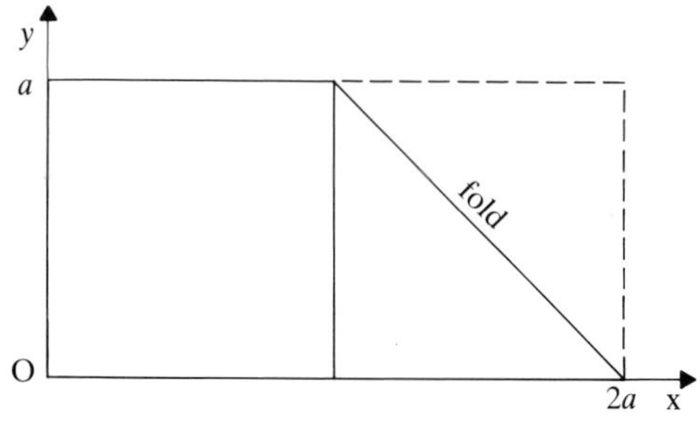

Figure 9.16

5. A hinged ruler consists of four sections each of length 15 cm. If one section is folded over, find the centre of mass.

6. An equilateral triangle of side $2a$ is folded so that one vertex touches the midpoint of the opposite side. Find the coordinates of the centre of mass.

7. Three corner squares of a chess board are removed and placed on the fourth corner. Find the distance of the centre of mass from the centre of the board.

8. A regular hexagon of side $2a$ has one of the constituent equilateral triangles removed.
   a) Find the distance of the centre of mass from the centre of the hexagon.
   b) If the removed section is placed on the opposite triangle, where is the centre of mass?
9. A rectangular lamina ABCD has sides AB $= 4a$ and AD $= 3a$. The corner at D is folded so that AD is along the side AB. A square of side a is removed from the corner B. Find the coordinates of the centre of mass of the resulting figure relative to axes BA and BC.
10. A uniform regular tetrahedron of side a is attached to the triangular face of a uniform prism of length $3a$. The triangular end of the prism is equilateral with side a. Find the position of the centre of mass.

9.4 Uses of integration

In section 9.2 we saw how symmetry arguments were used to determine the position of the centre of mass of simple continuous mass distributions. However, we cannot determine the centre of mass of the bodies in figure 9.17 by symmetry alone.

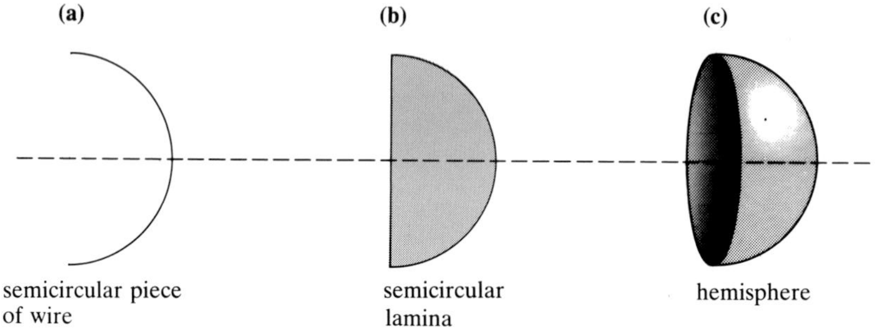

Figure 9.17

In all cases the centre of mass lies on the line of symmetry (dotted), but we need to use techniques of integration to locate the actual position on the line. Most of the examples we consider are of a geometrical nature and so the term centroid will be used rather than centre of mass.

a) Laminas and wires

Consider the region formed by the graph of $y = f(x)$, the x-axis and the lines $x = a$ and $x = b$, as shown in figure 9.18. The area of the region is

$$A = \int_a^b f(x)\,dx = \int_a^b y\,dx.$$

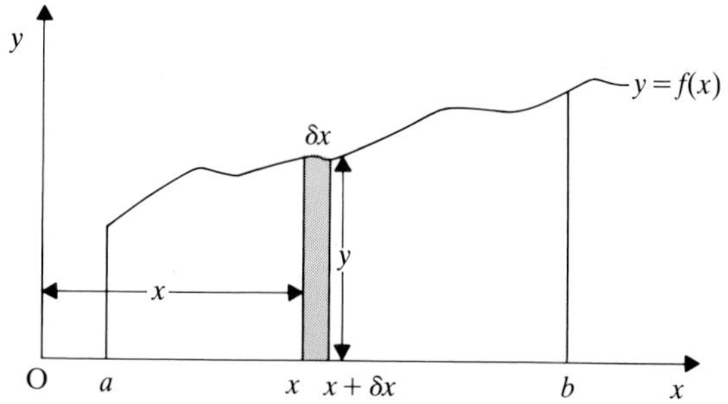

Figure 9.18

To derive this expression we divide the region into a series of rectangular strips of width δx and height y.

To find the centroid, we take the limit of the sum of all the moments about both axes of all such strips. The total moment about the y-axis is $\sum xy\delta x$.

Taking the limit as $\delta x \to 0$, the total moment is

$$\int_a^b xy\,\mathrm{d}x.$$

Thus, if (x_G, y_G) are the coordinates of the centroid,

$$Ax_G = \int_a^b xy\,\mathrm{d}x,$$

where $A = \int_a^b y\,\mathrm{d}x$. So that

$$x_G = \frac{\int_a^b xy\,\mathrm{d}x}{\int_a^b y\,\mathrm{d}x}.$$

To find y_G, we note that all points of each vertical strip are not the same distance y from the x-axis, and so we regard each strip as a particle concentrated at its centroid $(x, \frac{1}{2}y)$, see figure 9.19.

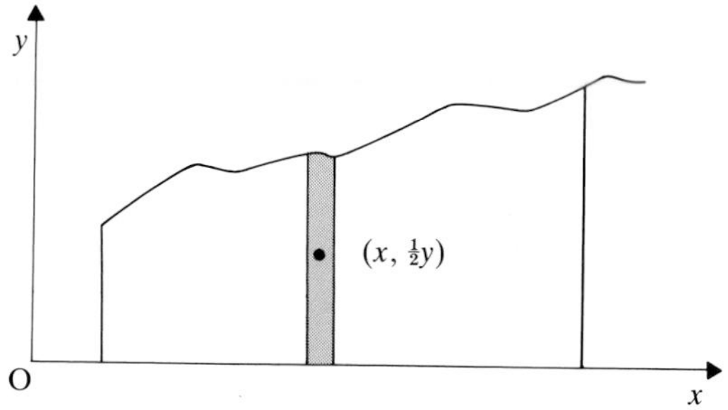

Figure 9.19

The total moment of the strips about the x-axis is $\Sigma \frac{1}{2}y\,y\,\delta x$, and, in the limit as $\delta x \to 0$, this moment is

$$\int_a^b \tfrac{1}{2}y^2\,\mathrm{d}x$$

Thus

$$y_G = \frac{\int_a^b \frac{1}{2}y^2\,\mathrm{d}x}{\int_a^b y\,\mathrm{d}x}$$

To summarise:

$$x_G = \frac{\int_a^b xy\,dx}{\int_a^b y\,dx}, \qquad y_G = \frac{\int_a^b \frac{1}{2}y^2\,dx}{\int_a^b y\,dx}.$$

EXAMPLE 1

Find the centroid of the region bounded by the curve $y = 8 - x^3$ and the positive x- and y-axes.

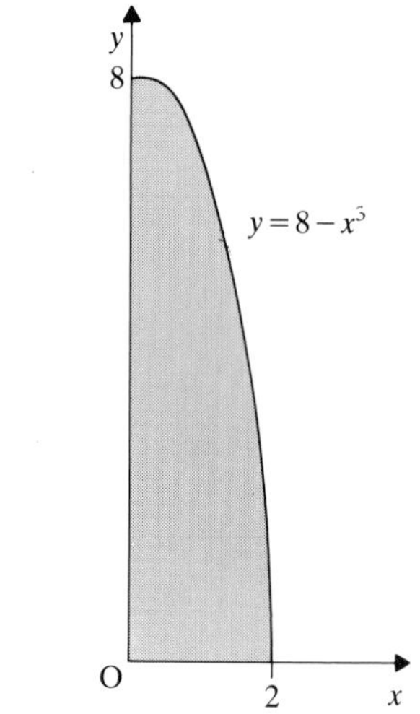

Figure 9.20

We first calculate the area of the region (see figure 9.20)

$$\begin{aligned} A &= \int_0^2 y\,dx \\ &= \int_0^2 (8 - x^3)\,dx \\ &= [8x - \tfrac{1}{4}x^4]_0^2 = 12. \end{aligned}$$

The moment of the area about the y-axis

$$\begin{aligned} \int_0^2 xy\,dx &= \int_0^2 (8x - x^4)\,dx \\ &= [4x^2 - \tfrac{1}{5}x^5]_0^2 = 9.6. \end{aligned}$$

The moment of the area about the x-axis

$$\begin{aligned} \int_0^2 \tfrac{1}{2}y^2\,dx &= \int_0^2 \tfrac{1}{2}(8 - x^3)^2\,dx \\ &= \int_0^2 \tfrac{1}{2}(64 - 16x^3 + x^6)\,dx \\ &= [32x - 2x^4 + \tfrac{1}{14}x^7]_0^2 = 41.1. \end{aligned}$$

Thus

$$x_G = \frac{\int_0^2 xy\,dx}{\int_0^2 y\,dx} = \frac{9.6}{12} = 0.8 \qquad y_G = \frac{\int_0^2 \frac{1}{2}y^2\,dx}{\int_0^2 y\,dx} = \frac{41.1}{12} = 3.43.$$

The centroid is at the point (0.8, 3.43).

EXAMPLE 2

Find the centroid of a piece of uniform wire in the shape of an arc of a circle of radius a, which subtends an angle 2α radians at its centre.

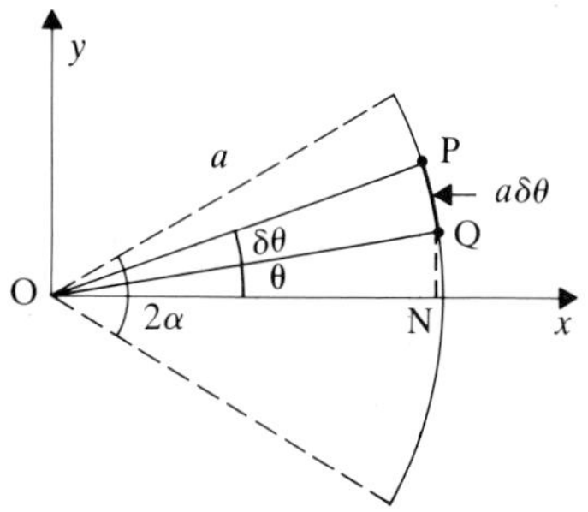

Figure 9.21

We take O as the origin and axes as shown in figure 9.21. We think of the wire as composed of a series of small elements PQ (particles) so that PQ $= a\delta\theta$. The moment of PQ about the y-axis is

$$a\delta\theta\,\mathrm{ON} \approx a\delta\theta a\cos\theta.$$

The total moment of all such elements is

$$\sum a^2\cos\theta\delta\theta,$$

where the summation is over the angles $\delta\theta$. In the limit, as $\delta\theta \to 0$, i.e. the sizes of the elements get smaller,

$$\sum a^2 \cos\theta\delta\theta \to \int a^2 \cos\theta \, d\theta.$$

Thus, the total moment of the wire about the y-axis is

$$\int_{-\alpha}^{\alpha} a^2 \cos\theta \, d\theta = a^2[\sin\theta]_{-\alpha}^{\alpha}$$

$$= 2a^2 \sin\alpha.$$

The total length of the arc is $2a\alpha$, so that x_G is given by

$$2a\alpha x_G = 2a^2 \sin\alpha,$$

$$x_G = \frac{a\sin\alpha}{\alpha}.$$

By symmetry, $y_G = 0$.

A special case of this is when we have a semicircular arc, in which $2\alpha = \pi$, so that

$$x_G = \frac{a\sin\frac{1}{2}\pi}{\frac{1}{2}\pi} = \frac{2a}{\pi} = 0.64a.$$

EXAMPLE 3

Find the centroid of a lamina in the shape of a sector of a circle of radius a, which subtends an angle 2α at its centre, as in figure 9.22.

We take O as the origin and axes as shown. PQ is an elementary strip in the shape of an arc of radius x and thickness δx, whose area is $2\alpha x\delta x$. The moment of PQ about the y-axis is

$$2\alpha x\delta x\frac{x\sin\alpha}{\alpha},$$

since PQ is like the wire in example 2. The total moment about the y-axis is

$$\int_0^a 2x^2 \sin\alpha \, dx = \tfrac{2}{3}a^3 \sin\alpha.$$

The total area is $\frac{1}{2}a^2 2\alpha = a^2\alpha$. Thus

$$x_G = \frac{2a\sin\alpha}{3\alpha}$$

and $y_G = 0$, by symmetry.

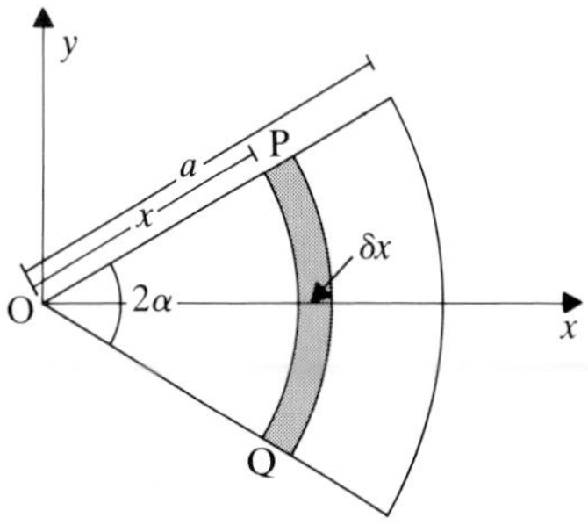

Figure 9.22

An alternative solution is as follows. We take an elementary strip OPQ, as shown in figure 9.23. Its centroid is $\frac{2}{3}a$ from O, since it is approximately a triangle. We can regard the lamina as equivalent to a single wire, distance $\frac{2}{3}a$ from O, composed of all the mass centres of the elementary strips. Hence, from example 2, the x-coordinate of its centroid is

$$x_G = \frac{2}{3}a\frac{\sin\alpha}{\alpha} = \frac{2a\sin\alpha}{3\alpha}, \qquad \text{as before.}$$

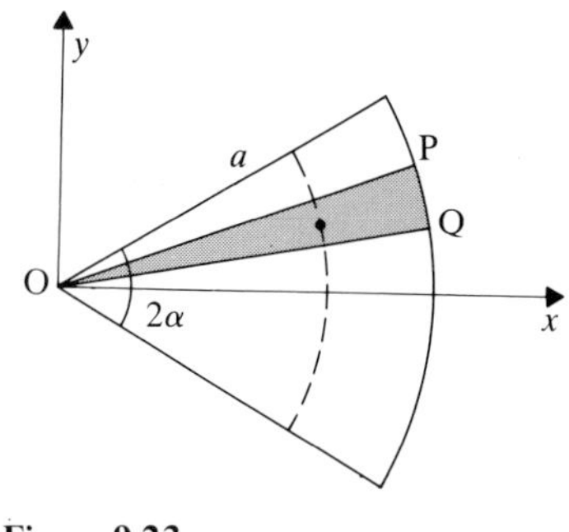

Figure 9.23

For a semicircular lamina, $2\alpha = \pi$, so that

$$x_G = \frac{2a \sin \frac{1}{2}\pi}{\frac{3}{2}\pi} = \frac{4a}{3\pi} = 0.42a.$$

EXERCISE 9D

1. Find the coordinates of the centroid of the region between the curve $y = x^2$ and the lines $x = 1$ and $y = 0$.

2. Find the coordinates of the centroid of the region between the curve $y = \sqrt{x}$ and the lines $x = 1$ and $y = 0$.

3. Find the coordinates of the centroid of the region between the quadrant with equation $y^2 = a^2 - x^2$ and the positive x- and y-axes.

4. Find the coordinates of the centroid of the region enclosed by the curves $y = x^2$ and $y = \sqrt{x}$.

5. Find the coordinates of the centroid of the region between the graph of $y = 4 - x^2$ and the positive x- and y-axes.

6. Find the coordinates of the centroid of the region between the graph of $y = 1/x$ and the lines $y = 0$, $x = 1$ and $x = 2$.

7. A wire is bent in the shape of a letter 'P'. It consists of a straight piece AB of length 12 cm, to which is attached at one end, B, a semicircle of radius 3 cm. Find the height of the centroid above A and its distance from AB.

8. A wire frame ABCD consists of a rectangle of length AB = 4 cm and width BC = 3 cm. Attached to the longer side AB is a piece of wire in the shape of a semicircular arc of radius 2 cm. Find the distance of the centroid from AB.

9.* Prove that the centroid of the area enclosed by the curve $r = a(1 - \cos\theta)$ is on the axis of symmetry $\frac{5}{8}a$ from the pole.

9.5 Volumes of revolution

We shall only consider volumes which are either solids of revolution or are composed of separate parts which are well-known uniform solids, e.g. cuboids and hemispheres. A more general discussion is beyond the scope of this book, as are solids with variable density.

By taking circular discs, as shown in figure 9.24, we can establish the volume as

$$V = \int_a^b \pi y^2 \, dx.$$

The total moment about the y-axis of the elementary discs is

$$\int_a^b x\pi y^2 \, dx.$$

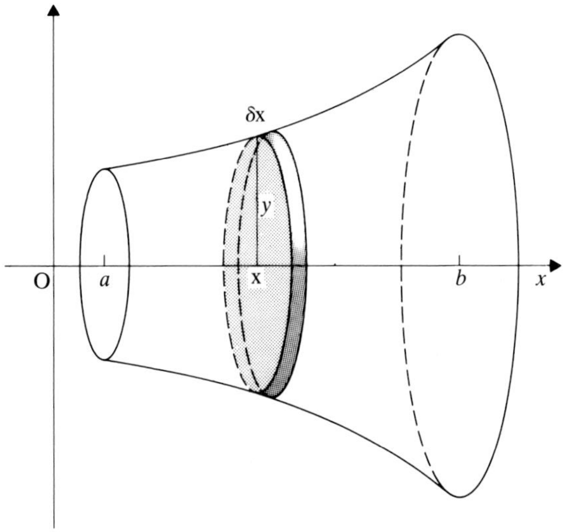

Figure 9.24

The x-coordinate of the centroid is

$$x_G = \frac{\int_a^b xy^2 \, dx}{\int_a^b y^2 \, dx}.$$

By symmetry, $y_G = 0$.

EXAMPLE 1

Find the centroid of a uniform solid hemisphere of radius a.

By symmetry, $y_G = 0$, see figure 9.25. The volume is given by

$$\begin{aligned} V &= \int_0^a \pi y^2 \, dx \\ &= \int_0^a \pi(a^2 - x^2) \, dx \\ &= \pi\left[a^2x - \tfrac{1}{3}x^3\right]_0^a \\ &= \tfrac{2}{3}\pi a^3. \end{aligned}$$

The total moment about the y-axis is

$$\begin{aligned} \int_0^a x\pi y^2 \, dx &= \pi \int_0^a x(a^2 - x^2) \, dx \\ &= \pi\left[\tfrac{1}{2}a^2x^2 - \tfrac{1}{4}x^4\right]_0^a \\ &= \tfrac{1}{4}\pi a^4. \end{aligned}$$

Thus

$$\begin{aligned} x_G &= \frac{\tfrac{1}{4}\pi a^4}{\tfrac{2}{3}\pi a^3} \\ &= \tfrac{3}{8}a. \end{aligned}$$

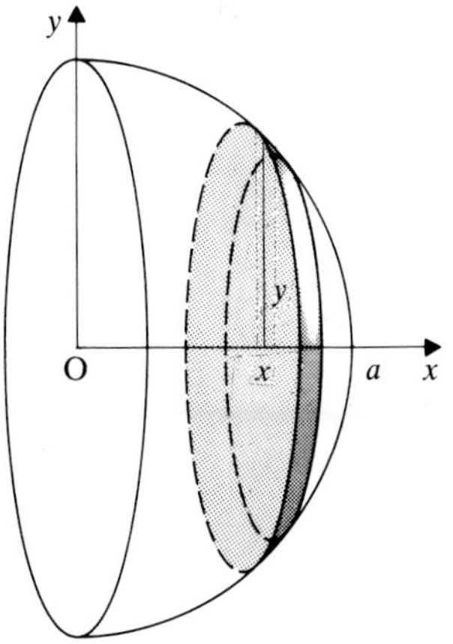

Figure 9.25

The centroid of a uniform solid hemisphere of radius a is $\tfrac{3}{8}a$ along the line of symmetry from the circular base.

EXAMPLE 2

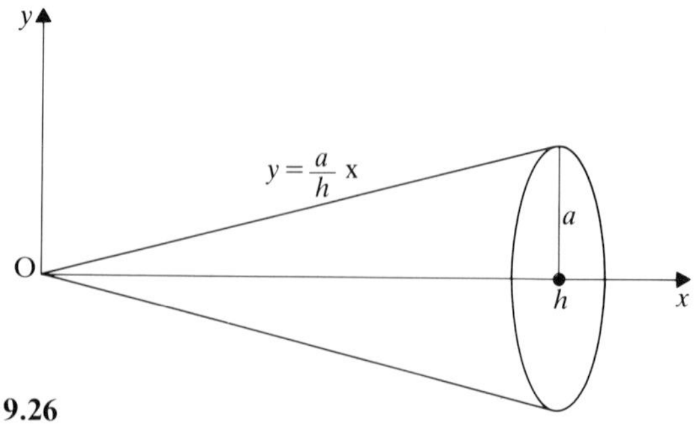

Figure 9.26

Find the centroid of a uniform cone of height h and base radius a.
The equation of the line OA in figure 9.26 is

$$y=\frac{a}{h}x.$$

The volume is

$$V=\int_0^h \pi y^2\,dx=\int_0^h \pi\frac{a^2}{h^2}x^2\,dx$$

$$=\pi\frac{a^2}{h^2}\left[\tfrac{1}{3}x^3\right]_0^h$$

$$=\tfrac{1}{3}\pi a^2 h.$$

The total moment about the y-axis is

$$\int_0^h \pi x\frac{a^2}{h^2}x^2\,dx=\pi\frac{a^2}{h^2}\left[\tfrac{1}{4}x^4\right]_0^h$$

$$=\tfrac{1}{4}\pi a^2h^2.$$

Thus

$$x_G=\frac{\frac{1}{4}\pi a^2h^2}{\frac{1}{3}\pi a^2h}$$

$$=\tfrac{3}{4}h.$$

By symmetry $y_G=0$.

The centroid of a cone of height h is $\frac{1}{4}h$ along the line of symmetry from the circular base.

EXAMPLE 3

Find the volume and the centroid formed when the area between the graph of $y=4-x^2$ and the positive x- and y-axes is rotated through 360° about the y-axis.

By symmetry $x_G=0$, see figure 9.27. The volume of revolution is given by

$$V=\int_0^4 \pi x^2\,dy=\int_0^4 \pi(4-y)\,dy$$

$$=\pi\left[4y-\tfrac{1}{2}y^2\right]_0^4=8\pi.$$

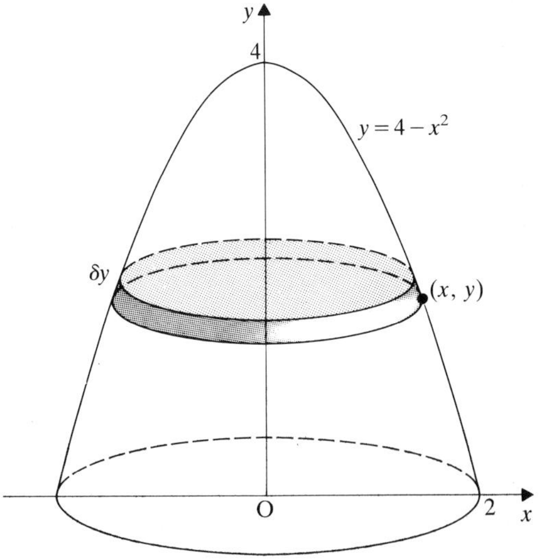

Figure 9.27

The total moment about the x-axis is

$$\int_0^4 y\pi x^2 \,\mathrm{d}y = \int_0^4 \pi y(4-y)\,\mathrm{d}y$$
$$= \pi[2y^2 - \tfrac{1}{3}y^3]_0^4 = \tfrac{32}{3}\pi$$

Hence $$y_G = \tfrac{32}{3}\pi/8\pi = \tfrac{4}{3}.$$

□□□□□

The following example illustrates how we use the results of the previous examples for composite bodies.

EXAMPLE 4

A solid is composed of a cylinder of radius a and height a which is attached to the frustum of height $3a$ taken from a cone of base radius $2a$, as shown in figure 9.28.

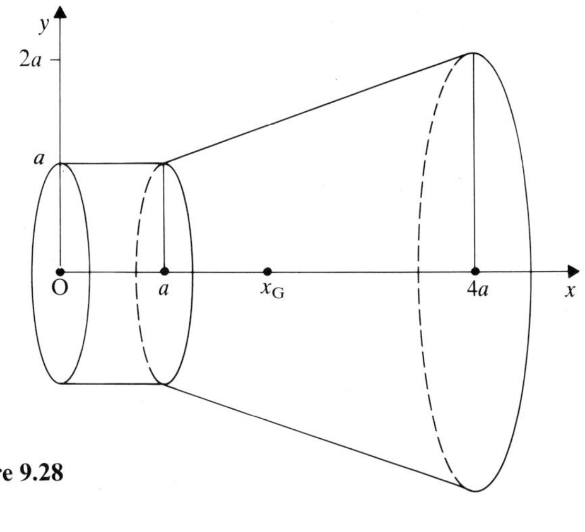

Figure 9.28

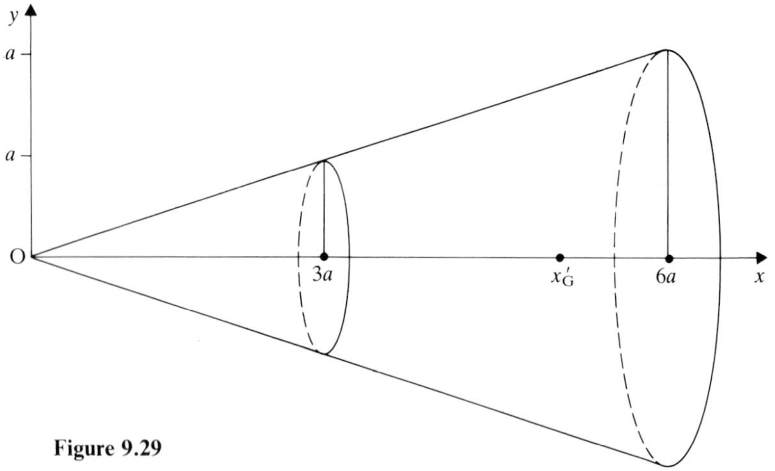

Figure 9.29

To determine the centroid of the frustum, we think of it as a cone of height $6a$ less a cone of height $3a$, as in figure 9.29. The origin is taken as the vertex of the cone, and its centroid at (x'_G, y'_G, z'_G). Clearly $y'_G = z'_G = 0$, i.e. the centroid lies along the x-axis. We compile a table of moments.

Solid	Volume V_i	Coordinate of centroid x_i	Moment $V_i x_i$
large cone	$\frac{1}{3}\pi(2a)^2 6a = 8\pi a^3$	$\frac{3}{4}6a = \frac{9}{2}a$	$36\pi a^4$
small cone	$\frac{1}{3}\pi a^2 3a = \pi a^3$	$\frac{3}{4}3a = \frac{9}{4}a$	$\frac{9}{4}\pi a^4$
frustum	$7\pi a^3$	x'_G	

Equating moments

$$7\pi a^3 x'_G = 8\pi a^3 \times \tfrac{9}{2}a - \pi a^3 \times \tfrac{9}{4}a,$$
$$x'_G = 4.82a.$$

We now take the whole solid with the origin at the end of the cylinder, so that x'_G now becomes $x'_G - 2a = 2.82a$. We compile a table of moments.

Solid	Volume V_i	Coordinate of centroid x_i	Moment $V_i x_i$
frustum	$7\pi a^3$	$2.82a$	$7\pi a^3 \times 2.82a$
cylinder	πa^3	$0.5a$	$\pi a^3 \times 0.5a$
complete solid	$8\pi a^3$	x_G	

Equating moments,

$$8\pi a^3 x_G = 7\pi a^3 \times 2.82a + \pi a^3 \times 0.5a,$$
$$x_G = 2.53a.$$

EXERCISE 9E

1. Find the coordinates of the centroid of the uniform solid formed when each of the regions with the following boundaries is rotated through 360° about the x-axis.

   a) $y = x^2$, $x = 1$ and $y = 0$.

   b) $y = x$, $x = 1$ and $y = 0$.

   c) $y^2 = a^2 - x^2$, $x = 0$ and $y = 0$

   d) $y = x^2$ and $y = x$.

   e) $y = 4 - x^2$, $x = 0$ and $y = 0$.

   f) $y = 1/x$, $x = 1$ and $x = 2$.

2. A cone of height t and base radius r is attached to one end of a cylinder of height h and base radius r. If the distance of the centre of mass from the circular base is $\frac{1}{3}$ of the total height, prove that $h = (\sqrt{10} - 2)t$.

3. Find the coordinates of the centre of mass of a uniform solid pyramid of height h whose base is a square of side $2a$, where the vertex is above the centre of the base.

4. From the pyramid in question 3 a smaller pyramid of height $\frac{1}{2}h$ is removed by cutting along a plane parallel to the base. Calculate the height of the centre of mass of the frustum remaining.

5. A uniform solid hemisphere of radius a is attached to the circular end of a cylinder of radius a and height $3a$. Find the coordinates of the centre of mass.

6. A uniform solid frustum of a cone is of height 5 cm. The radius of the larger circle is 3 cm and of the smaller is 2 cm. Find the coordinates of the centre of mass.

7. A cap height h is cut from a sphere of radius a. Prove that the distance of the centroid from the base is $h(4a - h)/4(3a - h)$.

8. The centroid of a thin hollow hemisphere is midway between its centre and its surface along the line of symmetry.
   A quantity of liquid of weight W is poured into a hemispherical bowl of radius a so that it fills to a height $\frac{1}{2}a$. If the weight of the bowl is $0.25W$, find the coordinates of the centre of mass.

9. Find the coordinates of the centroid of the solid formed by rotating the region between the graph of $y = \sin x$ and the x-axis between $x = 0$ and $x = \frac{1}{2}\pi$ through 360° about the x-axis.

Suspended bodies **9.6**

Suppose a body of weight W is suspended by a string from a point P, as shown in figure 9.30. Clearly, from section 7.5, the body will be in equilibrium if $T = W$ and if they lie in the same line. Hence, the body must hang with G vertically below P. If a body is suspended from

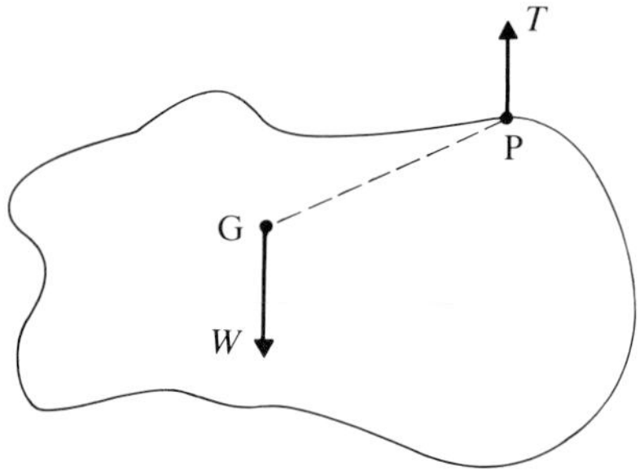

Figure 9.30

a point not on its line of symmetry, it is sometimes useful to find the inclination to the vertical of one of its faces or edges.

EXAMPLE 1

Find the centroid of the quadrilateral ABCD shown in figure 9.31. If this is suspended from A and hangs in equilibrium, what angle will AB make with the vertical?

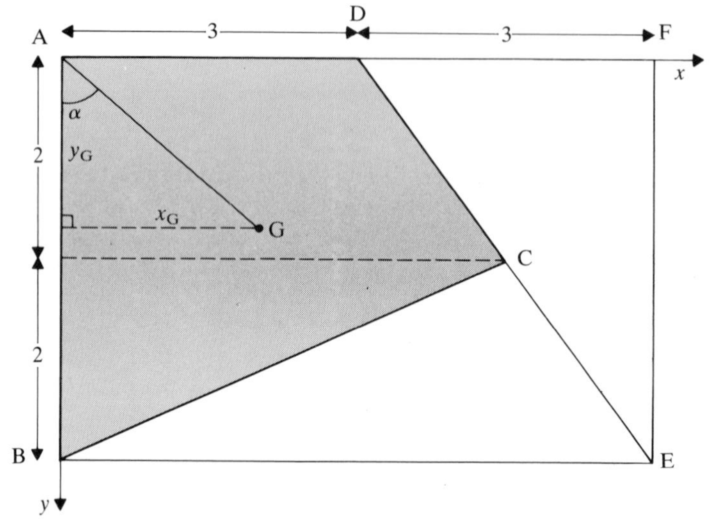

Figure 9.31

We take x- and y-axes along AF and AB, respectively.
To find the centroid, we enclose ABCD in a rectangle ABEF.
We compile a table of moments.

Shape	Area A_i	Coordinates of the centroid x_i	y_i	Moments A_ix_i	A_iy_i
ABEF	24	3	2	72	48
BEC	6	$\frac{7}{2}$	$\frac{10}{3}$	21	20
DEF	6	5	$\frac{4}{3}$	30	8
ABCD	12	x_G	y_G		

Taking moments about the y-axis

$$12x_G = 72 - 21 - 30,$$

$$x_G = \frac{7}{4}.$$

Taking moments about the x-axis

$$12y_G = 48 - 20 - 8,$$

$$y_G = \frac{5}{3}.$$

Relative to A, G is the point $(1\frac{3}{4}, 1\frac{2}{3})$. The angle between AG and the y-axis is given by

$$\tan \alpha = \frac{x_G}{y_G} = \frac{1\frac{3}{4}}{1\frac{2}{3}} = \frac{21}{20},$$
$$\alpha = 46.4°,$$

and this is the angle AB makes with the vertical when ABCD is suspended from A.

EXAMPLE 2

A lamina in the shape of a sector of a circle of angle $\frac{1}{3}\pi$ and radius a is suspended from the point A, as shown in figure 9.32. Find the angle OA makes with the vertical.

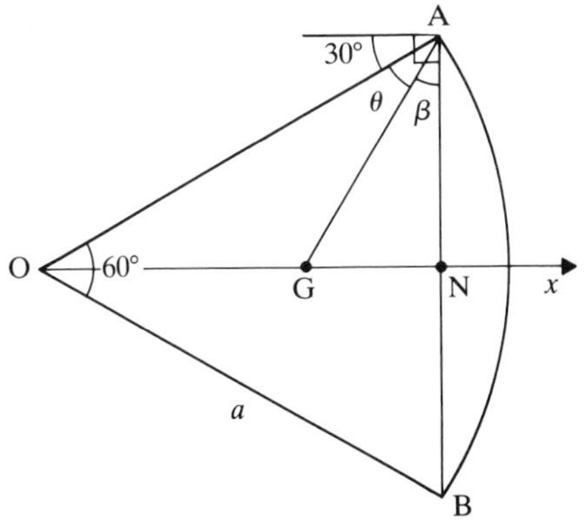

Figure 9.32

From example 3 of section 9.4,

$$OG = \frac{2a \sin \frac{1}{6}\pi}{3 \times \frac{1}{6}\pi} = 2a/\pi = 0.637a.$$

When suspended, the line AG will be vertical and so the inclination of OA is given by $O\hat{A}G = \theta$, where $\theta = 90° - 30° - \beta$. Now

$$\tan \beta = \frac{GN}{AN} = \frac{ON - OG}{AN}$$

$$= \frac{a \cos 30° - 2a/\pi}{a \sin 30°}$$

$$= \frac{0.866 - 0.637}{0.5} = 0.459$$

Hence $\beta = 24.6°$ and so $\theta = 90° - 30° - 24.6° = 35.4°$.

EXAMPLE 3

What is the magnitude of the horizontal force $\boldsymbol{F}$ acting at B needed in order to keep the line OA in the lamina above in a vertical position, as shown in figure 9.33, assuming the weight of the lamina is 0.5 kg?

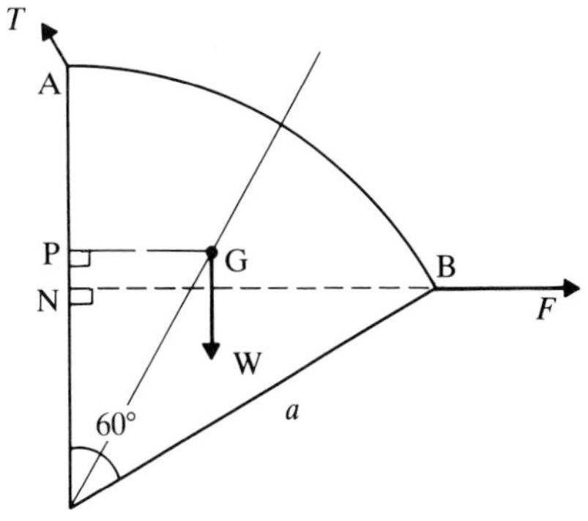

Figure 9.33

We take moments about A, since we do not require the value of the tension at A.

$$F \times \text{NA} = W \times \text{GP}$$
$$F(a - a\cos 60^\circ) = 0.5g \times \text{OG}\sin 30^\circ$$
$$Fa(1 - \cos 60^\circ) = \frac{0.5 \times 10 \times 2a \times 0.5}{\pi}$$
$$F = 10/\pi.$$

The horizontal force required is about 3.18 N.

9.7 Tipping and sliding

Figure 9.34a shows a cross-section of a triangular prism at rest in contact with a horizontal plane. For equilibrium, both the weight force $\boldsymbol{W}$ and the normal contact force $\boldsymbol{N}$ will pass through the centre of gravity G.

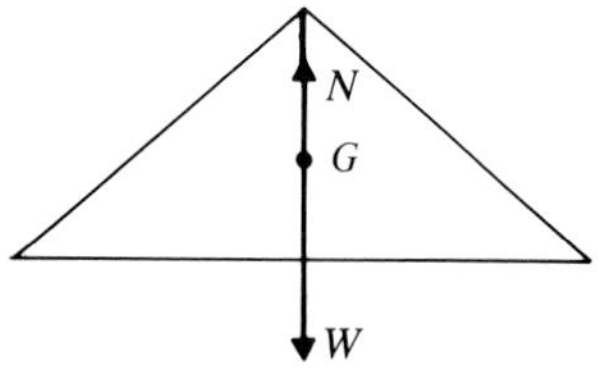

Figure 9.34 **(a)**

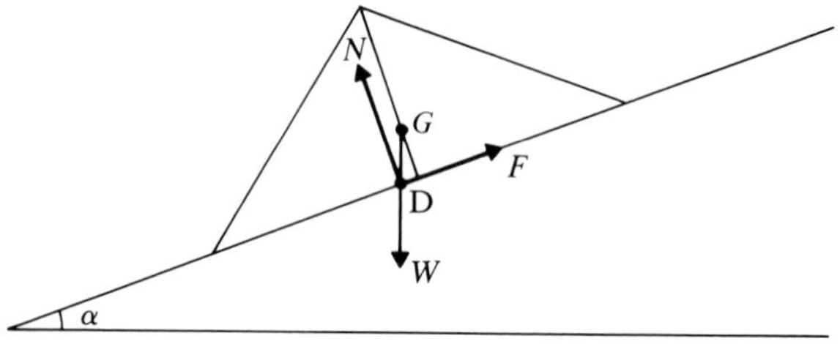

(b)

If the prism is placed on a plane inclined at an angle α to the horizontal, as in figure 9.34b, the concurrency condition tells us that the normal contact force must pass through the intersection of the lines of action of the other two forces acting, namely the frictional force and the weight force. Thus the contact force does not always pass through the centre of gravity G. The position of the centre of gravity sometimes enables us to determine whether or not objects will 'stand up' when placed on a plane.

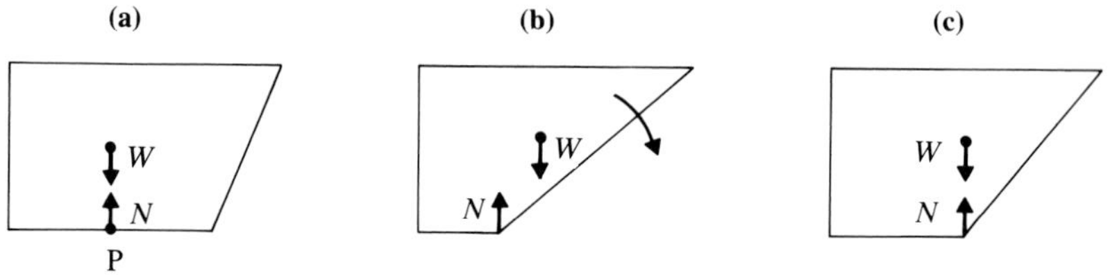

Figure 9.35

In figure 9.35a the system is in equilibrium with the resultant normal contact force acting at P. In figure 9.35b the system cannot remain in equilibrium since the line of action of W lies outside the area of contact of the body with the plane. The body will therefore tip over. Figure 9.35c shows the limiting case, when the line of action of W passes through the edge of the area of contact of the body with the plane.

EXAMPLE 1

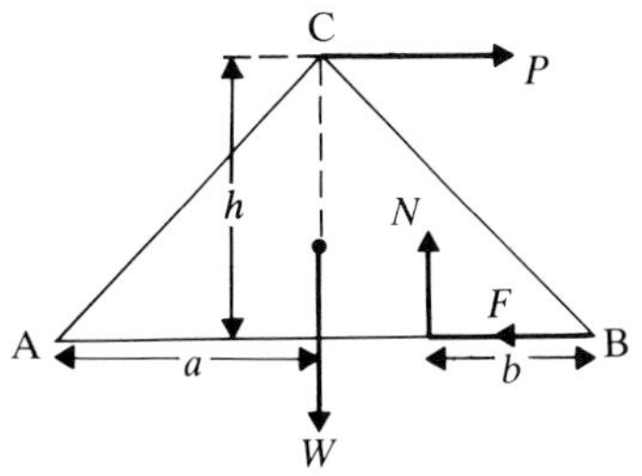

Figure 9.36

An isosceles triangular prism ABC of width $2a$, height h and weight W is at rest on a rough horizontal table. A horizontal force P is applied to the vertex C, as shown in figure 9.36. The coefficient of friction between the table and the prism is μ.

Discuss the breaking of equilibrium as P increases.

Resolving vertically $\quad W = N,$

where N is the normal contact force.
If the prism does not slide, resolving horizontally gives $P = F$.
Now $F \leqslant \mu W$, so the prism will not slide provided $P \leqslant \mu W$.
Taking moments about the vertex B, the prism will not tip if

$$Ph < Wa - Nb.$$

On the point of tipping, N will pass through B and so

$$P < \frac{a}{h} W.$$

The prism will tip before it will slide if

$$\frac{a}{h} < \mu.$$

For example, suppose AB = 16 cm, the height $h = 5$ cm and $\mu = 0.5$. Then $a/h = 8/5 = 1.6 > \mu = 0.5$, and so it will slide rather than tip.

This example illustrates that when rigid bodies are in contact with each other or with surfaces two types of motion may result when equilibrium is broken, namely sliding or tipping.

EXAMPLE 2

Figure 9.37

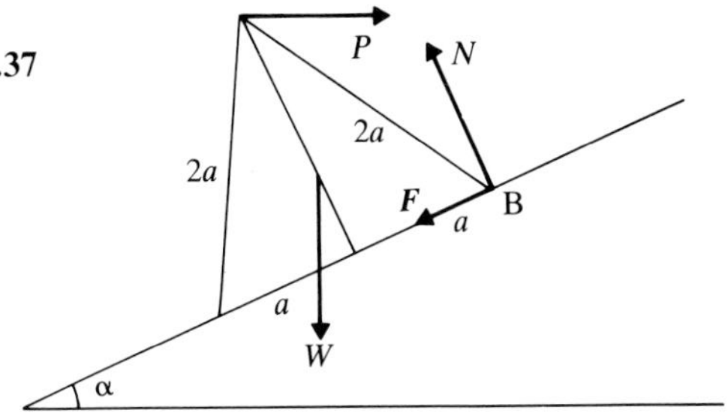

An equilateral prism of side $2a$ and weight W is at rest on a rough inclined plane of slope α. The coefficient of friction between the prism and the plane is μ. A horizontal force P is applied at the vertex,

as shown in figure 9.37. Find the conditions for (a) the prism not to slide up the plane, and (b) the prism not to rotate about B.
If $\tan\alpha = \frac{1}{4}$ and $\mu = \frac{1}{3}$, which will occur first, sliding or tipping?

a) Resolving along the plane

$$F = -W\sin\alpha + P\cos\alpha,$$

where F is the frictional force.
Resolving perpendicular to the plane

$$N = W\cos\alpha + P\sin\alpha,$$

where N is the normal contact force. The prism will not slide provided $F \leqslant \mu N$, i.e.

$$-W\sin\alpha + P\cos\alpha \leqslant \mu(W\cos\alpha + P\sin\alpha),$$
$$P(1 - \mu\tan\alpha) \leqslant W(\mu + \tan\alpha).$$

b) The prism will not tip about B provided the moment of P about B is less than or equal to the moment of W about B.

At this position N passes through B and has no moment about it. The clockwise moment of P about B is

$$P\cos\alpha \times 2a\sin 60^\circ - P\sin\alpha \times 2a\cos 60^\circ = Pa(\sqrt{3}\cos\alpha - \sin\alpha).$$

The anticlockwise moment of W about B is

$$W\cos\alpha \times 2a\cos 60^\circ + W\sin\alpha \times \tfrac{1}{3} \times 2a\sin 60^\circ$$
$$= Wa(\cos\alpha + \sqrt{\tfrac{1}{3}}\sin\alpha)$$

The prism will not tip provided

$$Pa(\sqrt{3}\cos\alpha - \sin\alpha) \leqslant Wa(\cos\alpha + \sqrt{\tfrac{1}{3}}\sin\alpha)$$
$$P(\sqrt{3} - \tan\alpha) \leqslant W(1 + \sqrt{\tfrac{1}{3}}\tan\alpha)$$

If $\tan\alpha = \frac{1}{4}$, $\mu = \frac{1}{3}$ then these two conditions become

$$\text{a)}\quad \frac{P}{W} \leqslant \frac{\frac{1}{3} + \frac{1}{4}}{1 - \frac{1}{3} \times \frac{1}{4}} = \frac{7}{11} = 0.636,$$

$$\text{b)}\quad \frac{P}{W} \leqslant \frac{1 + \sqrt{\frac{1}{3}} \times \frac{1}{4}}{3 - \frac{1}{4}} = \frac{4\sqrt{3} + 1}{12 - \sqrt{3}} = 0.772.$$

Thus the prism will slide rather than tip, since (a) will reach its limit before (b).

EXERCISE 9F

1. The letter 'U' of exercise 9C, question 1, is suspended by a string from its top left-hand corner. Find the inclination of the left-hand edge to the vertical.

2. The framework of exercise 9B, question 11, is suspended by a rope from its highest point. Find the inclination of the longest edge to the vertical.

3. A loop of wire in the shape of a letter 'D' consists of a semicircle of radius a and a diameter. It hangs freely from one end of the diameter. What angle does the diameter make with the vertical?

4. The volume of revolution described in example 3, section 9.5, is suspended freely from the point (2, 0). Find the inclination of the flat base to the vertical.

5. The frustum of exercise 9E, question 6, is suspended from a point on the edge of the smaller circular face. Find the inclination of this face to the horizontal.

6. An equilateral triangle ABC of side $2a$ forms one end of a prism and rests with BC on a horizontal table. A smaller prism with a triangular face which is equilateral with side $2x$ is removed from the corner at B. Find the centre of mass of the remaining solid relative to axes through B. What is the maximum size of x so that the prism will not tip over?

7. A weight w is suspended from the edge of a solid hemisphere of radius a and weight W. What is the size of w if the hemisphere is to lie with its curved surface on a horizontal table and its flat surface inclined at 30° to the horizontal?

8. A uniform cuboid of width a and height $4a$ is at rest on a rough ramp which is inclined at an angle α to the horizontal. The coefficient of friction between the cuboid and the ramp is μ. Find the minimum value of α for which the cuboid will topple rather than slide and find the corresponding value of μ.

9. A uniform cube of side a is at rest on a horizontal plane. A triangular prism is removed from one of the bottom corners, by cutting at 45° to form an isosceles triangle of side x. Show that the block will fall if $x > 0.56a$, approximately.

10. Show that the frustum described in exercise 9E, question 4, can stand with a side (a trapezium) on a smooth horizontal plane provided $17h^2 \geqslant 28a^2$.

11. A circular tray of radius r is attached at its centre to a cylindrical support of radius R. W is the total weight of the tray and its support. Find how far from the centre a weight w can be placed before the tray falls over.

12. A librarian piles a series of text books each measuring 26 cm × 21 cm × 3 cm, so that the end of each is protruding 5 cm over the 26 cm edge of the one beneath it. How many books can be placed on the pile before it tips over?

Summary

Centre of gravity

This is the point where the total weight force on a body may be considered to act. In a constant gravitational field this coincides with the centre of mass, and for uniform solids the centre of gravity also coincides with the centroid, or geometrical centre of the solid.

Suspended bodies

When a body is suspended by a string its centre of gravity must be in the same vertical line as the point of suspension.

Tipping and sliding

When a rigid body is in equilibrium resting on a surface and a force is applied to it, equilibrium may be broken by tipping or sliding. Examination of the forces acting, and their moments about the possible line of rotation will establish whether tipping or sliding occurs first.

EXAMINATION QUESTIONS

The following exercises consist of questions taken from recent A-level examination papers. They are arranged to correspond with the topics covered in the individual chapters in the main text. Where two exercises are given for a particular chapter, they are labelled A and B. Questions in exercises labelled A are generally of a straightforward nature, whilst those in B may be more demanding.

It is assumed that teachers and students will have access to complete past papers from their chosen Examination Board for use during final revision.

Abbreviation

(AEB)	Associated Examining Board for the General Certificate of Education
(C)	University of Cambridge Local Examinations Syndicate
(JMB)	Joint Matriculation Board
(L)	University Entrance and School Examinations Council, University of London
(O & C)	Oxford and Cambridge Schools Examination Board

Vectors

Revision exercise 1A

1. The points A, B, C have position vectors $\boldsymbol{a}$, $\boldsymbol{b}$, $\boldsymbol{c}$ respectively, with respect to an origin O. Write down, in terms of $\boldsymbol{a}$ and $\boldsymbol{b}$, the vector **BA** and find the position vector of the fourth vertex D of the parallelogram ABCD *(L)*

2. Given that $\mathbf{OA} = (-2\boldsymbol{i} - 3\boldsymbol{j})$ and $\mathbf{OB} = (5\boldsymbol{i} + t\boldsymbol{j})$, where t is a constant, determine the value of t when the points O, A and B are collinear. *(L)*

3. The resolved part of the force $\begin{pmatrix} 2c \\ -2c \\ c \end{pmatrix}$ N, in the direction of the vector $\begin{pmatrix} 1 \\ -2 \\ -2 \end{pmatrix}$, is 6 N. Find the constant c. *(JMB)*

4. Find the values of α in order that the angle between the vectors $\boldsymbol{i} + 2\boldsymbol{j} + 2\boldsymbol{k}$ and $\boldsymbol{i} + \alpha\boldsymbol{k}$ shall be
   a) $\frac{1}{2}\pi$,
   b) $\frac{1}{4}\pi$. *(O & C)*

5. The vectors $\boldsymbol{a}$ and $\boldsymbol{b}$ are such that $|\boldsymbol{a}| = 3$ and $|\boldsymbol{b}| = 5$. Calculate the magnitude of $\boldsymbol{a} + \boldsymbol{b}$ given that the angle between $\boldsymbol{a}$ and $\boldsymbol{b}$ is $\frac{1}{3}\pi$. *(L)*

6. The lines L_1 and L_2 have vector equations given by $\boldsymbol{r}_1 = 3\boldsymbol{i} + \boldsymbol{j} + t(2\boldsymbol{j} + \boldsymbol{k})$ and $\boldsymbol{r}_2 = 4\boldsymbol{k} + s(\boldsymbol{i} + \boldsymbol{j} - \boldsymbol{k})$ where t and s are parameters. Show that L_1 and L_2 intersect and find in surd form the cosine of the angle between these lines. *(JMB)*

7. The position vectors of two points A and B relative to an origin O are $\boldsymbol{a}$ and $\boldsymbol{b}$. You are given that $\boldsymbol{a}$ and $\boldsymbol{b}$ have unit length, and that the angle between these vectors is 60°. Write down the values of the products $\boldsymbol{a}\cdot\boldsymbol{a}$, $\boldsymbol{b}\cdot\boldsymbol{b}$ and $\boldsymbol{a}\cdot\boldsymbol{b}$.
   The point C on the line-segment AB is such that AC = 2CB. If $\boldsymbol{c}$ is the position vector of C, express $\boldsymbol{c}$ in terms of $\boldsymbol{a}$ and $\boldsymbol{b}$. Hence calculate (a) the length of $\boldsymbol{c}$, (b) the cosine of the angle between $\boldsymbol{a}$ and $\boldsymbol{c}$. *(O & C)*

Revision exercise 1B

1. *Gravity may be ignored in this question.*
   A particle of mass 4 units moves so that its position vector at time t is
   $$\boldsymbol{r} = \boldsymbol{i}\sin 2t + \boldsymbol{j}\cos 2t + \boldsymbol{k}(t^2 - 2t).$$
   Find
   a) the kinetic energy of the particle at time t,
   b) the work done by the resultant force in the time interval $t = 0$ to $t = 2$,
   c) the resultant force acting on the particle.
   d) the time when the acceleration of the particle is perpendicular to its direction of motion. *(AEB)*

2. *Gravity may be ignored in this question.*
A particle of mass 5 units is acted upon by the forces $\boldsymbol{F}_1 = \boldsymbol{i} + 3\boldsymbol{j} + 2\boldsymbol{k}$, $\boldsymbol{F}_2 = 5\boldsymbol{i} - \boldsymbol{j} - 2\boldsymbol{k}$ and $\boldsymbol{F}_3 = 9\boldsymbol{i} + 8\boldsymbol{j} + 5\boldsymbol{k}$ and at time $t = 0$ is at rest at the point with position vector $\boldsymbol{i} + 2\boldsymbol{j} + 3\boldsymbol{k}$. Find the momentum vector and the position vector of the particle at time t.
Show that, at time $t = 2$, the particle is at the point with position vector $7\boldsymbol{i} + 6\boldsymbol{j} + 5\boldsymbol{k}$ and find the work done on the particle from $t = 0$ to $t = 2$. If at time $t = 2$ the force $\boldsymbol{F}_3$ is removed, find the cosine of the angle between the directions of motion of the particle for $t = 1$ and $t = 7$. *(AEB)*

3. a) The position vectors of the points A, B and C are $\boldsymbol{a}$, $\boldsymbol{b}$ and $\boldsymbol{c}$, respectively, referred to the point O as origin. Given that $3\boldsymbol{a} + \boldsymbol{b} = 4\boldsymbol{c}$, prove that the points A, B and C are collinear and find the ratio AB : AC.

b) Three forces $7\boldsymbol{i} + 5\boldsymbol{j}$, $2\boldsymbol{i} + 3\boldsymbol{j}$ and $\lambda\boldsymbol{i}$ act at the origin O, where $\boldsymbol{i}$ and $\boldsymbol{j}$ are unit vectors parallel to the x-axis and the y-axis, respectively. The unit of force is the newton. If the magnitude of the resultant of the three forces is 17 N, calculate the two possible values of λ. Show that the two possible directions of the line of action of the resultant are equally inclined to Oy. *(AEB)*

4. At time $t = 0$, a boat is at position vector $\boldsymbol{b}$ relative to a lighthouse, and is moving with constant velocity $\boldsymbol{u}$. Show that the distance d of the boat from the lighthouse at time t satisfies

$$d^2 = (\boldsymbol{u}\cdot\boldsymbol{u})t^2 + 2(\boldsymbol{b}\cdot\boldsymbol{u})t + (\boldsymbol{b}\cdot\boldsymbol{b}).$$

By completing the square, or differentiating with respect to t, show that the boat is nearest to the lighthouse when

$$t = -(\boldsymbol{b}\cdot\boldsymbol{u})/(\boldsymbol{u}\cdot\boldsymbol{u}).$$

Evaluate this time to the nearest second, and find the minimum distance to the nearest metre, when the magnitudes of $\boldsymbol{b}$ and $\boldsymbol{u}$ are 1 km and 7 m s^{-1}, respectively, and the angle between $\boldsymbol{b}$ and $\boldsymbol{u}$ is 130°. *(O & C)*

5. a) In the regular hexagon ABCDEF, **AB** $= \boldsymbol{a}$ and **BC** $= \boldsymbol{b}$. Express, in terms of $\boldsymbol{a}$ and $\boldsymbol{b}$, the vectors (i) **AC**, (ii) **AD**, (iii) **AE**, (iv) **AF**.

b) The origin O, the point A with position vector $4\boldsymbol{i} + 3\boldsymbol{j}$ and the point C with position vector $3\boldsymbol{i} - 4\boldsymbol{j}$ are three vertices of a square OABC. Calculate the position vector of B.

Forces of magnitudes 5 N, $10\sqrt{2}$ N and 10 N act along **OA**, **OB** and **CO** respectively. Express each of these forces as a vector in terms of $\boldsymbol{i}$ and $\boldsymbol{j}$.
Hence show that the resultant of these forces acts along **OA** and calculate the magnitude of this resultant. *(AEB)*

Kinematics

Revision exercise 2A

1. A particle moves on the x-axis so that its displacement x from O is related to the time t by

$$t = x^2 + 2x.$$

Find the speed of the particle when $x = 1$. *(L)*

2. A particle moves in the x-y plane so that its position at time t is given by

$$x = t + \sin 2t, \quad y = 1 - 2\cos \tfrac{3}{2}t.$$

Find the values of t, in the interval $0 \leqslant t \leqslant 2\pi$, for which the particle is momentarily at rest. *(JMB)*

3. A ball is projected with speed 20 m s^{-1} at an angle of 60° to the horizontal. Find the time taken for the ball to travel 10 m horizontally. Find also the height of the ball above the level of the point of projection when it has travelled a horizontal distance of 10 m. (Take g as 10 m s^{-2}.) *(L)*

4. At time $t (> 0)$ a particle in a plane is at the point whose position vector relative to the origin is

$$\boldsymbol{r} = \begin{pmatrix} \cos t + t\sin t \\ \sin t - t\cos t \end{pmatrix}.$$

Find, in terms of t, the speed of the particle (i.e. the magnitude of its velocity) at this instant, giving your answer as simply as possible. *(O & C)*

5. The ship A is sailing with speed u in a direction N 30° E. The ship B is sailing with speed v in a direction Nθ° E. The velocity of B relative to A is due southwest. Show that

$$v(\cos\theta - \sin\theta) = \tfrac{1}{2}u(\sqrt{3} - 1).$$

The ship A changes course to N 60° E while continuing with the same speed; B continues with the same velocity. The velocity of B relative to A is now due west. Find $\tan\theta$°, leaving your answer in surd form. *(JMB)*

6. A particle is projected from a point O on horizontal ground with velocity V m s^{-1} at an angle of elevation α and passes through a point P which is at a distance x metres horizontally from O and at a height y metres above the ground. Prove that

$$y = x\tan\alpha - (gx^2/2V^2)\sec^2\alpha.$$

If $x = 30$, $y = 10$ and $V = 10.5\sqrt{10}$, find the two possible values of $\tan\alpha$. (Take g as 9.8; the use of tables or a calculator is not recommended.) *(O & C)*

7. A particle is projected with initial speed V and at an angle of inclination α above the horizontal from a point on horizontal ground. Obtain expressions for (a) the time of flight, (b) the horizontal range.

   A man throws a ball at an initial speed of 50 m s^{-1}. Show, taking g to be 10 m s^{-2}, that the times of flight corresponding to a horizontal range of 100 m are the positive roots of the equation

$$T^4 - 100T^2 + 400 = 0. \qquad (C)$$

8. At noon the position vectors of two ships, A and B, from a lighthouse are $\binom{18}{6}$ km and $\binom{4}{10}$ km, respectively. The constant velocities of the two ships are $\binom{1}{4}$ km h^{-1} and $\binom{3}{2}$ km h^{-1}, respectively. Find the displacement of A, relative to B, t hours after noon.

   Hence, or otherwise, determine the value of t for which the ships are closest together and show that this closest distance is $5\sqrt{2}$ km. *(JMB)*

9. Two particles P and Q are simultaneously projected, under gravity, from the points A and B, respectively, where AB is horizontal and of length d. The motion takes place in the vertical plane through A and B. The initial velocity of P is v_1 at an angle θ_1 to the horizontal, and the initial velocity of Q is v_2 at an angle θ_2 to the horizontal, as indicated in figure E.1. Show that, if the particles are to collide, it is necessary that

$$v_1 \sin\theta_1 = v_2 \sin\theta_2 .$$

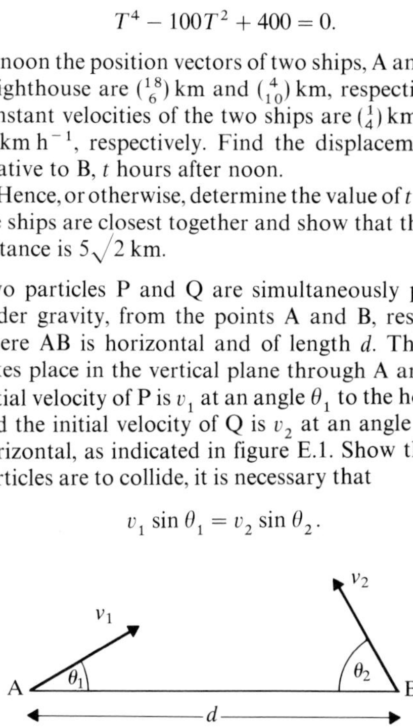

Figure E.1

Given that $d = 200$ m, $v_1 = 30$ m s^{-1}, $\sin\theta_1 = \frac{4}{5}$, $v_2 = 40$ m s^{-1}, $\sin\theta_2 = \frac{3}{5}$ and $g = 10$ m s^{-2}, verify that the particles will collide and find the height above AB of the point of collision.

Show that the angle between the directions of motion of the particles just before collision is approximately 112°. *(C)*

Revision exercise 2B

1. (i) Two points move in a plane, both starting from the origin, in such a way that, after time t seconds, their position vectors are

$$3(\cos t - 1)\mathbf{i} + (4\sin t)\mathbf{j}$$

and

$$(3\sin t)\mathbf{i} + 4(\cos t - 1)\mathbf{j}.$$

Find the value of t when the points are first moving in (a) opposite directions, (b) the same direction.

(ii) A particle moves in a straight line with acceleration

$$[(t-1)e^{-t} + 2\cos t]\text{m/s}^2,$$

starting from rest at the origin at time $t = 0$. Obtain the distance x m travelled in time t seconds. *(L)*

2. A certain bowler in a game of cricket projects the ball horizontally with speed 26 m s^{-1} from a height of 2 m above ground level. Taking g as 10 m s^{-2}, find the horizontal distance between the point of projection and the point at which the ball first strikes the ground.

   At the impact with the ground, the horizontal component of the velocity of the ball is unchanged and the vertical component is reversed in direction and halved in magnitude. The batsman hits the ball at a point which is at a horizontal distance of 19 m from the point of projection. Calculate
   (i) the length of the time interval between the ball striking the ground and the batsman hitting it,
   (ii) the height of the ball when it is hit,
   (iii) the angle made with the horizontal by the direction of motion of the ball just before it is hit. *(C)*

3. A particle P moves freely under gravity in the plane of a fixed horizontal axis Ox and a fixed upward vertical axis Oy. At time t the coordinates of P are (x, y). Write down the values of

$$\frac{d^2x}{dt^2} \text{ and } \frac{d^2y}{dt^2}.$$

The particle is projected from O, at time $t = 0$, with speed V at an angle α to Ox. Find by integration the values of x and y at time t, and deduce that

$$y = x\tan\alpha - \frac{gx^2}{2V^2}(1 + \tan^2\alpha).$$

The point O is on horizontal ground and AB is a vertical post of height $2h$ whose foot A is at the point $(3h, 0)$. Given that

$$V^2 = 9gh,$$

show that the particle will pass over the post provided that

$$1 < \tan\alpha < 5.$$

Show that in this case the particle will hit the ground at a distance greater than $\frac{6}{13}h$ from A. *(JMB)*

4. A car and a lorry are initially at rest side by side. The lorry moves off with uniform acceleration 0.8 m s^{-2}. After 5 s, the car moves off with uniform acceleration 1.8 m s^{-2}. Find how long the lorry has been in motion when it is overtaken by the car, and show that by this time it has travelled 90 m.

   When the lorry has been in motion for 20 s, both vehicles apply their brakes. The car then has a uniform deceleration of 3 m s^{-2}, and the lorry a uniform deceleration of x m s^{-2}. Find the total distance which each vehicle travels before coming to rest, and show that the lorry passes the car again if $x < \frac{32}{41}$.

   Show that, whatever the value of x, the lorry does not pass the car until after the car has come to rest. *(C)*

5. Two cars, A and B, are initially at rest side by side. A sets off and moves with a constant acceleration of $\frac{1}{3}$ m s^{-2}, and 5 s later B sets off in the same direction moving with a constant acceleration of $\frac{3}{4}$ m s^{-2}. Find the time for which B has been in motion when it overtakes A, and show that in this time B travels $37\frac{1}{2}$ m.
When B's speed is 12 m s^{-1}, it starts to decelerate at a constant rate of $\frac{13}{16}$ m s^{-2}. Find the speed of A relative to B when A overtakes B. *(C)*

6. Two ships A and B are travelling on straight courses at constant speeds.
a) Given that the ships will collide if their courses remain unchanged, what can be said about the direction of their relative velocity?
b) At 12 00 (noon), the ship A is at a distance of 10 km from the ship B and is due east of B. At 12 20, A is at a distance of 5 km from B and on a bearing N 60° E from B. Find, graphically or otherwise, the magnitude (in km h^{-1}) and direction of the velocity of A relative to B, and the shortest distance between the ships in the ensuing motion.
Given that A is travelling due north at a speed of 15 km h^{-1} find, in magnitude and direction, the velocity of B. *(C)*

7. A river flows at 5 m s^{-1} in a direction S 60° W and the velocity of a boat relative to the water is 8 m s^{-1} due N. Find the true velocity of the boat in magnitude and direction.
At a given instant the boat is in a direction S 30° E and at a distance 25 m from a buoy when a bird on the buoy flies off horizontally and in a straight line with speed 3.5 m s^{-1} so as to alight on the boat. Show, graphically or otherwise, that there are two routes it can take and find the time taken for each route. *(O & C)*

8. An aeroplane which flies at 90 m s^{-1} in still air is travelling in a (true) direction N 30° E. There is a 20 m s^{-1} wind blowing from the direction S 15° E. Show that the true speed of the aeroplane is about 103 m s^{-1}, and find the direction in which it is steering.
A train is travelling with constant speed along a straight track. At a given instant, the aeroplane is 5 km due west of the train, and one minute later it is 5 km NW of the train. Find the speed of the train, and the direction in which it is travelling.
(A graphical method is permitted for this question.) *(C)*

9. A particle is thrown directly upwards from the foot of a tower 25 m high with a speed of 8 m s^{-1}. At the same instant a second particle is projected horizontally from the top of the tower with a speed 6 m s^{-1}. Find their distance of closest approach and the time from the start of the motion at which it occurs.
Show that, when the particles are closest together, their relative velocity is perpendicular to the line joining them. *(O & C)*

10. A bird flies on a straight line course due east from A to to B, a distance 10 km, and then back again to A. The constant speed of the bird would be $20\sqrt{3}$ km h^{-1} in still air. On both journeys the bird encounters a wind blowing with a constant velocity 20 km h^{-1} in a direction from 30° east of south. Find the directions in which the bird must aim on the outward and return journeys and the time taken for the double journey. *(L)*

Dynamics

Revision exercise 3A

1. The position vector $\boldsymbol{r}$, at time t, of a particle of unit mass is given by

$$\boldsymbol{r} = 2\cos t\,\boldsymbol{i} + 2\sin t\,\boldsymbol{j} + 5t^2\boldsymbol{k}.$$

Find
a) the speed of the particle at time t,
b) the resultant force, $\boldsymbol{F}$, acting on the particle at time t,
c) the work done by $\boldsymbol{F}$ in the time interval $0 < t < t_1$. *(JMB)*

2. A man of mass 50 kg stands on the floor of a lift which descends with acceleration 1 m s^{-2}. Find, in newtons, the total force exerted between the floor of the lift and the man's feet. (Take $g = 9.8$ m s^{-2}.) *(L)*

3. A gas balloon, with its load and occupants, has a total mass of 400 kg. If it is descending with a constant speed of 5 m s^{-1}, how large is the combined force of buoyancy and air resistance? (Take the value of g to be 9.8 m s^{-2}.)
In order to slow down the descent, a mass x kg of ballast is thrown out, sufficient to produce a retardation of 0.2 m s^{-2}. If the buoyancy and air resistance are supposed to remain unaltered, what is the value of x? *(O & C)*

4. A particle of mass m is suspended from a fixed point O by a light inextensible string of length l. The particle moves in a vertical circle, of radius l and centre O, and its greatest speed is u. Find, in terms of m, g, l, u and θ, the tension in the string when the angle between

the string and the downward vertical is θ. Given that the maximum tension in the string is $10\,mg$,

a) show that $u = 3\sqrt{gl}$,

b) find the value of $\cos\theta$ at which the particle has no vertical acceleration. *(AEB)*

5. A particle of unit mass moves under the action of a constant force $\boldsymbol{i} + 2\boldsymbol{j}$. At time $t = 0$ the particle is stationary at the point with position vector $2\boldsymbol{i} + 5\boldsymbol{j}$. Find the velocity at any subsequent time t and the position vector of the particle at time $t = 2$. *(L)*

6. A particle of mass 3 kg moves so that its position vector after t seconds is given by

$$\boldsymbol{r} = (3t - 2t^3)\boldsymbol{i} - 2t\boldsymbol{j}$$

Find the force acting on the particle at time $t = 2$ s. *(L)*

Revision exercise 3B

1. A lift which, when empty, has mass 1000 kg is carrying a man of mass 80 kg. The lift is descending with a downward acceleration of $1\ \text{m s}^{-2}$. Taking g as $9.8\ \text{m s}^{-2}$ and ignoring friction, calculate the tension in the lift cable and the vertical force exerted on the man by the floor of the lift.

   The man drops a coin from a height of 2 m. Calculate, to 2 decimal places, the time taken for it to hit the floor of the lift.

   The lift is designed so that during any journey the magnitude of its acceleration reaches, but does not exceed, $1\ \text{m s}^{-2}$. Safety regulations do not allow the lift cable to bear a tension greater than 20 000 N. Making reasonable assumptions and showing your working, suggest the number of persons that the lift should be licensed to carry. (Hint: the maximum tension in the lift cable occurs when the lift is accelerating upwards.) *(O & C)*

2. The vertical descent of a lift cage is undertaken in three stages. During the first stage the lift uniformly accelerates from rest at $5k\ \text{m s}^{-2}$, during the second stage it moves at a constant speed of $10\ \text{m s}^{-1}$ and during the third stage it uniformly retards at $2k\ \text{m s}^{-2}$ until it comes to rest.

   a) Express, in terms of k, the times taken during the first and third stages of the descent.

   b) Given that the total distance covered by the lift during the descent is 350 m and that this distance is covered in 40 s, calculate the value of k.

   A tool box of mass 5 kg was placed on the floor of the lift cage before the descent.

   c) Find, in newtons, the force exerted by the floor of the lift cage on the tool box during each stage of the descent.

   (Take the acceleration due to gravity to be $10\,\text{m s}^{-2}$.) *(AEB)*

3. The Earth may be regarded as a sphere of radius 6370 km. The acceleration due to gravity at an external point is inversely proportional to the square of its distance from the centre of the Earth. A communications satellite travels in a circular orbit above the equator with a period of 24 hours. Find the height of such a satellite above the Earth's surface.

   Another satellite describes a circular orbit at a height of 280 km above the equator in the same sense as the Earth's rotation. At midday (12 00) the satellite is directly above an observatory. Show that it will next be directly above the observatory at about 13 36. *(C)*

4. A conical pendulum consists of a light inextensible string of length l with a particle of mass m attached to its free end. The particle describes a horizontal circle with angular speed ω and the string makes an angle of $60°$ with the vertical. Express l in terms of g and ω.

   A second conical pendulum consists of a light inextensible string of length L with a particle of mass M attached to its free end. The particle describes a horizontal circle with angular speed $\frac{1}{2}\omega$ and the string makes an angle of $30°$ with the vertical. Find the value of the fraction l/L, leaving your answer in surd form. *(JMB)*

5. A light inextensible string of length $5c$ has one end A tied at a fixed point. A particle of mass m is tied at the other end B of the string. The particle is made to rotate at constant speed u in a horizontal circle whose centre is at a distance $3c$ vertically below A. Find

   a) the tension in the string,

   b) an expression for u in terms of c and g.

   The particle is taken from the end B and tied at the midpoint of the string. The end B is attached to a fixed point at a distance $3c$ vertically below the point of attachment of A. The particle is set to move at constant speed v in a horizontal circle about the vertical through AB. Given that the tension in the upper portion of the string is twice the tension in the lower portion, find

   c) the tension in each half of the string,

   d) an expression for v in terms of c and g. *(AEB)*

6. A particle of mass m is placed on a rough plane inclined at an angle $\tan^{-1}\frac{5}{12}$ to the horizontal. The coefficient of friction between the plane and the particle is $\frac{1}{2}$. Prove that the particle will remain stationary.

   A light inextensible string is fastened to the particle, passes up a line of greatest slope, over a frictionless pulley at the top of the plane, and to its other end is attached a particle of mass $2m$, which hangs freely. Prove that the particles will move and find the magnitude of their acceleration.

   When the particle of mass $2m$ has descended a distance h, it hits a floor without rebounding. Prove that the particle of mass m will subsequently move a distance $\frac{5}{11}h$ up the slope. *(C)*

7. A mass of 5 kg is moved along a rough horizontal table by means of a light inextensible string which passes over a smooth light pulley at the edge of the table and is attached to a mass of 1 kg hanging over the edge of the

table. The system is released from rest with the string taut, each portion being at right angles to the edge of the table. If the masses take twice the time to acquire the same velocity from rest that they would have done had the table been smooth, prove that the coefficient of friction is $\frac{1}{10}$.

After falling a distance $\frac{1}{5}$ m, the 1 kg mass reaches the floor and comes to rest. Prove that the 5 kg mass then moves a further $\frac{1}{6}$ m before coming to rest.

(Assume throughout that the 5 kg mass does not leave the table.) *(O & C)*

8.

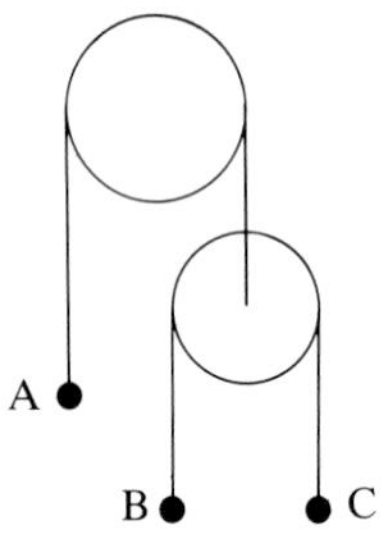

Figure E.2

Figure E.2 shows a smooth inextensible light string which passes over a smooth fixed peg. A particle A, of mass M, is attached to one end of this string and a smooth light pulley is attached to the other end. A second smooth inextensible light string passes over this pulley. To the ends of this second string are attached a particle B, of mass m, and a particle C of mass $2m$. The whole system is held at rest with the strings vertical and taut and then gently released. Show that the acceleration of B is

$$\left(\frac{5M - 8m}{3M + 8m}\right)g.$$

Find the accelerations of A and C and the tension in each string in terms of m, M and g.

Show that A descends if $3M > 8m$ and that C ascends if $8m < M$. *(C)*

9. A particle P of mass 0.5 kg is subject to a constant air resistance of 3.1 N. It is projected vertically upwards from the ground with speed 24 m s^{-1}. Find the maximum height it attains. Show that it returns to the ground after a total time of about 4.7 s, and find its speed just before it hits the ground.

The particle is again projected vertically upwards with speed 24 m s^{-1}. After a delay of T s, an identical particle Q (which is subject to the same resistance) is projected vertically upwards from the same point with speed 29 m s^{-1}. The particles collide at a height 6.75 m above the ground, whilst P is moving downwards and Q is moving upwards. Show that $T = 3.75$, and find the relative speed of the particles just before the collision. *(C)*

Motion in a straight line

Revision exercise 4

1. A particle is projected in a medium which exerts a resistance to motion proportional to the cube of the velocity, and no other forces act on the particle. In time t, the velocity of the particle decreases from v_1 to v_2 and the particle moves a distance s. Prove that

$$\frac{s}{t} = \frac{2v_1 v_2}{v_1 + v_2}.$$

(C)

2. A particle of mass m moves along the x-axis in the positive direction and at time t it has speed v. At time $t = 0$, it is at the origin and $v = u$. The only force acting on the particle opposes the motion of the particle and is of magnitude kv^α, where k and α are constants.

   a) Given that $\alpha = \frac{1}{2}$, show that $v = (\sqrt{u} - kt/2m)^2$. Show also that the particle comes to rest at a distance $2mu^{3/2}/(3k)$ from O.

   b) Given that $\alpha = 1$, find v in terms of m, u, k and t, and show that v is never zero. Show also that the distance of the particle from O is always less than mu/k. *(C)*

3. A particle is projected vertically upwards under (constant) gravity g from a point A on the Earth's surface with an initial speed k. At time t after projection, the particle is at height x above A and its speed is v; the air resistance is gv/k per unit mass.

   Show that, before the particle reaches its highest point,

$$\frac{dv}{dt} = -\frac{g}{k}(v + k),$$

   and $v = k(2e^{-gt/k} - 1)$. Hence find the corresponding value of x as a function of t. *(O & C)*

4. An automated goods train is programmed to move from rest under constant acceleration a m s^{-2} until it reaches its maximum speed 20 m s^{-1} in a distance of 300 m. The train can be brought to rest from its maximum speed under uniform retardation r m s^{-2} in a time of 15 s. Find the values of a and r.

   The distance between the stations A and B is 5 km and the train is programmed to stop at each station. Find the shortest possible time in which the distance AB can be covered. *(A E B)*

On a particular journey between A and B, the train has to stop midway between A and B, owing to signal failure. If it stops for 2 min, calculate the least extra time required for this journey compared with the journey covered in the shortest possible time. (*AEB*)

5. A particle of mass m is set in motion with speed u. Subsequently the only force acting upon the particle directly opposes its motion and is of magnitude $k(1 + v^2)$, where v is its speed at time t and k is constant. Show that the particle is brought to rest after a time $(m/k)\tan^{-1} u$ and find an expression in terms of m, k and u for the distance travelled by the particle in this time. (*JMB*)

6. A particle of mass m is projected vertically upwards under gravity with initial speed v_0. The air resistance to its motion has magnitude mkv^2, where v is the speed of the particle and k is a constant.

   a) Show that the greatest height attained in this motion is
   $$\frac{1}{2k}\log_e\left(\frac{g + kv_0^2}{g}\right).$$

   b) Given that the speed of the particle is v when it has fallen a distance y from its maximum height, show that
   $$y = \frac{1}{2k}\log_e\left(\frac{g}{g - kv^2}\right).$$

   c) Given that v_1 is the speed of return to the point of projection, show that
   $$(g + kv_0^2)(g - kv_1^2) = g^2. \qquad (JMB)$$

Momentum and impulse

Revision exercise 5A

1. A spacecraft of mass 20 000 kg is travelling at a speed of $2\,\text{km}\,\text{s}^{-1}$. After a 20 s burn, it is travelling at the same speed at 10° to the original direction. Find the magnitude and direction of the (constant) force exerted on the spacecraft during the burn. (Ignore the change in mass due to the loss of fuel during the burn.) (*O & C*)

2. A sphere A of mass $2m$ moving with speed u collides directly with a sphere B of mass $3m$ moving in the opposite direction with the same speed. Sphere B is brought to rest by the collision. Find the coefficient of restitution between the spheres. (*L*)

3. In a game of hockey the ball, whose mass is 0.15 kg, is travelling along the ground at a speed of $8\,\text{m}\,\text{s}^{-1}$. It is struck by a player's stick with a horizontal impulse of magnitude 0.8 N s, at an angle of 60°, as in Figure E.3. By means of an accurate diagram, or otherwise, find the angle through which the ball is deflected by the impact. (*O &C*)

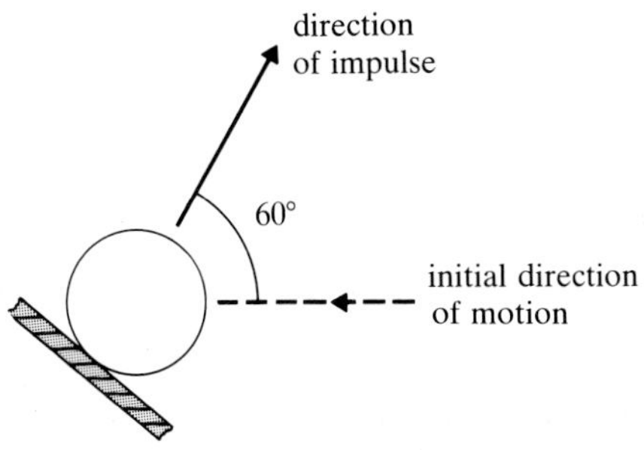

Figure E.3

4. A particle of mass 0.5 kg is in motion with velocity $(6\boldsymbol{i} + 4\boldsymbol{j})\,\text{m}\,\text{s}^{-1}$ when it strikes a fixed barrier and rebounds with velocity $(-2\boldsymbol{i} + 2\boldsymbol{j})\,\text{m}\,\text{s}^{-1}$. The particle is in contact with the barrier for 0.02 s. Find the average force exerted by the barrier on the particle.
   Calculate also the kinetic energy lost by the particle in the collision. (*JMB*)

5. Two boys are playing a game on a frozen pond. One skims a stone of mass 100 g across the surface of the ice; the other then tries to hit it sideways and deflect it with a stone of mass 60 g. Figure E.4 shows the velocities of the two stones; on this occasion the lighter stone is brought to rest by the impact. By representing the momentum of the stones in a vector diagram, or otherwise, find the velocity of the heavier stone after the impact, giving both its speed and the angle through which it is deflected. (You may find your answers either by calculation or by measurement.) (*O & C*)

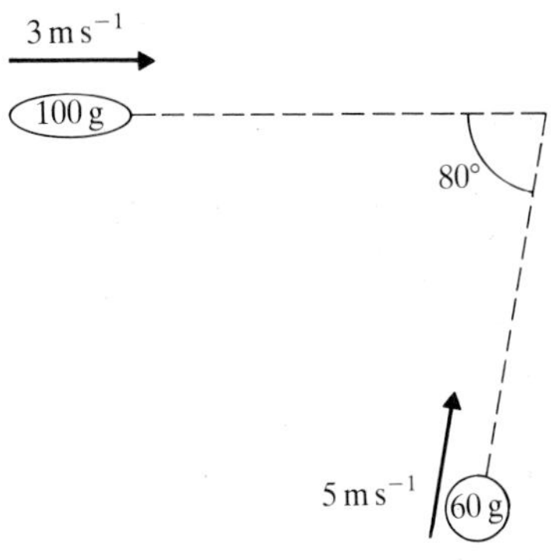

Figure E.4

6. Two points A and B lie on a smooth horizontal plane and are such that the line AB is perpendicular to a vertical wall standing on the plane, A being between B and the wall. A particle P of mass $2m$ is at rest at A and a particle Q of mass m is projected with velocity u from B directly towards A. Find the velocities of the particles immediately after the impact, given that the coefficient of restitution between them is $\frac{1}{3}$.

   P hits the wall and rebounds, hitting Q again. The coefficient of restitution between P and the wall is $\frac{1}{6}$. Does P hit the wall a second time? Justify your answer. *(O & C)*

Revision exercise 5B

1. Two small spheres of masses m and $2m$ are connected by a light inextensible string of length $2a$. When the string is taut and horizontal, its midpoint is fixed and the spheres are released from rest. The coefficient of restitution between the spheres is $\frac{1}{2}$. Show that the first impact brings the heavier sphere to rest, and that the second impact brings the lighter sphere to rest.

   Find the velocity of each sphere immediately after the third impact. *(L)*

2. A piece of wood of mass M is suspended from a fixed point O by a light inextensible string of length l. The wood is at rest vertically below O when it is struck by a bullet of mass m travelling horizontally. The bullet remains embedded in the wood. The maximum angle made by the string with the vertical in the subsequent motion is α, where $\alpha < \frac{1}{2}\pi$. Show that the speed of the bullet was

$$\left(1+\frac{M}{m}\right)[2gl(1-\cos\alpha)]^{1/2}.$$

   Show that, if α is small, the angular speed of the string when it makes an angle θ with the vertical in the subsequent motion is approximately

$$[(g/l)(\alpha^2-\theta^2)]^{1/2}.$$

   (O & C)

3. Two identical particles P and Q lie at rest on a smooth horizontal plane, P at A and Q at B. The line AB is perpendicular to a vertical barrier across the plane with B between A and the barrier. P is projected towards Q with speed u. During the collision with Q three-eighths of the kinetic energy of the system is lost. Find the coefficient of restitution between P and Q, and the velocities of P and Q immediately after the collision.

   The coefficient of restitution between Q and the barrier is e, where $0<e<1$. Show that Q hits the barrier on at least two occasions in the subsequent motion. *(C)*

4. A, B and C are three particles of masses m, $2m$ and $4m$ respectively. They are placed at the points P, Q and R respectively on a smooth horizontal table. P, Q and R lie in that order on a straight line and $PQ = QR = a$. The coefficient of restitution between any pair of particles is e. The particle A is projected towards B with speed u. Show that the speed of C just after it has been struck for the first time by B is $\frac{1}{9}u(1+e)^2$. Find the range of values of e for which A and B collide a second time.

   If $e=\frac{1}{4}$, show that A and B collide for the second time at X where $PX=\frac{17}{7}a$ and find the time taken for A to reach this point from its initial projection from P. *(C)*

5. A small sphere P of mass m is moving with speed u on a smooth horizontal plane along a straight line AO. At O the sphere collides with a smooth vertical wall which makes an acute angle θ with AO. Show that, if the coefficient of restitution at O is e, the sphere leaves O at an angle ϕ to the wall, where

$$\tan\phi = e\tan\theta.$$

   Find the value of θ for which the component, perpendicular to AO, of the velocity after collision is greatest.

   A sphere Q of mass $2m$, with the same radius as P, is at rest on the plane and OQ is perpendicular to AO. Show that if $\cot\theta=\sqrt{e}$, P strikes Q directly and at speed $u\sqrt{e}$. Given that the spheres are perfectly elastic, find the impulse exerted by P on Q. *(JMB)*

6. Three particles A, B and C, each of mass m, lie at rest in a straight line on a smooth horizontal plane with B between A and C. The particle A moves and collides directly with B, the coefficient of restitution between A and B being $\frac{1}{2}$. As a result of this collision B moves with speed $\frac{3}{4}u$. Calculate

   a) the velocity of A before the collision,

   b) the velocity of A after the collision,

   c) the loss in kinetic energy due to the collision.

   The particle B moves on with speed $\frac{3}{4}u$ until it collides directly with the particle C and the coefficient of restitution between B and C is e.

   d) Find, in terms of m, u and e, the magnitude of the impulse exerted by B on C due to their collision.

   e) Given that there are no further collisions between the particles after the collision between B and C, show that $e \leqslant \frac{1}{3}$. *(AEB)*

7. Write down the principle of conservation of momentum for two particles which move along the same straight line stating when it is applicable.

   A plank AB of length l and mass M is at rest on a fixed horizontal plane sheet of smooth ice. A man of mass m stands on the plank at A and then walks along the plank in such a way that, at time t after he has started, his velocity relative to the plank is ft, where f is constant. Find the velocity of the plank at time t.
   Find the distance through which the plank has moved when the man reaches B. *(JMB)*

8. (In this question take g to be 10 m s^{-2}.)
A particle is projected from a point O on horizontal ground with speed 15 m s^{-1} at an angle of elevation of $\tan^{-1}\frac{4}{3}$. The point O is 18 m in front of a vertical wall, and the particle moves in a vertical plane perpendicular to the wall. Calculate the height of the particle above ground level when it hits the wall.
At the impact with the wall the horizontal and vertical components of the velocity of the particle are each reduced to one-eighth of their previous values, and the horizontal component is reversed in direction. Calculate the magnitude and direction of the impulse on the particle due to this impact, given that the mass of the particle is 0.5 kg.
The particle hits the ground again at A. Show that OA = 17.1 m. (*C*)

Work and energy

Revision exercise 6A

1. A particle of mass m is moving with speed u when it receives an impulse which is of magnitude I and acting in the same direction as u. Find the speed of the particle immediately after the impulse and prove that the increase in the kinetic energy of the particle is

$$I(I + 2mu)/2m. \qquad (L)$$

2. A particle of mass m moving with speed $2u$ is overtaken by and coalesces with a particle of mass $2m$ moving with speed $3u$ in the same straight line. Calculate the loss in kinetic energy due to the collision. (*L*)

3. A pile-driver of mass M falls freely from a height h and strikes without rebounding the upper end of a vertical pile of mass m. The blow drives the pile a distance d into the ground. Find the resistance of the ground, assumed to be constant, in terms of M, m, h, d and g.
Find also the time for which the pile is in motion. (State the mechanical principle you are using at each stage of your argument.) (*O&C*)

4. A lorry of mass 2000 kg is subject to a constant frictional resistance of 2600 N. Find in kW the power at which the engine is working when the lorry is travelling along a level road at a steady speed of 45 km h^{-1}.
If the engine continues to work at this rate, find the steady speed in km h^{-1} at which the lorry ascends a a hill of inclination $\sin^{-1}\frac{1}{14}$.
(Take g to be 9.8 m s^{-2}.) (*O&C*)

5. The frictional resistance to the motion of a car of mass 1000 kg is kv N, where v m s^{-1} is its speed and k is constant. The car ascends a hill of inclination $\sin^{-1}\frac{1}{10}$ at a steady speed of 8 m s^{-1}, the power exerted by the engine being 9.76 kW. Prove that the numerical value of k is 30.
Find the steady speed at which the car ascends the hill if the power exerted by the engine is 12.8 kW.
When the car is travelling at this speed, the power exerted by the engine is increased by 2 kW. Find the immediate acceleration of the car.
(Take 9.8 m s^{-2} as the acceleration due to gravity.) (*O & C*)

6. Initially, a particle of mass m is stationary at the origin. The particle is then acted on by a force which is fixed in direction and which works at a constant power P, so that, after time t, the particle has a velocity v and is at a distance x from the origin. Find
a) v in terms of t, P and m,
b) v in terms of x, P and m,
c) x in terms of t, P and m. (*C*)

Revision exercise 6B

1. Three small smooth beads P, Q and R of mass $\frac{1}{2}m$, m and km, respectively, are threaded, in that order, on a long straight horizontal wire. Initially the beads are at rest. The bead Q is projected towards R with speed V. After the collision, Q is stationary, and the kinetic energy of R is two-thirds of the kinetic energy of Q immediately before the collision. Find the value of k and the speed of R after the collision.
Subsequently the bead P is projected with speed $2V$ towards Q, and these two beads coalesce in the collision. Find (a) the loss of kinetic energy resulting from this collision and (b) the magnitude of the impulse on Q.
Determine whether any further collisions take place. (*C*)

2. A load of 2000 kg is being pulled up a slope inclined at an angle α to the horizontal, where $\sin\alpha = 0.01$. The coefficient of friction between the load and the slope is 0.04. The acceleration of the load is directed up the slope, and has magnitude 0.21 m s^{-2}. Find the tension in the rope, taking $\cos\alpha$ to be 1 and g to be 9.8 m s^{-2}.
The load starts from rest. Find the work done by the rope on the load during the first 20 s of motion, and the power being developed at the end of the first 20 s of motion.
After 20 s of motion the rope breaks. How much further does the load travel up the slope? What happens to the load after it stops moving up the slope? (*O & C*)

3. Two particles P and Q, of mass $2m$ and $3m$, respectively, are connected by a light inelastic string which passes

over a smooth fixed pulley. The system is released from rest with the string taut and the hanging parts vertical. After time t, the particle P picks up a stationary particle of mass m. Show that the loss of kinetic energy of the system due to the impulse is $mg^2t^2/60$. (*L*)

4. An engine, of mass 10 t, is working at 1650 kW and is pulling carriages, of total mass 100 t, up a straight track inclined at an angle $\sin^{-1}\frac{1}{200}$ to the horizontal. The track resistances for both the engine and the carriages are constant at all speeds and have magnitude 160 N t^{-1}. Show that, when the train is moving at 15 m s^{-1}, the acceleration is 0.79 m s^{-2}. Find the tension in the coupling between the engine and the first carriage at this speed.

   Find also, in m s^{-1}, the greatest speed which the train could maintain up this incline with the engine working at 600 kW.

   (Take the acceleration due to gravity to be 10 m s^{-2}.) (*AEB*)

5. A pile of mass m and height h is placed upright on the ground. It is driven into the ground by n successive blows of a pile-driver of mass M. Prior to each blow the pile-driver is raised to a height H above the top of the pile. Each blow is delivered by releasing the driver to fall vertically under gravity only (through a distance H each time). The pile-driver and pile remain together until this composite body has been brought to rest by the resistance of the ground, which may be regarded as constant and of magnitude R whilst the pile is in motion. Show that the height H through which the pile-driver needs to be raised is given by the equation

$$nM^2gH = h(M+m)(R - Mg - mg).$$

   The impulse on the pile by its impact with the pile-driver must not be greater than I or the pile will split. Show that in this case

$$n \geqslant \frac{2m^2h(R - Mg - mg)}{(M+m)I^2}. \qquad (C)$$

6. A car has an engine capable of developing 15 kW. The maximum speed of the car on a level road is 120 km h^{-1}. Calculate the total resistance in newtons at this speed.

   Given that the mass of the car is 1000 kg and that the resistance to motion is proportional to the square of the speed, obtain the rate of working, in kW to two decimal places, of the engine when the car is moving at a constant speed of 40 km h^{-1} up a road of inclination θ, where $\sin\theta = \frac{1}{25}$.

   (Take $g = 9.8$ m s^{-2}.) (*L*)

7. A locomotive of mass 15 000 kg, working at the rate of 220 kW, pulls a train of mass 35 000 kg up a straight track which rises 1 m vertically for every 50 m travelled along the track. When the speed is 10 m s^{-1} the acceleration is 0.23 m s^{-2}. Find the frictional resistance at this speed.

   Given that the resistance is proportional to the speed of the train, find, in m s^{-1}, the greatest speed of the train up the slope if the rate of working is unchanged.

   (Take $g = 10$ m s^{-2}.) (*L*)

8. The engine of a car of mass 10^3 kg is working at a constant power of 1.8×10^4 W. At a certain instant the car is travelling along a level road and at this instant its speed is 30 m s^{-1} and its acceleration is 0.03 m s^{-2}. Show that the resistance to motion at this instant is 570 N.

   The resistance to motion, R N, when the car is travelling at a speed of v m s^{-1} is given by $R = av^2 + bv$, where a and b are positive constants. Use the result from the first paragraph to write down an equation relating a and b.

   Given also that the maximum speed when coasting (with the engine shut off) down a hill of inclination α to the horizontal, where $\sin\alpha = \frac{9}{1000}$, is 10 m s^{-1}, obtain a second equation relating a and b, and find the values of a and b.

   (Take the value of g to be 10 m s^{-2}.) (*C*)

Statics

Revision exercise 7A

1. A rectangle ABCD has AB = 3 cm and BC = 4 cm. Forces, all measured in newtons and of magnitudes 2, 4, 6, 8 and k, act along AB, BC, CD, DA and AC, respectively, the direction of each force being shown by the order of the letters. The resultant of the five forces is parallel to BD. Find k and show that the resultant has magnitude $\frac{5}{6}$ N. Find the distance from A of the line of action of the resultant. (*O & C*)

2. A particle of mass m is placed on a rough plane inclined at an angle $\tan^{-1}\frac{3}{4}$ to the horizontal. The coefficient of friction between the particle and the plane is $\frac{1}{3}$. A horizontal force P, directed towards the plane, acts on the particle. This force acts in a vertical plane through a line of greatest slope of the inclined plane. Prove that the particle remains stationary provided that

$$\tfrac{1}{3}mg \leqslant P \leqslant \tfrac{13}{9}mg. \qquad (C)$$

3. A uniform ladder of length 7 m rests against a vertical wall with which it makes an angle of 45°, the coefficients of friction between the ladder and the wall and the ladder and the (horizontal) ground being $\frac{1}{3}$ and $\frac{1}{2}$, respectively. A boy whose weight is one half that of the ladder slowly ascends the ladder. How far along the ladder will he be when the ladder slips?

   (Assume the ladder is a uniform rod which is perpendicular to the line of intersection of the wall and ground.) *(O & C)*

4. A particle is placed on the inner surface of a fixed rough hollow sphere of internal radius a. Given that the coefficient of friction between the particle and the sphere is $\frac{3}{4}$, show that the particle rests in limiting equilibrium at a depth $\frac{4}{5}a$ below the centre of the sphere. *(L)*

5. A uniform ladder of length $2a$ and weight W rests against a smooth vertical wall with its lower end on rough horizontal ground at a distance a from the foot of the wall. Find the force exerted by the wall on the ladder. *(L)*

6. In the triangle ABC, $AB = AC = 10a$ and $BC = 12a$. The point E on AC is such that angle BEC is 90° and D is the midpoint of BC. Forces of magnitudes $2P$, $10P$, $5P$ and $10P$ act along **CB, AD, BE** and **AC**, respectively. Calculate

   a) the sum of the resolved parts of these forces parallel to **BC**,

   b) the sum of the resolved parts of these forces parallel to **AD**,

   c) the magnitude of the resultant of these forces,

   d) the acute angle made by the line of action of the resultant with BC, giving your answer to the nearest degree.

   The line of action of the resultant of these forces cuts BC at the point F. Find the distance BF in terms of a. *(AEB)*

Revision exercise 7B

1. a) A particle is placed on a rough plane inclined at an angle α to the horizontal. A force of magnitude P, acting up a line of greatest slope of the plane, is needed to prevent the particle from sliding down the plane. A force of magnitude $3P$, acting in the same direction as before, is needed to cause the particle to be about to slide up the plane. Show that the coefficient of friction between the particle and the plane is $\frac{1}{2}\tan\alpha$.

   b) A particle of weight W is placed on a rough plane inclined at an angle β to the horizontal. The coefficient of friction between the particle and the plane is μ, where $\mu = \tan\lambda$ and $\lambda < \beta$. The particle is maintained in limiting equilibrium by a force of magnitude Q. Find the direction of this force when Q is least, and find this least value of Q. *(C)*

2. A uniform sphere of radius a and weight $W/\sqrt{3}$ rests on a rough horizontal table. A uniform rod AB of weight $2W$ and length $2a$ is freely hinged at A to a fixed point on the table and leans against the sphere so that the centre of the sphere and the rod lie in a vertical plane. The rod makes an angle of 60° with the horizontal. Show that the frictional force between the rod and the sphere is $\frac{1}{3}W$. The coefficient of friction at each point of contact is μ. What is the smallest value of μ which makes equilibrium possible? *(O & C)*

3. The points A, B have coordinates $(\sqrt{3}, 0)$, $(0, 1)$, respectively, relative to rectangular axes Ox, Oy. C is the midpoint of AB, and D is the midpoint of BC. Forces of magnitude $4\sqrt{3}$ N, 13 N, 11 N, $6\sqrt{3}$ N, 7 N act along OA, OB, CO, DO, AB, respectively, the direction of each force being indicated by the order of the letters. Show that the resultant of these forces has magnitude 14 N. Find the equation of the line of action of the resultant, and verify that it passes through the midpoint of AC.

   The above system is equivalent to forces of magnitude P N, Q N, R N acting along EA, EB, AB, respectively, where E is the point $(\sqrt{3}, 1)$. Find P, Q and R. *(C)*

4. A particle of mass m is on a rough horizontal plane. A force with its line of action making an angle θ with the plane is applied to the particle. Show that, if this force is just sufficient to pull the particle along the plane, the magnitude, P, of the force, is $[mg\sin\lambda]/\cos(\theta - \lambda)$ where $\tan\lambda$ is the coefficient of friction.

   State the least value of P.

   The particle is now placed on the same plane which is tilted at an angle α to the horizontal. A force of magnitude $mg\sin\lambda$ acting along the line of greatest slope is just sufficient to move the particle up the plane. Show that

   $$\sin(\lambda + \alpha) = \sin\lambda\cos\lambda.$$ *(L)*

5. A uniform ladder of length $2a$ rests in limiting equilibrium in a vertical plane with its lower end on rough horizontal ground and its upper end against a smooth vertical wall. The ladder makes an angle 60° with the ground. Show that the coefficient of friction is $\frac{1}{6}\sqrt{3}$.

   The ladder is lowered in its vertical plane whilst still resting against the smooth wall and the ground to make an angle 30° with the ground. The coefficient of friction between the ladder and the ground remains at $\frac{1}{6}\sqrt{3}$. A man whose weight is four times that of the ladder starts climbing up the ladder. Find how far he can climb up the ladder before it slips. *(L)*

6. A uniform square lamina ABCD of weight W and side $2a$ rests in a vertical plane with the vertex A in contact with a rough horizontal plane. The lamina is kept in equilibrium by a force P acting at the vertex C in the direction of DC produced. Given that the height of the vertex D above the horizontal plane is $\frac{6}{5}a$, show that $P = \frac{1}{10}W$.

   Find the coefficient of friction between the lamina and the plane if the lamina is in limiting equilibrium. *(L)*

7. Explain what is meant by (a) the coefficient of friction, (b) limiting friction.

A uniform rod AB, of mass $4M$ and length l, is smoothly jointed at the end A to a fixed straight horizontal wire AC. The end B is connected by means of a light inextensible string of length l to a bead of mass M which can slide on the wire, the coefficient of friction between the bead and the wire being μ. Show that, when the friction is limiting, the angle of inclination θ, of the rod to the horizontal wire is given by $\cot\theta = 2\mu$. *(AEB)*

8. A smooth fixed inclined plane has slope $\sin^{-1}\frac{5}{6}$. A uniform sphere has weight W and radius $7a$. A light inextensible string of length $18a$ joins a point P on the surface of the sphere to a fixed point A on the plane, and the sphere hangs in equilibrium against the plane. Show that the tension in the string is $\frac{125}{144}W$.

A particle is fastened to a point Q on the surface of the sphere, diametrically opposite to P. The sphere now hangs in equilibrium with PQ parallel to the plane. Find the weight of the particle, and show that the new tension in the string and the reaction between the sphere and the plane are both equal to $\frac{3}{4}W\sqrt{11}$. *(C)*

Elasticity and simple harmonic motion

Revision exercise 8A

1. A particle moves in a straight line with simple harmonic motion of period 8 s about a fixed point O in the line. At a certain time the particle is at a distance 3 m from O and two seconds later it is still on the same side of O but 4 m from O. Find the amplitude of the motion.

Show that after a further two seconds the particle is on the other side of O at a distance 3 m from O. Find the speed and acceleration of the particle in this position. Find also the time which elapses before the particle next passes through this position. *(AEB)*

2. A particle moves in simple harmonic motion along the x-axis. When $t = 0$ the particle is instantaneously at rest at $x = b$. The speed of the particle is u when $x = 2b$. When $t = 2$ the particle passes for the first time through the point $x = 3b$, which is the centre of the motion. Show that $4u = \pi b\sqrt{3}$.

Find the times at which the particle passes through the point $x = \frac{5}{2}b$ on the first and second occasions after $t = 0$. *(C)*

3. A particle is suspended from a fixed point O by a light elastic string which is of natural length a and which obeys Hooke's law. When the particle hangs at rest, the length of the string is $\frac{5}{4}a$. If the particle is released from rest at O, find the distance it falls before it first comes to rest. *(L)*

4. A rope is made of nylon which stretches under tension. Its unstretched length is 40 m. When it is stretched by x m, the force in the rope is $1200\,x$ N. Find the work done in stretching the rope to a length $(40 + l)$m, stating a unit.

A mountaineer of mass 80 kg, standing on a ledge, attaches one end of this rope to a metal ring anchored to the ledge, and fastens the other end to himself. He then falls from the ledge in a free vertical drop. If, when he *first* comes to rest, the rope is stretched by an amount l m, form an equation for l. Hence find how far below the ledge he is first brought to rest. Take g to be $10\,\text{m}\,\text{s}^{-2}$. *(O & C)*

5. One end of an elastic string of modulus mg and natural length a is attached to a fixed point O. To the other end A are attached two particles P and Q, P having mass $2m$ and Q having mass m. The particles hang down in equilibrium under gravity. If Q falls off, show that P subsequently performs simple harmonic motion and state the period and amplitude of this motion.

If on the other hand P falls off, find the distance from O of the highest point reached by Q. *(O & C)*

6. A horizontal platform is moving vertically so that its displacement x from a fixed horizontal plane at time t satisfies

$$x = a\sin^2\omega t,$$

where a and ω are positive constants. Prove that the platform is in simple harmonic motion with centre at $x = \frac{1}{2}a$. Find the amplitude and period of this motion.

A particle is placed on the platform when $x = 0$ and is observed to leave the platform, travelling vertically upwards, when $x = \frac{5}{6}a$. Show that $a\omega^2 = \frac{3}{4}g$. *(O & C)*

Revision exercise 8B

1. A light elastic string has natural length l and modulus of elasticity λ. It is slowly stretched until its length is $l + x$. Prove that the work done in so stretching it is $\frac{1}{2}\lambda x^2/l$. (Any statement made about 'average tension' must be proved.)

One end of a light elastic string of natural length a and modulus $2mg$ is fastened to the point O of a smooth plane whose inclination to the horizontal is 30°. The other end of the string is fastened to a particle P of mass m. P is held at O and then released. Show that it first comes to instantaneous rest at a distance $2a$ from O. Show also that the time taken from its release to its return to O is

$$\left(\frac{a}{2g}\right)^{1/2}\{4\sqrt{2} + 2\sin^{-1}(\tfrac{1}{3}) + \pi\}. \qquad (C)$$

2. A particle P of mass m is attached to A by a light elastic string of modulus λ and natural length a. It is also attached to B by a light elastic string of modulus 2λ and natural length $\frac{1}{2}a$. The points A and B are fixed on a smooth horizontal plane at a distance $4a$ apart. Find the distance of the position of equilibrium, E, of P from A. The particle P is projected from E towards A with speed u. After time t, the displacement of P from E in the direction BA is x. Show that as long as both strings remain taut

$$\frac{d^2x}{dt^2} + \frac{5\lambda}{am}x = 0.$$

Show that if $4mu^2 \leqslant 5a\lambda$ then P will execute complete cycles of simple harmonic motion.

If, on the other hand, $u = (5a\lambda/m)^{1/2}$, find the time between the instant of projection of P and the instant when PB first goes slack. *(C)*

3. A particle of mass m is suspended from a fixed point A by a light elastic string of natural length l and modulus of elasticity $4mg$. If the particle is given a small vertical displacement from the equilibrium position, show that it will move with simple harmonic motion of period $\pi\sqrt{(l/g)}$.

The particle is held at A and then released. It falls and comes momentarily to rest at a point B. Calculate the distance AB.

At the instant when the particle reaches B it picks up a second particle of mass $5m$ which was stationary at B. Find the amplitude of the subsequent motion and the time that elapses before the combined particle next comes to rest. *(AEB)*

4. One end of a light spring of natural length a and modulus of elasticity $2mg$ is fastened to a fixed point O. The spring hangs vertically and in equilibrium with a particle of mass m attached to its lower end. Write down an expression for the potential energy of the spring.

When a horizontal force F acts on the particle, the system is in equilibrium with the spring inclined at an angle of 45° to the vertical, the particle being below the level of O. Prove that the depth of the particle below O is then $\frac{1}{2}a(\sqrt{2}+1)$ and that the total potential energy of the particle and the spring has been increased by $\frac{1}{4}mga(5-2\sqrt{2})$. *(C)*

5. Two fixed points A and B on a smooth horizontal table are at a distance $10a$ apart. A particle of mass m lies between A and B. It is attached to A by means of a light elastic string of modulus λ and natural length $2a$ and to B by means of a light elastic string of modulus 2λ and natural length $5a$. M is the midpoint of AB and O the point at which the particle would rest in equilibrium. Prove that $\text{OM} = \frac{5}{3}a$.

The particle is released from rest at P, the midpoint of OM. Prove that it moves in simple harmonic motion of amplitude $\frac{5}{6}a$ and period $2\pi/n$, where $n^2 = 9\lambda/10am$.

Show that the speed of the particle when it passes through Q, the midpoint of OP, is $\frac{5}{12}\sqrt{3an}$ and find the time taken by the particle to move the distance from Q to O. *(O & C)*

6. AB is a line of greatest slope of a rough plane which is inclined to the horizontal at an angle θ, where $\sin\theta = \frac{3}{5}$. The point A is below the level of B and the distance AB is 1 m. A particle P, of mass 0.1 kg, rests on the plane at a point of AB between A and B, and two light elastic strings, each of natural length 0.4 m and modulus of elasticity 4 N, connect P to A and to B. The coefficient of friction between P and the plane is $\frac{1}{2}$. The lowest point on the line AB at which P can rest in equilibrium is L. Taking g as $10\ \text{m s}^{-2}$, show that AL = 0.45 m. (It may be assumed that neither string is slack at an equilibrium position.)

Calculate the work required to push P slowly up the plane from L to the midpoint of AB. *(C)*

7. A light elastic string has natural length l and modulus $2mg$. One end is attached to a particle P of mass m which is free to move on a fixed smooth horizontal table. The other end of the string is attached to a fixed point A which is at a distance $\frac{5}{4}l$ vertically above the point O of the table. The string passes through a small smooth ring which is fixed at a point distant l vertically below A. Show that while the particle is moving on the table the reaction between P and the table is independent of the distance OP.

The particle P is at rest at O. Another particle Q, of mass $3m$, is at a point B of the table where $OB = 3l$. The particle Q is projected along the table towards P with speed $4\sqrt{(2gl)}$ so that it collides with and adheres to P. Show that the subsequent motion of the composite particle is simple harmonic and find the period and amplitude of this motion. Show that the time taken from the initial projection of Q until its first return to B as a composite particle is

$$\frac{9+28\pi}{24}\sqrt{\left(\frac{2l}{g}\right)}.$$

(C)

8. A particle of mass m is attached to two elastic strings each of natural length a. The first string has modulus $3mg$ and its other end is attached to a fixed point A. The second string has modulus $6mg$ and its other end is attached to a fixed point B, which is at a distance $3a$ vertically below A. Show that the particle can rest in equilibrium at a point O between A and B with both strings taut. Find the distance y of O from A.

The particle is in motion in the line AB with both strings taut. At time t the particle is at P where OP = x. Prove that

$$\frac{d^2x}{dt^2} = -\frac{9g}{a}x.$$

The particle is projected vertically upwards from the point at a distance $2a$ below A with speed u. Find the maximum value of u for which the upper string does not become slack in the subsequent motion.

For this maximum value of u find the time taken for the particle to travel from O to its highest point. *(O & C)*

Centre of gravity

Revision exercise 9

1. A uniform solid right circular cone has its top removed by cutting the cone by a plane parallel to its base, leaving a truncated cone of height h, the radii of its ends being r and $4r$. Show that the distance of the centre of gravity of the truncated cone from its broader end is $\frac{9}{28}h$. *(O & C)*

2. Find the area of the finite region D contained between the x-axis and the curve $y = x(2-x)^2$, and find the volume of the solid of revolution obtained by rotating D through 2π radians about the x-axis.
   From your answers, deduce (without further integration) the y coordinate of the centroid of D. *(O & C)*

3. A uniform thin sheet of paper has the shape of a rectangle OABC, where OA = 20 cm and OC = 12 cm.
   The side AB is folded down so as to lie entirely along OA. Find the distances of the centre of gravity of the folded sheet from OA and OC. *(O & C)*

4. Use integration to prove that the centre of gravity of a uniform right circular cone of height h is at a distance $\frac{1}{4}h$ from the centre of the base.
   A uniform solid concrete pillar used in a motorway bridge construction is a frustum of a right circular cone. The radii of its circular ends are 3 m and 1 m, the centres of these ends being A and B, respectively, and AB is of length 26 m. Calculate the distance of the centre of gravity of the pillar from A.
   The pillar is lifted by two vertical cables, one attached at each end, and held at rest with AB horizontal. Find the ratio of the tensions in the two cables. *(AEB)*

5. State the position of G, the centre of gravity of a uniform triangular lamina ABC.
   Prove that the centre of gravity of three particles of equal mass, placed at A, B and C, is also at G.
   A uniform rectangular lamina PQRS has PQ $= 9a$ and QR $= 6a$. The point T is on RS and RT $= 3a$. The triangular lamina QRT is cut away to leave the lamina PQTS. Find the distances of the centre of gravity of the lamina PQTS from PQ and PS.
   The lamina PQTS hangs in equilibrium in a vertical plane with the vertex Q smoothly hinged to a fixed point. Calculate, to the nearest degree, the angle made by QP with the vertical. *(AEB)*

6. A solid hemisphere of radius a and a solid right circular cone of height h and base radius a are made from the same uniform material and are joined together with their plane faces completely in contact. O is the centre of the common base. Find the position of the centre of gravity of the whole body.
   a) The body is suspended freely from a point A on the edge of the common base and hangs in equilibrium under gravity. If $h = 3a$, find, correct to the nearest degree, the acute angle made by AO with the vertical.
   b) The body is found to rest in equilibrium when it is placed on a horizontal table with *any* point of its hemispherical surface in contact with the table. Find h in terms of a. *(O & C)*

7. Figure E.5 shows a uniform rectangular lamina OXZY with sides OX = YZ $= 4a$ and OY = XZ $= 3a$. The points P and Q on OX and YZ, respectively, are such that PX = QZ $= a$, and the points R and S on OY and PQ are such that RY = SQ $= a$. The lamina is folded through 180° about PQ. Find the coordinates of the centre of mass of the folded lamina relative to OX and OY as axes.

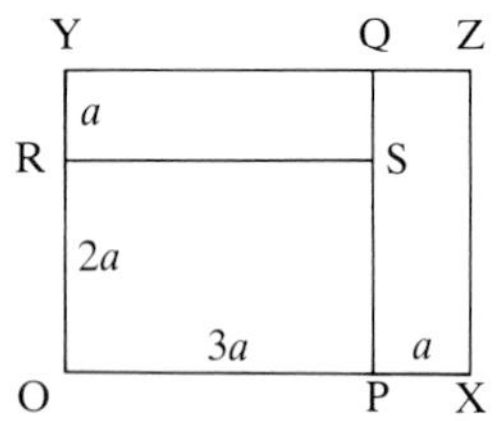

Figure E.5

The once-folded lamina is folded again, through 180° about RS. Find the coordinates of the centre of mass of the twice-folded lamina.
The twice-folded lamina is suspended from R and hangs in equilibrium. Find the tangent of the angle of inclination of RO to the vertical. *(C)*

8. A uniform semicircular lamina is of radius $3a$. The centre of its bounding diameter BC is O and its centre of gravity is at the point G. Show by integration that G is at a distance $4a/\pi$ from BC.

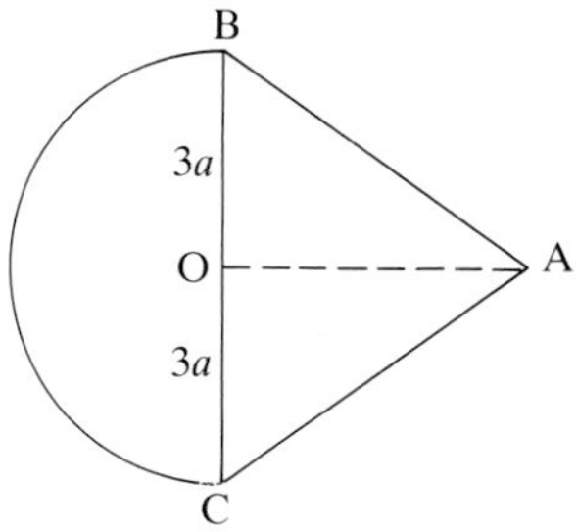

Figure E.6

The uniform plane lamina L shown in figure E.6 consists of the semicircular lamina and the isosceles triangular lamina ABC in which $OA = x$ and $AB = AC$. Given that the centre of gravity of L is at O, show that $x = 3a\sqrt{2}$.

The weight of L is W and a particle of weight W is attached at C. The lamina is smoothly hinged at A to a fixed point and can rotate freely in its own plane which is vertical. Calculate, in terms of a and W, the magnitude of the couple which would be required to keep L in equilibrium with AB horizontal. (*AEB*)

9. Prove that the centroid of a uniform solid hemisphere of radius a is at a distance $\frac{3}{8}a$ from O, the centre of its plane face.

   The hemisphere is suspended by two vertical strings, one fastened at O and the other at a point P on the rim of the plane face. Given that the tension in one string is three times the tension in the other string, find the two possible values of the tangent of the angle made by OP with the horizontal. (*L*)

10. The region defined by the inequalities

$$0 \leqslant x \leqslant a, \quad 0 \leqslant y^2 \leqslant 4ax, \quad y \geqslant 0$$

is rotated through 2π radians about the x-axis to give the solid of revolution V_1. Find, in terms of a and π,

a) the volume of V_1,

b) the position of the centroid of V_1.

The same region is rotated through 2π radians about the y-axis to give the solid of revolution V_2. Find, in terms of a and π, the volume of V_2. (*L*)

APPENDIX

Vectors and vector diagrams

On vector diagrams, vectors of unknown magnitude are generally shown by letters in bold type. If the magnitude is known, then this, together with the units is shown. In both cases the direction of the vector is indicated by an arrow, e.g., in figure A.1 **F** and **C** are of undisclosed magnitude.

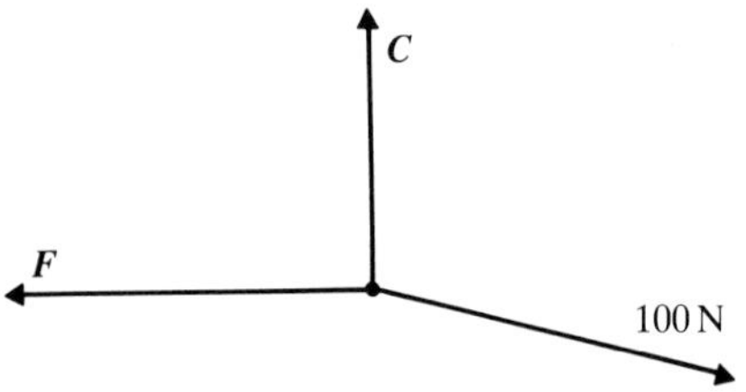

Figure A.1

In some cases, where forces of the same magnitude act in different directions, for example in problems involving connected particles, a letter is given to denote the magnitude of the force (not in bold type) and an arrow given to indicate the direction.

If the direction of a vector is unknown, it may be indicated by a wavy line, as shown in figure A.2.

Figure A.2

Use of double arrows

Acceleration and mass-acceleration vectors carry double arrows as in figure A.3. A double arrow may also be used to indicate the resultant in a vector polygon, e.g. if ***A***, ***B*** and ***C*** in figure A.4 are forces, ***R*** is their resultant.

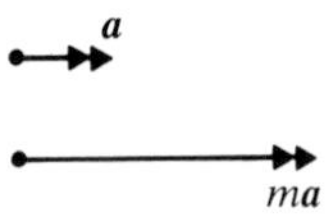

Figure A.3

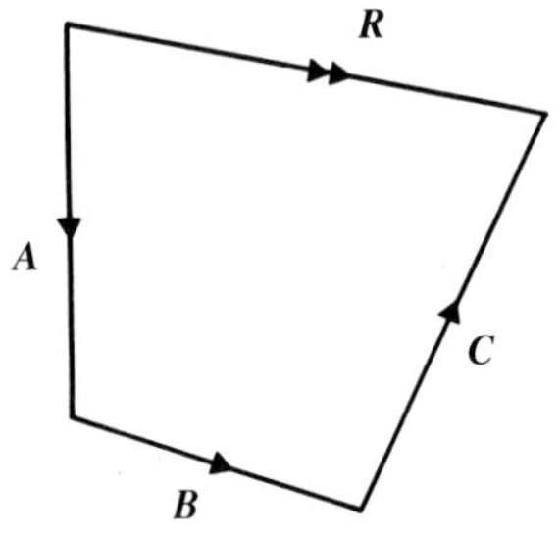

Figure A.4

Units and dimensions

The fundamental quantities in mechanics are mass (M), length (L) and time (T). All other quantities used are derived from these three. For example,

$$\text{speed} = \frac{\text{distance (length)}}{\text{time}}.$$

We denote mass, length and time by the symbols M, L and T, so so that speed is associated with the symbol

$$\frac{\mathrm{L}}{\mathrm{T}} = \mathrm{L\,T^{-1}}$$

We say that $\mathrm{L\,T^{-1}}$ are the dimensions of speed, and write

$$[\text{speed}] = \mathrm{L\,T^{-1}}$$

The dimensions of vector quantities are given by the dimensions of their components.

Thus $$[\text{velocity}] = [\text{speed}] = \mathrm{L\,T^{-1}}$$

If follows that $$[\text{acceleration}] = \mathrm{L\,T^{-2}}$$

In all equations involving physical quantities, the dimensions of all terms must be the same.

This rule is used to derive dimensions of important quantities as they appear in the text, although a summary of results is given in table 1.

SI units are used throughout this book, together with their decimal multiples, which are formed by attaching prefixes to them. Common examples are:

μ	10^{-6}	micro	M	10^{6}	mega
m	10^{-3}	milli	k	10^{3}	kilo
c	10^{-2}	centi	n	10^{9}	nano

Examples: 1 kg = 1000 g
1 m = 100 cm
1 km = 1000 m

Also of importance is 1 t (tonne) = 10^3 kg. The most common non-SI unit used is the hour. It is useful to remember the conversion factor

$$1\ \mathrm{km\,h^{-1}} \leftrightarrow \tfrac{5}{18}\ \mathrm{m\,s^{-1}}.$$

Table 1

Quantity	Unit	Dimensional symbol	Conventional variables
mass	kg	M	m
length	m	L	s, d, r, l
time	s	T	t
velocity	$\mathrm{m\,s^{-1}}$	$\mathrm{L\,T^{-1}}$	v
angular velocity	$\mathrm{rad\,s^{-1}}$	$\mathrm{T^{-1}}$	ω
acceleration	$\mathrm{m\,s^{-2}}$	$\mathrm{L\,T^{-2}}$	a, f
force	N	$\mathrm{M\,L\,T^{-2}}$	F, R, C, P, T
momentum	N s	$\mathrm{M\,L\,T^{-1}}$	p
moment	N m	$\mathrm{M\,L^2\,T^{-2}}$	G
impulse	N s	$\mathrm{M\,L\,T^{-1}}$	I
work	J	$\mathrm{M\,L^2\,T^{-2}}$	W
kinetic energy	J	$\mathrm{M\,L^2\,T^{-2}}$	T
power	W	$\mathrm{M\,L^2\,T^{-3}}$	P

In algebraic examples, standard SI units are understood and are not necessarily stated. Thus, if a force $\boldsymbol{F}$ acts on a particle of mass m, then the magnitude of $\boldsymbol{F}$ is understood to be in newtons and the mass m is understood to be in kilograms.

ANSWERS

Answers are given to 3 s.f., where appropriate.

Exercise 1A

1. $\boldsymbol{a} + 2\boldsymbol{b},\ -2\boldsymbol{a} + 3\boldsymbol{b},\ 2\boldsymbol{a} - \boldsymbol{b},\ \boldsymbol{a} - 3\boldsymbol{b},\ -\boldsymbol{a} - 2\boldsymbol{b},$
   $-2\boldsymbol{a} + \boldsymbol{b}$
2. (a) (1, 3) (b) (0.5, 2.5) (c) (3, 5)
3. (a) (3, 1), (1, 2), (− 1, 3), (− 3, 4), (− 5, 5)
   (b) $2y + x = 5$
4. (a) (0, 0), (1, 1), (2, 4), (3, 9)...
   (b) $y = x^2$
5. $y = 3 \sin x, 0 \leqslant x \leqslant 4\pi$
6. $\mathbf{OP} = 7\cos 20^\circ\, \boldsymbol{i} + 7 \sin 20^\circ\, \boldsymbol{j} = 6.58\boldsymbol{i} + 2.39\boldsymbol{j}$,
   $\mathbf{PQ} = -10 \sin 50^\circ\, \boldsymbol{i} + 10 \cos 50^\circ\, \boldsymbol{j} = -7.66\boldsymbol{i} + 6.43\boldsymbol{j}$,
   $\mathbf{OQ} = -1.08\boldsymbol{i} + 8.82\boldsymbol{j}$
7. 20.7 east, 77.3 south, 20.7 west, all in nautical miles
8. 30.5 km east, 26.8 km north
9. 234 km up, 95 km along, distance 253 km
10. $-6.43\hat{\boldsymbol{u}} - 7.66\hat{\boldsymbol{v}}$

Exercise 1B

1. (a) 108.4° (b) 60° (c) 78.7° (d) 120.2°
2. (a) 3.74 (b) $\dfrac{1}{\sqrt{14}}\begin{pmatrix}1\\2\\3\end{pmatrix} = \begin{pmatrix}0.267\\0.535\\0.802\end{pmatrix}$
3. (a) $t = 1$ (b) $t = \frac{4}{9}$
4. 12.1
5. (a) 22.8, 30.3° (b) 8.06, 60.3° (c) 7.09, 85.8°
6. (a) 3.61, bearing 011.3°
   (b) 3.61, bearing 191.3°
7. (b) 150, bearing 062.3°
8. 3.47, 8.79

Exercise 2A

1. (a) $-1.5\boldsymbol{i} + 0.5\boldsymbol{j}$ (b) $4.5\boldsymbol{i} - 3\boldsymbol{j}$ (c) $-4.5\boldsymbol{i} - 1.5\boldsymbol{j}$
   (d) $-0.5\boldsymbol{i} - 1.67\boldsymbol{j}$
2. $-6.88\boldsymbol{i} - 9.83\boldsymbol{j}$
3. $4\boldsymbol{i}$
4. (a) $y = \frac{1}{4}x^2 - 1$

interval:	0–1	1–2	2–3	3–4
average $\boldsymbol{v}$:	$2\boldsymbol{i} + \boldsymbol{j}$	$2\boldsymbol{i} + 3\boldsymbol{j}$	$2\boldsymbol{i} + 5\boldsymbol{j}$	$2\boldsymbol{i} + 7\boldsymbol{j}$

   (b)

t:	0	1	2	3	4
$\boldsymbol{v}$:	$2\boldsymbol{i}$	$2\boldsymbol{i} + 2\boldsymbol{j}$	$2\boldsymbol{i} + 4\boldsymbol{j}$	$2\boldsymbol{i} + 6\boldsymbol{j}$	$2\boldsymbol{i} + 8\boldsymbol{j}$

5. path: $y = 3 \sin x$,
   $\boldsymbol{v} = \boldsymbol{i} + 3 \cos 2\boldsymbol{j} = \boldsymbol{i} - 1.25\boldsymbol{j}$
6. $\binom{30}{6}$
7. $v = \sqrt{600} \approx 24.5$
8. $x^2 + y^2 = 16$

t:	0	0.5	1	1.5	2
$\boldsymbol{r}$	$4\boldsymbol{i}$	$4\boldsymbol{j}$	$-4\boldsymbol{i}$	$-4\boldsymbol{j}$	$4\boldsymbol{i}$

interval:	0 − 0.5	0.5 − 1	0 − 1	1 − 2
average $\boldsymbol{v}$:	$8\boldsymbol{j} - 8\boldsymbol{i}$	$-8\boldsymbol{i} - 8\boldsymbol{j}$	$-8\boldsymbol{i}$	$8\boldsymbol{i}$

9.

t:	0.5	1	1.5	2
$\boldsymbol{r}$:	$15\boldsymbol{i} + 3.75\boldsymbol{j}$	$30\boldsymbol{i} + 5\boldsymbol{j}$	$45\boldsymbol{i} + 3.75\boldsymbol{j}$	$60\boldsymbol{i}$
$\boldsymbol{v}$:		$30\boldsymbol{i}$		$30\boldsymbol{i} - 15\boldsymbol{j}$

   t: 2.5
   $\boldsymbol{r}$: $75\boldsymbol{i} - 6.25\boldsymbol{j}$

10. $\dfrac{4}{5\sqrt{5}}\begin{pmatrix}1\\2\end{pmatrix}$, $\boldsymbol{r} = \begin{pmatrix}0\\1\end{pmatrix} + \dfrac{4t}{5\sqrt{5}}\begin{pmatrix}1\\2\end{pmatrix} = \begin{pmatrix}0.358t\\1 + 0.716t\end{pmatrix}$

Exercise 2B

1. (a)

t:	0	1	2	3	4
$\boldsymbol{v}$:	$2\boldsymbol{i}$	$2\boldsymbol{i} + 2\boldsymbol{j}$	$2\boldsymbol{i} + 4\boldsymbol{j}$	$2\boldsymbol{i} + 6\boldsymbol{j}$	$2\boldsymbol{i} + 8\boldsymbol{j}$
av. $\boldsymbol{a}$:		$2\boldsymbol{j}$	$2\boldsymbol{j}$	$2\boldsymbol{j}$	$2\boldsymbol{j}$

   (b) $\boldsymbol{a} = 2\boldsymbol{j}$ (constant)
   (d) $y = \frac{1}{4}x^2$

2. $\boldsymbol{r} = 30\boldsymbol{i} + 30\boldsymbol{j} + 45\boldsymbol{k}$, $\boldsymbol{v} = 10\boldsymbol{i} + 10\boldsymbol{j} + 30\boldsymbol{k}$, $\boldsymbol{a} = 10\boldsymbol{k}$

3. $\boldsymbol{v} = \boldsymbol{i} + 3\cos t\,\boldsymbol{j}$, $\boldsymbol{a} = -3\sin t\,\boldsymbol{j}$, $\boldsymbol{v}\cdot\boldsymbol{a} = -9\sin t\cos t$

4. (i) $\boldsymbol{v} = (4t+8)\boldsymbol{i} + (20-3t)\boldsymbol{j}$ (ii) $\boldsymbol{a} = 4\boldsymbol{i} - 6t\boldsymbol{j}$
   (iii) $\boldsymbol{v}\cdot\boldsymbol{a} = 32 - 104t + 18t^3$

5. $\boldsymbol{v} = \binom{-4}{-8}$, $\boldsymbol{a} = \binom{-2}{-4}$, path: $y = 2x - 6$, $\boldsymbol{r}\cdot\boldsymbol{a} = 0$
   when $t = \sqrt{0.6} = 0.77$ s

6. $\boldsymbol{r} = 2\hat{\boldsymbol{u}} + 424t\,(\hat{\boldsymbol{n}} - \hat{\boldsymbol{e}})$

7. t: 0, 1, 2
   $\boldsymbol{v}$: $30\boldsymbol{i} + 10\boldsymbol{j}$, $30\boldsymbol{i}$, $30\boldsymbol{i} - 10\boldsymbol{j}$
   $\boldsymbol{a}$: $-10\boldsymbol{j}$, $-10\boldsymbol{j}$, $-10\boldsymbol{j}$

8. t: 0, $\frac{1}{2}\pi$, π
   $\boldsymbol{v}$: $2\boldsymbol{j}$, $-2\boldsymbol{i}$, $-2\boldsymbol{j}$
   $\boldsymbol{a}$: $-2\boldsymbol{i}$, $-2\boldsymbol{j}$, $2\boldsymbol{i}$
   path: $x^2 + y^2 = 4$

9. $\boldsymbol{v} = -2t\sin t\,\boldsymbol{i} + 2t\cos t\,\boldsymbol{j}$,
   $\boldsymbol{a} = -(2\sin t + 4t\cos t)\boldsymbol{i} + (2\cos t - 4t\sin t)\boldsymbol{j}$,
   path: $x^2 + y^2 = 1$

10. $\boldsymbol{v} = -2(1+t)^{-2}\boldsymbol{i} + 2\boldsymbol{j}$, $\boldsymbol{a} = 4(1+t)^{-3}\boldsymbol{j}$,
    path: $xy = 4$

Exercise 2C

1. $a = 3$ m s^{-2}, $s = 150$ m
2. 4.5 m s^{-2}
3. $\boldsymbol{v} = -3\boldsymbol{i} + 4\boldsymbol{j}$, (3, 10)
4. $\boldsymbol{v} = (1+3t)\boldsymbol{i} + (2-4t)\boldsymbol{j}$, $\boldsymbol{r} = (t + 1.5t^2)\boldsymbol{i} + (2t - 2t^2)\boldsymbol{j}$,
   $t = 1$
5. $\boldsymbol{v} = 20\boldsymbol{i} - 10t\boldsymbol{j}$, speed $= 22.4$ m s^{-1} at 26.6° below the horizontal
6. $a = 1$ m s^{-2}, speed 8.5 m s^{-1}
7. 7.5 m
9. 1.5 miles, 2 miles
10. B wins by 1 s, distance from the tape is 60 m

Exercise 2D

1. 7.75 m s^{-1}
2. 1.25 s, 2.19 m below the board
3. 3 s, 77.9 m
4. (a) 5 s (b) 130 m (c) 43.6 m s^{-1}
   (d) 53.4° to the horizontal
5. No, 8.5 m short
6. 20.9 m s^{-1} at 21.8° to the horizontal
7. (a) 2 m short (b) yes, by 0.1 m
8. 7.77 m s^{-1}, 65.9°
9. No

Exercise 2E

1. 1.02 m s^{-1}, 8.34 m s^{-2}
2. 251 rad s^{-1}
3. 29.7 km s^{-1}, 5.91×10^{-3} m s^{-2}
4. 2.62×10^{-3} rad s^{-1}
5. 61.7 rad s^{-1}
6. 20.6 m s^{-1}, 19.4 m s^{-1}
7. 25 rad s^{-1}, 50 rad s^{-1}
8. 6.67 rad s^{-1}
9. 11.1 rad s^{-1}
10. (a) 0.5 m s^{-1} (b) 10 rad s^{-1}, 5 rad s^{-1}
11. $$x = \frac{r^2\omega^2 \sin 2\theta}{2g} + r\sin\theta + \frac{r\omega\cos\theta}{g}\{r^2\omega^2\sin^2\theta + 2gr(1-\cos\theta)\}^{1/2}$$
12. (a) $v = 6t^2$ m s^{-1}, $\boldsymbol{a} = -18t^4\hat{\boldsymbol{r}} + 12t\hat{\boldsymbol{n}}$
    (b) 289 m s^{-2}, at an angle of 4.76° to the inward radius vector
13. on entering, $\boldsymbol{a} = 5\hat{\boldsymbol{u}} - 18\hat{\boldsymbol{r}}$, $a = 18.7$ m s^{-2}
    on leaving, $\boldsymbol{a} = 5\hat{\boldsymbol{u}} - 2.29\hat{\boldsymbol{r}}$, $a = 5.50$ m s^{-2}
14. 0 m s^{-1}, $r\omega^2$ m s^{-2} downwards,
    $v = \omega\{r\sin\theta + r^2\sin\theta\cos\theta(l^2 - r^2\sin^2\theta)^{-1/2}\}$

Exercise 2F

1. (a) 53.1° (b) 12.5 s
2. 33.2 m
3. 50.6° to the vertical
4. 80.6 km h^{-1}, 029.7°
5. AB: 8.27 s, BC: 10.33 s, CA: 12.9 s
6. 32.7 km
7. 27.7 m, 23.1 m, 15.4 m
8. 8.49 mph from NE

9. (a) 1.67 h (b) 2.43 h
10. 024.3°, 13 17
11. (a) $(1-t)\hat{\boldsymbol{e}} - 6t\hat{\boldsymbol{n}} + 3t\hat{\boldsymbol{u}}$
    (b) $-\hat{\boldsymbol{e}} - 6\hat{\boldsymbol{n}} + 3\hat{\boldsymbol{u}}$
    (c) $\frac{1}{46}$
12. $\boldsymbol{v}_A(B) = (20 \sin t - 25 \sin \frac{5}{6}t)\boldsymbol{i} + (25 \cos \frac{5}{6}t - 20 \cos t)\boldsymbol{j}$,
    18.8 s

Exercise 3B

1. (a) 9N (b) 75 N (c) 0.6 N (d) 0.006 N (c) 0.045 N
2. 16.7 s
3. 4 s, $\binom{23}{-14}$
4. 4 m s^{-2}
5. 2.5 m s^{-2}
6. 20 N
7. 25 N
8. 3 m s^{-2}, 6 N, both are directed towards the centre of the circle
9. 1389 N
10. $\boldsymbol{v} = \begin{pmatrix} -2 \sin t \\ 2 \cos t \end{pmatrix}$, $\boldsymbol{a} = \begin{pmatrix} -2 \cos t \\ -2 \sin t \end{pmatrix}$, $\boldsymbol{F} = \begin{pmatrix} -6 \cos t \\ -6 \sin t \end{pmatrix}$,
    $F = 6 \text{ N}$
11. (a) $2.75 \times 10^8 \text{ m s}^{-1}$ (b) $2.14 \times 10^8 \text{ m s}^{-1}$
12. 2000 N
13. (a) 29.2 m s^{-1}, at 59° to the original direction
    (b) 21.8 m s^{-1}, 83.4°
    (c) 14.2 m s^{-1}, 118°
14. 0.0366 N
15. (a) $-1600 \cos 2t\, \boldsymbol{i} - 1600 \sin 2t\, \boldsymbol{j} - 900 \sin 3t\, \boldsymbol{k}$
    (b) tension/thrust in the arm, gravity, air resistance
    (c) $-640 \cos 2t\, \boldsymbol{i} - 640 \sin 2t\, \boldsymbol{j} - 360 \sin 3t\, \boldsymbol{k}$, contact forces between the child and the seat, gravity
16. (a) none, it is dimensionless
    (b) T^{-1}
    (c) $\text{M L}^{-1} \text{T}^{-2}$
17. (a) 100 N (b) 300 N
18. (a) $(-11.9\boldsymbol{i} - 4.66\boldsymbol{j}) \text{ m s}^{-2}$ (b) $(-2.98\boldsymbol{i} - 1.17\boldsymbol{j})$ N
19. $\begin{pmatrix} 5\frac{1}{3} \\ 8 \end{pmatrix} \text{m s}^{-1}$, $\begin{pmatrix} 2\frac{2}{3} \\ 5\frac{1}{3} \end{pmatrix} \text{m}$
20. (a) $\boldsymbol{v} = 0.25\boldsymbol{i} + \cos 4\boldsymbol{j} = 0.25\boldsymbol{i} - 0.654\boldsymbol{j}$
    (b) $\boldsymbol{F} = -0.5\boldsymbol{i} + 8 \sin 4\boldsymbol{j} = -0.5\boldsymbol{i} - 6.05\boldsymbol{j}$

Exercise 3D

1. 6.6×10^{-7} N
2. 6.02×10^{24} kg
3. 2.34×10^{-6}
4. $\frac{1}{100}$
5. 1.41 h
6. 116 N
7. 0.3%
8. 4.2×10^4 km
9. (a) $r\omega^2 = g$
10. $F_A/F_O = 1 + 2R/r$, $F_B/F_O = 1 - 2R/r$, RF_O/r

Exercise 3E

2. (a) 392 N (b) 318 N (c) 352 N
3. (b) (i) 13 m s^{-2} (ii) 11.3 m s^{-2}
4. 3.03 m s^{-2}
5. 1000 N
6. 32 N
7. 1531 N, 0.98 m s^{-2}
8. 0.263 m s^{-2}
9. 5.88 m s^{-2}, 23.34 m s^{-2}, 58.2 m downwards
10. 18.8 m s^{-1}
11. 5850 N, 910 N
12. 1.75 m s^{-2}, 11 m s^{-1}, 18.3 m s^{-1}
13. 1 min, 900 m
14. 13.3 s, 133 m
15. 95.6 km h^{-1}

Exercise 3F

1. 489 N
2. 48.7 N, 3.09 m s^{-2}
3. 3490 N, 0.266 m s^{-2}
4. 0.0894 m s^{-2}

5. In the direction of the 35 N force
6. $0.268\ \mathrm{m\,s^{-2}}$
7. $0.871\ \mathrm{m\,s^{-2}}$, $28.8°$
8. $2.5\ \mathrm{m\,s^{-2}}$, bearing $250°$
9. 459.8 N
10. 9.17×10^4 N, 6.34×10^6 N
11. $0.978\ \mathrm{m\,s^{-2}}$, 6.89×10^5 N
12. 7.73×10^5 N, $0.849\ \mathrm{m\,s^{-2}}$

Exercise 3G

1. 3×10^4 N, $0.0143\ \mathrm{m\,s^{-2}}$
2. 5000 N (a) 10 000 N (b) 5710 N
3. 866 N, 2500 N
   initial acceleration $5\ \mathrm{m\,s^{-2}}$ at $30°$ to the horizontal
4. (a) 1.1×10^4 N, 1×10^3 N
   (b) 1.32×10^4 N, 1.2×10^3 N
   (c) 8.8×10^3 N, 8×10^2 N
5. (a) 300 N (b) 100 N
6. (a) $0.5\ \mathrm{m\,s^{-2}}$ (b) 4 N
7. (a) 15 750 N (b) (i) $0.678\ \mathrm{m\,s^{-2}}$ (ii) $16.6\ \mathrm{m\,s^{-1}}$
   (c) (i) $1.36\ \mathrm{m\,s^{-2}}$ downwards
   (ii) $10.5\ \mathrm{m\,s^{-1}}$ downwards
8. (a) $1.13\ \mathrm{m\,s^{-2}}$ (b) $0.088\ \mathrm{m\,s^{-2}}$
9. $0.226\ \mathrm{m\,s^{-2}}$, 66.4 s (a) 1.41×10^5 N
   (b) 2.82×10^4 N
10. (a) $0.209\ \mathrm{m\,s^{-2}}$ (b) 1284 N
11. (i) (a) 8000 N (b) 500 N
    (ii) (a) 10 400 N (b) 650 N
    (iii) (a) 5600 N (b) 350 N
12. 6970 N, 595 N, 9430 N, 805 N
13. 2.4×10^4 N, 600 N, $0.0107\ \mathrm{m\,s^{-2}}$, 6.86×10^3 N

Exercise 3H

1. $1.43\ \mathrm{m\,s^{-2}}$, 34.3 N
2. $5.71\ \mathrm{m\,s^{-2}}$, 17.1 N
3. $1.53\ \mathrm{m\,s^{-2}}$, 19.6 N, $59°$
4. $\dfrac{2m_1m_2g}{(m_1+m_2)}, \dfrac{(m_1-m_2)g}{(m_1+m_2)}$
5. (a) $2.5\ \mathrm{m\,s^{-2}}$ (b) 0.75 N (c) 1.5 N
6. $2.41\ \mathrm{m\,s^{-2}}$, 37.9 N
7. $T_1 = 20.9$ N, $T_2 = 23.6$ N, $0.536\ \mathrm{m\,s^{-2}}$
8. 14.4 N, $0.188\ \mathrm{m\,s^{-2}}$ up the slope
9. $\dfrac{(m_1-m_2)g}{(m_1+m_2+M)}$
10. (a) $2\ \mathrm{m\,s^{-2}}, 2\ \mathrm{m\,s^{-2}}, 6\ \mathrm{m\,s^{-2}}$ (b) 64 N, 32 N, 16 N
11. $12\frac{6}{7}$ N, $\frac{10}{7}\ \mathrm{m\,s^{-2}}$, $\frac{20}{7}\ \mathrm{m\,s^{-2}}$
12. (a) $2\ \mathrm{m\,s^{-2}}$, 48 N
    (b) $\frac{10}{9}\ \mathrm{m\,s^{-2}}$, $\frac{10}{9}\ \mathrm{m\,s^{-2}}$, $\frac{10}{3}\ \mathrm{m\,s^{-2}}$

Exercise 3I

1. 312.5 N
2. $16.7°$
3. $19.1\ \mathrm{m\,s^{-1}}$
4. $50\ \mathrm{m\,s^{-2}}$, 2800 N, 4200 N
5. $104\ \mathrm{m\,s^{-1}}$, 1.06×10^6 N
6. $\sqrt{50}\ \mathrm{rad\,s^{-1}}$
7. (a) 0.27 N (b) $56.3°$
8. 6.94 cm
9. 2 cm, $\sqrt{5}\ \mathrm{rad\,s^{-1}}$
10. $2.23\ \mathrm{m\,s^{-1}}$
11. 394 N, 364 N, 1300 N
12. $\tan^{-1}\frac{3}{5} = 30.96°$, $\tan^{-1}\frac{1}{2} = 26.57$
13. $\omega^2 = \dfrac{g\cot\theta}{(r + l\cos\theta)}$
14. $5.48\ \mathrm{m\,s^{-1}}$
15. (a) $\dfrac{-48}{\pi}\boldsymbol{i}$ (b) $\dfrac{-48\,000}{\pi}\boldsymbol{i}$
    (c) 7.27×10^4 N at $8.06°$ to the line AC
    (d) 7.27×10^4 N at $8.06°$ to the line CA
16. (a) $(10\boldsymbol{i} - 17.3\boldsymbol{j})\ \mathrm{m\,s^{-1}}$ (b) $(7.93\boldsymbol{i} - 4\boldsymbol{j})\ \mathrm{m\,s^{-2}}$
    (c) $(357\boldsymbol{i} - 180\boldsymbol{j})$ N
17. (a) $T = m(g\cos\alpha + l\omega^2\sin^2\alpha)$,
    $R = m\sin\alpha\,(g + l\omega^2\cos\alpha)/\cos 2\alpha$

Exercise 4A

1. 11.3 s
2. $2\ \mathrm{m\,s^{-2}}$, 200 m
4. $3\frac{1}{3}\ \mathrm{m\,s^{-1}}$, $\frac{1}{18}\ \mathrm{m\,s^{-2}}$, 19 m, 54 s
5. $1.15\ \mathrm{m\,s^{-1}}$

6. 15 s, 2.29 m s^{-2}
7. 23 m s^{-1}, 143.5 m
8. $\frac{4}{5}$
9. 1 m s^{-1}
10. 35.4 s

Exercise 4B

1. $v = 13\frac{2}{3}$, $s = 29\frac{1}{15}$
2. t = 1 s. s = 10.75
3. $v = 4\pi^2 \approx 39.5$
   $s = \frac{1}{3}\pi(8\pi^2 - 3) \approx 79.5$
4. 1.06 s
5. $v = 0.9$, $s = 9 - \ln 10$
6. (a) $10\frac{2}{3}$ m (b) 3.46 s
7. $k = 1$, 45 m.
8. (a) 2.4 km (b) $4(e^{1/2} - 1) = 2.59$ h
9. 111 m s^{-1}, 1304 m

Exercise 4C

1. 2.3×10^3 m s^{-1}
2. 2.40 km s^{-1}
5. $\dfrac{\pi}{6\sqrt{k}}$

Exercise 4D

3. (b) 0.462 s (c) 0.231 m
4. 45 m, 6 s
   (a) 32.1 m
   (b) 2.4 s
   (c) 21.8 m s^{-1}
   (d) 2.68 s
5. (a) 23.3 m
   (b) 1.83 s

Exercise 5A

1. (a) 3.3×10^4 (b) 0.15 (c) 1×10^9 (d) 3
2. 2.2×10^4 N s
3. 1 N s
4. 15.5 N s at 152° with the initial direction
5. $(6\boldsymbol{i} - 6\boldsymbol{k})Ns(4\boldsymbol{i} + 2\boldsymbol{j} + 2\boldsymbol{k})$m s^{-1}
6. 0.748 N s
7. 22.0° to the $\boldsymbol{j}$-direction, 24.7 m s^{-1}
8. 6×10^4 N s
9. 4.10 N s at 73.5° to boards
10. (a) 96.6° (b) 43.6 m s^{-1}

Exercise 5B

1. (a) 6000 N s (b) 27 m s^{-1}
2. (a) 3 N s (b) O N s (c) gravity, 2 s (d) only (a)
3. (a) 300 N (b) 60 N
4. $(9\boldsymbol{i} + 3\boldsymbol{j} + 1.5\boldsymbol{k})$N s,
   $(0.5\boldsymbol{i} + 4.5\boldsymbol{j} - 1.25\boldsymbol{k})$m s^{-1}
5. (a) 300 N s (b) 27 N s (c) 80 N s (d) 0.586 N s
6. (a) $(2\boldsymbol{i} + 8\boldsymbol{k})$N s (b) $(\frac{1}{4}\pi\boldsymbol{i} + \frac{1}{4}\pi\boldsymbol{j})$N s
7. 1100
8. (a) 15 m s^{-1} (b) 11.25 m s^{-1}, no (c) 15 m s^{-1}
9. $-\frac{1}{3}\boldsymbol{j}$ N s, $-\frac{1}{3}\boldsymbol{j}$ N s

Exercise 5C

1. (a) 3.5 m s^{-1} (b) 3000 N s
2. $(1.8\boldsymbol{i} + 0.8\boldsymbol{j})$ m s^{-1}, 8.74 N s
3. $8\frac{1}{3}$ m s^{-1}, 36.8°
4. 11.0 m s^{-1}
5. 6.68×10^{-27} kg
6. 4.41 m s^{-1}, 2.82 m s^{-1}
7. 2.37 m s^{-1}, 17.6°
8. (a) 1.71 m s^{-1} (b) 329 N s
9. (a) $\frac{5}{16}u\sqrt{3}$ (b) $\frac{3}{8}mu$
10. (a) 69.3 N s (b) 1 m s^{-1}, neither
11. (a) 0.1 m s^{-1} (b) 150 N
12. (a) $\frac{1}{24}$ (b) $\frac{48}{41}d/u$ (c) $\frac{1}{41}d$

Exercise 5D

1. u, $5u$
2. 0.5 kg, 143° to the direction of the 2 kg piece. Yes
3. 6000 Ns
4. 4 m s^{-1}
5. 2.29 m s^{-1}, 346 Ns
6. (a) 1.49 m s^{-1} (b) 60.2° (c) 299 m s^{-1}
7. 0.3125 m s^{-1}, 35 s

8. (a) $2.79\ \text{m s}^{-1}$ (b) 0.173°

Exercise 5E

1. $0.2\ \text{m s}^{-1}$, $1.7\ \text{m s}^{-1}$

3. 0.2

4. $\dfrac{1+e}{1-e}\sqrt{\dfrac{2h}{g}}$

6. 0.5

8. 3

9. 3

10. (a) $\dfrac{d}{u}\left(1+\dfrac{1}{e}\right)$ (b) $\frac{1}{2}u$ (c) $\frac{1}{2}meu$

Exercise 5F

3. 14.5°

6. $4h\,e(e+1)\sin\alpha$

8. (a) $u\sqrt{\frac{1}{3}}$ (b) $\frac{1}{3}$ (c) $mu\sqrt{\frac{1}{3}}$, along the line of centres

Exercise 6A

1. (a) 3500 (b) 90 (c) 2.08×10^5

2. (a) $1.25\ \text{m s}^{-2}$ (b) 422 J

3. 60 000 N

4. 1.44×10^7 N

5. 11 150 N

6. $4\ \text{m s}^{-1}$, 8 m

7. 1.6×10^9 N

8. (a) -18 J (b) -13 J (c) 2 J (d) 18 J

9. 1386 J, $7.68\ \text{m s}^{-1}$

10. 47.3 N

11. $1.67\ \text{m s}^{-1}$

12. $1\ \text{m s}^{-1}$

13. 122.9 J, $2.20\ \text{m s}^{-1}$

Exercise 6B

1. $7.07\ \text{m s}^{-1}$

2. $6\ \text{m s}^{-1}$

3. 4169 N

4. 5.02×10^5 N

5. (a) 2.33×10^7 J (b) 5.83×10^7 J

6. 32.25 N, $15.8\ \text{m s}^{-1}$

7. 921 N

8. $5.48\ \text{m s}^{-1}$, 4.06 m from the bottom of the wall

9. $24.2\ \text{m s}^{-1}$

Exercise 6C

1. $10.2\ \text{m s}^{-1}$, 1632 N, 15.2 m above the ground

2. $3.65\ \text{m s}^{-1}$, 0.668 m

3. $4.16\ \text{m s}^{-1}$, 1.40 m above the lowest point
   Note that the speed was $8.32\ \text{m s}^{-1}$ before the string became taut, but momentum is destroyed radially by the impulsive tension.

4. (a) rises to a height of 0.2 m
   (b) rises to a height of 0.8 m

5. 127°, $2.45\ \text{m s}^{-1}$, 0.192 m

6. $3.75\ \text{m s}^{-1}$, 44.0 N

7. 25.8°

8. $3.16\ \text{m s}^{-1}$

9. $4.83\ \text{m s}^{-1}$, 48.2°, 0.436 m

Exercise 6D

1. $8.37\ \text{m s}^{-1}$

3. $9.42\ \text{m s}^{-1} = 33.9\ \text{km h}^{-1}$

4. $9\ \text{m s}^{-1}$

Exercise 6E

1. $3.67\ \text{m s}^{-1}$, 667 J

2. $\frac{4}{3}\ \text{m s}^{-1}$, $\frac{11}{3}\ \text{m s}^{-1}$, no change in total KE

3. 3.1 cm

4. 6.05×10^5 N

5. $\cos^{-1}(\frac{4}{9}) = 63.6^\circ$

6. (a) $5.44\ \text{m s}^{-1}$ (b) 1.03×10^5 N

7. $3.61\ \text{m s}^{-1}$, 2.86 m

8. $9.33\ \text{km h}^{-1}$, 900 J

9. 9.06°

12. 50.9°

Exercise 6F

1. 25 kW

2. 1.125×10^3 N, 35.6 kW

3. 1562 kW
4. (a) $10\ \text{m s}^{-1}$ (b) 50 W
   (c) 3000 J (d) 5 m
5. 1.543 kW
6. 0.045 kW
7. 622 kW
8. B = 180 N, $107\ \text{km h}^{-1}$, 9.6 min
9. (a) $T = m\int_0^W \frac{v\,dv}{P - Av - Bv^2}$ (b) 2.77 min
10. 8.48×10^4 N.

Exercise 7A

1. 142 N, 181 N
2. 251.2 N
3. (a) $mg \sin\alpha$ (b) $mg \tan\alpha$
4. 13.28 N at an angle 111.3° with the 10 N force
5. 8.39 N
6. (a) $2\cos^{-1}\frac{3}{4} = 82.8°$ (b) 90°
7. $T = 566.7$ N, S = 387.6 N
8. $T_3 = 895$ N, $T_1 = T_2 = 361$ N

Exercise 7B

1. 0.4
2. 0.3, 144 N
3. 3500 N
4. $3333\ \text{Nm}^{-2}$
5. (a) 26.1 N (b) 27.1 N
6. (a) 8–40 N (b) 7.27–80 N
10. $\mu = 2\sin\alpha\frac{1 - \cos\alpha}{2\cos\alpha + \cos 2\alpha}$

Exercise 7C

1. (a) 0.4 (b) 18.6 N at 21.8° to the horizontal
2. (a) 0.566 (b) 19.7 N at 29.5° to the horizontal
3. (a) no (b) 303 N
   (c) 92 N at 36.9° to the line of greatest slope
4. $\alpha = 52.5°$, $\lambda = 7.5°$
5. (a) $mg \sin\alpha$ at α to the horizontal
   (b) $mg \sin 3\alpha$ at 3α to the horizontal

Exercise 7D

1. 0.58
2. (a) 32 N, $8.5\ \text{m s}^{-2}$ (b) 0, 0 (c) 66.6 N, 0
4. 12.5 m
5. 5.36 m
6. (a) yes (b) $\frac{2}{3}g(\tan\alpha - \sin\alpha)$
7. $9.76\ \text{rad s}^{-1}$
8. (a) 9.26 m above B (b) 5.52 s
9. 40 cm
10. $t = \frac{\mu}{g(\sin\alpha + \mu\cos\alpha)}\left[1 + \frac{\sin\alpha + \mu\cos\alpha}{\sin\alpha - \mu\cos\alpha}\right]^{1/2}$

Exercise 7E

1. 27.3 cm
2. 1.875 m from the pivot
3. 40 t, 5 m
4. 1.63 N
5. 4.58×10^4 N
6. 3.44×10^4 N
7. 1803 N
8. 35.2 N
9. At A: 3.56×10^4 N
   At B: 3.44×10^4 N

Exercise 7F

1. 4 N, $y = \frac{1}{4}$
2. -16 N m
3. 2 N, $y = -3$
4. (a) $(3\boldsymbol{i} + 4\boldsymbol{j})$N, -8 N m
   (b) 5 N, $4x - 3y = -8$
5. (a) $(3\boldsymbol{i} - 2\boldsymbol{j})$N, -8 N m
   (b) $(3\boldsymbol{i} - 3\boldsymbol{j})$N, -3 N m
   (c) $\sqrt{13}$ N, $3y + 2x = 8$
6. $\sqrt{97}$ N, $9y - 4x = 31$
7. $\sqrt{50}$ N, $y + 7x = 18$
8. $\sqrt{3}$ N, $\boldsymbol{F} = -\frac{1}{2}\begin{pmatrix} 3 \\ \sqrt{3} \end{pmatrix}$ through P, where **AP** = 2**CA**
9. (a) $4\sqrt{2}$ along AC, $-5a$
   (b) $4\sqrt{2}$, $y - x = -\frac{5}{4}a$
10. $3\sqrt{2}$, $-\sqrt{2}$, $6a$

11. $x = -3,\ y = 3,\ z = -4;$
$x = -7,\ y = 7,\ z = -6$

12. 2 N, $y = \sqrt{3}(2a - x)$

13. 15 N along FA and AO, 21 N along OF

Exercise 7G

1. 520 N, 74° to the horizontal
2. 0.288
3. 0.272
4. 5.81 m
5. AC: 4×10^4 N, BC: 3×10^4 N
6. AC: 5.62×10^4 N, BC: 7.03×10^4 N
7. 0.249W
8. 0.072W
9. $\mu = \cos\theta \sin\theta/(1 + \sin^2\theta)$
10. 0.288
11. 37.9°

Exercise 7H

1. $(Wl \sin 2\alpha)/4a$
2. T is negative
3.

	horizontally	vertically
	$\frac{1}{4}W \cot\alpha(1 + k)$	$\frac{1}{4}W(3 + k)$
	$\frac{1}{4}W \cot\alpha(1 + k)$	$\frac{1}{4}W(1 + 3k)$

4. A, 43.7°
5. $\mu < 3 \cot\alpha$
7. (a) $W\cos\alpha/2\sin(\alpha + \beta)$
(b) horizontal: $W\cos\alpha\cos\beta/2\sin(\alpha+\beta)$,
vertical: $W[2\sin(\alpha + \beta) - \cos\alpha\sin\beta]/2\sin(\alpha + \beta)$
8. $W/\sqrt{2}$
12. $2\, tan^{-1}\, \mu$
13. $\cos^3\theta = \dfrac{2r}{a}$
15. $W/2\sqrt{3}$

Exercise 8A

1. 25 N
2. 4×10^4 N
3. 74.2 N
5. 3/2
6. 0.6 m, 75 N
7. $\frac{5}{4}a$
8. The particle will rise
9. (a) $mg/\sqrt{3}$ (b) $(1 + 2/\sqrt{3})l \approx 2.15l$

Exercise 8B

1. (a) 1.875 J
(b) 5.625 J
(c) 16.875 J
2. 1.5 J
(a) 17.3 m s^{-1}
(b) 13.4 m s^{-1}
3. 10^6 N, 5×10^6 N m^{-1}, 30 cm
4. 8 m s^{-1}, negligible
5. (a) 1.3 m (b) 0.9 m
6. (b) 1 m
7. 168.75 N, 4.67 m s^{-1}
9. 5000 N, not quite!
10. $l + lc + l\sqrt{(c^2 - 2c)}$
12. (a) $\frac{1}{4}l$

Exercise 8C

1. (a) $2l$ (b) $2\sqrt{(lg)}$
2. (a) $1.637l$
(b) $1.167\sqrt{(lg)}$
3. 0.2, 2.38 m
5. 2
6. 1

Exercise 8D

1. 5 m, π s, 15.7 m s^{-1}.
2. (a) $\pi/6\omega$ (b) $\pi/3\omega$
3. 0.08 m
4. 2.51 s. 1.6 m
5. 197 m s^{-2}
6. 4.43 s
9. (a) $\ddot{x} = -4x$ (b) $\ddot{x} = -4x$
(c) $\ddot{x} = -4(x - 3)$
10. $x = 2 \sin 3t$
11. $x = -4 \cos \pi t$
13. $v = a\omega$

16. at the top of the motion

Exercise 8E

1. $\sqrt{(ma/\lambda)}[\frac{1}{2}\pi + a/(b-a)]$
2. (a) $2\pi\sqrt{(d/g)}$ (b) $\sqrt{(d/g)}\{\pi + 2\sin^{-1}\frac{4}{5} + \frac{3}{2}\}$
6. $\sqrt{(a\lambda/m)}$
7. $g/\pi^2 \simeq 1.01$ m $(g = 10)$
10. $2\pi\sqrt{(mh/\lambda)}$, $u\sqrt{(mh/\lambda)}$

Exercise 9A

1. 0.94 m
2. 0.094 m from 0.5 kg mass.
3. (0.125, 0.175)
4. (− 3.3, − 4.1)
5. (0.63, 1.73)
6. (4.1, 4.3)
7. (− 8, 10)
8. (− 1.01, 2.32)

Exercise 9B

1. 1.02 m
2. 1.15 m
3. 1.67 m from the top
4. 28.75 cm
5. 34 cm
6. 31.4 cm
7. 6.09 m above the ground
8. 0.809 cm from longest side
9. 1.07 cm above base,
   1.14 cm above base
10. 2.95 cm above base
11. 1.066 m, 0.89 m
12. 1.483 m, 0.309 m

Exercise 9C

1. 5.25 cm from top of letter
2. − 0.44 cm
3. (a) $(1.07a, 1.07a, 0.93a)$ (b) $(1.02a, 1.02a, 0.98a)$
4. $(\frac{11}{12}a, \frac{5}{12}a)$
5. 26.25 cm from the unfolded end
6. $0.433a$ above the base
7. $7\sqrt{2}a/32$, where a is the side of a small square
8. (a) $0.23a$
   (b) $0.38a$
9. $(1.45a, 1.18a)$
10. $1.64a$ above the base

Exercise 9D

1. (0.75, 0.3)
2. (0.6, 0.375)
3. $(4a/3\pi, 4a/3\pi)$
4. (0.45, 0.45)
5. (0.75, 1.6)
6. (1.44, 0.36)
7. 7.32 cm, 0.84 cm
8. 0.64 cm

Exercise 9E

1. (a) $(\frac{5}{6}, 0)$ (b) $(\frac{3}{4}, 0)$ (c) $\frac{3}{8}a$
   (d) $(\frac{5}{8}, 0)$ (e) $(0.625, 0)$ (f) $(2\ln 2, 0)$
3. $(0, \frac{1}{4}h)$
4. $\frac{1}{8}h$
5. (0, 1.84)
6. (0, 2.17)
8. $0.64a$
9. 1.1

Exercise 9F

1. 29.7°
2. 23.7°
3. 21.3°
4. 33.7°
5. 35.2°
6. $\left(\dfrac{a^3 - x^3}{a^2 - x^2}, \dfrac{a^3 - x^3}{\sqrt{3}(a^2 - x^2)}\right)$, $x = \frac{1}{2}a(\sqrt{5} - 1)$.
7. $0.217W$
8. 14.03°, 0.25
11. $x = WR/w$
12. 7

INDEX